Frank

MW00598220

LINEAR ROBUST CONTROL

PRENTICE HALL INFORMATION AND SYSTEM SCIENCES SERIES

Thomas Kailath, Editor

ANDERSON & MOORE	*Optimal Control: Linear Quadratic Methods*
ANDERSON & MOORE	*Optimal Filtering*
ASTROM & WITTENMARK	*Computer-Controlled Systems: Theory and Design, 2/E*
BASSEVILLE & NIKIROV	*Detection of Abrupt Changes: Theory & Application*
BOYD & BARRATT	*Linear Controller Design: Limits of Performance*
DICKINSON	*Systems: Analysis, Design and Computation*
FRIEDLAND	*Advanced Control System Design*
GARDNER	*Statistical Spectral Analysis: A Nonprobabilistic Theory*
GRAY & DAVISSON	*Random Processes: A Mathematical Approach for Engineers*
GREEN & LIMEBEER	*Linear Robust Control*
HAYKIN	*Adaptive Filter Theory*
HAYKIN	*Blind Deconvolution*
JAIN	*Fundamentals of Digital Image Processing*
JOHANSSON	*Modeling and System Identification*
JOHNSON	*Lectures on Adaptive Parameter Estimation*
KAILATH	*Linear Systems*
KUNG	*VLSI Array Processors*
KUNG, WHITEHOUSE, & KAILATH, EDS.	*VLSI and Modern Signal Processing*
KWAKERNAAK & SIVAN	*Signals and Systems*
LANDAU	*System Identification and Control Design Using P.I.M. + Software*
LJUNG	*System Identification: Theory for the User*
LJUNG & GLAD	*Modeling of Dynamic Systems*
MACOVSKI	*Medical Imaging Systems*
MOSCA	*Stochastic and Predictive Adaptive Control*
NARENDRA & ANNASWAMY	*Stable Adaptive Systems*
RUGH	*Linear System Theory*
SASTRY & BODSON	*Adaptive Control: Stability, Convergence, and Robustness*
SOLIMAN & SRINATH	*Continuous and Discrete-Time Signals and Systems*
SOLO & KONG	*Adaptive Signal Processing Algorithms: Stability & Performance*
VISWANADHAM & NARAHARI	*Performance Modeling of Automated Manufacturing Systems*
WILLIAMS	*Designing Digital Filters*

FUTURE TITLES: 1996

SRINATH, RAJASEKARAN, & VISWANATHAN	*Introduction to Statistical Signal Processing with Applications*

LINEAR ROBUST CONTROL

MICHAEL GREEN
Australian National University
Canberra, Australia

DAVID J.N. LIMEBEER
Professor of Control Engineering
Imperial College of Science, Technology and Medicine
University of London
London, U.K.

PRENTICE HALL, Englewood Cliffs, New Jersey 07632

Library of Congress Cataloging-in-Publication Data

Green, Michael
Linear robust control
p. cm.
Includes bibliological references and index.
ISBN: 0-13-102278-4
1. Automatic control. 2. Linear systems. I. Limebeer, David J. N.
II. Title.
TJ213.G755 1995
629.8'32--dc20
93-22441
CIP

Acquisitions editor: **LINDA RATTS**
Editorial/production supervision
and interior design: **RICHARD DeLORENZO**
Copy editor: **BARBARA ZEIDERS**
Production coordinator: **DAVID DICKEY**
Editorial assistant: **JENNIFER KLEIN**

©1995 by Prentice-Hall, Inc.
A Paramount Communications Company
Englewood Cliffs, New Jersey 07632

All rights reserved. No part of this book may be reproduced, in any form or by any means, without permission in writing from the publisher.

The author and publisher of this book have used their best efforts in preparing this book. These efforts include the development, research, and testing of the theories and programs to determine their effectiveness. The author and publisher make no warranty of any kind, expressed or implied, with regard to these programs or the documentation contained in this book. The author and publisher shall not be liable in any event for incidental or consequential damages in connection with, or arising out of, the furnishing, performance, or use of these programs.

Printed in the United States of America

10 9 8 7 6 5 4 3 2 1

ISBN 0-13-102278-4

Prentice-Hall International (UK) Limited, London
Prentice-Hall of Australia Pty. Limited, Sydney
Prentice-Hall Canada Inc., Toronto
Prentice-Hall Hispanoamericana, S.A., Mexico
Prentice-Hall of India Private Limited, New Delhi
Prentice-Hall of Japan, Inc., Tokyo
Simon & Schuster Asia Pte. Ltd., Singapore
Editora Prentice-Hall do Brasil, Ltda., Rio de Janeiro

ISBN 0-13-102278-4

90000

9 780131 022782

Contents

Preface

Plant variability and uncertainty are formidable adversaries. An anecdote which serves as a reminder of this fact can be found in Harold Black's retrospective on his invention of the feedback amplifier [30]. At one point, he describes the operating procedure for his newly invented feedforward amplifier: "...every hour on the hour—twenty four hours a day—somebody had to adjust the filament current to its correct value. In doing this, they were permitted plus or minus 0.5 to 1 dB variation in the amplifier gain, whereas, for my purpose the gain had to be absolutely perfect. In addition, every six hours it became necessary to adjust the battery voltage, because the amplifier gain would be out of hand. There were other complications too...". Despite his subsequent discovery of the feedback principle and the tireless efforts of many researchers, the problem of plant variability and uncertainty is still with us.

Systems that can tolerate plant variability and uncertainty are called robust—Black's original feedforward amplifier was not robust. The aim of this book is to present a theory of feedback system analysis, design and synthesis that is able to optimize the performance and robustness of control systems. We contrast this with traditional optimal control methods, such as the Linear Quadratic Gaussian (LQG) theory, which optimizes performance but not robustness.

In determining the scope of this endeavour, we see two considerations as being paramount:

1. The theory should offer a quantitative measure of performance and robustness that leads directly to an optimization problem for which a synthesis procedure is available. Once the design objectives are specified, the synthesis theory should determine whether or not they can be achieved. If they can, the theory should synthesize a controller that meets them.

2. The theory must be accessible to engineers. We believe there is little point in offering a theory that, because of its complexity, is unlikely to find its way into engineering practice.

Over the last fifteen years singular values have been developed as a tool for analyzing the robustness and performance of feedback systems. We shall argue that they form the core of an accessible yet advanced optimal control theory, because they facilitate a natural generalization of many classical single-loop feedback analysis ideas. In general terms, the controller should be chosen so that the closed-loop transfer function matrix has certain characteristics that are derived from the specifications. An optimal design minimizes the maximum singular value of the discrepancy between the closed-loop transfer function matrix and the desired loop shape, subject to a closed-loop stability constraint. This is an $\mathcal{H}_\infty$ optimization problem, for which considerable mathematical theory is available.

The mathematical prerequisites for studying the book are modest, because for the most part we deal with finite dimensional linear systems. The background assumed of any reader is: (a) linear algebra and matrix theory; (b) linear differential equations; (c) a course in classical control theory that covers transfer functions, frequency responses, Bode plots and the Nyquist stability theorem; (d) linear systems theory, including a treatment of state-space system descriptions. The notions of controllability and observability are used without explanation. We recommend that students have some exposure to linear systems and optimal control at a graduate level before tackling the synthesis theory chapters of this book. Chapters 1 and 2 only require a modest background and could be included in senior undergraduate or Masters level courses.

A good idea of the scope of the book may be obtained from a perusal of the list of contents. Chapter 1 introduces the idea of $\mathcal{H}_\infty$ optimization by considering a number of simple scalar examples which are solved using Nevanlinna-Pick-Schur interpolation theory. In this way the reader knows what $\mathcal{H}_\infty$ optimal control is about after reading only a few pages. Chapter 2 deals with the use of singular values in multivariable control system design. A multivariable generalization of the Nyquist stability theorem and the interpretation of the minimum singular value of a matrix as a measure of the distance to a singular matrix are used to establish robustness results for linear time-invariant systems. The interpretation of the maximum singular value as the maximum gain is then used to show how performance issues may be addressed. Chapter 3 reviews background material on signals and systems and introduces the small gain theorem and the bounded real lemma. The small gain theorem states that stable systems can be connected to form a stable closed-loop if the loop gain product is less than unity; it is the basis for the general robust stability results. The bounded real lemma gives a condition for a linear time-invariant system to have less than unity gain. Chapter 4 discusses linear fractional transformations and their role in control systems. It is argued that various closed-loop and open-loop design problems can be posed in terms of a linear fractional transformation involving a fixed system known as the generalized plant and a to-be-designed system known as the controller. Linear fractional transformations therefore provide a general framework for controller synthesis theory and for computational software. The synthesis problem we consider is to find a controller that achieves a specified norm bound on a linear fractional transformation involving the controller and the generalized plant. Because the established theory and sign conventions of linear fractional transformations induce a positive sign convention on feedback problems, we use a positive feedback sign convention throughout the book.

Chapters 5 to 8 develop the control system synthesis theory. We begin with a brief treatment of the Linear Quadratic Guassian problem in Chapter 5. Chapters 6, 7 and 8 are the core of the book and concentrate on the synthesis of controllers that meet $\mathcal{H}_\infty$-norm objectives. The main result is that a controller that satisfies the objectives exists if and only if two Riccati equations have appropriate solutions. In this case, all controllers that satisfy the objectives can be given in terms of a linear fractional transformation involving a stable, norm bounded, but otherwise unconstrained, parameter. The development of the LQG and $\mathcal{H}_\infty$ synthesis theories is split into two parts. In the first, we analyze a finite-horizon version of the problem. For this part the plant may be assumed to be time-varying. The second part tackles the infinite-horizon extension by invoking limiting arguments. The infinite-horizon results are only developed in a time-invariant setting—we restrict ourselves to time-invariant plant before taking limits. Our approach to the synthesis theory is based, therefore, on time-domain techniques which are deeply rooted in the existing and widely known theory of linear quadratic optimal control. The application to $\mathcal{H}_\infty$ optimization requires that we consider a quadratic objective function which is not positive definite, but which connects precisely with the theory of linear, zero-sum differential games with quadratic pay-off functions. This time-domain, optimal-control based approach has several advantages. Firstly, the techniques are widely known and are covered in excellent texts such as [11], [33] and [125]. Secondly, they require almost no advanced mathematical theory. For the most part, a solid background in linear algebra and differential equations is sufficient. Thirdly, the main ideas and equations can be developed in a finite time horizon setting in which stability issues do not arise. The sufficiency theory in this case is almost trivial, amounting to little more than "completing the square". Finally, they are applicable to time-varying problems and are amenable to generalization to nonlinear systems.

In order to provide the reader with some insight into the alternative approaches that have been developed, we have: (a) included two complete proofs of the bounded real lemma, one algebraic and one based on optimal control; (b) covered the four-block general distance problem in some detail; (c) explored the connection with factorization methods in several of the problems. The approach based on the four-block problem is given fairly detailed coverage because it is the only approach that has yielded a complete treatment of the optimal cases and because it is able to deal (easily) with problems involving optimization subject to the constraint that the solution contains no more than a prespecified number of unstable poles. This problem is of interest in frequency weighted model reduction applications which are also covered.

Chapters 9 to 11 deal with the approximation of high-order systems by others of lower order. This approximation process is known as model reduction. The inclusion of model reduction is motivated by our belief that control system design cannot be separated from the process of plant modelling. Any serious application of the optimal synthesis methods in this book is bound to involve some model reduction. In addition, the similarity of the mathematical techniques involved in model reduction and $\mathcal{H}_\infty$ optimal control makes it appropriate to include this material.

Chapter 12 contains two design case studies. The first considers the design of a controller to stabilize the vertical dynamics of the elongated plasma in a tokamak fusion reactor and the second considers the design of a composition controller for a high-purity distillation column.

For completeness, internal stability theory is covered in Appendix A, although an advantage of our approach to the synthesis problem is that a detailed knowledge of internal stability theory is not required. Appendix B offers a brief treatment of the discrete-time synthesis theory.

Section summaries are included to help readers review their progress and highlight the main issues. Each chapter ends with student exercises; some are straightforward, while others are much more challenging. The easy exercises offer practise in formula manipulation and are designed to help students increase their confidence in the subject. On the whole, they add only minor embellishments to the text. On the other hand, the more difficult exercises expand the text and even develop aspects of the subject we could not touch on in the main body. Answering the more difficult problems requires real work—mastering control theory is not a spectator sport! The exercises are an integral part of the text and there is no doubt that a serious attempt to answer them will greatly improve one's understanding of the subject. A solution to each of the problems is available in a separate solutions manual.

There is enough material in Chapters 1 to 8 for a 45 hour course in $\mathcal{H}_\infty$ controller synthesis. If time is short, or if students have had recent exposure to linear quadratic optimal control theory, Chapter 5 can be omitted. The material in Chapters 9 to 11 is self contained (excepting for some elementary material in Chapters 3 and 4) and could be used for a 20 hour course on model reduction. Chapter 2 is self-contained and could be used as the basis of 2 to 5 hours of lectures on singular values in a course on multivariable control systems. Indeed, this chapter has evolved from lecture notes that have been used in the Masters course at Imperial College. Chapter 12 can also be incorporated in a course on multivariable control system design and will, we hope, be of interest to engineers who want to find out how these new methods can be used on real-life problems.

Our aim in writing this book is to generate an accessible text that develops along a single line of argument. In any exercise of this sort, the selection of material is bound to involve compromise. We have made no attempt to review all the material that could be construed as being relevant. Rather, we have restricted our attention to work that we believe will be of most help to readers in developing their knowledge of the subject, and to material that has played a direct role in educating us or in helping us prepare the manuscript. In the case of well established theory, we have referred to well known texts rather than duplicate their extensive bibliographies. Despite our best efforts, there is bound to be important work that has escaped our attention. To those authors, we offer our sincerest apologies.

This work is the result of seven years of collaboration and every part of this book is the result of our joint efforts.

Acknowledgments

We owe a debt of gratitude to many of our colleagues and friends.

Brian Anderson, who was instrumental in bringing us together, deserves special mention as a mentor, collaborator, colleague and friend. We dedicate this book to him.

The theory of $\mathcal{H}_\infty$ control design and synthesis is the result of the efforts of many researchers. We acknowledge countless discussions with Mark Davis, John Doyle, Tryphon Georgiou, Keith Glover, Sam Hung, Tom Kailath, Huibert Kwakernaak, David Mayne, Mike Safonov, Uri Shaked, Rafi Sivan, Malcolm Smith, Allen Tannenbaum and George Zames.

The case studies in Chapter 12 are the result of the collaborative efforts of several people. The tokamak study would not have been possible without the contributions of Malcolm Haines, Ebrahim Kasenally and Alfredo Portone. The distillation column design owes much to the contributions made by Elling Jacobsen, Nefyn Jones, Ebrahim Kasenally and John Perkins.

We are grateful to Bo Bernhardsson and Bjorn Wittenmark for the opportunity to present this work, in early form, as a short course to graduate students at the Lund Institute of Technology.

We were pleasantly surprised by the willingness of colleagues to read draft chapters and offer their advice. In particular, we would like to thank Bob Bitmead, Francesco Crusa, Izchak Lewkowicz, David Mayne, Gjerrit Meinsma, John Perkins and Vincent Wertz.

The people who really made this exercise worthwhile were our students and post-docs. They gave this project more support and momentum than they will ever realize. We would like to thank Mahmoud Al-Husari, Matthieu Biron, Tong Chiang, Britta Hendel, David Hoyle, Imad Jaimoukha, Nefyn Jones, Ebrahim Kasenally, Jeremy Matson, Nick Rubin, Alfredo Portone and Michael Zervos for their comments and hours of tireless proof reading.

Above all, we are grateful to Eliza and Sue for their understanding and patience while we wrote this book.

MICHAEL GREEN
DAVID LIMEBEER

London

We gratefully acknowledge the support of: the British Science and Engineering Research Council; the Centre for Process Systems Engineering, Imperial College; the Department of Systems Engineering and the Department of Engineering, Australian National University; and the Cooperative Research Centre for Robust and Adaptive Systems, under the Cooperative Research Centre Program of the Commonwealth of Australia.

LINEAR
ROBUST CONTROL

1

Introduction

1.1 Goals and origins of $\mathcal{H}_\infty$ optimal control

Most engineering undergraduates are taught to design proportional-integral-derivative (PID) compensators using a variety of different frequency response techniques. With the help of a little laboratory experience, students soon realize that a typical design study involves juggling with conflicting design objectives such as the gain margin and the closed-loop bandwidth until an acceptable controller is found. In many cases these "classical" controller design techniques lead to a perfectly satisfactory solution and more powerful tools hardly seem necessary. Difficulties arise when the plant dynamics are complex and poorly modelled, or when the performance specifications are particularly stringent. Even if a solution is eventually found, the process is likely to be expensive in terms of design engineer's time.

When a design team is faced with one of these more difficult problems, and no solution seems forthcoming, there are two possible courses of action. These are either to compromise the specifications to make the design task easier, or to search for more powerful design tools. In the case of the first option, reduced performance is accepted without ever knowing if the original specifications could have been satisfied, as classical control design methods do not address existence questions. In the case of the second option, more powerful design tools can only help if a solution exists.

Any progress with questions concerning achievable performance limits and the existence of satisfactory controllers is bound to involve some kind of optimization theory. If, for example, it were possible to optimize the settings of a PID regulator, the design problem would either be solved or it would become apparent that the specifications are impossible to satisfy (with a PID regulator). We believe that answering existence questions is an important component of a good design methodology. One does not want to waste time trying to solve a problem that has no solution, nor does one want to accept specification compromises without knowing that these are necessary. A further benefit of optimization is that it provides an absolute scale of merit against which any design can be measured—if a design is already all but perfect, there is little point in trying to improve it further.

The aim of this book is to develop a theoretical framework within which one may address complex design problems with demanding specifications in a systematic way.

Wiener-Hopf-Kalman optimal control

The first successes with control system optimization came in the 1950s with the introduction of the Wiener-Hopf-Kalman (WHK) theory of optimal control.[1] At roughly the same time the United States and the Soviet Union were funding a massive research program into the guidance and maneuvering of space vehicles. As it turned out, the then new optimal control theory was well suited to many of the control problems that arose from the space program. There were two main reasons for this:

1. The underlying assumptions of the WHK theory are that the plant has a known linear (and possibly time-varying) description, and that the exogenous noises and disturbances impinging on the feedback system are stochastic in nature, but have known statistical properties. Since space vehicles have dynamics that are essentially ballistic in character, it is possible to develop accurate mathematical models of their behavior. In addition, descriptions for external disturbances based on white noise are often appropriate in aerospace applications. Therefore, at least from a modelling point of view, the WHK theory and these applications are well suited to each other.

2. Many of the control problems from the space program are concerned with resource management. In the 1960s, aerospace engineers were interested in minimum fuel consumption problems such as minimizing the use of retrorockets. One famous problem of this type was concerned with landing the lunar excursion module with a minimum expenditure of fuel. Performance criteria of this type are easily embedded in the WHK framework that was specially developed to minimize quadratic performance indices.

Another revolutionary feature of the WHK theory is that it offers a true synthesis procedure. Once the designer has settled on a quadratic performance index to be minimized, the WHK procedure supplies the (unique) optimal controller without any further intervention from the designer. In the euphoria that followed the introduction of optimal control theory, it was widely believed that the control system

[1] Linear Quadratic Gaussian (LQG) optimal control is the term now most widely used for this type of optimal control.

designer had finally been relieved of the burdensome task of designing by trial and error. As is well known, the reality turned out to be quite different.

The wide-spread success of the WHK theory in aerospace applications soon led to attempts to apply optimal control theory to more mundane industrial problems. In contrast to experience with aerospace applications, it soon became apparent that there was a serious mismatch between the underlying assumptions of the WHK theory and industrial control problems. Accurate models are not routinely available and most industrial plant engineers have no idea as to the statistical nature of the external disturbances impinging on their plant. After a ten year re-appraisal of the status of multivariable control theory, it became clear that an optimal control theory that deals with the question of plant modelling errors and external disturbance uncertainty was required.

Worst-case control and $\mathcal{H}_\infty$ optimization

$\mathcal{H}_\infty$ optimal control is a frequency-domain optimization and synthesis theory that was developed in response to the need for a synthesis procedure that *explicitly* addresses questions of modelling errors. The basic philosophy is to treat the worst case scenario: if you don't know what you are up against, plan for the worst and optimize. For such a framework to be useful, it must have the following properties:

1. It must be capable of dealing with plant modelling errors and unknown disturbances.

2. It should represent a natural extension to existing feedback theory, as this will facilitate an easy transfer of intuition from the classical setting.

3. It must be amenable to meaningful optimization.

4. It must be able to deal with multivariable problems.

In this chapter, we will introduce the infinity norm and $\mathcal{H}_\infty$ optimal control with the aid of a sequence of simple single-loop examples. We have carefully selected these in order to minimize the amount of background mathematics required of the reader in these early stages of study; all that is required is a familiarity with the *maximum modulus principle*. Roughly speaking, this principle says that if a function $\boldsymbol{f}$ (of a complex variable) is analytic inside and on the boundary of some domain $\mathcal{D}$, then the maximum modulus (magnitude) of the function $\boldsymbol{f}$ occurs on the boundary of the domain $\mathcal{D}$. For example, if a feedback system is closed-loop stable, the maximum of the modulus of the closed-loop transfer function over the closed right-half of the complex plane will always occur on the imaginary axis.

To motivate the introduction of the infinity norm, we consider the question of robust stability optimization for the feedback system shown in Figure 1.1. The transfer function $\boldsymbol{g}$ represents a nominal linear, time-invariant model of an open-loop system and the transfer function $\boldsymbol{k}$ represents a linear, time-invariant controller to be designed. If the "true" system is represented by $(1+\boldsymbol{\delta})\boldsymbol{g}$, we say that the modelling

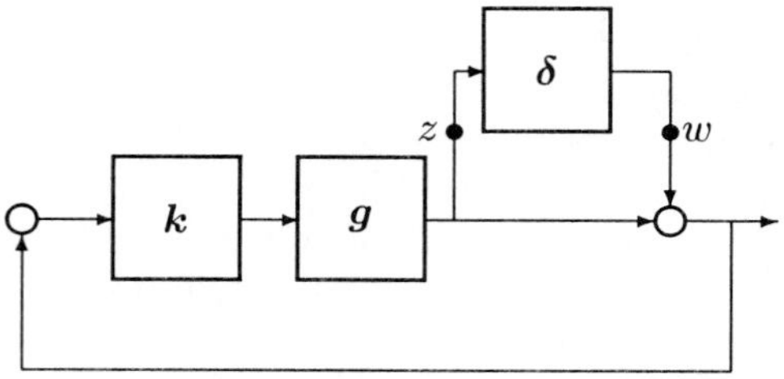

Figure 1.1: The problem of robust stability optimization.

error is represented by a multiplicative perturbation $\boldsymbol{\delta}$ at the plant output. For this introductory analysis, we assume that $\boldsymbol{\delta}$ is an unknown linear, time-invariant system.

Since

$$z = (1 - \boldsymbol{gk})^{-1}\boldsymbol{gk}w,$$

the stability properties of the system given in Figure 1.1 are the same as those given in Figure 1.2, in which

$$\boldsymbol{h} = (1 - \boldsymbol{gk})^{-1}\boldsymbol{gk}.$$

If the perturbation $\boldsymbol{\delta}$ and the nominal closed-loop system given by $\boldsymbol{h}$ are both

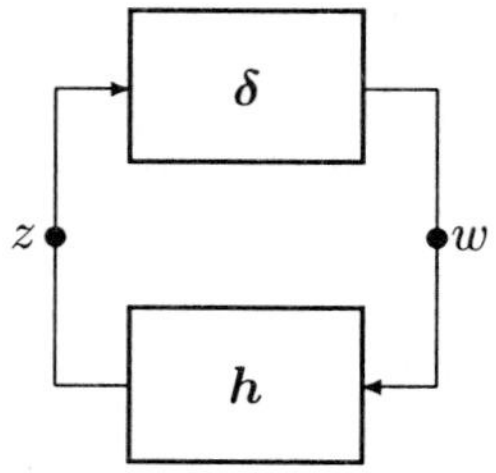

Figure 1.2: The small gain problem.

stable, the Nyquist criterion says that the closed-loop system is stable if and only if the Nyquist diagram of $\boldsymbol{h\delta}$ does not encircle the $+1$ point. We use the $+1$ point rather than the -1 point because of our positive feedback sign convention. Since the condition

$$\sup_{\omega} |\boldsymbol{h}(j\omega)\boldsymbol{\delta}(j\omega)| < 1. \tag{1.1.1}$$

ensures that the Nyquist diagram of $\boldsymbol{h\delta}$ does not encircle the $+1$ point, we conclude that the closed-loop system is stable provided (1.1.1) holds.

Since $\boldsymbol{\delta}$ is unknown, it makes sense to replace (1.1.1) with an alternative sufficient condition for stability in which $\boldsymbol{h}$ and $\boldsymbol{\delta}$ are separated. We could for example test the condition

$$\sup_\omega |\boldsymbol{h}(j\omega)| \sup_\omega |\boldsymbol{\delta}(j\omega)| < 1.$$

If $\boldsymbol{\delta}$ is stable and bounded in magnitude, so that

$$\sup_\omega |\boldsymbol{\delta}(j\omega)| = M,$$

the feedback loop given in Figure 1.1 will be stable provided a stabilizing controller can be found such that

$$\sup_\omega |\boldsymbol{h}(j\omega)| < \frac{1}{M}.$$

The quantity $\sup_\omega |\boldsymbol{h}(j\omega)|$ satisfies the axioms of a norm, and is known as the *infinity norm*. Specifically,

$$\|\boldsymbol{h}\|_\infty = \sup_\omega |\boldsymbol{h}(j\omega)|.$$

Electrical engineers will immediately recognize $\|\boldsymbol{h}\|_\infty$ as the highest gain value on a Bode magnitude plot. The quantity $\|\cdot\|_\infty$ is a norm, since it satisfies the following axioms:

1. $\|\boldsymbol{h}\|_\infty \geq 0$ with $\|\boldsymbol{h}\|_\infty = 0$ if and only if $\boldsymbol{h} = 0$.
2. $\|\alpha\boldsymbol{h}\|_\infty = |\alpha|\|\boldsymbol{h}\|_\infty$ for all scalars α.
3. $\|\boldsymbol{h} + \boldsymbol{g}\|_\infty \leq \|\boldsymbol{h}\|_\infty + \|\boldsymbol{g}\|_\infty$.

In addition, $\|\cdot\|_\infty$ satisfies

4. $\|\boldsymbol{hg}\|_\infty \leq \|\boldsymbol{h}\|_\infty\|\boldsymbol{g}\|_\infty$.

The fourth property is the crucial submultiplicative property which is central to all the robust stability and robust performance work to be encountered in this book. Note that not all norms have this fourth property.

With this background, the optimal robust stability problem is posed as one of finding a stabilizing controller $\boldsymbol{k}$ that minimizes $\|(1 - \boldsymbol{gk})^{-1}\boldsymbol{gk}\|_\infty$. Note that $\boldsymbol{k} = 0$ gives $\|(1 - \boldsymbol{gk})^{-1}\boldsymbol{gk}\|_\infty = 0$ and is therefore optimal in this sense provided the plant itself is stable. Thus, when the plant is stable and there are no performance requirements other than stability, the optimal course of action is to use no feedback at all! When $\boldsymbol{k} = 0$ is not allowed because the plant is unstable, the problem is more interesting and the optimal stability margin and the optimal controller are much harder to find. We will return to the analysis of this type of problem in Section 1.4.

In order to lay the groundwork for our analysis of optimal disturbance attenuation and optimal stability robustness, we consider the optimal command response problem. This problem is particularly simple because it contains no feedback. Despite this, it contains many of the essential mathematical features of more difficult (feedback) problems.

1.2 Optimizing the command response

As an introduction to the use of the infinity norm in control system optimization, we analyze the design of reference signal prefilters in command tracking applications. This is our first example of an $\mathcal{H}_\infty$ optimal controller synthesis problem.

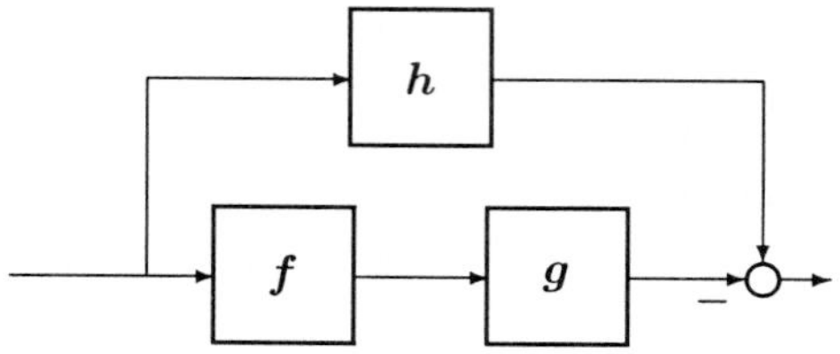

Figure 1.3: Command response optimization.

In the configuration illustrated in Figure 1.3, we suppose that the plant model $\boldsymbol{g}$ is a given stable rational transfer function and that $\boldsymbol{h}$ is a given stable rational transfer function with desired command response properties. The design task is to find a stable rational prefilter with transfer function $\boldsymbol{f}$ such that $\|\boldsymbol{h} - \boldsymbol{g}\boldsymbol{f}\|_\infty$ is minimized. An unstable prefilter is unacceptable in practical applications because it results in unbounded control signals and actuator saturation.

In the case that $\boldsymbol{g}$ has no zeros in the closed-right-half plane, the solution is easy since we may simply set $\boldsymbol{f} = \boldsymbol{g}^{-1}\boldsymbol{h}$. If $\boldsymbol{g}$ has right-half-plane zeros, however, the plant inverse leads to an unstable prefilter unless the right-half-plane poles of $\boldsymbol{g}^{-1}$ happen to be cancelled by zeros of $\boldsymbol{h}$. Thus, when $\boldsymbol{g}$ has right-half-plane zeros, the requirement that the prefilter be stable forces us to accept some error between $\boldsymbol{g}\boldsymbol{f}$ and $\boldsymbol{h}$ which we denote

$$\boldsymbol{e} = \boldsymbol{h} - \boldsymbol{g}\boldsymbol{f}. \tag{1.2.1}$$

This gives

$$\boldsymbol{f} = \boldsymbol{g}^{-1}(\boldsymbol{h} - \boldsymbol{e}). \tag{1.2.2}$$

If the right-half-plane zeros of $\boldsymbol{g}$ are $z_1, z_2, \ldots, z_m$ and are of multiplicity one, the prefilter will be stable if and only if

$$\boldsymbol{e}(z_i) = \boldsymbol{h}(z_i), \qquad i = 1, 2, \ldots, m. \tag{1.2.3}$$

This is because the unstable poles of $\boldsymbol{g}^{-1}$ will be cancelled by the zeros of $\boldsymbol{h} - \boldsymbol{e}$.

The conditions given in (1.2.3) are called *interpolation constraints.* Any error system $\boldsymbol{e}$ resulting from a stable prefilter must satisfy the conditions (1.2.3) and, conversely, the satisfaction of these constraints ensures that all the right-half-plane poles of $\boldsymbol{g}^{-1}$ will be cancelled by zeros of $\boldsymbol{h} - \boldsymbol{e}$ when forming the prefilter. The optimization problem is to find a stable transfer function $\boldsymbol{e}$ of minimum infinity norm such that the interpolation constraints given in (1.2.3) are satisfied. This is an example of a *Nevanlinna-Pick interpolation* problem. A general solution to problems of this type is complicated and was found early this century. Once the optimal error function is found, $\boldsymbol{f}$ follows by back substitution using (1.2.2). We shall now consolidate these ideas with a numerical example.

Example 1.2.1. Suppose $\boldsymbol{g}$ and $\boldsymbol{h}$ are given by

$$\boldsymbol{g} = \left(\frac{s-1}{s+2}\right), \qquad \boldsymbol{h} = \left(\frac{s+1}{s+3}\right).$$

The transfer function $\boldsymbol{g}$ has a single zero at $s = 1$, so there is a single interpolation constraint given by

$$\boldsymbol{e}(1) = \left(\frac{s+1}{s+3}\right)\bigg|_{s=1} = \frac{1}{2}.$$

Since $\boldsymbol{e}$ is required to be stable, the maximum modulus principle ensures that

$$\begin{aligned} \|\boldsymbol{e}\|_\infty &= \sup_{s=j\omega} |\boldsymbol{e}(s)| \\ &= \sup_{R_e(s)\geq 0} |\boldsymbol{e}(s)| \\ &\geq |\boldsymbol{e}(1)| = \frac{1}{2}. \end{aligned}$$

The minimum infinity norm interpolating function is therefore the constant function $\boldsymbol{e} = \frac{1}{2}$ and the associated norm is $\|\boldsymbol{e}\|_\infty = \frac{1}{2}$. Back substitution using (1.2.2) yields

$$\boldsymbol{f} = \left(\frac{s+2}{s-1}\right)\left(\frac{s+1}{s+3} - \frac{1}{2}\right) = \frac{1}{2}\left(\frac{s+2}{s+3}\right).$$

▽

Interpolating a single data point is particularly simple because the optimal interpolating function is a constant. Our next example, which contains two interpolation constraints, shows that the general interpolation problem is far more complex.

Example 1.2.2. Consider the command response optimization problem in which

$$\boldsymbol{g} = \frac{(s-1)(s-2)}{(s+3)^2}, \qquad \boldsymbol{h} = \frac{2}{3(s+3)}.$$

The transfer function $\boldsymbol{g}$ has right-half-plane zeros at $z_1 = 1$ and $z_2 = 2$, so we must find a stable transfer function $\boldsymbol{e}$ of minimum norm such that:

$$\boldsymbol{e}(1) = \boldsymbol{h}(1) = \frac{1}{6} = h_1 \tag{1.2.4}$$

and

$$\boldsymbol{e}(2) = \boldsymbol{h}(2) = \frac{2}{15} = h_2. \tag{1.2.5}$$

It follows from the maximum modulus principle that any such $\boldsymbol{e}$ must satisfy

$$\|\boldsymbol{e}\|_\infty \geq \max\left\{\frac{1}{6}, \frac{2}{15}\right\} = \frac{1}{6}.$$

Since we have two values to interpolate, simply setting $\boldsymbol{e} = \frac{1}{6}$ will not do!

The Nevanlinna-Pick interpolation theory says that there is a stable interpolating function $\boldsymbol{e}$ with $\|\boldsymbol{e}\|_\infty \leq \gamma$ if and only if the *Pick matrix* given by

$$\Pi(\gamma) = \begin{bmatrix} \frac{\gamma^2 - h_1^2}{2} & \frac{\gamma^2 - h_1 h_2}{3} \\ \frac{\gamma^2 - h_1 h_2}{3} & \frac{\gamma^2 - h_2^2}{4} \end{bmatrix}$$

is nonnegative definite. Since $\Pi(\gamma_1) \geq \Pi(\gamma_2)$ if $\gamma_1 \geq \gamma_2$, our desired optimal norm is the largest value of γ for which the Pick matrix $\Pi(\gamma)$ is singular. Alternatively, the optimal value of γ (call it γ_{opt}) is the square root of the largest eigenvalue of the symmetric matrix pencil

$$\gamma^2 \begin{bmatrix} \frac{1}{2} & \frac{1}{3} \\ \frac{1}{3} & \frac{1}{4} \end{bmatrix} - \begin{bmatrix} \frac{h_1^2}{2} & \frac{h_1 h_2}{3} \\ \frac{h_1 h_2}{3} & \frac{h_2^2}{4} \end{bmatrix}.$$

Carrying out this calculation gives $\gamma_{opt} \approx 0.207233$. The Nevanlinna-Pick theory also gives the optimal interpolating function as

$$\boldsymbol{e} = \gamma_{opt}\left(\frac{a - s}{a + s}\right),$$

with a given by

$$\begin{aligned} a &= z_i \frac{\gamma_{opt} + h_i}{\gamma_{opt} - h_i} \quad \text{(in which } i \text{ is either 1 or 2)} \\ &\approx 9.21699. \end{aligned}$$

(It is easy to check that this $\boldsymbol{e}$ satisfies the interpolation constraints.) Notice that the optimal interpolating function is a constant multiplied by a stable transfer function with unit magnitude on the imaginary axis, which is a general property of optimal interpolating functions. Since $\|\frac{a-s}{a+s}\|_\infty = 1$, it is clear that $\|\boldsymbol{e}\|_\infty = \gamma_{opt}$. Since $\boldsymbol{f} = \boldsymbol{g}^{-1}(\boldsymbol{h} - \boldsymbol{e})$, it follows that the optimal prefilter is

$$\boldsymbol{f} = \gamma_{opt}\left(\frac{s + 3}{s + a}\right).$$

▽

We conclude from this example that an increase in the number of interpolation constraints makes the evaluation of the interpolating function much harder. Despite this, the error function retains the "constant magnitude on the imaginary axis" property associated with constants. We will not address (or require) a general solution to the Nevanlinna-Pick interpolation problem, although the solution to the $\mathcal{H}_\infty$ optimal control problem we shall develop also provides a solution to the Nevanlinna-Pick interpolation problem. We shall say more about this in Chapter 6.

1.3 Optimal disturbance attenuation

The aim of this section is to solve a simple $\mathcal{H}_\infty$ control problem involving feedback by recasting the optimal disturbance attenuation problem as an optimization problem constrained by interpolation conditions.

In the system illustrated in Figure 1.4, it is assumed that the plant model $\boldsymbol{g}$ is a given stable rational transfer function and that the frequency domain signal d represents some *unknown* disturbance. The aim is to find a compensator $\boldsymbol{k}$ with the following two properties:

1. It must stabilize the loop in a sense to be specified below.

2. It must minimize the infinity norm of the transfer function that maps d to y.

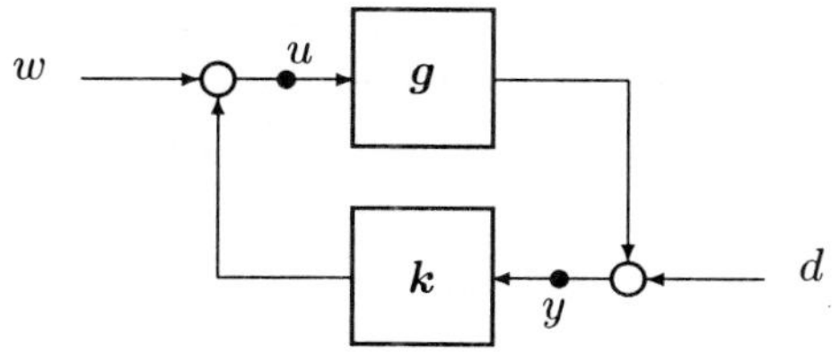

Figure 1.4: The disturbance attenuation problem.

If $w = 0$, it is immediate from Figure 1.4 that

$$\begin{aligned} y &= (1 - \boldsymbol{gk})^{-1} d \\ &= (1 + \boldsymbol{gk}(1 - \boldsymbol{gk})^{-1})d, \end{aligned}$$

and we note that the closed-loop transfer function is a nonlinear function of $\boldsymbol{k}$. To restore an affine parametrization of the type given in (1.2.1), we set

$$\boldsymbol{q} = \boldsymbol{k}(1 - \boldsymbol{gk})^{-1}, \tag{1.3.1}$$

which is the transfer function between the disturbance d and the plant input u. The closed-loop mapping d to y may now be written as

$$y = (1 + \boldsymbol{gq})d, \tag{1.3.2}$$

which is affine in the unknown parameter $\boldsymbol{q}$. Before continuing, we need to introduce the notion of internal stability and discover the properties required of $\boldsymbol{q}$ in order that the resulting controller be internally stabilizing.

1.3.1 Internal stability theory for stable plants

Definition 1.3.1 *The feedback system given in Figure 1.4 is called internally stable if each of the four transfer functions mapping w and d to u and y are stable.*

If the feedback system in Figure 1.4 is internally stable, we say that $\boldsymbol{k}$ is an internally-stabilizing controller for $\boldsymbol{g}$.[2]

Internal stability is a more stringent stability requirement than the simple input-output stability of closed-loop transfer functions, because it also bans all right-half-plane pole-zero cancellations between cascaded subsystems within the feedback loop.

Example 1.3.1. The transfer functions $\boldsymbol{g} = \left(\frac{-s}{s+1}\right)$ and $\boldsymbol{k} = \left(\frac{s+3}{s}\right)$ produce the stable transfer function $(1 - \boldsymbol{gk})^{-1} = \left(\frac{s+1}{2(s+2)}\right)$ mapping d to y. However, the closed-loop transfer function between d and u is $\boldsymbol{k}(1-\boldsymbol{gk})^{-1} = \left(\frac{(s+1)(s+3)}{2s(s+2)}\right)$, which is unstable due to the closed-loop pole at the origin. We therefore conclude that the system in Figure 1.4 is not internally stable for this particular plant and controller combination, although it is input-output stable. ∇

We will now prove our first result on internal stability.

Lemma 1.3.1 *The feedback loop in Figure 1.4 is internally stable if and only if*

$$\begin{bmatrix} 1 & -\boldsymbol{k} \\ -\boldsymbol{g} & 1 \end{bmatrix}^{-1} \tag{1.3.3}$$

is stable.

Proof. It is immediate from Figure 1.4 that

$$\begin{aligned} u &= \boldsymbol{k}y + w \\ y &= \boldsymbol{g}u + d, \end{aligned}$$

or equivalently

$$\begin{bmatrix} w \\ d \end{bmatrix} = \begin{bmatrix} 1 & -\boldsymbol{k} \\ -\boldsymbol{g} & 1 \end{bmatrix} \begin{bmatrix} u \\ y \end{bmatrix}.$$

This gives

$$\begin{bmatrix} u \\ y \end{bmatrix} = \begin{bmatrix} 1 & -\boldsymbol{k} \\ -\boldsymbol{g} & 1 \end{bmatrix}^{-1} \begin{bmatrix} w \\ d \end{bmatrix}$$

and the result follows from Definition 1.3.1. ∎

[2]The terms internally-stabilizing controller and stabilizing controller are synonymous in this book—internally-stabilizing controller is used to draw special attention to the requirement of internal stability.

We will now discover the properties required of the q-parameter defined in (1.3.1) for internal stability in the stable plant case. Since

$$\begin{bmatrix} 1 & -k \\ -g & 1 \end{bmatrix} = \begin{bmatrix} 1 & 0 \\ -g & 1 \end{bmatrix} \begin{bmatrix} 1 & -k \\ 0 & 1-gk \end{bmatrix},$$

we get

$$\begin{aligned} \begin{bmatrix} 1 & -k \\ -g & 1 \end{bmatrix}^{-1} &= \begin{bmatrix} 1 & k(1-gk)^{-1} \\ 0 & (1-gk)^{-1} \end{bmatrix} \begin{bmatrix} 1 & 0 \\ g & 1 \end{bmatrix} \\ &= \begin{bmatrix} 1 & q \\ 0 & 1+gq \end{bmatrix} \begin{bmatrix} 1 & 0 \\ g & 1 \end{bmatrix} \end{aligned}$$

on substituting from (1.3.1). Since g is assumed stable, it is apparent that

$$\begin{bmatrix} 1 & -k \\ -g & 1 \end{bmatrix}^{-1}$$

is stable if and only if q is stable. This gives the following result:

Lemma 1.3.2 *Suppose g is stable. Then k is an internally-stabilizing controller for the feedback loop in Figure 1.4 if and only if $q = k(1-gk)^{-1}$ is stable. Equivalently, k is an internally-stabilizing controller if and only if $k = q(1+qg)^{-1}$ for some stable q.*

1.3.2 Solution of the disturbance attenuation problem

We may now return to the disturbance attenuation problem given in (1.3.2). Since the transfer functions that maps d to y is given by

$$h = 1 + gq, \tag{1.3.4}$$

one obtains

$$q = g^{-1}(h-1).$$

For the loop to be internally stable, we need to ensure that q is stable.

When g^{-1} is stable we could, in principle, set $q = -g^{-1}$, since this results in $h = 0$ and perfect disturbance attenuation. Unfortunately, such a q is not achievable by a realizable controller since k has infinite gain. We may, however, use $q = -(1-\epsilon)g^{-1}$ for an arbitrarily small ϵ. This gives $h = \epsilon$ and

$$k = -(\frac{1-\epsilon}{\epsilon})g^{-1}.$$

The controller is simply the negative of the inverse of the plant together with an arbitrarily high gain factor. This is not a surprising conclusion, because high gain improves disturbance attenuation and we know from classical root locus theory that a plant will be closed-loop stable for arbitrarily high gain if all the plant zeros are in the open-left-half plane.

In the case that $\boldsymbol{g}^{-1}$ is not stable, $\boldsymbol{q}$ will be stable if and only if

$$\boldsymbol{h}(z_i) = 1, \qquad i = 1, 2, \ldots, m, \tag{1.3.5}$$

for each zero, z_i, of $\boldsymbol{g}$ such that $\mathrm{R}_e(z_i) \geq 0$ (provided each of the zeros z_i is of multiplicity one). The optimal disturbance attenuation problem therefore requires us to find a stable closed-loop transfer function $\boldsymbol{h}$, of minimum infinity norm, which satisfies the interpolation constraints given in (1.3.5). It follows from (1.3.4) that the corresponding optimal $\boldsymbol{q}$ may be interpreted as the best stable approximate inverse of $-\boldsymbol{g}$, in the infinity norm sense.

It follows from the maximum modulus principle that the constraints $\boldsymbol{h}(z_i) = 1$ make it impossible to achieve $\|\boldsymbol{h}\|_\infty < 1$ when the plant has a right-half-plane zero. Since the plant is stable, we can set $\boldsymbol{k} = 0$ to achieve $y = d$, which is optimal in this case. The presence of a right-half-plane zero makes broadband disturbance attenuation impossible.

If some spectral information is available about the disturbance d, one may be able to improve the situation by introducing frequency response weighting. If d is bandlimited, we could seek to minimize $\|\boldsymbol{w}\boldsymbol{h}\|_\infty$ in which $\boldsymbol{w}$ is some low-pass stable and minimum phase weighting function. If $\|\boldsymbol{w}\boldsymbol{h}\|_\infty < 1$, it follows that $|\boldsymbol{h}(j\omega)| < |\boldsymbol{w}^{-1}(j\omega)|$ for all real ω. Since $|\boldsymbol{w}^{-1}(j\omega)|$ is small at low frequency due to the low pass nature of $\boldsymbol{w}$, it follows that $|\boldsymbol{h}(j\omega)|$ will also be small there. The idea is that $|\boldsymbol{h}(j\omega)|$ should be small over the range of frequencies for which $|d(j\omega)|$ is large. If we set $\widehat{\boldsymbol{h}} = \boldsymbol{w}\boldsymbol{h}$, one obtains

$$\widehat{\boldsymbol{h}} = \boldsymbol{w} + \boldsymbol{w}\boldsymbol{g}\boldsymbol{q}$$

and consequently that

$$\boldsymbol{q} = \boldsymbol{g}^{-1}\boldsymbol{w}^{-1}(\widehat{\boldsymbol{h}} - \boldsymbol{w}).$$

Under these conditions the $\boldsymbol{q}$-parameter will be stable if and only if the interpolation constraints

$$\widehat{\boldsymbol{h}}(z_i) = \boldsymbol{w}(z_i), \qquad i = 1, 2, \ldots, m,$$

are satisfied. If the right-half-plane plant zeros occur beyond the bandwidth of the weighting function, the $\boldsymbol{w}(z_i)$'s will be small and it is at least possible that an $\widehat{\boldsymbol{h}}$ can be found such that $\|\widehat{\boldsymbol{h}}\|_\infty < 1$. Since $\|\widehat{\boldsymbol{h}}\|_\infty < 1 \;\Rightarrow\; |\boldsymbol{h}(j\omega)| < |\boldsymbol{w}^{-1}(j\omega)|$ for all ω, we conclude that $|\boldsymbol{h}(j\omega)| < \epsilon$ whenever $|\boldsymbol{w}(j\omega)| \geq 1/\epsilon$. Consequently, by designing $\boldsymbol{w}$, one can guarantee an appropriate level of disturbance attenuation provided a controller exists such that $\|\widehat{\boldsymbol{h}}\|_\infty < 1$. Conversely, if $\boldsymbol{w}(z_i) > 1$ for at least one z_i, we must have $\|\widehat{\boldsymbol{h}}\|_\infty > 1$ and $|\boldsymbol{w}(j\omega)| \geq 1/\epsilon$ no longer ensures $|\boldsymbol{h}(j\omega)| < \epsilon$.

Main points of the section

1. The optimal disturbance attenuation problem is a feedback problem and it is possible to replace the nonlinear parametrization of $\boldsymbol{h}$ in terms of stabilizing controllers $\boldsymbol{k}$, by an affine parametrization of $\boldsymbol{h}$ in terms of stable functions $\boldsymbol{q}$. So far we have only established this fact for the stable plant case, but it is true in general.
2. The optimization problem requires us to find a stable transfer function $\boldsymbol{h}$ of minimum norm that satisfies the interpolation constraints given in (1.3.5). This is a classical Nevanlinna-Pick interpolation problem and satisfaction of the interpolation constraints guarantees the internal stability of the feedback system. We note that minimizing $\|\boldsymbol{h}\|_\infty$ is equivalent to finding a stable approximate inverse of the plant.
3. If the plant has a right-half-plane zero, the constraint $\boldsymbol{h}(z_i) = 1$ makes it impossible to achieve $\|\boldsymbol{h}\|_\infty < 1$ thereby attenuating unknown disturbances. In this case the best one can do is set $\boldsymbol{k} = 0$, since this will give $y = d$. If some spectral information about the disturbance is available, the situation may be improved if the right-half-plane zero is outside the bandwidth in which there is significant disturbance energy.

1.4 A robust stability problem

When a design team is faced with the problem of designing a controller to meet certain closed-loop performance specifications, they will hardly ever have a perfect model of the plant. As a consequence, the design process is complicated by the fact that the controller has to be designed to operate satisfactorily for all plants in some model set. The most fundamental of all design requirements is that of finding a controller to stabilize all plants in some class; we call this the robust stabilization problem. To set this problem up in a mathematical optimization framework, we need to decide on some representation of the model error. If the nominal plant model is $\boldsymbol{g}$, we can use an additive representation of the model error by describing the plant as $\boldsymbol{g} + \boldsymbol{\delta}$ in which the stable transfer function $\boldsymbol{\delta}$ represents the unknown dynamics; this is an alternative to the multiplicative description of model error given in Section 1.1.

Let us consider the robust stabilization problem in which some nominal plant model $\boldsymbol{g}$ is given, and we seek a stabilizing controller for all plants of the form $\boldsymbol{g} + \boldsymbol{\delta}$ in which the allowable $\|\boldsymbol{\delta}\|_\infty$ is maximized. A controller that maximizes $\|\boldsymbol{\delta}\|_\infty$ is optimally robust in the sense that it stabilizes the largest ball of plants with center $\boldsymbol{g}$. A block diagram of the set-up under consideration is given in Figure 1.5 and

$$z = (1 - \boldsymbol{kg})^{-1}\boldsymbol{k}w.$$

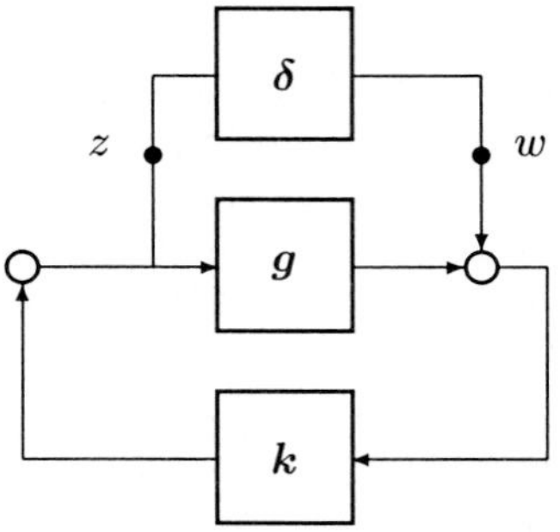

Figure 1.5: A robust stability problem.

If $\boldsymbol{\delta}$ and the nominal closed-loop system are stable, it follows from an earlier "small gain" argument based on the Nyquist criterion that the perturbed closed loop will also be stable provided

$$\|\boldsymbol{\delta}\|_\infty \|(1-\boldsymbol{kg})^{-1}\boldsymbol{k}\|_\infty < 1.$$

The optimal robustness problem therefore requires a stabilizing controller that minimizes $\|(1-\boldsymbol{kg})^{-1}\boldsymbol{k}\|_\infty$.

As before, in the case that the plant is stable, the solution is trivially obtained by setting $\boldsymbol{k}=0$; note, however, that $\boldsymbol{k}=0$ offers no protection against unstable perturbations however small! Before substituting

$$\boldsymbol{q}=(1-\boldsymbol{kg})^{-1}\boldsymbol{k},$$

we need the conditions on $\boldsymbol{q}$ that lead to a stable nominal closed-loop system. The mere stability of $\boldsymbol{q}$ is not enough in the unstable plant case. Since

$$\begin{bmatrix} 1 & -\boldsymbol{k} \\ -\boldsymbol{g} & 1 \end{bmatrix}^{-1} = \begin{bmatrix} 1+\boldsymbol{qg} & \boldsymbol{q} \\ (1+\boldsymbol{qg})\boldsymbol{g} & 1+\boldsymbol{gq} \end{bmatrix},$$

it is clear that the nominal closed loop will be stable if and only if

1. $\boldsymbol{q}$ is stable,

2. $\boldsymbol{gq}$ is stable, and

3. $(1+\boldsymbol{qg})\boldsymbol{g}$ is stable.

If $\boldsymbol{g}$ is stable and Condition 1 is satisfied, Conditions 2 and 3 follow automatically. If $(p_1, p_2, \ldots, p_m)$ are the right-half-plane poles of $\boldsymbol{g}$, it follows from Condition 2 that internal stability requires satisfaction of the interpolation constraints

2′. $\boldsymbol{q}(p_i)=0$, for $i=1,2,\ldots,m$,

while Condition 3 demands

3′. $(1+\boldsymbol{gq})(p_i)=0$, for $i=1,2,\ldots,m$.

To keep things simple, we will assume for the present that each unstable pole has multiplicity one and that $\mathrm{R}_e(p_i)>0$.

Since the closed-loop transfer function of interest is $\boldsymbol{q}$, the solution of the robust stabilization problem requires a stable $\boldsymbol{q}$ of minimum infinity norm that satisfies the interpolation constraints of Conditions 2′ and 3′.

As we will now show, it is possible to reformulate the problem so that there is one, rather than two, interpolation constraints per right-half-plane pole. To effect the reformulation, we introduce the completely unstable function[3]

$$\boldsymbol{a}=\prod_{i=1}^{m}\left(\frac{\bar{p}_i+s}{p_i-s}\right) \tag{1.4.1}$$

which has the property that $|\boldsymbol{a}(j\omega)|=1$ for all real ω. If we define $\tilde{\boldsymbol{q}}:=\boldsymbol{aq}$ it follows that:

1. $\|\boldsymbol{q}\|_\infty=\|\tilde{\boldsymbol{q}}\|_\infty$.
2. If $\tilde{\boldsymbol{q}}$ is stable, so is $\boldsymbol{q}$.
3. If $\tilde{\boldsymbol{q}}$ is stable, $\boldsymbol{q}(p_i)=0$, because $\boldsymbol{q}=\tilde{\boldsymbol{q}}\prod_{i=1}^{m}\left(\frac{p_i-s}{\bar{p}_i+s}\right)$.
4. $\tilde{\boldsymbol{q}}(p_i)=-(\boldsymbol{ag}^{-1})(p_i)\Rightarrow(1+\boldsymbol{qg})(p_i)=0$.

In its new form, the robust stabilization problem is one of finding a stable $\tilde{\boldsymbol{q}}$ of minimum infinity norm such that

$$\tilde{\boldsymbol{q}}(p_i)=-(\boldsymbol{ag}^{-1})(p_i) \qquad i=1,2,\ldots,m, \tag{1.4.2}$$

which is yet another Nevanlinna-Pick interpolation problem . The corresponding (optimal) controller may be found by back substitution as

$$\boldsymbol{k}=(\boldsymbol{a}+\tilde{\boldsymbol{q}}\boldsymbol{g})^{-1}\tilde{\boldsymbol{q}}. \tag{1.4.3}$$

Example 1.4.1. Suppose the plant is given by

$$\boldsymbol{g}=\frac{s+2}{(s+1)(s-1)}.$$

Since there is a single right-half-plane pole at $+1$, it follows that the allpass function given in equation (1.4.1) is

$$\boldsymbol{a}=\left(\frac{1+s}{1-s}\right)$$

[3]Such functions are sometimes known as Blaschke products.

in this particular case. As a consequence

$$-\boldsymbol{a}\boldsymbol{g}^{-1} = \frac{(s+1)^2}{(s+2)},$$

and the interpolation condition follows from (1.4.2) as

$$\tilde{\boldsymbol{q}}(1) = -\boldsymbol{a}\boldsymbol{g}^{-1}\big|_{s=1} = \frac{4}{3}.$$

It is now immediate from the maximum modulus principle that $\|\tilde{\boldsymbol{q}}\|_\infty \geq 4/3$, so that $\tilde{\boldsymbol{q}} = 4/3$ is optimal. Substitution into (1.4.3) yields

$$\boldsymbol{k} = -\frac{4(s+1)}{(3s+5)}$$

as the optimal controller that will stabilize the closed-loop system for all stable $\boldsymbol{\delta}$ such that $\|\boldsymbol{\delta}\|_\infty < 3/4$. ∇

Our second robust stabilization example shows that it is impossible to robustly stabilize a plant with a right-half-plane pole-zero pair that almost cancel. We expect such a robust stability problem to be hard, because problems of this type have an unstable mode that is almost uncontrollable.

Example 1.4.2. Consider the unstable plant

$$\boldsymbol{g} = \left(\frac{s-\alpha}{s-1}\right), \quad \alpha \neq 1,$$

which has a zero at α. As with the previous example, we require

$$\boldsymbol{a} = \left(\frac{1+s}{1-s}\right)$$

which gives

$$-\boldsymbol{a}\boldsymbol{g}^{-1} = \left(\frac{s+1}{s-\alpha}\right).$$

The only interpolation constraint is therefore

$$\tilde{\boldsymbol{q}}(1) = -\boldsymbol{a}\boldsymbol{g}^{-1}\big|_{s=1} = \frac{2}{1-\alpha}.$$

Invoking the maximum modulus principle yields $\tilde{\boldsymbol{q}} = 2/(1-\alpha)$ as the optimal interpolating function. Substitution into (1.4.3) gives

$$\boldsymbol{k} = \frac{2}{1+\alpha}$$

as the optimal controller. The closed loop will therefore be stable for all stable $\boldsymbol{\delta}$ such that $\|\boldsymbol{\delta}\|_\infty < |(1-\alpha)/2|$. From this we conclude that the stability margin measured by the maximum allowable $\|\boldsymbol{\delta}\|_\infty$ vanishes as $\alpha \to 1$. ∇

Our final example considers the robust stabilization of an integrator.

Example 1.4.3. Consider the case of

$$g = \frac{1}{s}.$$

At first sight this appears to be an awkward problem because the interpolation constraint occurs at $s = 0$, and the allpass function in (1.4.1) degenerates to 1. Suppose we ignore this difficulty for the moment and restrict our attention to constant controllers given by $k \leq 0$. This gives

$$\boldsymbol{q} = (1 - \boldsymbol{kg})^{-1}\boldsymbol{k} = \frac{ks}{s-k}$$

with

$$\begin{aligned} \|(1 - \boldsymbol{kg})^{-1}\boldsymbol{k}\|_\infty &= \left\| \frac{sk}{s-k} \right\|_{s=\infty} \\ &= |k|. \end{aligned}$$

To solve the problem we observe that if we want to stabilize the closed loop for any stable $\boldsymbol{\delta}$ such that $\|\boldsymbol{\delta}\|_\infty < 1/\epsilon$, we simply set $\boldsymbol{k} = -\epsilon$; ϵ may be arbitrarily small! In problems such as this one, which has an interpolation constraint on the imaginary axis, it is not possible to achieve the infimal value of the norm. For any positive number, we can achieve a closed-loop with that number as its infinity norm, but we cannot achieve a closed-loop infinity norm of zero. ∇

1.5 Concluding comments and references

We will now conclude this introductory chapter with a few remarks about the things we have already learned and the things we still hope to achieve.

1. $\mathcal{H}_\infty$ control problems can be cast as constrained minimization problems. The constraints come from an internal stability requirement and the object we seek to minimize is the infinity norm of some closed-loop transfer function. The constraints appear as interpolation constraints and stable closed-loop transfer functions that satisfy the interpolation data may be found using the classical Nevanlinna-Schur algorithm. This approach to control problems is due to Zames [227] and is developed in Zames and Francis [228] and Kimura [118]. In our examples we have exploited the fact that there is no need for the Nevanlinna algorithm when there is only one interpolation constraint.

2. We will not be discussing the classical Nevanlinna-Pick-Schur theory on analytic interpolation in this book. The interested reader may find this material in several places such as Garnett [69] and Walsh [207] for a purely function theoretic point of view, and [53, 43, 44, 129, 221, 227, 228], for various applications of analytic interpolation to system theory.

3. The reader may be puzzled as to why the interpolation theory approach to $\mathcal{H}_\infty$ control problems is being abandoned at this early stage of our book. There are several reasons for this:

   (a) Interpolation theoretic methods become awkward and unwieldy in the multivariable case and in situations where interpolation with multiplicities is required; if there are several interpolation constraints associated with a single right-half-plane frequency point, we say that the problem involves interpolation with multiplicities.

   (b) It is our opinion that interpolation theoretic methods are computationally inferior to the state-space methods we will develop in later chapters of the book. Computational issues become important in realistic design problems in which one is forced to deal with systems of high order.

   (c) Frequency domain methods (such as interpolation theory) are restricted to time-invariant problems. The state-space methods we will develop are capable of treating linear time varying problems.

   (d) It is not easy to treat multitarget problems in an interpolation based framework. To see this we cite one of many possible problems involving robust stabilization with performance. Take the case of disturbance attenuation with robust stability, in which we require a characterization of the set

$$\arg\min_{\boldsymbol{k}\in\mathcal{S}} \left\| \begin{bmatrix} (1-\boldsymbol{gk})^{-1} \\ \boldsymbol{k}(1-\boldsymbol{gk})^{-1} \end{bmatrix} \right\|_\infty$$

   with $\mathcal{S}$ denoting the set of all stabilizing controllers. If the plant is stable, we may introduce the $\boldsymbol{q}$-parameter to obtain

$$\arg\min_{\boldsymbol{q}\in\mathcal{H}_\infty} \left\| \begin{bmatrix} 1 \\ 0 \end{bmatrix} + \begin{bmatrix} \boldsymbol{g} \\ 1 \end{bmatrix} \boldsymbol{q} \right\|_\infty .$$

   Problems of this type are not directly addressable via interpolation due to the nonsquare nature of $\begin{bmatrix} \boldsymbol{g} \\ 1 \end{bmatrix}$; we will not pursue this point at this stage.

4. Solving each $\mathcal{H}_\infty$ control problem from scratch, as we have done so far, is a practice we will now dispense with. This approach is both effort intensive and an intellectually clumsy way to proceed. Rather, we will develop a single solution framework that captures many $\mathcal{H}_\infty$ optimization problems of general interest as special cases. A large part of the remainder of the book will be devoted to the development of a comprehensive theory for multivariable, multitarget problems.

5. The solutions to the problems we have considered so far have a common theme. With the exception of the robust stabilization of an integrator, the

magnitudes of the optimal closed-loop transfer functions are a constant function of frequency. It turns out that this is a general property of the solutions of all single-input, single-output problems that are free of imaginary axis interpolation constraints. In each case, the optimal closed-loop transfer function is a scalar multiple of a rational inner function. Inner functions are stable allpass functions, and rational allpass functions have the form

$$\boldsymbol{a} = \prod_{i=1}^{m} \left(\frac{\bar{p}_i + s}{p_i - s} \right)$$

which we have already encountered. Since the poles and zeros of allpass functions are symmetrically located about the imaginary axis, it is not hard to see that they have the property $|\boldsymbol{a}(j\omega)| = 1$ for all real ω. The "flat frequency response" property of optimal closed-loop transfer functions is fundamental in the design of frequency weighting functions.

1.6 Problems

Problem 1.1. Prove that $\|\cdot\|_\infty$ is a norm and that $\|\boldsymbol{gh}\|_\infty \le \|\boldsymbol{g}\|_\infty \|\boldsymbol{h}\|_\infty$.

Problem 1.2. Consider the frequency weighted disturbance attenuation problem of finding a stabilizing controller that minimizes $\|\boldsymbol{w}(1-\boldsymbol{gk})^{-1}\|_\infty$. If

$$\boldsymbol{g} = \left(\frac{s-\alpha}{s+2} \right), \qquad \boldsymbol{w} = \left(\frac{s+4}{2(s+1)} \right),$$

in which α is real, show that when $0 \le \alpha \le 2$ there is no stabilizing controller such that

$$|(1-\boldsymbol{gk})^{-1}(j\omega)| < |\boldsymbol{w}^{-1}(j\omega)|, \qquad \text{for all } \omega.$$

Problem 1.3. Consider the command tracking problem in which

$$\boldsymbol{g} = \left(\frac{(s-1)^2}{(s+2)(s+3)} \right), \qquad \boldsymbol{h} = \frac{1}{s+4}.$$

Show that the error $\boldsymbol{e} = \boldsymbol{h} - \boldsymbol{gf}$ must satisfy the interpolation constraints

$$\boldsymbol{e}(1) = \frac{1}{5}, \qquad \frac{d\boldsymbol{e}}{ds}(1) = \frac{-1}{25}.$$

The construction of such an $\boldsymbol{e}$ requires the solution of an interpolation problem with derivative constraints.

Problem 1.4. Suppose an uncertain plant is described by $\boldsymbol{g}(1+\boldsymbol{\delta})$ in which $\boldsymbol{g}$ is a given unstable transfer function and $\boldsymbol{\delta}$ is a stable but otherwise unknown linear perturbation bounded in magnitude by $\|\boldsymbol{\delta}\|_\infty < \alpha$.

1. Give an interpolation theoretic procedure for finding the optimal controller that stabilizes every $\boldsymbol{g}(1+\boldsymbol{\delta})$ of the type described and with α maximized. (Hint: you need to introduce the stable minimum phase spectral factor $\boldsymbol{m}$ that satisfies $\boldsymbol{g}\boldsymbol{g}^{\sim} = \boldsymbol{m}\boldsymbol{m}^{\sim}$.)
2. Give two reasons why α must always be strictly less than one.
3. Suppose $\boldsymbol{g} = \left(\frac{s-2}{s-1}\right)$. Show that the largest achievable value of α is $\alpha_{max} = \frac{1}{3}$, and that the corresponding controller is $\boldsymbol{k} = \frac{3}{4}$.

Problem 1.5. Suppose an uncertain plant is described by $\boldsymbol{g} + \boldsymbol{\delta}$ in which $\boldsymbol{g}$ is a given unstable transfer function and $\boldsymbol{\delta}$ is a stable but otherwise unknown linear perturbation such that $|\boldsymbol{\delta}(j\omega)| < |\boldsymbol{w}(j\omega)|$ for all ω. The function $\boldsymbol{w}$ is a stable and minimum phase frequency weight.

1. Show that $\boldsymbol{k}$ will stabilize all $\boldsymbol{g} + \boldsymbol{\delta}$ with $\boldsymbol{\delta}$ in the above class provided it stabilizes $\boldsymbol{g}$ and $\|\boldsymbol{w}\boldsymbol{k}(1-\boldsymbol{g}\boldsymbol{k})^{-1}\|_\infty \le 1$.
2. Explain how to find a stabilizing controller that minimizes $\|\boldsymbol{w}\boldsymbol{k}(1-\boldsymbol{g}\boldsymbol{k})^{-1}\|_\infty$.
3. If $\boldsymbol{g} = \left(\frac{s+1}{s-2}\right)$ and $\boldsymbol{w} = \left(\frac{s+1}{s+4}\right)$, find a controller (if one exists) that will stabilize every $\boldsymbol{g} + \boldsymbol{\delta}$ in which $\boldsymbol{\delta}$ is stable with $|\boldsymbol{\delta}(j\omega)| < |\boldsymbol{w}(j\omega)|$ for all ω.

Problem 1.6. Consider the multivariable command response optimization problem in which the stable transfer function matrices $\boldsymbol{G}$ and $\boldsymbol{H}$ are given and a stable prefilter $\boldsymbol{F}$ is required such that $\boldsymbol{E} = \boldsymbol{H} - \boldsymbol{G}\boldsymbol{F}$ is small in some sense.

1. If $\boldsymbol{G}$ is nonsingular for almost all s and $\boldsymbol{F}$ is to be stable, show that $\boldsymbol{H} - \boldsymbol{E}$ must have a zero at each right-half-plane zero of $\boldsymbol{G}$, taking multiplicities into account.
2. If all the right-half-plane zeros z_i, $i = 1, 2, \ldots, m$, of $\boldsymbol{G}$ are of multiplicity one, show that $\boldsymbol{F}$ is stable if and only if there exist vectors $w_i \neq 0$ such that

$$w_i^* \begin{bmatrix} \boldsymbol{H}(z_i) - \boldsymbol{E}(z_i) & \boldsymbol{G}(z_i) \end{bmatrix} = 0.$$

   Conclude from this that multivariable problems have vector valued interpolation constraints. What are they?

The relationship between vector interpolation and $\mathcal{H}_\infty$ control is studied in detail in Limebeer and Anderson [129] and Kimura [119].

2

Multivariable Frequency Response Design

2.1 Introduction

By the 1950s, classical frequency response methods had developed into powerful design tools widely used by practicing engineers. There are several reasons for the continued success of these methods for dealing with single-loop problems and multi-loop problems arising from some multi-input-multi-output (MIMO) plant. Firstly, there is a clear connection between frequency response plots and data that can be experimentally acquired. Secondly, trained engineers find these methods relatively easy to learn. Thirdly, their graphical nature provides an important visual aid that is greatly enhanced by modern computer graphics. Fourthly, these methods supply the designer with a rich variety of manipulative and diagnostic aids that enable a design to be refined in a systematic way. Finally, simple rules of thumb for standard controller configurations and processes can be developed. The most widespread of these is the Ziegler-Nichols method for tuning PID controller parameters based on the simple "process reaction curve" model. Unfortunately, these classical techniques can falter on MIMO problems that contain a high degree of cross-coupling between the controlled and measured variables.

In order to design controllers for MIMO systems using classical single-loop techniques, one requires decomposition procedures that split the design task into a set of single-loop problems that may be regarded as independent. Such decomposition methods have many attractive features and are certainly applicable in some cases, but there are also some fundamental difficulties. How does one find design specifications for the derived single-loop problems that are in some sense equivalent to the specifications for the multivariable problem? Do good gain and phase margins for the single loop problems imply good stability properties for the multivariable problem?

A completely different approach to frequency response design emerged from Wiener's work on prediction theory for stochastic processes. By invoking a variational argument, he showed that certain design problems involving quadratic integral performance indices may be solved analytically. It turned out that the solution involved an integral equation which he had studied ten years earlier with E. Hopf—thus the term Wiener-Hopf optimization. These optimization based design procedures have the advantage that they automatically uncover inconsistent design specifications. In addition, because of their optimization properties, the designer is never left with the haunting thought that a better solution might be possible.

In its early form, the Wiener-Hopf theory could not tackle MIMO or time-varying problems. These limitations were overcome with Kalman's introduction of state-space methods. The key observation was that the solution of the Wiener-Hopf equation, and hence the optimal control law, may be obtained from the solution of a quadratic matrix equation known as a Riccati equation.

These ideas formed the core of what was for a long time known as "Modern Control", although this term has now fallen into disuse. The theory of minimizing quadratic integral performance indices subject to linear state-space dynamics driven by Gaussian white noise is commonly known as Linear Quadratic Gaussian (LQG) optimal control; the term $\mathcal{H}_2$ optimal control is sometimes used for deterministic versions of this problem. The mathematics and the insight that the "Modern" era brought into the field has an important bearing on the mathematical techniques and computational procedures used in the theory and computation of $\mathcal{H}_\infty$ optimal controllers.

Despite the success of LQG optimal control and optimal estimation in the aerospace sector, applications in the process industries have been few and far between. As a result, a number of authors raised objections to the theory, complaining that it fails to address the real issues of feedback control. In an attempt to rectify this situation, there was a resurgence of interest in classical frequency response ideas and several attempts were made to generalize the Nyquist criterion to the multivariable case. An early version of the generalized Nyquist criterion came from the relationship

$$\begin{aligned}\det(I - \boldsymbol{G}) &= \det\big((\boldsymbol{D} - \boldsymbol{N})\boldsymbol{D}^{-1}\big)\\ &= \frac{\det(\boldsymbol{D} - \boldsymbol{N})}{\det(\boldsymbol{D})}\\ &= \frac{\text{closed loop characteristic polynomial}}{\text{open loop characteristic polynomial}},\end{aligned}$$

in which $\boldsymbol{G} = \boldsymbol{N}\boldsymbol{D}^{-1}$ is a coprime polynomial matrix fraction description. This relationship allows closed-loop stability to be tested by counting the number of encirclements of the origin by the Nyquist diagram of $\det(I - \boldsymbol{G})$, but is of limited value in design because of the complexity of the relationship between the entries of a matrix and its determinant. Later refinements were based on Nyquist diagrams of the diagonal entries of $\boldsymbol{G}$ and on plots of the eigenvalues of $\boldsymbol{G}$. Since

$$\begin{aligned} \det(I - \boldsymbol{G}) &= \prod_{i=1}^{m} \lambda_i(I - \boldsymbol{G}) \\ &= \prod_{i=1}^{m} \big(1 - \lambda_i(\boldsymbol{G})\big), \end{aligned}$$

we see that the number of encirclements of the origin by $\det(I - \boldsymbol{G})$ is the sum of the number of encirclements of $+1$ by the eigenvalues of $\boldsymbol{G}$. The controller design problem may then be considered as a problem requiring the shaping of the open-loop eigenvalue loci.[1]

The relationship between a matrix and its eigenvalues is complex, but the eigenvalues are known to lie in circles centered on the diagonal entries of the matrix. The radii of these circles depend on magnitude of the off-diagonal entries—in the case of triangular matrices, the diagonal entries are the eigenvalues.[2] These ideas form the basis of Nyquist array design methodologies. Crucial to these eigenvalue-based techniques is the belief that control objectives for the overall multivariable plant can be posed as objectives on the eigenvalue loci. The generalized Nyquist criterion certainly means that stability can be assessed via a consideration of the eigenvalues. What is less clear is whether eigenvalue "gain margins" and eigenvalue "phase margins" imply anything about stability robustness for the overall system. In general, they do not.

It also became apparent that LQG optimal controllers could exhibit poor stability robustness properties. This came as something of a surprise, because full state-feedback LQ optimal controllers and Kalman filters, considered separately, have impressive robust stability properties including at least 60° of phase margin, an infinite gain margin and a 50% gain-reduction tolerance. In contrast, the robustness of an LQG optimal design must be analyzed *a posteriori*—LQG optimality does not automatically ensure stability robustness.

During the 1970s, robust stability for MIMO systems and methods of achieving it emerged as a key problem in feedback design. It cannot be addressed by considering the eigenvalues of the plant, nor is it guaranteed by LQG optimality. We will now illustrate these points by examining two examples.

Example 2.1.1. Early frequency response methods for designing controllers for multivariable systems use diagonalization techniques to decompose the design into a number of single-loop problems. In Figure 2.1, the plant $\boldsymbol{G}$ is given and a controller $\boldsymbol{K}$ is required. The designer may introduce loop transformations M

[1] The eigenvalue loci are called the "characteristic loci" by many authors. Since we shall argue that the eigenvalues of the plant are anything but characteristic of control system performance and robust stability, we prefer to use the descriptive term "eigenvalue loci".

[2] See Gershgorin's theorem in [172, 144].

and N as shown in Figure 2.2. If M and N can be chosen so that $\widehat{\boldsymbol{G}} = N\boldsymbol{G}M$ is diagonal, then a diagonal $\widehat{\boldsymbol{K}}$ can be found using single-loop methods. The controller is then obtained from a reversal of the scaling to give $\boldsymbol{K} = M\widehat{\boldsymbol{K}}N$.

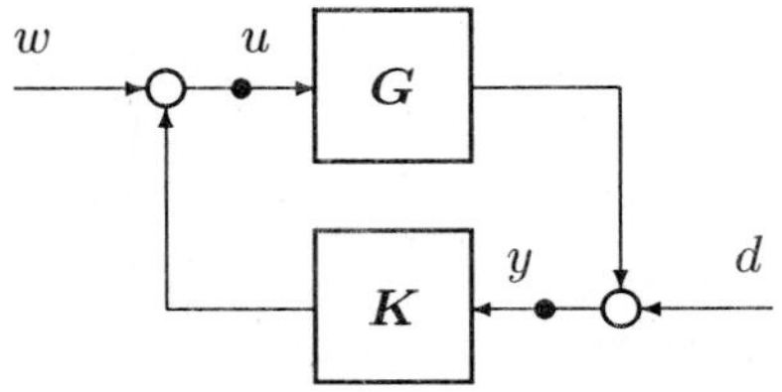

Figure 2.1: A typical feedback loop.

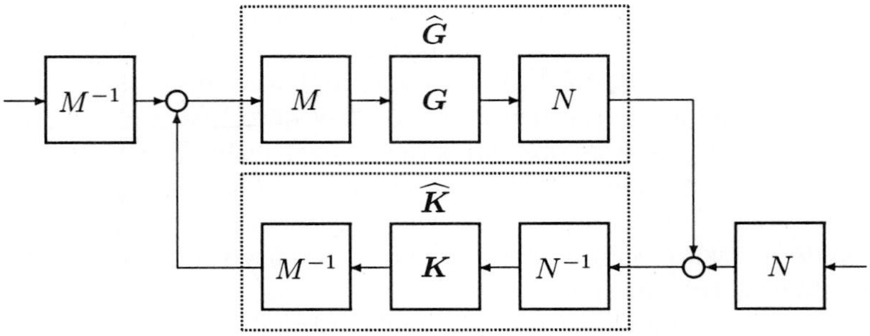

Figure 2.2: Analysis and design configuration.

From the point of view of nominal stability, there is nothing wrong with this approach. The difficulties arise when robust stability is considered.

To see this, suppose the transfer function matrix $\boldsymbol{G}$ in Figure 2.1 is given by

$$\boldsymbol{G} = \frac{1}{(s+1)(s+2)} \begin{bmatrix} 2-47s & 56s \\ -42s & 50s+2 \end{bmatrix},$$

which may be decomposed as

$$\boldsymbol{G} = \begin{bmatrix} 7 & 8 \\ 6 & 7 \end{bmatrix} \begin{bmatrix} \frac{1}{s+1} & 0 \\ 0 & \frac{2}{s+2} \end{bmatrix} \begin{bmatrix} 7 & -8 \\ -6 & 7 \end{bmatrix},$$

giving

$$M = \begin{bmatrix} 7 & 8 \\ 6 & 7 \end{bmatrix}, \quad \widehat{\boldsymbol{G}} = \begin{bmatrix} \frac{1}{s+1} & 0 \\ 0 & \frac{2}{s+2} \end{bmatrix}, \quad N = \begin{bmatrix} 7 & -8 \\ -6 & 7 \end{bmatrix}.$$

Since $M = N^{-1}$, the eigenvalues of $\boldsymbol{G}$ are given by the diagonal entries of $\widehat{\boldsymbol{G}}$. The closed loop will be stable for

$$\widehat{\boldsymbol{K}} = \begin{bmatrix} \widehat{k}_1 & 0 \\ 0 & \widehat{k}_2 \end{bmatrix}$$

provided $-\infty < \widehat{k}_i < 1$ for $i = 1, 2$. The Nyquist diagrams of $\widehat{\boldsymbol{G}}_{11}$ and $\widehat{\boldsymbol{G}}_{22}$ also reveal that both these systems have phase margins of 180° if $\widehat{k}_1$ and $\widehat{k}_2$ are set to -1. Therefore, if we treat $\widehat{\boldsymbol{G}}_{11}$ and $\widehat{\boldsymbol{G}}_{22}$ as single loop systems, it would appear that the feedback loop in Figure 2.2 with $\widehat{\boldsymbol{K}} = -I$ has desirable closed-loop stability properties. This yields $\boldsymbol{K} = M\widehat{\boldsymbol{K}}N = -I$ as the controller for the actual closed loop of Figure 2.1.

To see that this controller does *not* result in a robustly stable closed loop, consider the (nondynamic) controller

$$\boldsymbol{K} = \begin{bmatrix} k_1 & 0 \\ 0 & k_2 \end{bmatrix}.$$

If we set $k_1 = k + \delta$ and $k_2 = k - \delta$, it may be shown that the closed-loop characteristic polynomial is given by

$$s^2 + (3 - 3k + 97\delta)s + 2\big((1-k)^2 - \delta^2\big).$$

Closed-loop stability therefore requires

$$\begin{aligned} 3 - 3k + 97\delta &> 0 \\ \Leftrightarrow 3 - 50k_2 + 47k_1 &> 0, \end{aligned}$$

since $k = \frac{k_1+k_2}{2}$ and $\delta = \frac{k_1-k_2}{2}$, and

$$\begin{aligned} (1-k)^2 - \delta^2 &> 0 \\ \Leftrightarrow \left(1 - \frac{k_1+k_2}{2}\right)^2 - \left(\frac{k_1-k_2}{2}\right)^2 &> 0 \\ \Leftrightarrow 1 - k_1 - k_2 + k_1k_2 &> 0. \end{aligned}$$

With k_1 set at its nominal value of -1, the loop is *unstable* if $k_2 \geq -44/50 = -0.88$, since this would make the linear term of the closed-loop characteristic polynomial nonpositive. If $k_2 = -1$, the loop is *unstable* if $k_1 \leq -53/47 = -1.128$. Indeed, the gains $(k_1, k_2) = (-1.09, -0.9)$, a distance of 0.1345 from the nominal $(-1, -1)$ point, creates an unstable loop.[3] This lack of stability robustness is not evident from the eigenvalue loci of $\widehat{\boldsymbol{G}}$.

We conclude that the eigenvalue loci of a multivariable plant are not good robust stability indicators. Eigenvalues may also be misleading indicators of performance,

[3] It may be shown that $(k_1, k_2) = (-1.0599, -0.9363)$ minimizes the distance from the line $3 - 50k_2 + 47k_1 = 0$ to the point $(-1, -1)$. The minimum distance is 0.0874.

since they cannot always account for loop interactions. For example, suppose a transfer function has the form

$$\boldsymbol{G} = \begin{bmatrix} 1 & \phi(s) \\ 0 & 1 \end{bmatrix}.$$

The eigenvalues of $\boldsymbol{G}$ are independent of the off-diagonal term $\phi(s)$, so they provide no indication of the fact that $\phi(s)$ may cause significant inter-loop coupling between the second input and the first output. ∇

The next example demonstrates that an LQG optimal controller may lead to a closed loop that is arbitrarily close to instability.

Example 2.1.2. Consider the LQG problem with dynamics

$$\begin{aligned} \begin{bmatrix} \dot{x}_1 \\ \dot{x}_2 \end{bmatrix} &= \begin{bmatrix} 1 & 1 \\ 0 & 1 \end{bmatrix} \begin{bmatrix} x_1 \\ x_2 \end{bmatrix} + \begin{bmatrix} 0 \\ 1 \end{bmatrix} u + \begin{bmatrix} 1 \\ 1 \end{bmatrix} w \\ y &= \begin{bmatrix} 1 & 0 \end{bmatrix} \begin{bmatrix} x_1 \\ x_2 \end{bmatrix} + v. \end{aligned}$$

The vector $x = \begin{bmatrix} x_1 & x_2 \end{bmatrix}'$ is the state vector, u is the control input, y is the measured output and w and v are independent Gaussian white noises with intensities $\sigma \geq 0$ and 1 respectively. The performance index is

$$J = \mathcal{E}\left\{ \lim_{T\to\infty} \frac{1}{T} \int_0^T \rho(x_1 + x_2)^2 + u^2 \, dt \right\},$$

in which $\mathcal{E}(\cdot)$ is the expectation operator and ρ is a real nonnegative parameter. The optimal controller is given by

$$u = \boldsymbol{k} y,$$

in which

$$\boldsymbol{k} = \frac{\alpha\beta(1 - 2s)}{s^2 + (\alpha + \beta - 2)s + 1 + \alpha\beta}$$

with

$$\alpha = 2 + \sqrt{4 + \rho}, \qquad \beta = 2 + \sqrt{4 + \sigma}.$$

Now consider the closed-loop system shown in Figure 2.3, in which κ is a gain with nominal value $+1$.

A calculation shows that only the linear and constant terms in the closed-loop characteristic polynomial are functions of κ and that these terms are given by

$$\beta + \alpha - 4 + 2(\kappa - 1)\alpha\beta \quad \text{and} \quad 1 + (1 - \kappa)\alpha\beta$$

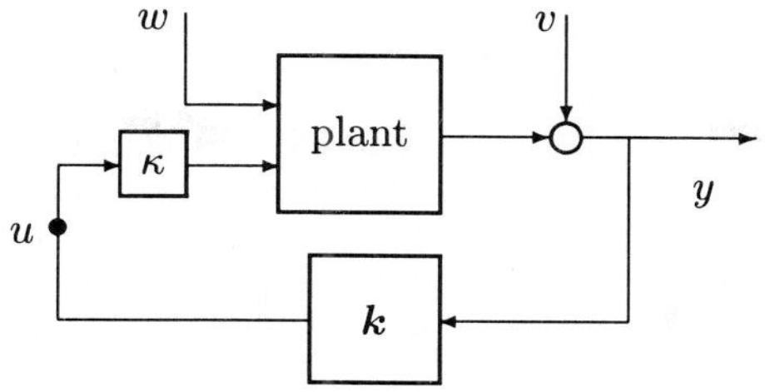

Figure 2.3: LQG closed loop with variable gain.

respectively. A necessary condition for stability is that both these terms are positive. This is easily seen to be true for the nominal loop $\kappa = 1$. However, for $\alpha,\ \beta = 4$ (*i.e.*, $\rho = 0$ and $\sigma = 0$), the necessary condition for stability is

$$1 - \frac{1}{8} < \kappa < 1 + \frac{1}{16}.$$

The situation deteriorates if α and β are large. For the case $\beta = \alpha$, the necessary condition for stability becomes

$$1 + \frac{2}{\alpha^2} - \frac{1}{\alpha} < \kappa < 1 + \frac{1}{\alpha^2}.$$

The gain margin can therefore be made arbitrarily small by selecting α and β (equivalently, ρ and σ) sufficiently large.

We conclude that LQG optimality does not guarantee stability robustness. ∇

Main points of the section

1. Single-loop design techniques may be used for MIMO systems when the cross-coupling is relatively weak.
2. The eigenvalues of the open-loop plant $\boldsymbol{G}$ may be used to assess the stability of the nominal closed-loop system. Despite this, the eigenvalues of $\boldsymbol{G}$ do not give reliable information about the robust stability or performance of the closed loop.
3. LQG optimality does not automatically ensure good robustness properties. The robust stability of a LQG optimal closed loop must be checked *a posteriori*. This fundamental drawback associated with quadratic norm minimization methods was one of the triggers that initiated research into infinity norm minimization approaches.
4. Robustness is a key feedback objective which must be addressed. A set of robust stability (and robust performance) indicators for multivariable systems is required. In this chapter, we will motivate the use of singular values in this role.

2.2 Singular values

The singular value decomposition (SVD) is one of the most important tools in modern numerical linear algebra and numerical analysis. Owing to the linear algebraic nature of many control problems and the importance of the robust stability issue, the singular value decomposition has found its way into control and system theory. The aim of this section is to introduce the singular value decomposition and to examine some of the properties of singular values. Subsequent sections will show how singular values may be used to analyze the robustness and performance of control systems.

In order to avoid excessive notational clutter when dealing with vectors and matrices, dimensions are only rarely mentioned explicitly. Whenever a sum of matrices such as $Q+R$ appears, it is assumed that the dimensions are compatible for addition. A similar assumption is made in the case of matrix products. When an inverse such as Q^{-1} is written, it is assumed that the matrix Q is square and that the inverse exists.

2.2.1 The singular value decomposition

In this section we will establish some of the fundamental properties of the singular value decomposition (SVD). Our first result ensures the existence of the SVD.

Lemma 2.2.1 *For any $m \times p$ complex matrix Q, there exist $m \times m$ and $p \times p$ unitary matrices Y and U, and a real matrix Σ, such that*

$$Q = Y \begin{bmatrix} \Sigma & 0 \\ 0 & 0 \end{bmatrix} U^*, \tag{2.2.1}$$

in which $\Sigma = diag(\sigma_1, \ldots, \sigma_r)$ with $\sigma_1 \geq \sigma_2 \geq \ldots \geq \sigma_r > 0$ and $\min(m,p) \geq r$. When Q is real, Y and U may be chosen orthogonal. Expression (2.2.1) is called a singular value decomposition (SVD) of Q.

Proof. A proof appears in many places—see Stewart [198] for example. ■

Since $\sigma_1, \sigma_2, \ldots, \sigma_r$ are the positive square roots of the positive eigenvalues of Q^*Q or QQ^*, they are uniquely determined by Q. All the nonnegative square roots of the eigenvalues of Q^*Q will be called the *singular values of* Q:

$$\sigma_1, \sigma_2, \ldots, \sigma_r > 0, \text{ while } \sigma_{r+1} = \ldots = \sigma_p = 0. \tag{2.2.2}$$

The set of singular values, the *maximum singular value* and the *minimum singular value* of Q will be denoted by

$$\begin{aligned} \sigma(Q) &= \{\sigma_i : i = 1, \ldots, p\} && (2.2.3) \\ \overline{\sigma}(Q) &= \sigma_1 && (2.2.4) \\ \underline{\sigma}(Q) &= \sigma_p. && (2.2.5) \end{aligned}$$

Since Y and U are nonsingular, the rank of Q is the same as that of Σ, which is equal to the number of nonzero singular values:

$$\text{rank}(Q) = r.$$

A matrix Q has no zero singular values (*i.e.*, $\underline{\sigma}(Q) > 0$) if and only if Q has full column rank. When Q is square, $\underline{\sigma}(Q) > 0$ if and only if Q is nonsingular. In this case $Q^{-1} = U\Sigma^{-1}Y^*$ and the singular values of Q^{-1} are $\sigma_r^{-1}, \sigma_{r-1}^{-1}, \ldots, \sigma_1^{-1}$. In particular

$$\overline{\sigma}(Q^{-1}) = \frac{1}{\underline{\sigma}(Q)}.$$

To give the SVD an operator theoretic interpretation, we regard the matrix Q as a linear map from the vector space $\mathbb{C}^p$ into the vector space $\mathbb{C}^m$, defined by

$$\begin{aligned} Q &: \mathbb{C}^p \mapsto \mathbb{C}^m \\ &: u \mapsto Qu. \end{aligned}$$

The operator theoretic interpretation of a matrix is important in the analysis of the input-output properties of system transfer functions. Suppose u_i and y_i denote the columns of the unitary matrices U and Y in the SVD (2.2.1). Then the SVD of Q may be written in the form of the dyadic expansion

$$Q = \sum_{i=1}^{r} \sigma_i y_i u_i^*.$$

Since U is unitary, $u_i^* u_j = \delta_{ij}$ (the Kronecker delta) and it follows that u_j is mapped into $\sigma_j y_j$ by Q:

$$Qu_j = \left(\sum_{i=1}^{r} \sigma_i y_i u_i^* \right) u_j = \sigma_j y_j.$$

We may therefore regard the singular value σ_j as a dilation or gain factor for the matrix Q restricted to the one-dimensional subspace spanned by u_j.

The maximum singular value $\overline{\sigma}(Q)$ and the minimum singular value $\underline{\sigma}(Q)$ play a particularly important role in our analysis and are given by the identities

$$\overline{\sigma}(Q) = \max_{\|u\|=1} \|Qu\| \tag{2.2.6}$$

$$\underline{\sigma}(Q) = \min_{\|u\|=1} \|Qu\|, \tag{2.2.7}$$

in which the vector norm is the Euclidean norm. Thus $\overline{\sigma}(Q)$ and $\underline{\sigma}(Q)$ are respectively the maximum gain and the minimum gain of the matrix Q.

To verify (2.2.6) and (2.2.7), note that

$$\begin{aligned} \|Qu\|^2 &= u^* U \Sigma Y^* Y \Sigma U^* u \\ &= x^* \Sigma^2 x \end{aligned}$$

where $x = U^* u$. Since $\|x\| = \|u\|$, it follows that

$$\max_{\|u\|=1} \|Qu\| = \max_{\|x\|=1} \|\Sigma x\|.$$

Now

$$\|\Sigma x\|^2 = \sum_{i=1}^{p} \sigma_i^2 |x_i|^2,$$

subject to $\|x\|^2 = 1$, is maximized by setting $x_1 = 1$ and $x_i = 0$ for all $i \neq 1$ and is minimized by setting $x_p = 1$ and $x_i = 0$ for all $i \neq p$. This verifies that (2.2.6) and (2.2.7) hold.

Identities (2.2.6) and (2.2.7) are in fact special cases of a general minimax characterization of singular values:

$$\begin{aligned} \sigma_i(Q) &= \min_{dim(\mathcal{S})=p-i+1} \max_{\substack{u\in\mathcal{S}\\ \|u\|=1}} \|Qu\| & (2.2.8)\\ &= \max_{dim(\mathcal{S})=i} \min_{\substack{u\in\mathcal{S}\\ \|u\|=1}} \|Qu\|, & (2.2.9) \end{aligned}$$

in which Q is $m \times p$ (see [198]). Identities (2.2.6) and (2.2.7) follow from (2.2.8) and (2.2.9) by setting $i = 1$ and $i = p$.

The identity (2.2.6) implies that $\overline{\sigma}(Q)$ is the norm of the operator Q induced by the Euclidean norm:

$$\begin{aligned} \overline{\sigma}(Q) &= \|Q\| & (2.2.10)\\ &= \max_{\|u\|=1} \|Qu\| \\ &= \max_{u\neq 0} \frac{\|Qu\|}{\|u\|}. \end{aligned}$$

It is easy to show that $\|Q\|$ is indeed a norm using the properties of the Euclidean norm on $\mathbb{C}^m$ and $\mathbb{C}^p$:

1. $\|Q\| \geq 0$ is obvious, and $\|Q\| = 0 \Leftrightarrow \|Qu\| = 0\ \forall u \Leftrightarrow Q = 0$.
2. Let $\alpha \in \mathbb{C}$. Then $\|\alpha Q\| = \max_{\|u\|=1} \|\alpha Qu\| = \max_{\|u\|=1} |\alpha| \|Qu\| = |\alpha| \|Q\|$.
3. $\|Q + R\| = \max_{\|u\|=1} \|Qu + Ru\| \leq \max_{\|u\|=1}(\|Qu\| + \|Ru\|) \leq \|Q\| + \|R\|$. Thus
$$\|Q + R\| \leq \|Q\| + \|R\|. \qquad (2.2.11)$$

In addition to these three properties, which all norms must share, induced norms satisfy

4. The submultiplicative property:

$$\|QR\| \leq \|Q\|\|R\|. \tag{2.2.12}$$

To prove this, note that if $R = 0$ the inequality is trivial. Otherwise, for $R \neq 0$, we have

$$\begin{aligned}
\|QR\| &= \max_{\|u\|=1} \|QRu\| \\
&= \max_{\|u\|=1} \left(\frac{\|QRu\|}{\|Ru\|} \|Ru\| \right) \\
&\leq \max_{v \neq 0} \frac{\|Qv\|}{\|v\|} \max_{\|u\|=1} \|Ru\| \\
&= \|Q\|\|R\|.
\end{aligned}$$

2.2.2 Singular value inequalities

Using fact that the maximum singular value defines an induced norm, we have the following inequalities:

$$\overline{\sigma}(Q+R) \leq \overline{\sigma}(Q) + \overline{\sigma}(R) \tag{2.2.13}$$

$$\overline{\sigma}(QR) \leq \overline{\sigma}(Q)\overline{\sigma}(R). \tag{2.2.14}$$

These inequalities and some elementary consequences of them are fundamental to the singular value analysis of feedback systems.

Lemma 2.2.2

$$|\overline{\sigma}(Q) - \overline{\sigma}(R)| \leq \overline{\sigma}(Q+R) \leq \overline{\sigma}(Q) + \overline{\sigma}(R) \tag{2.2.15}$$

$$\underline{\sigma}(Q)\overline{\sigma}(R) \leq \overline{\sigma}(QR) \leq \overline{\sigma}(Q)\overline{\sigma}(R) \tag{2.2.16}$$

$$\max\{\underline{\sigma}(R) - \overline{\sigma}(Q), \underline{\sigma}(Q) - \overline{\sigma}(R)\} \leq \underline{\sigma}(Q+R) \leq \underline{\sigma}(Q) + \overline{\sigma}(R) \tag{2.2.17}$$

$$\underline{\sigma}(Q)\underline{\sigma}(R) \leq \underline{\sigma}(QR) \leq \overline{\sigma}(Q)\underline{\sigma}(R). \tag{2.2.18}$$

Proof. The right-hand inequality in (2.2.15) is just (2.2.13). The left-hand inequality follows by replacing Q and R with $Q+R$ and $-R$ respectively in (2.2.13). In the same way, we can replace Q and R with $Q+R$ and $-Q$ respectively in (2.2.13).

The right-hand inequality in (2.2.16) follows from (2.2.14). For the left-hand inequality we argue as follows:

$$\begin{aligned}
\overline{\sigma}(QR) &= \max_{\|u\|=1} \|QRu\| \\
&= \max_{\|u\|=1, Ru \neq 0} \left(\frac{\|QRu\|}{\|Ru\|} \|Ru\| \right)
\end{aligned}$$

$$
\begin{aligned}
& \quad \text{(as the maximum must occur for } Ru \neq 0) \\
\geq & \min_{Ru\neq 0} \frac{\|QRu\|}{\|Ru\|} \max_{\|u\|=1} \|Ru\| \\
\geq & \underline{\sigma}(Q)\overline{\sigma}(R).
\end{aligned}
$$

The right-hand inequality in (2.2.17) follows from (2.2.7) as follows:

$$
\begin{aligned}
\underline{\sigma}(Q+R) &= \min_{\|u\|=1} \|Qu + Ru\| \\
&\leq \min_{\|u\|=1} (\|Qu\| + \|Ru\|) \\
&\leq \min_{\|u\|=1} \|Qu\| + \max_{\|u\|=1} \|Ru\| \\
&= \underline{\sigma}(Q) + \overline{\sigma}(R).
\end{aligned}
$$

The left-hand inequality follows by replacing Q and R with $Q+R$ and $-R$, or $Q+R$ and $-Q$, respectively in the right-hand inequality.

For (2.2.18), first consider the case $\underline{\sigma}(QR) = 0$. The right-hand inequality is trivial and $\underline{\sigma}(QR) = \min_{\|u\|=1}(QRu)$ implies there is a $u \neq 0$ such that $Ru = 0$, or a $v \neq 0$ such that $Qv = 0$, so $\underline{\sigma}(Q)\underline{\sigma}(R) = 0$ and the left-hand inequality is verified. Assume therefore that $\underline{\sigma}(QR) > 0$ (which implies that $\underline{\sigma}(R) > 0$). Then

$$
\begin{aligned}
\underline{\sigma}(QR) &= \min_{\|u\|=1} \|QRu\| \\
&= \min_{\|u\|=1} \frac{\|QRu\|}{\|Ru\|}\|Ru\| \\
&\geq \min_{\|v\|=1} \|Qv\| \min_{\|u\|=1} \|Ru\| \\
&= \underline{\sigma}(Q)\underline{\sigma}(R),
\end{aligned}
$$

which proves the left-hand inequality. For the right-hand inequality, we argue

$$
\begin{aligned}
\underline{\sigma}(QR) &= \min_{\|u\|=1} \|QRu\| \\
&= \min_{\|u\|=1} \frac{\|QRu\|}{\|Ru\|}\|Ru\| \\
&\leq \max_{\|v\|=1} \|Qv\| \min_{\|u\|=1} \|Ru\| \\
&= \overline{\sigma}(Q)\underline{\sigma}(R).
\end{aligned}
$$

■

There are similar inequalities for the other singular values which can be derived from the identities (2.2.8) and (2.2.9). It may be shown that the following identities hold whenever the indices are defined:

$$
\begin{aligned}
\sigma_{i+j+1}(Q+R) &\leq \sigma_{i+1}(Q) + \sigma_{j+1}(R) \\
\sigma_{i+j+1}(QR) &\leq \sigma_{i+1}(Q)\sigma_{j+1}(R).
\end{aligned}
$$

Our next corollary shows that the minimum singular value of a square matrix gives a measure of "closeness to singularity".

Corollary 2.2.3 *Let Q and R be $p \times p$ complex matrices and suppose also that Q is nonsingular. Then*

$$\overline{\sigma}(R) < \underline{\sigma}(Q) \Rightarrow (Q+R) \textit{ is nonsingular} \quad (2.2.19)$$

$$\min_{R:\,\det(Q+R)=0} \overline{\sigma}(R) = \underline{\sigma}(Q). \quad (2.2.20)$$

Proof. Suppose $\overline{\sigma}(R) < \underline{\sigma}(Q)$. Then (2.2.17) implies $\underline{\sigma}(Q+R) \geq \underline{\sigma}(Q) - \overline{\sigma}(R) > 0$. Therefore $Q+R$ is nonsingular.

If R is such that $\det(Q+R) = 0$, then $\overline{\sigma}(R) \geq \underline{\sigma}(Q)$ by (2.2.19). Consequently

$$\min_{\det(Q+R)=0} \overline{\sigma}(R) \geq \underline{\sigma}(Q).$$

It remains to show that the bound is attained by some R with $\overline{\sigma}(R) = \underline{\sigma}(Q)$. Let Q have SVD $Q = Y\Sigma U^*$ and set $R = -\sigma_p y_p u_p^*$ where y_p and u_p are the last columns of Y and U respectively. Clearly $\overline{\sigma}(R) = \underline{\sigma}(Q)$ and $Q+R$ is singular. ■

Main points of the section

1. The set of columns of the singular-vector matrices U and Y define orthogonal bases for the domain $\mathbb{C}^p$ and range $\mathbb{C}^m$ of Q. For this choice of bases, the map Q takes the jth basis vector u_j of $\mathbb{C}^p$ to a vector lying along the direction of the jth basis vector y_j of $\mathbb{C}^m$. The corresponding singular value σ_j can be regarded as a dilation (or gain) factor for the restricted map $Q|_{u_j}$.
2. $\overline{\sigma}(Q)$ and $\underline{\sigma}(Q)$ are the minimum and maximum gains of the matrix Q.
3. $\|Q\| = \overline{\sigma}(Q)$ is the norm of the operator Q induced by the Euclidean norm. Induced norms have the submultiplicative property $\|QR\| \leq \|Q\|\|R\|$.
4. The maximum and minimum singular values of a sum or product of matrices are bounded above and below by simple formulas involving the maximum and minimum singular values of the individual matrices.
5. The minimum singular value of a square matrix is a measure of the distance from that matrix to one which is singular.

2.3 Singular values and the sensitivity operator

In his classic treatise on feedback amplifier design, Bode analyzed the sensitivity of closed-loop systems to variations in the constituent elements of the loop. He showed that the sensitivity of the closed-loop system to variations in the plant is governed by the sensitivity function. If the sensitivity function is less than one, he concluded that the feedback system is less sensitive to plant variations than the open-loop system. In general, the "robustness" of the closed-loop system to plant variations is improved by making the sensitivity function small. We now show that the singular values of the sensitivity operator have a role to play in generalizing these ideas to the multivariable setting.

The *sensitivity* of a quantity α to changes in a quantity β is defined to be

$$S_\beta^\alpha = \frac{\partial \alpha}{\partial \beta}\frac{\beta}{\alpha},$$

which is a measure of the relative (or percentage) change in α due to a relative (or percentage) change in β.

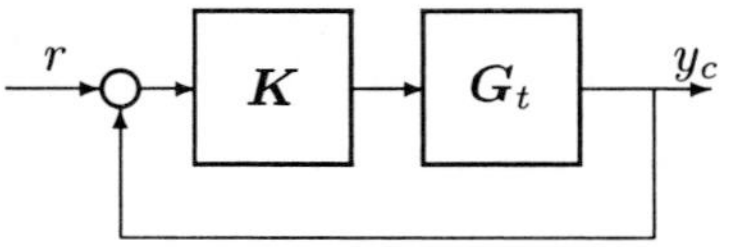

Figure 2.4: Unity feedback loop.

If the controller and plant in the unity feedback loop shown in Figure 2.4 are described by scalar transfer functions $\boldsymbol{k}$ and $\boldsymbol{g}_t$, we may evaluate the sensitivity of the closed-loop transfer function $\boldsymbol{h}$ that maps r to y_c to changes in the plant transfer function $\boldsymbol{g}_t$. Since

$$\boldsymbol{h} = \frac{\boldsymbol{g}_t\boldsymbol{k}}{1-\boldsymbol{g}_t\boldsymbol{k}},$$

the sensitivity of the closed-loop transfer function to changes in the plant is

$$\begin{aligned}
\boldsymbol{s}_g^h &= \frac{\partial \boldsymbol{h}}{\partial \boldsymbol{g}_t}\frac{\boldsymbol{g}_t}{\boldsymbol{h}} \\
&= \frac{\boldsymbol{k}}{(1-\boldsymbol{g}_t\boldsymbol{k})^2}\frac{1-\boldsymbol{g}_t\boldsymbol{k}}{\boldsymbol{k}} \\
&= \frac{1}{1-\boldsymbol{g}_t\boldsymbol{k}}.
\end{aligned}$$

Plant variations will have a small or large effect on the closed-loop transfer function according to the size of the sensitivity function $\boldsymbol{s}_g^h$.

To generalize this analysis to multivariable loops, consider the two control schemes shown in Figures 2.4 and 2.5. Since

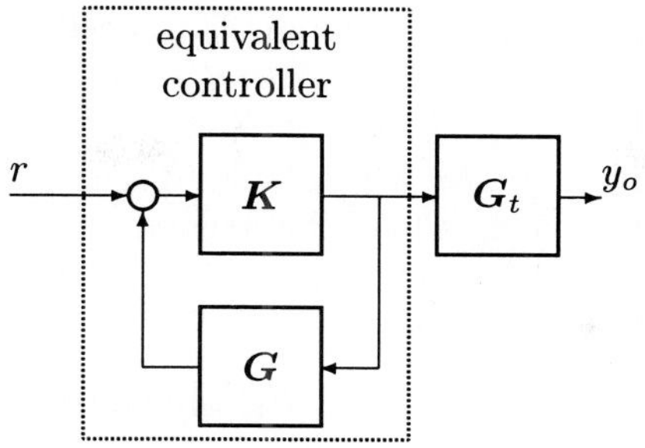

Figure 2.5: The equivalent open loop.

$$\begin{aligned} y_c &= \boldsymbol{G}_t\boldsymbol{K}(I - \boldsymbol{G}_t\boldsymbol{K})^{-1}r \\ y_o &= \boldsymbol{G}_t\boldsymbol{K}(I - \boldsymbol{G}\boldsymbol{K})^{-1}r, \end{aligned}$$

it follows that $y_c = y_o$ for all r if the system $\boldsymbol{G}_t$ and the model $\boldsymbol{G}$ are identical.

Suppose the plant $\boldsymbol{G}_t$ depends on a parameter δ, so that $\boldsymbol{G}_t$ becomes $\boldsymbol{G}_t(\delta)$. The effect of changes in δ on y_c and y_o can now be evaluated:

$$\frac{\partial y_c}{\partial \delta} = (I - \boldsymbol{G}_t\boldsymbol{K})^{-1}\frac{\partial \boldsymbol{G}_t}{\partial \delta}\boldsymbol{K}(I - \boldsymbol{G}_t\boldsymbol{K})^{-1},$$

while

$$\frac{\partial y_o}{\partial \delta} = \frac{\partial \boldsymbol{G}_t}{\partial \delta}\boldsymbol{K}(I - \boldsymbol{G}\boldsymbol{K})^{-1}.$$

Assume now that the model $\boldsymbol{G}$ is obtained by using a nominal value for δ, so that $\boldsymbol{G} = \boldsymbol{G}_t(\delta_{nom})$. Then

$$\left.\frac{\partial y_c}{\partial \delta}\right|_{\delta=\delta_{nom}} = (I - \boldsymbol{G}\boldsymbol{K})^{-1}\left.\frac{\partial y_o}{\partial \delta}\right|_{\delta=\delta_{nom}}.$$

This means that the *sensitivity operator*

$$\boldsymbol{S} = (I - \boldsymbol{G}\boldsymbol{K})^{-1} \tag{2.3.1}$$

determines how changes in the plant affect the output of the closed-loop scheme given changes in the nominally equivalent open-loop scheme. Again, the closed-loop scheme will be more or less sensitive to changes in the plant depending on the "size" of $\boldsymbol{S}$.

Using (2.2.6) and (2.2.7) we have

$$\left\|\frac{\partial y_c(j\omega)}{\partial \delta}\right\|_{\delta=\delta_{nom}} \leq \overline{\sigma}(\boldsymbol{S}(j\omega))\left\|\frac{\partial y_o(j\omega)}{\partial \delta}\right\|_{\delta=\delta_{nom}}$$

and

$$\left\|\frac{\partial y_c(j\omega)}{\partial \delta}\right\|_{\delta=\delta_{nom}} \geq \underline{\sigma}(\boldsymbol{S}(j\omega))\left\|\frac{\partial y_o(j\omega)}{\partial \delta}\right\|_{\delta=\delta_{nom}}.$$

The closed-loop scheme is uniformly less sensitive to changes in system parameters than the open-loop scheme when $\overline{\sigma}\big(\boldsymbol{S}(j\omega)\big) < 1$ and is uniformly more sensitive when $\underline{\sigma}\big(\boldsymbol{S}(j\omega)\big) > 1$. If neither of the above inequalities are satisfied, the closed-loop scheme will only offer a reduction in sensitivity for signals in the subspace (of the output space) spanned by the singular vectors corresponding to the singular values that are less than one.

A feedback design objective might be to ensure that

$$\overline{\sigma}\big(\boldsymbol{S}(j\omega)\boldsymbol{w}(j\omega)\big) < 1 \tag{2.3.2}$$

for some scalar valued frequency dependent weighting function $\boldsymbol{w}$. The weighting function should satisfy $|\boldsymbol{w}(j\omega)| \geq 1$ over the range of frequencies in which sensitivity reduction is desired. The objective (2.3.2) ensures that $\overline{\sigma}\big(\boldsymbol{S}(j\omega)\big) < 1$ over the range of frequencies of interest.

Using (2.2.17), it follows that

$$\begin{aligned}\overline{\sigma}\big(\boldsymbol{S}(j\omega)\boldsymbol{w}(j\omega)\big) < 1 \quad &\Leftrightarrow \quad \underline{\sigma}\big(I - \boldsymbol{G}(j\omega)\boldsymbol{K}(j\omega)\big) > |\boldsymbol{w}(j\omega)| \\ &\Rightarrow \quad \underline{\sigma}\big(\boldsymbol{G}(j\omega)\boldsymbol{K}(j\omega)\big) > |\boldsymbol{w}(j\omega)| - 1.\end{aligned} \tag{2.3.3}$$

Therefore, good sensitivity reduction (*i.e.*, $|\boldsymbol{w}(j\omega)| \gg 1$ in (2.3.2)) demands high loop gain ($\underline{\sigma}\big(\boldsymbol{G}(j\omega)\boldsymbol{K}(j\omega)\big) \gg 1$). Also,

$$\underline{\sigma}\big(\boldsymbol{G}(j\omega)\boldsymbol{K}(j\omega)\big) > |\boldsymbol{w}(j\omega)| + 1 \Rightarrow \overline{\sigma}\big(\boldsymbol{S}(j\omega)\boldsymbol{w}(j\omega)\big) < 1, \tag{2.3.4}$$

which shows that high loop gain ensures good sensitivity reduction.

In the above, we introduced the sensitivity operator via a special parametric sensitivity analysis. As we will discover as we progress through the book, the sensitivity operator also has an important role to play in the assessment of other feedback objectives such as disturbance rejection and closed-loop tracking.

2.4 Robust stability analysis

Control systems are designed using mathematical models that are only approximate representations of the real hardware. Since discrepancies between a system and its mathematical representation may lead to a violation of some performance specification, or even closed-loop instability, accounting for modelling errors is necessarily an integral part of the design process. The modelling of a physical system is therefore only complete when the modelling errors have been quantified. By their very nature, modelling errors defy precise mathematical description and must be quantified in terms of bounds or probability distributions of some type.

In this section, we analyze the stability robustness of closed-loop systems with respect to modelling errors quantified in terms of singular values. The treatment given in this chapter is restricted to systems described by rational matrix functions with real coefficients. A more general situation is considered following the introduction of the small gain theorem in Chapter 3.

The difference between the model and the true system may be represented in several ways. The simplest is the absolute or additive representation

$$\boldsymbol{G}_t = \boldsymbol{G} + \boldsymbol{A},$$

in which $\boldsymbol{G}$ is the nominal model, $\boldsymbol{G}_t$ represents the true system and $\boldsymbol{A}$ is an additive perturbation.

The model error may also be represented in the relative or multiplicative form

$$\boldsymbol{G}_t = (I + \boldsymbol{\Delta}_1)\boldsymbol{G},$$

so that $\boldsymbol{\Delta}_1 = (\boldsymbol{G}_t - \boldsymbol{G})\boldsymbol{G}^{-1}$ is the modelling error relative to the nominal model. An alternative multiplicative representation is to take the model error relative to the true system, so that $\boldsymbol{\Delta}_2 = (\boldsymbol{G}_t - \boldsymbol{G})\boldsymbol{G}_t^{-1}$, which gives

$$\boldsymbol{G}_t = (I - \boldsymbol{\Delta}_2)^{-1}\boldsymbol{G}.$$

In each case, the size of the modelling error at any frequency is determined by its maximum singular value at that frequency. Robust stability may be quantified in terms of the maximum modelling error that will not destabilize a nominally stable closed loop.

If $\boldsymbol{G}$ and $\boldsymbol{G}_t$ are the same in each case, the various representations are related by the identities

$$\begin{aligned}
\boldsymbol{A} &= \boldsymbol{\Delta}_1\boldsymbol{G} \\
\boldsymbol{A} &= (I - \boldsymbol{\Delta}_2)^{-1}\boldsymbol{\Delta}_2\boldsymbol{G} \\
&\approx \boldsymbol{\Delta}_2\boldsymbol{G} \text{ (for } \overline{\sigma}(\boldsymbol{\Delta}_2) \ll 1) \\
\boldsymbol{\Delta}_2 &= I - (I + \boldsymbol{\Delta}_1)^{-1} \\
&\approx \boldsymbol{\Delta}_1 \text{ (for } \overline{\sigma}(\boldsymbol{\Delta}_1) \ll 1).
\end{aligned}$$

The various representations of modelling error are therefore equivalent and any particular selection is purely a matter of convenience. For example, if $\overline{\sigma}\big(\boldsymbol{\Delta}_1(j\omega)\big)$ is small, the model is accurate in absolute terms when $\overline{\sigma}\big(\boldsymbol{G}(j\omega)\big)$ is small also, since

$$\begin{aligned}
\overline{\sigma}(\boldsymbol{A}) &= \overline{\sigma}(\boldsymbol{\Delta}_1\boldsymbol{G}) \\
&\leq \overline{\sigma}(\boldsymbol{\Delta}_1)\overline{\sigma}(\boldsymbol{G}).
\end{aligned}$$

On the other hand, if $\overline{\sigma}\big(\boldsymbol{A}(j\omega)\big)$ is small, the model is accurate in relative terms when $\underline{\sigma}\big(\boldsymbol{G}(j\omega)\big)$ is large since

$$\begin{aligned}
\overline{\sigma}(\boldsymbol{\Delta}_1) &= \overline{\sigma}(\boldsymbol{A}\boldsymbol{G}^{-1}) \\
&\leq \overline{\sigma}(\boldsymbol{A})\overline{\sigma}(\boldsymbol{G}^{-1}) \\
&= \frac{\overline{\sigma}(\boldsymbol{A})}{\underline{\sigma}(\boldsymbol{G})}.
\end{aligned}$$

It may be the case that different representations of modelling error are useful over different frequency ranges.

In contrast to Section 2.3, the modelling error here is not parametric and is usually referred to as an unstructured modelling error or as unstructured uncertainty. Its main purpose is to allow for high-frequency phenomena that are poorly modelled or completely neglected. Neglected high-frequency mechanical resonance is a typical example. Parametric errors also induce modelling errors which may be represented in the unstructured way considered in this section. However, conclusions about parametric errors that are based on a nonparametric analysis may be conservative, since the parametric nature of the error is not taken into account.

The robust stability analysis we will present here is based on a Nyquist type stability theorem.

2.4.1 A Nyquist stability theorem

Following a multivariable version of the basic internal stability lemma, a Nyquist type test for nominal closed-loop stability will be given in terms of the determinant of the return-difference matrix.

Definition 2.4.1 *Suppose $\boldsymbol{G}$ and $\boldsymbol{K}$ as given in Figure 2.1 are proper*[4] *rational transfer function matrices and let $\boldsymbol{H}$ denote the closed-loop transfer function matrix mapping $\begin{bmatrix} w' & d' \end{bmatrix}'$ to $\begin{bmatrix} u' & y' \end{bmatrix}'$. Then*

1. *The feedback loop is well-posed if $\boldsymbol{H}$ is proper;*
2. *The feedback loop is internally stable if $\boldsymbol{H}$ is stable.*

Lemma 2.4.1 *Suppose $\boldsymbol{G}$ and $\boldsymbol{K}$ in Figure 2.1 are proper rational transfer function matrices. Then the feedback loop shown in Figure 2.1 is well-posed if and only if $\det\big(I - \boldsymbol{G}(\infty)\boldsymbol{K}(\infty)\big) \neq 0$ and is internally stable if and only if*

$$\boldsymbol{H} = \begin{bmatrix} I & -\boldsymbol{K} \\ -\boldsymbol{G} & I \end{bmatrix}^{-1} \tag{2.4.1}$$

is stable.

Proof. From Figure 2.1 we obtain

$$\begin{bmatrix} w \\ d \end{bmatrix} = \begin{bmatrix} I & -\boldsymbol{K} \\ -\boldsymbol{G} & I \end{bmatrix} \begin{bmatrix} u \\ y \end{bmatrix},$$

which shows that the closed-loop transfer function matrix $\boldsymbol{H}$ mapping $\begin{bmatrix} w' & d' \end{bmatrix}'$ to $\begin{bmatrix} u' & y' \end{bmatrix}'$ is given by (2.4.1). In addition,

$$\begin{aligned} \det\begin{bmatrix} I & -\boldsymbol{K} \\ -\boldsymbol{G} & I \end{bmatrix} &= \det\begin{bmatrix} I & 0 \\ -\boldsymbol{G} & I-\boldsymbol{GK} \end{bmatrix} \det\begin{bmatrix} I & -\boldsymbol{K} \\ 0 & I \end{bmatrix} \\ &= \det(I - \boldsymbol{GK}). \end{aligned}$$

[4] A rational transfer function matrix is *proper* if it is bounded at infinity.

Therefore $\boldsymbol{H}$ will be proper if and only if $\det\big(I - \boldsymbol{G}(\infty)\boldsymbol{K}(\infty)\big) \neq 0$. We conclude that the loop is internally stable if and only if $\boldsymbol{H}$ is stable. ■

Theorem 2.4.2 *Let $\boldsymbol{G}$ and $\boldsymbol{K}$ in Figure 2.1 be given proper rational transfer functions that form a well-posed closed loop, and let $\boldsymbol{G}$ and $\boldsymbol{K}$ have n_G and n_K poles (counting multiplicities) respectively in the closed-right-half plane (CRHP). Now suppose that D_R is the Nyquist "D" contour of radius R and with semi-circular indentations of radius ϵ into the left-half plane whenever $\boldsymbol{G}$ or $\boldsymbol{K}$ has a pole on the imaginary axis.*[5]

The feedback loop of Figure 2.1 is internally stable if and only if the Nyquist diagram $\Gamma = \det\big(I - \boldsymbol{GK}(s)\big)$, $s \in D_R$, makes $n_G + n_K$ anticlockwise encirclements of the origin (without crossing it).

Proof. Let $\boldsymbol{G} = \boldsymbol{N}\boldsymbol{D}^{-1}$ and $\boldsymbol{K} = \boldsymbol{P}\boldsymbol{Q}^{-1}$ be right coprime polynomial matrix fraction descriptions of $\boldsymbol{G}$ and $\boldsymbol{K}$, so that n_G and n_K are the number of CRHP zeros of $\det(\boldsymbol{D})$ and $\det(\boldsymbol{Q})$ respectively.[6] The closed-loop transfer function matrix $\boldsymbol{H}$ in (2.4.1) has right matrix fraction description

$$\begin{bmatrix} I & -\boldsymbol{K} \\ -\boldsymbol{G} & I \end{bmatrix}^{-1} = \begin{bmatrix} \boldsymbol{D} & 0 \\ 0 & \boldsymbol{Q} \end{bmatrix} \begin{bmatrix} \boldsymbol{D} & -\boldsymbol{P} \\ -\boldsymbol{N} & \boldsymbol{Q} \end{bmatrix}^{-1}, \qquad (2.4.2)$$

which is coprime as a consequence of the coprimeness of $\boldsymbol{N}$ and $\boldsymbol{D}$ and of $\boldsymbol{P}$ and $\boldsymbol{Q}$. Hence, the poles of the closed-loop transfer function matrix $\boldsymbol{H}$ are the zeros of the polynomial

$$\begin{aligned} \phi &= \det\begin{bmatrix} \boldsymbol{D} & -\boldsymbol{P} \\ -\boldsymbol{N} & \boldsymbol{Q} \end{bmatrix} \\ &= \det\begin{bmatrix} I & 0 \\ -\boldsymbol{G} & I - \boldsymbol{GK} \end{bmatrix} \det\begin{bmatrix} \boldsymbol{D} & -\boldsymbol{P} \\ 0 & \boldsymbol{Q} \end{bmatrix} \\ &= \det(\boldsymbol{D})\det(\boldsymbol{Q})\det(I - \boldsymbol{GK}). \end{aligned}$$

Since the factorization in (2.4.2) is coprime, no zero of $\det(\boldsymbol{D})$ in D_R or $\det(\boldsymbol{Q})$ in D_R can be a zero of ϕ in D_R. Consequently, every zero of ϕ in D_R is a zero of $\det(I - \boldsymbol{GK})$ in D_R and every pole of $\det(I - \boldsymbol{GK})$ in D_R is a zero of $\det(\boldsymbol{D})$ or a zero of $\det(\boldsymbol{Q})$ in D_R since ϕ is polynomial. Thus, the closed loop has no poles in D_R if and only if $\det(I - \boldsymbol{GK})$ has no zeros in D_R and exactly $n_G + n_K$ poles there. By applying the Principle of the Argument to $\det(I - \boldsymbol{GK})$ on the Nyquist contour D_R, we conclude that the closed loop has no poles in D_R if and only if $\det\big(I - \boldsymbol{GK}(s)\big)$, $s \in D_R$, makes $n_G + n_K$ anticlockwise encirclements of the origin (without crossing it). ■

[5] In this, and all other Nyquist type theorems, we assume that D_R is given a clockwise orientation and that R is chosen large enough to contain the CRHP poles of $\boldsymbol{G}$, $\boldsymbol{K}$ and of the closed-loop transfer function matrix $\boldsymbol{H}$. The parameter ϵ must be such that none of the left-half-plane poles of $\boldsymbol{G}$, $\boldsymbol{K}$ or $\boldsymbol{H}$ are contained within D_R.

[6] See, for example, Kailath [105].

2.4.2 Additive model error

Consider the feedback configuration shown in Figure 2.6, in which $\boldsymbol{G}$ is a nominal system transfer function, $\boldsymbol{A}$ is an additive perturbation and $\boldsymbol{K}$ is a controller selected to ensure the internal stability of the nominal closed loop. We would like to know how large $\overline{\sigma}\big(\boldsymbol{A}(j\omega)\big)$ can become before the closed loop becomes unstable.

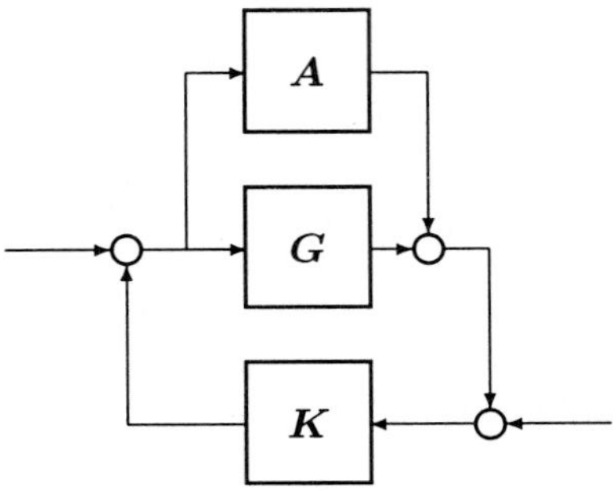

Figure 2.6: Feedback loop with additive model error.

Since the nominal closed loop (*i.e.*, when $\boldsymbol{A}=0$) is assumed stable, the roots of $\det(I-\boldsymbol{GK})$ all lie in the open-left-half plane. Thus

$$\det\big(I-\boldsymbol{GK}(j\omega)\big)\neq 0$$

for all real ω. Now suppose that $\boldsymbol{A}$ brings the perturbed system to the stability boundary, so that for some frequency ω_0

$$\begin{aligned} 0 &= \det\big(I-\boldsymbol{GK}(j\omega_0)-\boldsymbol{AK}(j\omega_0)\big)\\ &= \det\big(\big(I-\boldsymbol{AK}(I-\boldsymbol{GK})^{-1}(j\omega_0)\big)\big(I-\boldsymbol{GK}(j\omega_0)\big)\big)\\ &= \det\big(I-\boldsymbol{AK}(I-\boldsymbol{GK})^{-1}(j\omega_0)\big)\det\big(I-\boldsymbol{GK}(j\omega_0)\big), \end{aligned}$$

which is equivalent to

$$0=\det\big(I-\boldsymbol{AK}(I-\boldsymbol{GK})^{-1}(j\omega_0)\big)$$

since $\det\big(I-\boldsymbol{GK}(j\omega_0)\big)\neq 0$. By Corollary 2.2.3, this situation cannot arise if

$$\overline{\sigma}\big(\boldsymbol{AK}(I-\boldsymbol{GK})^{-1}(j\omega)\big)<1 \quad \text{for all real } \omega. \tag{2.4.3}$$

This inequality still depends on the detailed structure of $\boldsymbol{A}$, which is unknown. However, the inequality (2.4.3) is implied by

$$\overline{\sigma}\big(\boldsymbol{A}(j\omega)\big)<\frac{1}{\overline{\sigma}\big(\boldsymbol{K}(I-\boldsymbol{GK})^{-1}(j\omega)\big)} \quad \text{for all real } \omega \tag{2.4.4}$$

and one is led to the conjecture that this is a sufficient condition on the size of $\overline{\sigma}(\boldsymbol{A}(j\omega))$ for the closed-loop stability of the perturbed system. The next theorem shows that this is indeed the case.

Theorem 2.4.3 *Let $\boldsymbol{G}$ and $\boldsymbol{K}$ in Figure 2.6 be given rational transfer function matrices. Then the feedback loop of Figure 2.6 is internally stable if the following conditions are satisfied:*

1. *The nominal closed-loop system is internally stable;*
2. *The model error $\boldsymbol{A}$ is a rational transfer function matrix such that $\boldsymbol{G}$ and $\boldsymbol{G}+\boldsymbol{A}$ have the same number of poles in the closed-right-half plane;*
3. *The model error $\boldsymbol{A}$ satisfies the bound*

$$\overline{\sigma}(\boldsymbol{A}(s)) < \frac{1}{\overline{\sigma}\big(\boldsymbol{K}(I-\boldsymbol{G}\boldsymbol{K})^{-1}(s)\big)} \quad \textit{for all } s \in D_R.$$

Furthermore, there exists a rational transfer function matrix $\boldsymbol{A}$ satisfying Condition 2 and

$$\overline{\sigma}(\boldsymbol{A}(j\omega)) \le \frac{1}{\overline{\sigma}\big(\boldsymbol{K}(I-\boldsymbol{G}\boldsymbol{K})^{-1}(j\omega)\big)} \quad \textit{for all real } \omega$$

such that the closed loop is not *internally stable.*

Proof. Let D_R be a Nyquist contour as in Theorem 2.4.2. Since the nominal closed loop is stable, the curve Γ_0 defined by

$$\Gamma_0 = \det\big(I - \boldsymbol{G}K(s)\big), \quad s \in D_R,$$

makes $n_G + n_K$ anticlockwise encirclements of the origin. By Condition 2, the perturbed system will have no poles in D_R provided the curve Γ defined by

$$\Gamma = \det\big(I - (\boldsymbol{G}+\boldsymbol{A})\boldsymbol{K}(s)\big), \quad s \in D_R, \tag{2.4.5}$$

also has $n_G + n_K$ anticlockwise encirclements of the origin. By an elementary result from algebraic topology, the two curves Γ_0 and Γ will encircle the origin the same number of times if one curve may be continuously deformed into the other without crossing the origin. Consider the curve

$$\Gamma_\epsilon = \det\big(I - (\boldsymbol{G}+\epsilon\boldsymbol{A})\boldsymbol{K}(s)\big) \text{ for } s \in D_R \text{ and } \epsilon \in [0,1].$$

Since the determinant is a continuous function of ϵ, Γ_0 deforms continuously into Γ as ϵ varies from 0 to 1. We therefore need to show that Γ_ϵ does not cross the origin for any $\epsilon \in [0,1]$. That is, that

$$\det\big(I - (\boldsymbol{G}+\epsilon\boldsymbol{A})\boldsymbol{K}(s)\big) \neq 0 \text{ for all } s \in D_R \text{ and all } \epsilon \in [0,1].$$

Since $I - \boldsymbol{GK}(s)$ is nonsingular on D_R, and since

$$I - (\boldsymbol{G} + \epsilon \boldsymbol{A})\boldsymbol{K} = \left(I - \epsilon \boldsymbol{AK}(I - \boldsymbol{GK})^{-1}\right)(I - \boldsymbol{GK}),$$

it follows that the closed loop will have no poles in D_R provided

$$\det\left(I - \epsilon \boldsymbol{AK}(I - \boldsymbol{GK})^{-1}(s)\right) \neq 0 \tag{2.4.6}$$

for all $s \in D_R$ and for all $\epsilon \in [0, 1]$. From Condition 3 and (2.2.16),

$$\overline{\sigma}\left(\epsilon \boldsymbol{AK}(I - \boldsymbol{GK})^{-1}(s)\right) < 1 \text{ for } s \in D_R \text{ and } \epsilon \in [0, 1].$$

Corollary 2.2.3 therefore implies that (2.4.6) holds for all $s \in D_R$ and for all $\epsilon \in [0, 1]$. The loop is therefore internally stable.

To establish the existence of a destabilizing perturbation with the required properties, let

$$\omega_0 = \arg\min_{\omega} \frac{1}{\overline{\sigma}\left(\boldsymbol{K}(I - \boldsymbol{GK})^{-1}(j\omega)\right)} \tag{2.4.7}$$

and let

$$\boldsymbol{K}(I - \boldsymbol{GK})^{-1}(j\omega_0) = \sum_{i=1}^{m} \sigma_i u_i y_i^*$$

be an SVD. Let $A = {\sigma_1}^{-1} y_1 u_1^*$, which is a constant, but complex, matrix. Then $\overline{\sigma}(A) = \sigma_1^{-1}$ and $I - A\boldsymbol{K}(I - \boldsymbol{GK})^{-1}(j\omega_0)$ is singular. To realize the destabilizing perturbation as a physical system, set

$$y_1 = \begin{bmatrix} a_1 e^{i\theta_1} \\ \vdots \\ a_m e^{i\theta_m} \end{bmatrix} \quad \text{and} \quad u_1^* = \begin{bmatrix} b_1 e^{i\phi_1} & \ldots & b_m e^{i\phi_m} \end{bmatrix},$$

in which the a_i's and b_i's are real numbers. The signs of these numbers are selected to ensure that $\theta_i,\ \phi_i \in [0, -\pi)$ for $i = 1, 2, \ldots, m$. It is now possible to find positive numbers α_i and β_i so that θ_i is the phase of $\left(\frac{j\omega_0 - \alpha_i}{j\omega_0 + \alpha_i}\right)$ and ϕ_i is the phase of $\left(\frac{j\omega_0 - \beta_i}{j\omega_0 + \beta_i}\right)$. Setting

$$\boldsymbol{A} = \sigma_1^{-1} \begin{bmatrix} a_1 \left(\frac{s - \alpha_1}{s + \alpha_1}\right) \\ \vdots \\ a_m \left(\frac{s - \alpha_m}{s + \alpha_m}\right) \end{bmatrix} \begin{bmatrix} b_1 \left(\frac{s - \beta_1}{s + \beta_1}\right) & \ldots & b_m \left(\frac{s - \beta_m}{s + \beta_m}\right) \end{bmatrix}$$

gives $\boldsymbol{A}$ stable with $\boldsymbol{A}(j\omega_0) = A = \sigma_1^{-1} y_1 u_1^*$. Furthermore, $\overline{\sigma}\left(\boldsymbol{A}(j\omega)\right) = \sigma_1^{-1}$ for all real ω. Consequently, by the choice of ω_0 in (2.4.7),

$$\overline{\sigma}\left(\boldsymbol{A}(j\omega)\right) \leq \frac{1}{\overline{\sigma}\left(\boldsymbol{K}(I - \boldsymbol{GK})^{-1}(j\omega)\right)}$$

for all ω, with equality at $\omega = \omega_0$.

The instability of the loop under the influence of this perturbation follows from the fact that the closed loop will have imaginary-axis poles at $\pm j\omega_o$. ■

If $\boldsymbol{G}$ has right-half-plane poles, the result allows them to be perturbed, but no poles are allowed to cross the imaginary axis (in either direction). That is, $\boldsymbol{G}$ *must contain exactly as many unstable poles as the true system* $\boldsymbol{G} + \boldsymbol{A}$.[7]

In the scalar case, with $\boldsymbol{k} = 1$, Condition 3 says that robustness to additive modelling error degrades in proportion to the distance between the Nyquist diagram of $\boldsymbol{g}$ and the critical $+1$ point. If

$$\frac{1}{|1 - \boldsymbol{g}(j\omega)|} < \gamma$$

for all real ω and $\gamma > 0$, the Nyquist diagram of $\boldsymbol{g}$ cannot enter the circle of radius $1/\gamma$ with center at $+1$ (see Figure 2.7).

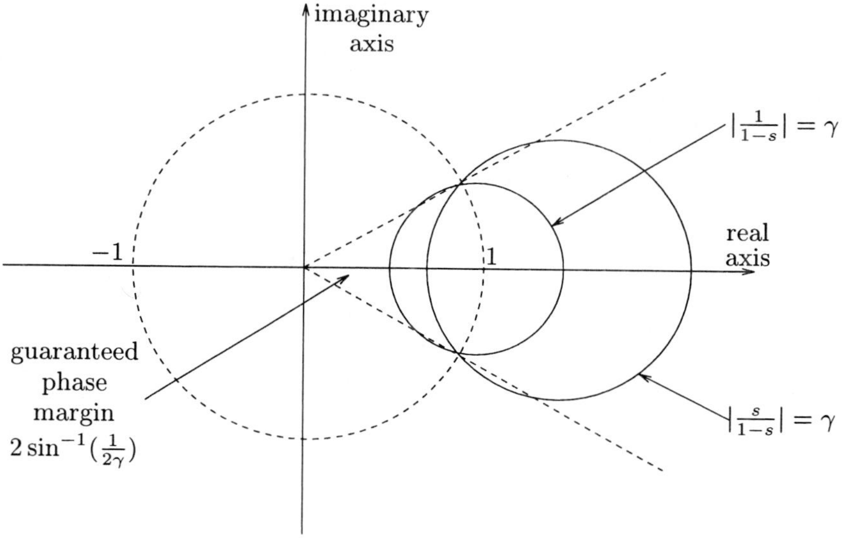

Figure 2.7: The circles $|\frac{1}{1-s}| = \gamma$ and $|\frac{s}{1-s}| = \gamma$.

In the case that $\boldsymbol{G}$ is stable, $\boldsymbol{K} = 0$ will lead to a nominally stable closed loop. In this case the quantity $\overline{\sigma}\big(\boldsymbol{K}(I - \boldsymbol{G}\boldsymbol{K})^{-1}\big)$ is zero and the robust stability margin is arbitrarily large; this is a trivial illustration of low controller gain leading to good

[7] A robustness theorem that allows a different number of unstable poles in the nominal model and the true system will be presented in Chapter 12.

robustness margins. In the general case it may be shown using Lemma 2.2.2 that

$$\overline{\sigma}\big(\boldsymbol{K}(I-\boldsymbol{G}\boldsymbol{K})^{-1}(j\omega)\big) \leq \gamma \quad \Rightarrow \quad \overline{\sigma}\big(\boldsymbol{K}(j\omega)\big) \leq \frac{\gamma}{1-\gamma\overline{\sigma}\big(\boldsymbol{G}(j\omega)\big)} \qquad (2.4.8)$$

$$\text{if } 1-\gamma\overline{\sigma}\big(\boldsymbol{G}(j\omega)\big) > 0$$

and

$$\overline{\sigma}\big(\boldsymbol{K}(I-\boldsymbol{G}\boldsymbol{K})^{-1}(j\omega)\big) \leq \gamma \Leftarrow \overline{\sigma}\big(\boldsymbol{K}(j\omega)\big) \leq \frac{\gamma}{1+\gamma\overline{\sigma}\big(\boldsymbol{G}(j\omega)\big)}. \qquad (2.4.9)$$

Verifiction of these implications is requested in an exercise. The first inequality shows that if the robust stability margin is large, (*i.e.*, the closed loop is stable for all perturbations satisfying Condition 2 in Theorem 2.4.3) and $\overline{\sigma}(\boldsymbol{A}) < \gamma^{-1}$ for a small value of γ, then the controller gain is necessarily small. Conversely, it follows from the second inequality that a low controller gain ensures good robust stability margins (provided such a controller can stabilize the nominal plant).

2.4.3 Multiplicative model error

A disadvantage of the additive representation of modelling error is that the error in $\boldsymbol{G}$ is not the error in the compensated loop-gain operator $\boldsymbol{GK}$. This is because $(\boldsymbol{G}+\boldsymbol{A})\boldsymbol{K} \neq \boldsymbol{GK}+\boldsymbol{A}$. It is therefore difficult to envisage the effect of the additive perturbation $\boldsymbol{A}$ on $\boldsymbol{GK}$. Multiplicative representations of model error do not suffer from this disadvantage because a multiplicative perturbation on $\boldsymbol{G}$ is also a multiplicative perturbation on $\boldsymbol{GK}$. To see this we observe that $\big((I+\boldsymbol{\Delta}_1)\boldsymbol{G}\big)\boldsymbol{K} = (I+\boldsymbol{\Delta}_1)\boldsymbol{GK}$ and $\big((I-\boldsymbol{\Delta}_2)^{-1}\boldsymbol{G}\big)\boldsymbol{K} = (I-\boldsymbol{\Delta}_2)^{-1}\boldsymbol{GK}$.

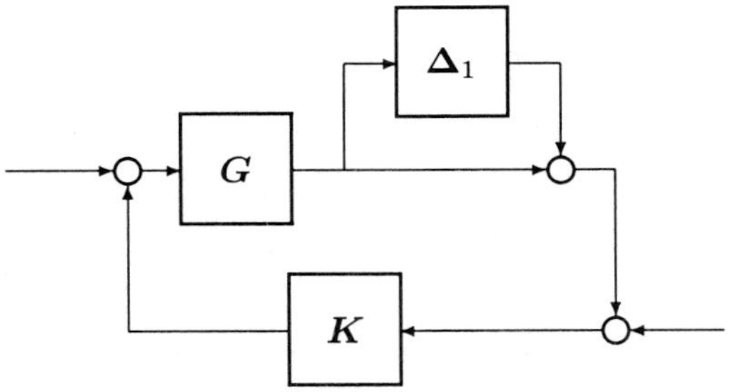

Figure 2.8: Loop with multiplicative model error.

Theorem 2.4.4 *Let $\boldsymbol{G}$ and $\boldsymbol{K}$ be given rational transfer function matrices. Then the feedback loop of Figure 2.8 is internally stable if the following conditions are satisfied:*

1. *The nominal closed loop is internally stable;*

2. *The model error* $\mathbf{\Delta}_1$ *is a rational transfer function matrix such that* $\boldsymbol{G}$ *and* $(I + \mathbf{\Delta}_1)\boldsymbol{G}$ *have the same number of poles in the closed-right-half plane;*

3. *The model error* $\mathbf{\Delta}_1$ *satisfies*

$$\overline{\sigma}(\mathbf{\Delta}_1(s)) < \frac{1}{\overline{\sigma}(\boldsymbol{GK}(I - \boldsymbol{GK})^{-1}(s))} \quad \textit{for all } s \in D_R. \tag{2.4.10}$$

Furthermore, there exists a rational $\mathbf{\Delta}_1$ *that satisfies Condition 2 and*

$$\overline{\sigma}(\mathbf{\Delta}_1(j\omega)) \leq \frac{1}{\overline{\sigma}(\boldsymbol{GK}(I - \boldsymbol{GK})^{-1}(j\omega))} \quad \textit{for all real } \omega$$

such that the closed loop is not *stable.*

Proof. The proof is similar to that of Theorem 2.4.3 and makes use of the identity

$$I - (I + \epsilon\mathbf{\Delta}_1)\boldsymbol{GK} = \big(I - \epsilon\mathbf{\Delta}_1\boldsymbol{GK}(I - \boldsymbol{GK})^{-1}\big)(I - \boldsymbol{GK}).$$

The details are requested as an exercise. ■

In the scalar case, Condition 3 says that robustness to multiplicative perturbations degrades in inverse proportion to $|\frac{\boldsymbol{q}}{1-\boldsymbol{q}}|$, with $\boldsymbol{q} = \boldsymbol{gk}$, which has an M-circle interpretation. Bounds on the gain and phase margins can be obtained from this objective. Suppose

$$\frac{|\boldsymbol{q}(j\omega)|}{|1 - \boldsymbol{q}(j\omega)|} < \gamma \tag{2.4.11}$$

for some $\gamma > 0$. Then the Nyquist diagram of $\boldsymbol{q}$ cannot cross the circle defined by $|s| = \gamma|1 - s|$. Since this circle intersects the real axis at $\gamma/(\gamma + 1)$ and $\gamma/(\gamma - 1)$, the loop will be stable for all gains in the range $(1 + \frac{1}{\gamma}, 1 - \frac{1}{\gamma})$. In other words, if we consider the gain variations to be a multiplicative model error, (2.4.11) and Theorem 2.4.4 will guarantee closed-loop stability provided the relative gain variation is less than $\pm 1/\gamma$. To determine the phase margin, we consider the intersection of the circles $|s| = 1$ and $|s| = \gamma|1 - s|$. If $\gamma < 1/2$, $|s| = \gamma|1 - s|$ implies $|s| < 1$, so the circles $|s| = \gamma|1 - s|$ and $|s| = 1$ do not intersect and the phase margin is infinite. Otherwise, for $\gamma \geq 1/2$, the circles $|s| = 1$ and $|s| = \gamma|1 - s|$ intersect at two points $e^{\pm j\theta}$ (see Figure 2.7). By the cosine rule,

$$\begin{aligned} \frac{1}{\gamma^2} &= 2(1 - \cos\theta) \\ &= 4\sin^2(\theta/2). \end{aligned}$$

The phase margin θ_m therefore satisfies

$$|\theta_m| > 2\sin^{-1}(\frac{1}{2\gamma}) \tag{2.4.12}$$

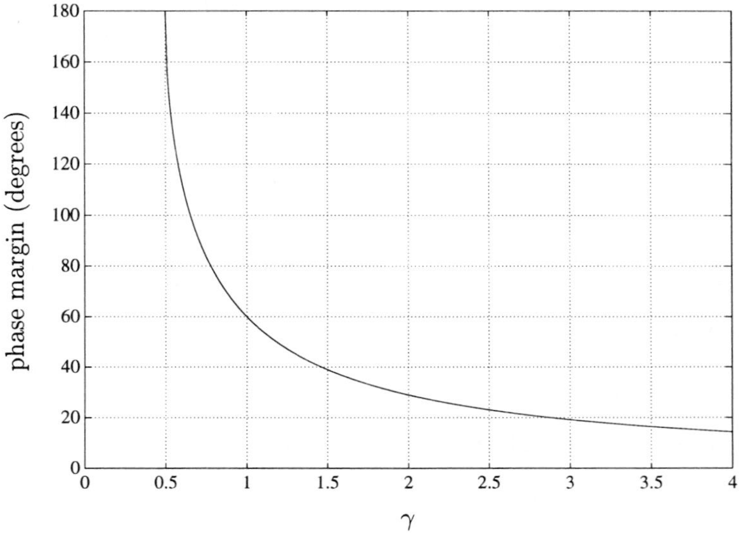

Figure 2.9: Guaranteed phase margin as a function of γ.

for $\gamma \geq 1/2$. A plot of θ_m versus γ is shown in Figure 2.9.

Once again, the bound (2.4.10) is arbitrarily large if $\boldsymbol{GK} = 0$. Otherwise, with $\boldsymbol{Q} = \boldsymbol{GK}$,

$$\overline{\sigma}\big(\boldsymbol{Q}(I-\boldsymbol{Q})^{-1}(j\omega)\big) \leq \gamma \begin{cases} \Rightarrow \overline{\sigma}\big(\boldsymbol{Q}(j\omega)\big) \leq \frac{\gamma}{1-\gamma} \text{ if } \gamma < 1 \\ \\ \Leftarrow \overline{\sigma}\big(\boldsymbol{Q}(j\omega)\big) \leq \frac{\gamma}{1+\gamma}. \end{cases} \tag{2.4.13}$$

The first inequality shows that if $\gamma \ll 1$, the loop gain $\overline{\sigma}\big(\boldsymbol{Q}(j\omega)\big)$ is small. Notice, however, that $\gamma < 1$ is not achievable if the open-loop is unstable, since the perturbation $\boldsymbol{\Delta}_1 = -I$ will open the feedback loop. The second inequality says that good robustness margins will be guaranteed if it is possible to stabilize the nominal plant with a controller that results in $\overline{\sigma}\big(\boldsymbol{Q}(j\omega)\big)$ being small.

The last theorem of this section considers multiplicative model error representations of the form $\boldsymbol{G}_t = (I - \boldsymbol{\Delta}_2)^{-1}\boldsymbol{G}$.

Theorem 2.4.5 *Let $\boldsymbol{G}$ and $\boldsymbol{K}$ be given rational transfer function matrices. Then the feedback loop of Figure 2.10 is internally stable if the following conditions are satisfied:*

1. *The nominal closed loop is internally stable;*

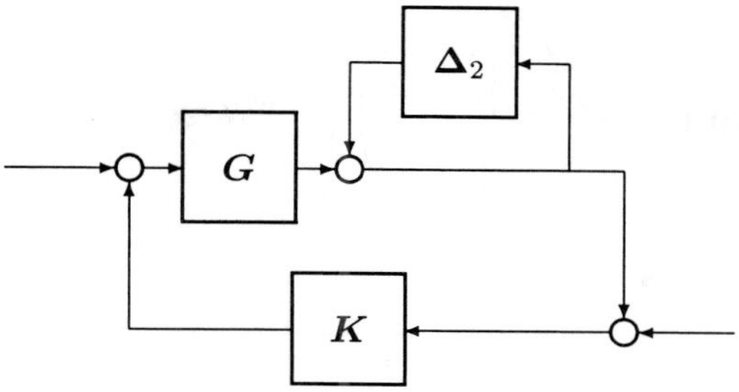

Figure 2.10: Loop with feedback multiplicative model error.

2. *The model error* $\boldsymbol{\Delta}_2$ *is a rational transfer function matrix such that* $\boldsymbol{G}$ *and* $(I - \boldsymbol{\Delta}_2)^{-1}\boldsymbol{G}$ *have the same number of poles in the closed-right-half plane;*

3. *The model error* $\boldsymbol{\Delta}_2$ *satisfies*

$$\overline{\sigma}\big(\boldsymbol{\Delta}_2(s)\big) < \min\{1, \underline{\sigma}((I - \boldsymbol{GK})(s))\} \quad \text{for all } s \in D_R. \tag{2.4.14}$$

$$\left(\textit{Note that } \underline{\sigma}\big(I - \boldsymbol{GK}(s)\big) = \frac{1}{\overline{\sigma}\big(\boldsymbol{S}(s)\big)}.\right)$$

Furthermore, there exists a rational $\boldsymbol{\Delta}_2$ *satisfying Condition 2 and*

$$\overline{\sigma}\big(\boldsymbol{\Delta}_2(j\omega)\big) \le \min\{1, \underline{\sigma}((I - \boldsymbol{GK})(j\omega))\} \quad \text{for all real } \omega$$

such that the closed loop is not *stable.*

Proof. Note that $\overline{\sigma}\big(\boldsymbol{\Delta}_2(s)\big) < 1$ and Corollary 2.2.3 ensures that $\big(I - \epsilon\boldsymbol{\Delta}_2(s)\big)$ is nonsingular for all $\epsilon \in [0, 1]$. This means that $\big(I - \epsilon\boldsymbol{\Delta}_2(s)\big)$ has no zeros on the Nyquist D_R contour. The proof now proceeds along lines similar the proof of Theorem 2.4.3 by making use of the identity

$$I - (I - \epsilon\boldsymbol{\Delta}_2)^{-1}\boldsymbol{Q} = (I - \epsilon\boldsymbol{\Delta}_2)^{-1}(I - \boldsymbol{Q} - \epsilon\boldsymbol{\Delta}_2).$$

The details are requested as an exercise. ■

In the scalar case, Condition 3 says that the robustness margin degrades in proportion to the distance between the Nyquist diagram of $\boldsymbol{q} = \boldsymbol{gk}$ and the critical $+1$ point.

2.4.4 Examples

We will now illustrate the robust stability analysis by revisiting our two earlier examples.

Example 2.4.1. Consider the feedback loop shown in Figure 2.1 with $\boldsymbol{K} = -I$ and

$$\boldsymbol{G} = \begin{bmatrix} 7 & 8 \\ 6 & 7 \end{bmatrix} \begin{bmatrix} \frac{1}{s+1} & 0 \\ 0 & \frac{2}{s+2} \end{bmatrix} \begin{bmatrix} 7 & 8 \\ 6 & 7 \end{bmatrix}^{-1}$$

as in Example 2.1.1.

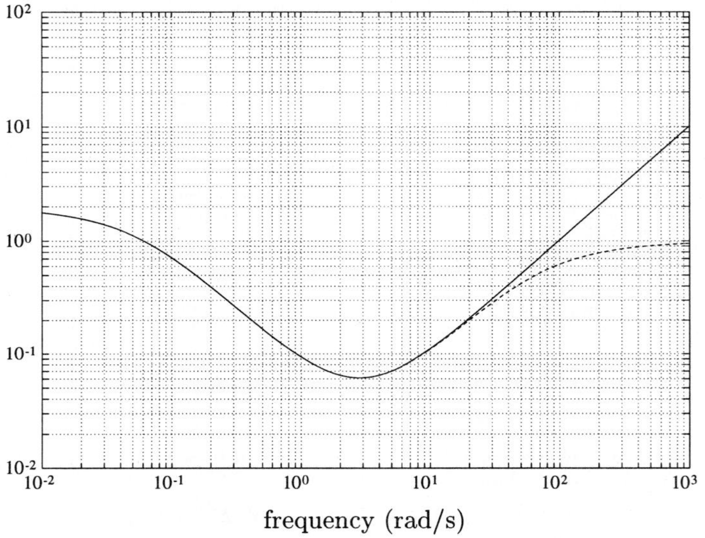

Figure 2.11: Singular value plots of $1/\overline{\sigma}\big(\boldsymbol{GKS}(j\omega)\big)$ (solid) and $1/\overline{\sigma}\big(\boldsymbol{KS}(j\omega)\big)$ (dashed).

Figure 2.11 shows singular value plots indicating the robust stability margins for multiplicative (solid) and additive (dashed) perturbations. At 3 rad/s, these curves drop down to a minimum value of 0.0612, indicating that a multiplicative or additive perturbation of infinity norm 0.0612 could destabilize the loop.

To show that this system can be destabilized by a stable rational additive perturbation with $\overline{\sigma}\big(\boldsymbol{A}(j\omega)\big) \leq 0.0612$ for all real ω, we will construct such an additive perturbation. Using the singular value decomposition of $\boldsymbol{K}(I - \boldsymbol{GK})^{-1}(j3)$, we obtain the perturbation

$$\boldsymbol{A} = 0.0612 \begin{bmatrix} 0.6886 \\ -0.7252\left(\frac{s-0.0509}{s+0.0509}\right) \end{bmatrix} \begin{bmatrix} -0.7851\left(\frac{s-0.0341}{s+0.0341}\right) \\ -0.6194\left(\frac{s-0.0864}{s+0.0864}\right) \end{bmatrix}'$$

using the techniques described in the proof of Theorem 2.4.3; the details are requested in the exercises.

It can be seen that $\boldsymbol{A}$ is stable, that $\overline{\sigma}(\boldsymbol{A}(j\omega)) = 0.0612$ and that $\boldsymbol{A}$ it is destabilizing. The destabilization property follows from the fact that

$$I - \boldsymbol{A}\boldsymbol{K}(I - \boldsymbol{G}\boldsymbol{K})^{-1}(j3)$$

is singular. This means that the closed-loop system will have imaginary-axis poles at $\pm j3$.

The important point is that the singular values of closed-loop operators such as $\boldsymbol{K}(I - \boldsymbol{G}\boldsymbol{K})^{-1}$ and $\boldsymbol{G}\boldsymbol{K}(I - \boldsymbol{G}\boldsymbol{K})^{-1}$ give information about the ability of the loop to tolerate modelling errors.

If we designed an optimally robust controller ignoring all other possible requirements, the solution would simply be $\boldsymbol{K} \equiv 0$! $\triangledown$

Example 2.4.2. In this example, we consider the design of optimally robust controllers. We will examine optimal robustness with respect to an additive model error representation, a multiplicative model error representation and then a combination of both. Our purpose is to illustrate the properties of controllers and closed loops that are optimal with respect to these different model error representations.

The optimal robustness problem for the model error representations introduced so far is only interesting if the plant is unstable. We therefore consider the unstable system

$$\boldsymbol{g} = \frac{1}{(s-1)^2}.$$

The fact that $\boldsymbol{g}$ is a simple scalar transfer function allows our insights to develop in a familiar environment where Nyquist diagrams and criteria such as gain and phase margins may be used.

Elementary considerations reveal that the loop will be unstable for any constant gain controller and hence some form of dynamic compensation is required. Such a compensator can easily be designed using classical control techniques. Our approach is to optimize robustness with respect to certain model error representations.

Taking the additive model error representation first, we seek a controller that stabilizes all plants $\boldsymbol{g}_t = \boldsymbol{g} + \boldsymbol{a}$ with $\|\boldsymbol{a}\|_\infty < 1/\gamma$ and with γ minimized. This is achieved by minimizing $\gamma = \|\boldsymbol{k}(1 - \boldsymbol{g}\boldsymbol{k})^{-1}\|_\infty$ over the class of all controllers that stabilize the nominal loop.

Although a solution using the elementary maximum modulus principle argument of Chapter 1 is no longer possible, we can make use of more advanced techniques covered later in the book to show that $\gamma_{opt} = 4\sqrt{3 + 2\sqrt{2}}$ and that the optimal controller is

$$\boldsymbol{k}_a = \frac{4 - \gamma_{opt} s}{s + 3 + \sqrt{2}}.$$

This controller will stabilize the loop for all additive model errors $\boldsymbol{a}$ such that $\|\boldsymbol{a}\|_\infty < 1/\gamma_{opt} \approx 0.1035$. In the parlance of classical control, $\boldsymbol{k}_a$ allows gain variations in the interval $(0.85, 1.1)$, while the phase margin is $6.3°$. These are not good margins and yet the controller is optimally robust! This apparent contradiction arises because gain and phase margins are indicators of robustness to certain multiplicative model errors. Optimal robustness with respect to additive model error is not a good criterion if one is only interested in good gain and phase margins.

At high frequencies $\boldsymbol{g}(j\omega) \approx 0$ and so $\|\boldsymbol{k}(1-\boldsymbol{gk})^{-1}\|_\infty \leq \gamma$ implies that $\lim_{\omega\to\infty} |\boldsymbol{k}(j\omega)| \leq \gamma$. Thus, the additive robustness criterion limits the high-frequency gain of the compensator. In effect, we have found a stabilizing controller with a high-frequency gain limit.

We now turn our attention to optimizing robustness with respect to multiplicative model errors. We seek a controller that stabilizes all plants $\boldsymbol{g}_t = (1+\boldsymbol{\delta})\boldsymbol{g}$ such that $\|\boldsymbol{\delta}\|_\infty < 1/\gamma$ with γ minimized. To achieve this, we minimize $\gamma = \|\boldsymbol{q}(1-\boldsymbol{q})^{-1}\|_\infty$, in which $\boldsymbol{q} = \boldsymbol{gk}$. Because the objective involves only $\boldsymbol{q}$, and not $\boldsymbol{g}$ or $\boldsymbol{k}$ separately, the optimization problem is relatively easy to solve.

We require the Nyquist diagram to encircle the $+1$ point anticlockwise twice, while remaining in the region of the complex plane defined by $|s/(1-s)| < \gamma$. Note that the circle $|s/(1-s)| = \gamma$ has center $\gamma^2/(\gamma^2-1)$, radius $\gamma/(\gamma^2-1)$ and intersects the real axis at $\gamma/(\gamma \pm 1)$ (see Figure 2.7). It is therefore clear that we must have $\gamma > 1$ in order that the Nyquist plot encircles $+1$. It is easy to see that for any $\gamma > 1$, the Nyquist diagram of

$$\boldsymbol{q} = \frac{\gamma}{\gamma^2-1}\left(\left(\frac{1+s}{1-s}\right)^2 + \gamma\right)$$

is precisely the circle defined by $|s/(1-s)| = \gamma$ and that it makes two anticlockwise encirclements of the $+1$ point. The corresponding controller is

$$\boldsymbol{k}_m = \frac{\gamma}{\gamma^2-1}\left((s+1)^2 + \gamma(s-1)^2\right),$$

which is not proper. If a proper controller is required, we may use $\boldsymbol{k}_m/(\tau s+1)^2$ with τ sufficiently small. This illustrates an important feature of $\mathcal{H}_\infty$ optimal control designs. In this case, the objective requires that the Nyquist diagram be excluded from an M-circle of some particular radius. The resulting optimum occurs when the Nyquist diagram is tight against the M-circle boundary.

In this case, there is no minimum achievable value of γ and one can only approach the greatest lower bound of 1.

Since $\boldsymbol{gk}_m$ follows the circle $|s/(1-s)| = \gamma$ exactly, the allowable gain range is $[1-1/\gamma, 1+1/\gamma]$ and the phase margin is $2\sin^{-1}(\frac{1}{2\gamma})$. These impressive margins should be viewed with some caution, however, because the controller has very high gain at high frequencies and is therefore not implementable in practice. This phenomenon occurs because the objective involves only the loop-gain function $\boldsymbol{q} = \boldsymbol{gk}$ and there is nothing in the optimization criterion to ensure the controller is reasonable in any engineering sense.

We have seen that the additive robustness optimization problem places an explicit limit on the high-frequency controller gain, while the multiplicative version of the problem gives good gain and phase margins . In order to reap the benefits associated with both problems, we will now represent the plant by

$$g_t = (1 + \delta_1)g + \delta_2 \epsilon,$$

in which ϵ a design parameter. The modelling error is given by

$$g_t - g = \begin{bmatrix} \delta_1 & \delta_2 \end{bmatrix} \begin{bmatrix} g \\ \epsilon \end{bmatrix},$$

and we will design a controller that accommodates $\| \begin{bmatrix} \delta_1 & \delta_2 \end{bmatrix} \|_\infty < \gamma^{-1}$ with γ minimized. Since g is low pass, the multiplicative part of the model error representation, δ_1, will be emphasized at low frequencies where $|g(j\omega)| \gg \epsilon$. The additive part of the model error representation, δ_2, will then come into play at high frequencies.

Since $1 - g_t k$ can be written as

$$\left(1 - \begin{bmatrix} \delta_1 & \delta_2 \end{bmatrix} \begin{bmatrix} g \\ \epsilon \end{bmatrix} k(1 - gk)^{-1}\right)(1 - gk),$$

it follows that the objective will be achieved by minimizing

$$\gamma = \sup_\omega \overline{\sigma}\left(\begin{bmatrix} g \\ \epsilon \end{bmatrix} k(1 - gk)^{-1}\right).$$

Note that this objective implies that $\|gk(1 - gk)^{-1}\|_\infty < \gamma$ and that $\|k(1 - gk)^{-1}\|_\infty < \gamma/\epsilon$.

Taking $\epsilon = 1/10$, the optimal value of γ is $\gamma_{opt} = 2.38$ and the optimal controller is

$$k = \frac{4.856 - 23.818s}{s + 6.9049}.$$

The infinity norm bound means the loop will be stable for all multiplicative model errors $|\delta_1(j\omega)| < 1/\gamma_{opt} \approx 0.4198$ as well as all additive model errors $|\delta_2(j\omega)| < 1/(10\gamma_{opt}) \approx 0.04198$. The multiplicative model error bound implies the loop will be stable for gains in the range $[0.5802, 1.4198]$ and that the phase margin is at least $\pm 24°$.

It follows from the Nyquist diagram of gk shown in Figure 2.12 that the actual stable operating gain range is $(0.5731, 1.4241)$ and that the phase margin is $24.1°$. Note that the low-frequency region of the Nyquist diagram is close to the $1/\gamma_{opt}$ M-circle defined by $|s/(1 - s)| = 1/\gamma_{opt}$. At the same time, the additive part of the design criterion is limiting the controller gain to $10\gamma_{opt} = 23.82$. ▽

Main point of the section

Singular values can be used to generalize the classical intuition that the distance to +1 (or −1 for a negative feedback sign convention) is a

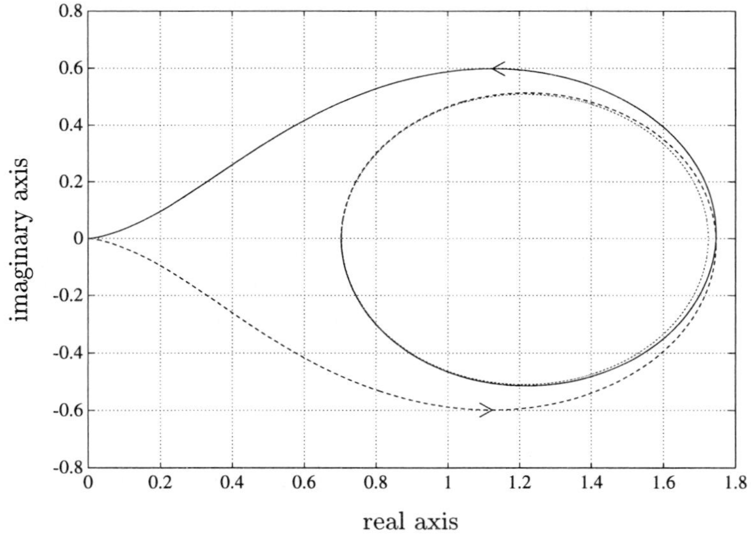

Figure 2.12: Compensated Nyquist diagram and the $1/\gamma_{opt}$ M-circle.

measure of robust stability. Theorems 2.4.3, 2.4.4 and 2.4.5 make these notions precise in the context of additive, multiplicative and inverse multiplicative model error representations respectively.

2.5 Performance analysis and enhancement

The stabilization of a system is only rarely the major reason for introducing feedback control. Indeed, in the case of stable plants, we have seen that feedback control can only have a detrimental effect on the stability robustness of the system in the sense we have discussed it. The most common reason for introducing feedback control is the enhancement of performance in the presence of uncertainty. In this context, performance enhancing goals include such things as disturbance attenuation, sensitivity reduction, the reduction of nonlinear effects and command tracking enhancement.

It is well known that the benefits of feedback control accrue from high gain and it is also known that high gain exacerbates the danger of loop instability, actuator saturation and sensor noise amplification. This conflict between the high- and low-gain requirements is what makes control system design interesting (and difficult). In broad terms, a feedback system designer will try to "shape" the loop gain as a function of frequency so that the low-frequency, high-gain requirements are met without infringing on the high-frequency, low-gain limits imposed by plant model errors, sensor errors and actuator limits.

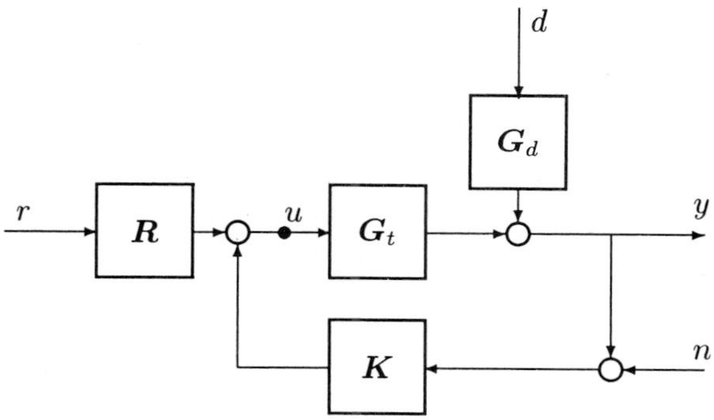

Figure 2.13: Closed-loop system.

In this section, our aim is to analyze various performance criteria and limits using singular values. The closed-loop configuration we will use for much of this discussion is shown in Figure 2.13.

2.5.1 Disturbance attenuation

The signal d represents an exogenous disturbance such as a load variation or wind gust that affects the output y of the system via a transfer function matrix $\boldsymbol{G}_d$ in an undesirable way. The disturbance attenuation problem is to find some means of reducing or eliminating the influence of d on the output y. Before embarking on the design of a feedback controller, it is as well to note that the disturbance attenuation problem may also be addressed by other means.

It may be possible to modify the system in such a way that the disturbance is eliminated or reduced in magnitude: the effect of wind gusts may be reduced by constructing a wind-break around the system. Unwanted induced signals in an electronic circuit may be attenuated by careful component layout, grounding and shielding. A well designed suspension system reduces the influence of road surface irregularities on the occupants of an automobile.

If plant modifications are not possible (or practical), one could measure the disturbance and compensate for its effect via a feedforward compensator $\boldsymbol{F}$ as shown in Figure 2.14. In the open-loop situation with $\boldsymbol{K} = 0$, the transfer function matrix from d to y is $\boldsymbol{G}_d + \boldsymbol{G}_t\boldsymbol{F}$ so that the effect of the disturbance may be eliminated if $\boldsymbol{G}_t$ is square and has no right-half-plane zeros by choosing $\boldsymbol{F} = -\boldsymbol{G}_t^{-1}\boldsymbol{G}_d$. Complete cancellation is not possible if $\boldsymbol{G}_t$ has right-half-plane zeros. In this case, the effect

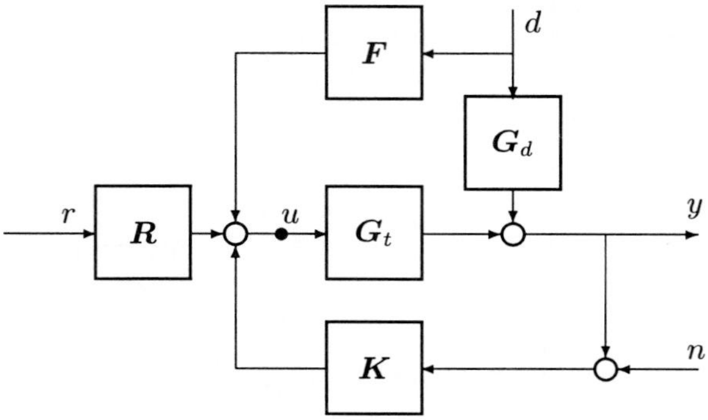

Figure 2.14: Disturbance attenuation via feedforward compensation.

of d may be reduced by making $\boldsymbol{G}_d + \boldsymbol{G}_t\boldsymbol{F}$ small. Specifically,

$$\overline{\sigma}\big((\boldsymbol{G}_d + \boldsymbol{G}_t\boldsymbol{F})(j\omega)\big) \leq \gamma$$

ensures that

$$\|y(j\omega)\| \leq \gamma\|d(j\omega)\|.$$

This gives rise to an optimization problem of the same type as the command response optimization problem discussed in Section 1.2.

Finally, a feedback controller may be used to attenuate the output disturbance. In this case, the transfer function matrix from d to y in Figure 2.14 is

$$(I - \boldsymbol{G}_t\boldsymbol{K})^{-1}(\boldsymbol{G}_d + \boldsymbol{G}_t\boldsymbol{F})$$

and we see that the sensitivity operator

$$\boldsymbol{S}_t = (I - \boldsymbol{G}_t\boldsymbol{K})^{-1} \tag{2.5.1}$$

plays a role in disturbance attenuation using feedback. In particular,

$$\overline{\sigma}\big(\boldsymbol{S}_t(\boldsymbol{G}_d + \boldsymbol{G}_t\boldsymbol{F})(j\omega)\big) \leq \gamma \tag{2.5.2}$$

ensures that

$$\|y(j\omega)\| \leq \gamma\|d(j\omega)\|.$$

Using the singular value inequalities (2.2.16) and (2.2.17), assuming $\gamma < 1$, we have

$$\begin{array}{rrcl} & \underline{\sigma}(\boldsymbol{G}_t\boldsymbol{K}) & \geq & \overline{\sigma}(\boldsymbol{G}_d + \boldsymbol{G}_t\boldsymbol{F})/\gamma + 1 \\ \Rightarrow & \underline{\sigma}(\boldsymbol{G}_t\boldsymbol{K} - I) & \geq & \overline{\sigma}(\boldsymbol{G}_d + \boldsymbol{G}_t\boldsymbol{F})/\gamma \\ \Rightarrow & \overline{\sigma}(\boldsymbol{S}_t)\overline{\sigma}(\boldsymbol{G}_d + \boldsymbol{G}_t\boldsymbol{F}) & \leq & \gamma \\ \Rightarrow & \overline{\sigma}\big(\boldsymbol{S}_t(\boldsymbol{G}_d + \boldsymbol{G}_t\boldsymbol{F})\big) & \leq & \gamma. \end{array}$$

Good attenuation ($\gamma \ll 1$) will be achieved if the minimum loop gain $\underline{\sigma}\big(\boldsymbol{G}_t\boldsymbol{K}(j\omega)\big)$ is high ($\gg 1$).

2.5.2 Tracking

The tracking or servo problem is to design the system in Figure 2.13 in such a way that the output y tracks the command or reference signal r. Ideally, the transfer function matrix relating r and y should be made equal to the identity matrix. As indicated in Section 1.2, we may attack this as an open-loop compensation problem where we seek to design the reference prefilter $\boldsymbol{R}$. With no feedback ($\boldsymbol{K} = 0$), the transfer function matrix from reference r to error $r - y$ is $I - \boldsymbol{G}_t\boldsymbol{R}$ so

$$\overline{\sigma}\big(I - \boldsymbol{G}_t\boldsymbol{R}(j\omega)\big) \leq \gamma$$

ensures that the error satisfies

$$\|r(j\omega) - y(j\omega)\| \leq \gamma\|r(j\omega)\|. \tag{2.5.3}$$

Again, if the plant is square and has no right-half-plane zeros, the obvious (and optimal) prefilter is $\boldsymbol{R} = \boldsymbol{G}_t^{-1}$. If the feedback loop is closed, the transfer function matrix from reference r to error $r - y$ becomes

$$\boldsymbol{S}_t\big(I - \boldsymbol{G}_t(\boldsymbol{K} + \boldsymbol{R})\big),$$

in which $\boldsymbol{S}_t$ is the sensitivity matrix (2.5.1), so that

$$\overline{\sigma}\big(\boldsymbol{S}_t\big(I - \boldsymbol{G}_t(\boldsymbol{K} + \boldsymbol{R})\big)(j\omega)\big) \leq \gamma \tag{2.5.4}$$

ensures the objective (2.5.3). The common unity feedback situation corresponds to the case where the restriction $\boldsymbol{R} = -\boldsymbol{K}$ is imposed and in this case (2.5.4) simplifies to an objective on the sensitivity operator:

$$\overline{\sigma}\big(\boldsymbol{S}_t(j\omega)\big) \leq \gamma. \tag{2.5.5}$$

Since

$$\underline{\sigma}\big(\boldsymbol{G}_t\boldsymbol{K}(j\omega)\big) \geq \frac{\overline{\sigma}\big(I - \boldsymbol{G}_t(\boldsymbol{K} + \boldsymbol{R})(j\omega)\big)}{\gamma} + 1$$

implies (2.5.4) (verify this as an exercise), good tracking ($\gamma \ll 1$) is ensured if the minimum loop gain $\underline{\sigma}\big(\boldsymbol{G}_t\boldsymbol{K}(j\omega)\big)$ is high ($\gg 1$) where $\overline{\sigma}\big(I - \boldsymbol{G}_t(\boldsymbol{K} + \boldsymbol{R})(j\omega)\big)$ is significant.

2.5.3 Sensor errors

The proper operation of any feedback system relies on accurate measurements of the feedback quantities. Since sensors are never absolutely accurate or noise free, the measurements they make differ from the signals they represent. As with disturbances, the effect of sensor errors is deleterious to the performance of the control system and their influence on the system output should be reduced as far as possible.

Given that sensor errors are inevitable, it is important that their effect be considered in the feedback system analysis and design process. In Figure 2.13, sensor errors are represented by the signal n and the transfer function from n to y is $\boldsymbol{G}_t\boldsymbol{K}\boldsymbol{S}_t$, in which $\boldsymbol{S}_t$ is the sensitivity operator (2.5.1). Therefore

$$\overline{\sigma}\big(\boldsymbol{G}_t\boldsymbol{K}(j\omega)\boldsymbol{S}_t\big) \leq \gamma \tag{2.5.6}$$

ensures that

$$\|y(j\omega)\| \leq \gamma\|n(j\omega)\|.$$

Note that $\boldsymbol{G}_t\boldsymbol{K}\boldsymbol{S}_t$ and $\boldsymbol{S}_t$ are algebraically related by

$$\begin{aligned} \boldsymbol{S}_t - \boldsymbol{G}_t\boldsymbol{K}\boldsymbol{S}_t &= (I - \boldsymbol{G}_t\boldsymbol{K})\boldsymbol{S}_t \\ &= I, \end{aligned} \tag{2.5.7}$$

which shows that $\boldsymbol{S}_t$ and $\boldsymbol{G}_t\boldsymbol{K}\boldsymbol{S}_t$ cannot be small simultaneously. As a result of this identity $\boldsymbol{G}_t\boldsymbol{K}\boldsymbol{S}_t$ is sometimes called the *complementary sensitivity operator.* It follows that

$$\underline{\sigma}\big(\boldsymbol{G}_t\boldsymbol{K}\boldsymbol{S}_t(j\omega)\big) > 1 - \overline{\sigma}\big(\boldsymbol{S}_t(j\omega)\big)$$

and hence that

$$\|y(j\omega)\| > \big(1 - \overline{\sigma}\big(\boldsymbol{S}_t(j\omega)\big)\big)\,\|n(j\omega)\|.$$

Objectives requiring that $\overline{\sigma}\big(\boldsymbol{S}_t(j\omega)\big)$ be small ($\ll 1$), such as disturbance attenuation and tracking, imply that sensor errors $n(j\omega)$ will pass (almost) unattenuated into the output signal $y(j\omega)$. As a result, *there must be a frequency separation between the requirement (2.5.6) and the objectives (2.5.2) and (2.5.5).* Sensors must be accurate over the operating bandwidth of any high-performance feedback system. A sufficient condition for (2.5.6) in terms of the loop-gain operator is obtained as follows:

$$\begin{aligned} & & \overline{\sigma}(\boldsymbol{G}_t\boldsymbol{K}) &\leq \tfrac{\gamma}{1+\gamma} \\ &\Rightarrow & \overline{\sigma}(\boldsymbol{G}_t\boldsymbol{K}) &\leq \gamma\big(1 - \overline{\sigma}(\boldsymbol{G}_t\boldsymbol{K})\big) \\ &\Rightarrow & \overline{\sigma}(\boldsymbol{G}_t\boldsymbol{K}) &\leq \gamma\underline{\sigma}(I - \boldsymbol{G}_t\boldsymbol{K}) \\ &\Rightarrow & \overline{\sigma}(\boldsymbol{G}_t\boldsymbol{K})\overline{\sigma}(\boldsymbol{S}_t) &\leq \gamma \\ &\Rightarrow & \overline{\sigma}(\boldsymbol{G}_t\boldsymbol{K}\boldsymbol{S}_t) &\leq \gamma. \end{aligned}$$

The effects of sensor errors are reduced by having low loop gain—in the extreme case of open-loop control ($\boldsymbol{K} = 0$), sensor errors have no effect on the output y!

This confirms that sensor noise attenuation conflicts with objectives requiring high loop gain. Ensuring that sensor errors do not destroy high-gain objectives such as disturbance attenuation generates an important trade-off in the design of the feedback control system.

2.5.4 The control signal

It has been shown that many of the objectives of control system design are enhanced by high loop gain. Our next calculation shows that high gain can produce excessive actuator activity and that the closed-loop bandwidth cannot be made significantly greater than that of the open loop without invoking high controller gain.

It follows from Figure 2.13 that the control signal is given by

$$\begin{aligned} u &= (I - \boldsymbol{K}\boldsymbol{G}_t)^{-1}(\boldsymbol{R}r + \boldsymbol{K}n + \boldsymbol{K}\boldsymbol{G}_d d) \\ &= (I - \boldsymbol{K}\boldsymbol{G}_t)^{-1}\boldsymbol{K}(-r + n + \boldsymbol{G}_d d) \;\text{ when } \boldsymbol{R} = -\boldsymbol{K}. \end{aligned} \tag{2.5.8}$$

The matrix $(I - \boldsymbol{K}\boldsymbol{G}_t)^{-1}\boldsymbol{K} = \boldsymbol{K}\boldsymbol{S}_t$, which also arises in the analysis of stability robustness with respect to additive model error, plays a vital role in assessing the impact of external influences on the control signal.

From the identity (2.5.7), we may write

$$\boldsymbol{K}\boldsymbol{S}_t = \boldsymbol{G}_t^{-1}(\boldsymbol{S}_t - I)$$

if $\boldsymbol{G}_t$ is nonsingular. Therefore

$$\underline{\sigma}\big(\boldsymbol{K}\boldsymbol{S}_t(j\omega)\big) \geq \frac{1 - \overline{\sigma}\big(\boldsymbol{S}_t(j\omega)\big)}{\overline{\sigma}\big(\boldsymbol{G}_t(j\omega)\big)} \quad \text{for } \overline{\sigma}\big(\boldsymbol{S}_t(j\omega)\big) < 1. \tag{2.5.9}$$

This shows that if the sensitivity is smaller than 1 at frequencies beyond the open-loop bandwidth, where $\overline{\sigma}\big(\boldsymbol{G}_t(j\omega)\big) \ll 1$, the external signals are amplified at u. The bandwidth over which the sensitivity may be made small is therefore limited by actuator performance.

By considering the inequality

$$\underline{\sigma}\big(\boldsymbol{K}(j\omega)\big) \geq \frac{\underline{\sigma}\big(\boldsymbol{G}_t\boldsymbol{K}(j\omega)\big)}{\overline{\sigma}\big(\boldsymbol{G}_t(j\omega)\big)},$$

we see that any objective requiring high loop gain (*i.e.*, $\underline{\sigma}\big(\boldsymbol{G}_t\boldsymbol{K}(j\omega)\big) \gg 1$) beyond the open-loop bandwidth will demand high gain from the controller.

2.5.5 Robust performance

So far, we have analyzed performance assuming the true plant is known. Yet feedback control is fundamentally concerned with achieving performance objectives despite modelling errors. We now consider the effect of plant model errors on performance. We choose the multiplicative model error representation and summarize performance by a sensitivity objective. Of course, a similar analysis can be performed for other model error representations and performance objectives.

Suppose a nominal model $\boldsymbol{G}$ of a system $\boldsymbol{G}_t$ is given. Suppose also that $\boldsymbol{G}_t$ lies in a neighborhood of $\boldsymbol{G}$ defined by

$$\boldsymbol{G}_t = (I + \boldsymbol{\Delta})\boldsymbol{G} \tag{2.5.10}$$

with

$$\overline{\sigma}\big(\boldsymbol{\Delta}(j\omega)\big) \leq \delta(j\omega) \quad \text{for all real } \omega. \tag{2.5.11}$$

Here, $\delta(j\omega)$ is a given real-valued positive function. Typically, $\delta(j\omega)$ is an increasing function of frequency—the model is a relatively good representation of the physical system at low frequencies, but is less reliable at high frequencies. In very general terms, the design problem is to find a controller $\boldsymbol{K}$ such that:

1. The system is internally stable for all plants described by (2.5.10) and (2.5.11).

2. The closed-loop performance is acceptable as specified by tracking accuracy, disturbance attenuation, sensitivity reduction and the reduction of nonlinear effects.

3. The control signal is of reasonable bandwidth and magnitude.

By Theorem 2.4.4, the stability requirements are ensured provided the nominal closed loop is internally stable, $\boldsymbol{G}_t$ and $\boldsymbol{G}$ have the same number of poles in the closed-right-half plane and

$$\overline{\sigma}\big(\boldsymbol{GKS}(j\omega)\big) < \frac{1}{\delta(j\omega)}, \tag{2.5.12}$$

in which $\boldsymbol{S}$ is the (nominal) sensitivity operator

$$\boldsymbol{S} = (I - \boldsymbol{GK})^{-1}.$$

The performance requirements may be translated into a condition such as

$$\rho(j\omega)\overline{\sigma}\big(\boldsymbol{S}_t(j\omega)\big) < 1 \quad \text{for all real } \omega \tag{2.5.13}$$

on the (true) sensitivity operator $\boldsymbol{S}_t = (I - \boldsymbol{G}_t\boldsymbol{K})^{-1}$. In (2.5.13), $\rho(j\omega)$ is some positive performance indicator, which will usually be large ($\gg 1$) at low frequencies and smaller at high frequencies. The frequency range over which $\rho(j\omega)$ is large is usually constrained by the need to avoid control signals of unacceptable bandwidth or amplitude.

Noting that

$$\boldsymbol{S}_t = \boldsymbol{S}(I - \boldsymbol{\Delta GKS})^{-1},$$

it may be shown (exercise) that

$$\begin{aligned} &\rho(j\omega)\overline{\sigma}\big(\boldsymbol{S}(j\omega)\big) + \delta(j\omega)\overline{\sigma}\big(\boldsymbol{GKS}(j\omega)\big) < 1 \\ \Rightarrow\ &\rho(j\omega)\overline{\sigma}\big(\boldsymbol{S}_t(j\omega)\big) < 1. \end{aligned} \tag{2.5.14}$$

We also notice that (2.5.14) ensures (2.5.12); the simultaneous satisfaction of (2.5.12) and (2.5.13) is an example of robust performance. We also conclude from (2.5.14) that achieving performance objectives when a modelling error is present requires additional gain.

To obtain a specification on the nominal sensitivity operator involving only $\rho(j\omega)$ and $\delta(j\omega)$, we note that $\boldsymbol{S} - \boldsymbol{GKS} = I$ implies

$$\overline{\sigma}\big(\boldsymbol{GKS}(j\omega)\big) \le 1 + \overline{\sigma}\big(\boldsymbol{S}(j\omega)\big).$$

Consequently,

$$\overline{\sigma}\big(\boldsymbol{S}(j\omega)\big) < \frac{1 - \delta(j\omega)}{\rho(j\omega) + \delta(j\omega)}$$

ensures (2.5.14).

2.5.6 Analytic limits on performance

We have already studied the design limitations imposed by algebraic identities such as

$$\boldsymbol{S} - \boldsymbol{GKS} = I. \tag{2.5.15}$$

If equations of this type were the only restriction, we could make $\overline{\sigma}\big(\boldsymbol{S}(j\omega)\big)$ small for $\omega \in [0, \omega_B]$ and $\overline{\sigma}\big(\boldsymbol{GKS}(j\omega)\big)$ small for $\omega \in (\omega_B, \infty)$. Under these conditions we could achieve high performance in the frequency range $[0, \omega_B]$ without compromising stability. Unfortunately, the rapid change of the loop gain in the vicinity of ω_B implied by this situation is not achievable.

Consider the scalar case with $\boldsymbol{q} = \boldsymbol{gk}$ stable and minimum phase.[8] The Bode gain-phase relation given by

$$\arg\big(\boldsymbol{q}(j\omega_0)\big) - \arg\big(\boldsymbol{q}(0)\big) = \frac{1}{\pi}\int_{-\infty}^{\infty} \frac{d\log|\boldsymbol{q}(j\omega)|}{d\omega} \log\left|\frac{\omega+\omega_0}{\omega-\omega_0}\right| d\omega \tag{2.5.16}$$

indicates that the phase at any frequency ω_0 is largely determined by the rate of change of gain in the vicinity of the frequency ω_0. This follows from the logarithmic singularity at $\omega = \omega_0$ in the weighting factor. For frequencies much larger than ω_0, the weighting factor is approximately $2\omega_0/\omega$, while at frequencies much less than ω_0 it is approximately $2\omega/\omega_0$. If $|\boldsymbol{q}(j\omega)|$ varies according to

$$\frac{d|\boldsymbol{q}(j\omega)|}{d\omega} \approx -n/\omega \tag{2.5.17}$$

(that is, $-n \times 20\ dB$ per decade) for ω between ω_0 and $\omega_B > 5\omega_0$, it is well known that

$$\arg\big(\boldsymbol{q}(j\omega_B)\big) - \arg\big(\boldsymbol{q}(0)\big) \approx -n \times 90^\circ.$$

As we will now show, this observation has implications for closed-loop stability.

Let us suppose that $|\boldsymbol{q}(j\omega_0)| \approx 1$ and that $n = 3$ in (2.5.17). Then the resulting 270° of phase change over the frequency interval $[\omega_0, \omega_B]$ may well drive the closed-loop system into instability (by producing an anticlockwise encirclement of $+1$). Even if n in (2.5.17) is only 2 at the unity-gain cross-over frequency, the phase change of about 180° could result in a small phase margin. Consequently, it is normally recommended that the gain should decrease at no more than 20 dB per decade ($n = 1$ in (2.5.17)) in the vicinity of the unity-gain cross-over frequency.

The requirement that the closed loop be stable therefore imposes analytic constraints on the allowed behavior of the loop gain as a function of frequency. These analytic constraints are consequences of Cauchy's integral formula.

A clear statement of these constraints is Bode's conservation of sensitivity theorem:

[8]This means that $\boldsymbol{q}$ has no poles or zeros in the closed-right-half plane, although it is allowed infinite zeros.

Theorem 2.5.1 *Suppose that* $\boldsymbol{q}$ *has relative degree at least 2. If* $\boldsymbol{s} = (1 - \boldsymbol{q})^{-1}$ *is stable, then*

$$\int_0^\infty \log |\boldsymbol{s}(j\omega)|\, d\omega = \pi \sum_i \mathrm{R}_e(p_i), \tag{2.5.18}$$

in which p_i *are the right-half-plane poles of* $\boldsymbol{q}$*. If* $\boldsymbol{q}$ *has no right-half-plane pole, then the right-hand side of (2.5.18) is zero.*

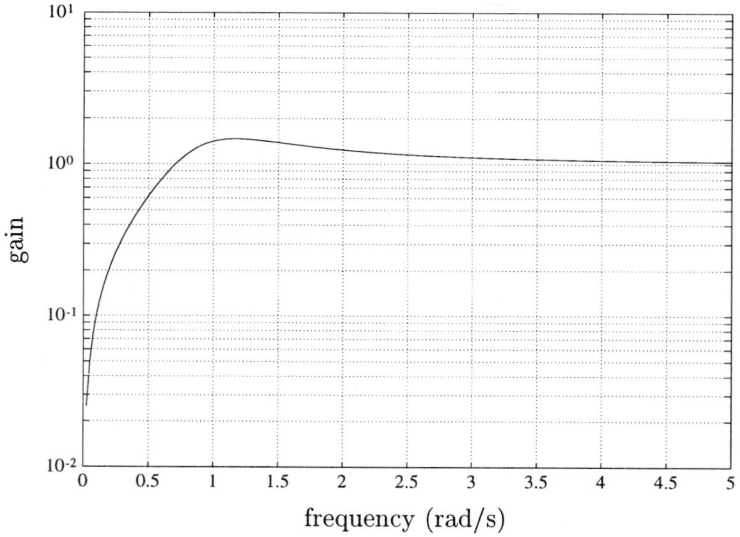

Figure 2.15: Plot of sensitivity on a logarithmic scale versus frequency on a linear scale.

This theorem states that the average of the logarithm of the sensitivity is conserved. All controllers such that the right-half-plane poles of $\boldsymbol{q} = \boldsymbol{gk}$ are at p_i will have the same average logarithmic sensitivity. If we make $|\boldsymbol{s}(j\omega)| < 1$ in the frequency range $[0, \omega_B]$, we must pay this back with $|\boldsymbol{s}(j\omega)| > 1$ in the high-frequency region. Figure 2.15 shows this phenomena for $\boldsymbol{q} = -1/s(s+1)$.

Equation (2.5.18) may not appear to be a serious restriction, since the debt incurred in making $|\boldsymbol{s}(j\omega)| < 1$ in the frequency range $[0, \omega_B]$ may be repaid, in theory, over the infinite frequency interval (ω_B, ∞). In reality, however, the controller bandwidth is limited and the repayment must be made in the active frequency range of the controller. To clarify the implications of this fact, suppose ω_{max} is chosen such that

$$|\boldsymbol{q}(j\omega)| \leq \frac{1}{(10\omega/\omega_{max})^2} \quad \text{for } \omega \geq \omega_{max}.$$

Then

$$\int_{\omega_{max}}^{\infty} \log|\boldsymbol{s}(j\omega)|\, d\omega \le M < \infty,$$

in which M depends only on ω_{max}.[9] Hence, if $|\boldsymbol{s}(j\omega)| < 1$ on the frequency range $[0, \omega_B]$, the debt must be repaid with $|\boldsymbol{s}(j\omega)| > 1$ on the finite frequency interval $[\omega_B, \omega_{max}]$. Specifically, if $|\boldsymbol{s}(j\omega)| \le 1/N$ for $\omega \in [0, \omega_B]$, then

$$(\omega_{max} - \omega_B)\log(\|\boldsymbol{s}\|_\infty) \ge \log(N)\omega_B - M + \pi \sum_i \mathrm{R}_e(p_i). \qquad (2.5.19)$$

As we press for more performance over a wider bandwidth (faster and more accurate tracking for example), stability robustness will be degraded, since $|\boldsymbol{gks}(j\omega)| \ge |\boldsymbol{s}(j\omega)| - 1$ when $|\boldsymbol{s}(j\omega)| \ge 1$. The inequality (2.5.19) therefore imposes a constraint that must be respected in choosing the performance target. Note that unstable open-loop poles make this analytic design trade-off even more restrictive.

It is possible to show that right-half-plane zeros in the open-loop transfer function also introduce an analytic design trade-off. If $|\boldsymbol{s}(j\omega)| \le 1/N$ for $\omega \in [0, \omega_B]$, then (irrespective of how $\boldsymbol{q}$ behaves at infinity)

$$\|\boldsymbol{s}\|_\infty \ge \alpha_2 \log N + \alpha_1 \log|\boldsymbol{s}^{-1}(z)|, \qquad (2.5.20)$$

in which z is a zero of $\boldsymbol{q}$ with $\mathrm{R}_e(z) > 0$ and α_1 and α_2 are constants depending only on ω_B and z.

These phenomena have come to be known as the "waterbed effect". Push the sensitivity down in one range of frequencies and it must pop up somewhere else.

The following theorem summarizes the results that are available in the multivariable case:

Theorem 2.5.2 *Suppose that $\boldsymbol{Q} = \boldsymbol{GK}$ is $n \times n$ and has entries which are each of relative degree at least 2. If $\boldsymbol{S} = (I - \boldsymbol{Q})^{-1}$ is stable, then*

$$\int_0^\infty \log|\det(\boldsymbol{S}(j\omega))|\, d\omega = \pi \sum_i \mathrm{R}_e(p_i) \qquad (2.5.21)$$

$$\sum_j^n \int_0^\infty \log \sigma_j(\boldsymbol{S}(j\omega))\, d\omega = \pi \sum_i \mathrm{R}_e(p_i) \qquad (2.5.22)$$

$$\int_0^\infty \log \underline{\sigma}(\boldsymbol{S}(j\omega))\, d\omega \le \frac{\pi}{n} \sum_i \mathrm{R}_e(p_i) \qquad (2.5.23)$$

$$\int_0^\infty \log \overline{\sigma}(\boldsymbol{S}(j\omega))\, d\omega \ge \frac{\pi}{n} \sum_i \mathrm{R}_e(p_i), \qquad (2.5.24)$$

in which the p_i's are the right-half-plane poles of $\boldsymbol{Q}$.

---

[9] $M = \omega_{max}[\ln(99/100) + \ln(11/9)/10] \approx \omega_{max}/100$.

Equations (2.5.21) and (2.5.22) provide conservation results for the multivariable sensitivity operator. Any decrease in $\overline{\sigma}(\boldsymbol{S}(j\omega))$ on $[0, \omega_B]$ must be compensated for by an increase in sensitivity at other frequencies *or in other directions.* There is the tantalizing prospect that a reduction in $\overline{\sigma}(\boldsymbol{S}(j\omega))$ on the interval $[0, \omega_B]$ might be traded against an increase in $\underline{\sigma}(\boldsymbol{S}(j\omega))$ on the interval $[0, \infty)$ (or $[0, \omega_{max}]$) without $\overline{\sigma}(\boldsymbol{S}(j\omega))$ becoming large—the singular values might be squeezed closer together. Inequalities (2.5.23) and (2.5.24) show the extent to which this is possible. When all the singular values have been squeezed together, so that $\overline{\sigma}(\boldsymbol{S}(j\omega)) = \underline{\sigma}(\boldsymbol{S}(j\omega))$, (2.5.24) will hold with equality and the scalar situation is recovered.

Main points of the section

1. Performance objectives can be analyzed using singular values.
2. Disturbance attenuation and tracking are improved by making the sensitivity operator small. This requires high loop gain.
3. Robust stability, and actuator and sensor constraints, limit the use of high gain.
4. Uncertainty about the plant makes the trade-off between high- and low-gain objectives more difficult to achieve.
5. Analytic constraints arising from Cauchy's integral formula impose "conservation laws" on stable closed-loop systems.

2.6 Example

We will now illustrate the use of singular values as an analysis tool by studying the unstable batch reactor process first described by Rosenbrock ([172], page 213).

A linearized model of this process is

$$\begin{aligned} \dot{x} &= \begin{bmatrix} 1.38 & -0.2077 & 6.715 & -5.676 \\ -0.5814 & -4.29 & 0 & 0.675 \\ 1.067 & 4.273 & -6.654 & 5.893 \\ 0.048 & 4.273 & 1.343 & -2.104 \end{bmatrix} x + \begin{bmatrix} 0 & 0 \\ 5.679 & 0 \\ 1.136 & -3.146 \\ 1.136 & 0 \end{bmatrix} u \\ y &= \begin{bmatrix} 1 & 0 & 1 & -1 \\ 0 & 1 & 0 & 0 \end{bmatrix} x. \end{aligned}$$

Since the eigenvalues of the A-matrix are $(1.99,\ 0.064,\ -5.057,\ -8.67)$ the reactor is unstable.

The two main aims of the control system are the stabilization of the process and the improvement of its step response. Since the actual batch process is nonlinear, we require stability robustness of the nominal linear closed loop. In order to achieve zero steady-state tracking error we require $\overline{\sigma}(\boldsymbol{S}(0)) = 0$. An adequate speed of response comes from ensuring that $\overline{\sigma}\big(\boldsymbol{S}(j\omega)\big) \le \epsilon$ for all $\omega \in [0, \omega_B]$ where ϵ is sufficiently small and ω_B is sufficiently large.

The objectives call for high loop gain ($\underline{\sigma}\big(\boldsymbol{GK}(j\omega)\big) \gg 1$) over a frequency range that is wide enough to meet the sensitivity specification. The uncompensated plant singular values $\sigma\big(G(j\omega)\big)$ are shown in Figure 2.16. Clearly some low-frequency gain is required, because $\underline{\sigma}\big(\boldsymbol{G}(j10^{-2})\big) \le 0.4$ implies that $\overline{\sigma}\big(\boldsymbol{S}(j10^{-2})\big) \ge 10/14$.

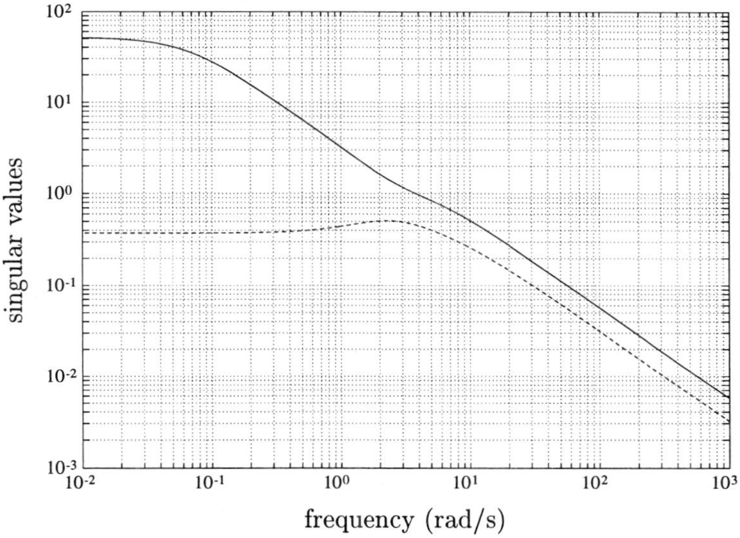

Figure 2.16: The two singular values uncompensated batch process.

There are many ways of designing control systems and many problems can be solved without the aid of the latest theory. Simply using modern methods such as $\mathcal{H}_\infty$ optimization for everything, without thought, may lead one to overlook simple and elegant solutions. $\mathcal{H}_\infty$ optimization is only one tool and we do not wish to convey the impression that it is the only tool.

By studying the batch process' inverse Nyquist array, Rosenbrock deduced that the control system design task is simplified by crossing over the two inputs and negating the sign of the first new loop. He then found that the system could easily be controlled using proportional-plus-integral control. In our study we use

$$u = K_p(y_{ref} - y) + K_i \int_0^t (y_{ref} - y)dt$$

where

$$K_p = \begin{bmatrix} 0 & 2 \\ -5 & 0 \end{bmatrix} \quad \text{and} \quad K_i = \begin{bmatrix} 0 & 2 \\ -8 & 0 \end{bmatrix}.$$

The proportional part is taken from Rosenbrock, while the integral part is ours—Rosenbrock did not specify the integral term in his writing. The elegance and simplicity of this solution is self evident.

From the singular values of the compensated plant $\sigma\big(\boldsymbol{GK}(j\omega)\big)$ shown in Figure 2.17, we see that the tracking requirements will now be met. Indeed, since $\underline{\sigma}\big(\boldsymbol{GK}(j\omega)\big) > 1+\sqrt{2}$ implies that $\overline{\sigma}\big(\boldsymbol{S}(j\omega)\big) < 1/\sqrt{2}$ and $\overline{\sigma}\big(\boldsymbol{S}(j\omega)\big) < 1/\sqrt{2}$ implies that $\underline{\sigma}\big(\boldsymbol{GK}(j\omega)\big) > \sqrt{2}-1$, the closed-loop bandwidth must be between 1.8 rad/s and 27.3 rad/s. These calculations illustrate the importance of simple singular value inequalities in the selection of frequency shaping functions during the design process.

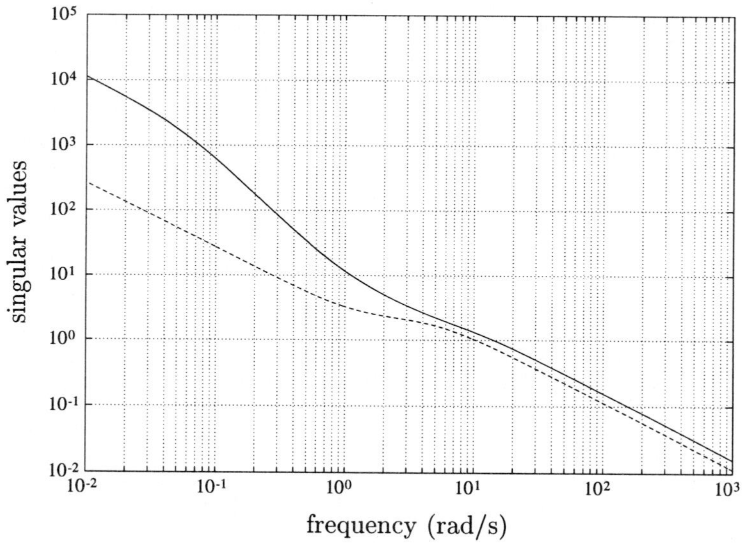

Figure 2.17: The two singular values of the loop-gain operator of the batch process compensated by Rosenbrock's controller.

Figure 2.18 shows the characteristics of $\sigma\big(\boldsymbol{S}(\omega)\big)$ that are necessary for tracking step reference inputs. These same characteristics will ensure the attenuation of step-like disturbances at the system output. The closed-loop bandwidth is about 15.2 rad/s. The step response of the closed-loop system is given in Figure 2.19.

We may examine robust stability to multiplicative model error by plotting the singular values of the complementary sensitivity $\boldsymbol{GKS}(j\omega)$, which are shown in

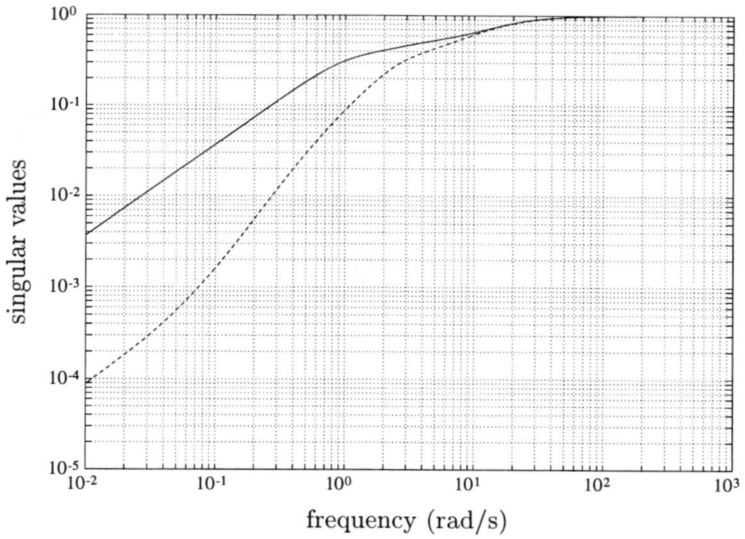

Figure 2.18: The two singular values of the sensitivity operator of the batch process.

Figure 2.20. Since $\overline{\sigma}(\boldsymbol{GKS}(j\omega)) \ll 1$ beyond about 100 rad/s, considerable high-frequency model error is tolerable. The peak of 1.34 at about 2.5 rad/s indicates that the loop will be stable for all stable multiplicative perturbations $\boldsymbol{\Delta}$ to $\boldsymbol{G}$ such that $\overline{\sigma}(\boldsymbol{\Delta}(j\omega)) < 1/1.34 = 0.75$ for all ω. However, there is a $\boldsymbol{\Delta}$ with $\overline{\sigma}(\boldsymbol{\Delta}(j\omega)) \leq 1/1.34 = 0.75$ that will destabilize the loop (Problem 2.15). Sensor errors are unlikely to be a problem if they are small at frequencies below about 100 rad/s.

2.7 Notes and References

There is a large literature on Nyquist array and characteristic locus methods and some excellent books on the subject are available. We refer the interested reader to MacFarlane [143], Rosenbrock [172] and Maciejowski [144].

Example 2.1.1 is from Doyle [50] (also Doyle and Stein [55]), who introduced it to make much the same points. Example 2.1.2 is taken from Doyle [49], who showed that LQG regulators have no guaranteed robust stability margins. For a treatment of the robustness properties of the linear quadratic regulator, see Anderson and Moore [11, 13] and Safonov and Athans [179].

The singular value decomposition and singular value inequalities are discussed in many places. Three useful references are Golub and van Loan [81], Horn and

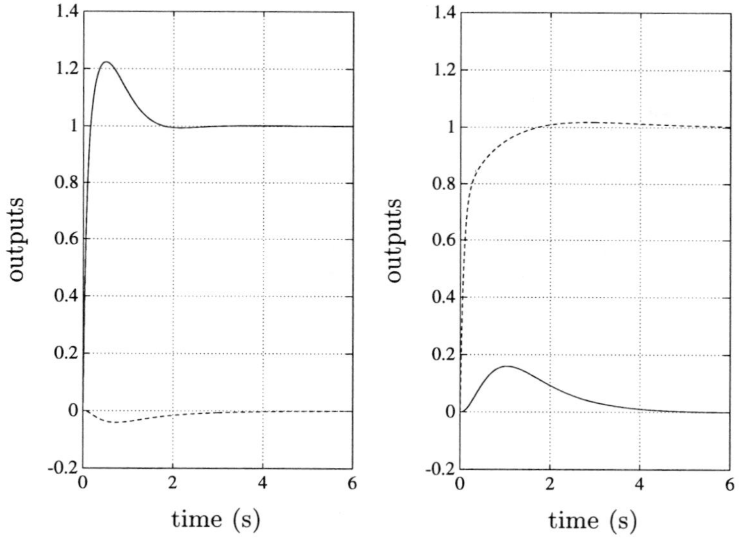

Figure 2.19: Step response of the batch process compensated with Rosenbrock's controller. The first diagram shows the response to a step input of the form $y_{ref} = H(t)[1\ 0]'$, while the second is the response to $y_{ref} = H(t)[0\ 1]'$.

Johnson [94] and Stewart [198]. Readers interested in interlacing inequalities on the sums and products of matrix valued operators are referred to Ky Fan [59].

The importance of the sensitivity operator in feedback design dates back to the classical texts of Bode [31] and Horowitz [95]. The multivariable case was analyzed in the early 1960s by Cruz and Perkins [38]. The parametric analysis in Section 2.3 follows that given in Anderson and Moore [13], page 112.

The use of singular values for the stability robustness analysis of multivariable control systems began in the late 1970s. The papers by Safonov [176], Stein and Doyle [197], and Sandell [190] in the *16th Annual Allerton Conference on Communications, Control and Computing*, 1978, appear to be the first references containing analysis along the lines presented in Section 2.4. The derivation using the generalized Nyquist theorem is due to Doyle [50]—Safonov derives his results (which allow a larger class of model errors) from the sector bounded stability results in his Ph.D. thesis [175] (see also [177]), while Sandell uses operator theoretic arguments. The paper by Sandell contains the acknowledgment:

> "The ideas in this paper arose during the course of discussions with M. Athans, J.C. Doyle, A.J. Laub, M.G. Safonov and G. Stein."

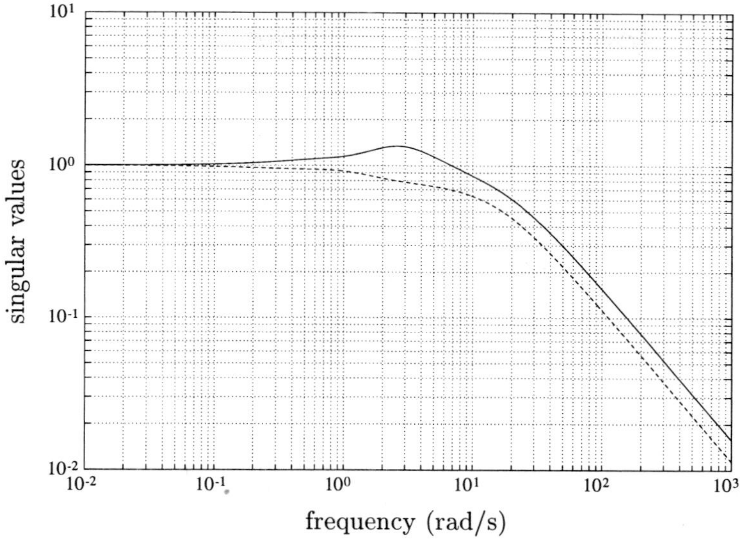

Figure 2.20: The two singular values of the complementary sensitivity operator of the batch process compensated with Rosenbrock's controller.

The journal papers on the singular value analysis of multivariable control systems by MacFarlane and Scott-Jones [142]; Doyle and Stein [55]; Safonov, Laub and Hartmann [182]; and Postlethwaite, Edmunds and MacFarlane [166] appeared a year or so later—all but one are in the *IEEE Transactions on Automatic Control* Special Issue on Linear Multivariable Control Systems [185] published in January 1981.

Analytic constraints on closed-loop performance date from the work of Bode [31], who developed the famous gain-phase relations that bear his name and proved the conservation of sensitivity result (Theorem 2.5.1) for the case of stable systems (see page 285 of [31]). The result was generalized by Freudenberg and Looze [67] to include open-loop unstable systems. An inequality similar to (2.5.19) appears in the monograph by Freudenberg and Looze [68], page 53. The limits on performance imposed by right-half-plane zeros have been studied at least since Horowitz [95]. An explicit statement of the design trade-off equivalent to (2.5.20) is given in Francis and Zames [66]. Multivariable extensions of the sensitivity conservation law were developed by Boyd and Desoer [32] and Freudenberg and Looze [68].

The unstable batch reactor example first appeared in Rosenbrock [172].

2.8 Problems

Problem 2.1. Suppose $\overline{\sigma}(\boldsymbol{Q}) < 1$.

1. Show that $(I - \boldsymbol{Q})$ is nonsingular.
2. Show that the series $\sum_{k=0}^{\infty} \boldsymbol{Q}^k$ converges.
3. Show that $(I - \boldsymbol{Q})^{-1} = \sum_{k=0}^{\infty} \boldsymbol{Q}^k$.

Problem 2.2. Prove the following identities

$$\begin{aligned} \boldsymbol{Q}(I-\boldsymbol{Q})^{-1} &= (I-\boldsymbol{Q})^{-1}\boldsymbol{Q} \\ (I-\boldsymbol{Q})^{-1} &= I + \boldsymbol{Q}(I-\boldsymbol{Q})^{-1} \\ \boldsymbol{K}(I-\boldsymbol{G}\boldsymbol{K})^{-1} &= (I-\boldsymbol{K}\boldsymbol{G})^{-1}\boldsymbol{K}. \end{aligned}$$

Problem 2.3. Let Q be a $p \times p$ matrix with ordered singular values $\sigma_1 \geq \sigma_2 \geq \ldots \geq \sigma_p > 0$.

1. Show that $\overline{\sigma}(Q^{-1}) = \frac{1}{\underline{\sigma}(Q)}$.
2. Show that $\sigma_p^{-1} \geq \ldots \geq \sigma_1^{-1}$ are the ordered singular values of Q^{-1}.

Problem 2.4. Let Q be a $p \times p$ matrix with $\lambda_i(Q)$, $i = 1, 2, \ldots, p$, the eigenvalues of Q.

1. Show that
$$\det(Q) = \prod_{i=1}^{p} \lambda_i(Q) = e^{i\theta} \prod_{i=1}^{p} \sigma_i(Q)$$
for some phase θ.
2. Show that $\underline{\sigma}(Q) \leq |\lambda_i(Q)| \leq \overline{\sigma}(Q)$, $i = 1, \ldots, p$.

Problem 2.5. Assume the feedback loop of Figure 2.1 is internally stable and that the Nyquist diagram of each eigenvalue $\lambda_i(s)$ has the property $|1 - \lambda_i(j\omega)| > \alpha_i > 0$ for constants α_i. What can one say about the stability robustness of the feedback loop?

Problem 2.6. Suppose

$$\boldsymbol{G} = \begin{bmatrix} 7 & 8 \\ 6 & 7 \end{bmatrix} \begin{bmatrix} \frac{1}{s+1} & 0 \\ 0 & \frac{2}{s+2} \end{bmatrix} \begin{bmatrix} 7 & 8 \\ 6 & 7 \end{bmatrix}^{-1}.$$

1. Sketch the Nyquist diagrams for the eigenvalues of $\boldsymbol{G}$.
2. Show that $\boldsymbol{G}$ has the following state-space realization:

$$\begin{aligned} \dot{x} &= \begin{bmatrix} -1 & 0 \\ 0 & -2 \end{bmatrix} x + \begin{bmatrix} 7 & -8 \\ -12 & 14 \end{bmatrix} u \\ y &= \begin{bmatrix} 7 & 8 \\ 6 & 7 \end{bmatrix} x. \end{aligned}$$

3. By evaluating the linear term of $\det(sI - A - BKC)$ with

$$K = \begin{bmatrix} k_1 & 0 \\ 0 & k_2 \end{bmatrix},$$

show that $3 - 50k_2 + 47k_1 > 0$ is a necessary condition for the stability of the feedback loop of Figure 2.1.
(Hint: you can simplify your calculations by setting $k_1 = k+\delta$ and $k_2 = k-\delta$.)

Problem 2.7. (M.C. Smith) The aim of this exercise is to demonstrate that the m eigenvalue loci of $m \times m$ transfer functions do not necessarily form m closed curves. To see this, plot the eigenvalue loci of

$$G = \begin{bmatrix} \left(\frac{1+\epsilon}{s+1}\right) & \left(\frac{-5s-8}{s+2}\right) \\ \left(\frac{1+\epsilon}{s+1}\right) & \left(\frac{-2s-6}{s+2}\right) \end{bmatrix}$$

for $\epsilon = -0.005, 0.000, +0.005$ and note the number of closed curves in each case.

Problem 2.8. By mimicking the arguments used in the proof of Theorem 2.4.3, establish Theorem 2.4.4.

Problem 2.9. By mimicking the arguments used in the proof of Theorem 2.4.3, establish Theorem 2.4.5.

Problem 2.10. Derive the implications expressed in (2.4.8), (2.4.9) and (2.4.13).

Problem 2.11. The aim of this exercise is to check the calculations in Example 2.4.1.

1. By making use of a computer package such as MATLAB[10], reconstruct Figure 2.11, thereby checking that

$$\min_{\omega} \left\{1/\overline{\sigma}\big(K(I - GK)^{-1}(j\omega)\big)\right\} = 0.0612$$

with

$$\arg\min_{\omega} \left\{1/\overline{\sigma}\big(K(I - GK)^{-1}(j\omega)\big)\right\} = 3.$$

2. If

$$K(I - GK)^{-1}(j3) = \sum_{i=1}^{2} \sigma_i v_i u_i^*,$$

show that $I - \Delta K(I - GK)^{-1}(j3)$ is singular if $\Delta = \sigma_1^{-1} u_1 v_1^*$.
3. Find a rational stable perturbation such that $\|\Delta\|_\infty \leq \sigma_1^{-1}$ and $\Delta(j3) = \sigma_1^{-1} u_1 v_1^*$. Compare your answer with the solution given in the text of Example 2.1.1.

[10]MATLAB is a registered trademark of The MathWorks, Inc.

Problem 2.12. Show that

$$\underline{\sigma}(\boldsymbol{GK}(j\omega)) \geq \frac{\overline{\sigma}(I - \boldsymbol{G}(\boldsymbol{K}+\boldsymbol{R})(j\omega))}{\gamma} + 1$$

ensures satisfaction of the reference tracking objective $\|r(j\omega) - y(j\omega)\| \leq \gamma\|r(j\omega)\|$ for the loop in Figure 2.13.

Problem 2.13. Show that (2.5.14) implies (2.5.13). Show also that (2.5.13) implies that $\rho(j\omega)\overline{\sigma}(\boldsymbol{S}(j\omega)) \leq 1 + \delta(j\omega)\overline{\sigma}(\boldsymbol{GKS}(j\omega))$.

Problem 2.14. Suppose a controller has been designed for the feedback loop in Figure 2.4 such that $\|r(j\omega) + y_c(j\omega)\| \leq \rho(j\omega)\|r(j\omega)\|$ for all $r(j\omega)$ and some nonnegative function $\rho(j\omega)$. Suppose also that $\boldsymbol{G}_t = (I + \boldsymbol{\Delta}_2)^{-1}\boldsymbol{G}$, in which $\boldsymbol{\Delta}_2$ satisfies $\overline{\sigma}(\boldsymbol{\Delta}_2(j\omega)) \leq \delta(j\omega) < 1$ for some other nonnegative function $\delta(j\omega)$. Show that this objective will be achieved if

$$\overline{\sigma}(\boldsymbol{S}(j\omega)) \leq \frac{\rho(j\omega)}{1 + \delta(j\omega)\big(1 + \rho(j\omega)\big)},$$

in which $\boldsymbol{S} = (I - \boldsymbol{GK})^{-1}$ is the nominal sensitivity function.

Problem 2.15. Consider the unstable batch reactor described in Example 2.6, together with the controller

$$\boldsymbol{K} = \begin{bmatrix} 0 & 2 \\ -5 & 0 \end{bmatrix} + \frac{1}{s}\begin{bmatrix} 0 & 2 \\ -8 & 0 \end{bmatrix}.$$

1. Using MATLAB[11] or otherwise, plot $\overline{\sigma}(\boldsymbol{GK}(I - \boldsymbol{GK})^{-1}(j\omega))$. Show that

$$\min_{\omega} \frac{1}{\overline{\sigma}(\boldsymbol{GK}(I - \boldsymbol{GK})^{-1}(j\omega))} = 0.7451,$$

and that

$$\arg\min_{\omega} \frac{1}{\overline{\sigma}(\boldsymbol{GK}(I - \boldsymbol{GK})^{-1}(j\omega))} \approx 2.5$$

2. Find a singular value decomposition of $\boldsymbol{GK}(I - \boldsymbol{GK})^{-1}(j2.5)$.
3. Show that

$$\boldsymbol{\Delta} = 0.7451 \begin{bmatrix} 0.9787 \\ 0.2052\left(\frac{s-1.7651}{s+1.7651}\right) \end{bmatrix} \begin{bmatrix} 0.9915\left(\frac{s-0.1656}{s+0.1656}\right) \\ -0.1299\left(\frac{s-3.5936}{s+3.5936}\right) \end{bmatrix}'$$

is a stable destabilizing perturbation satisfying $\|\boldsymbol{\Delta}\|_\infty \leq 0.7451$.

[11] MATLAB is a registered trademark of The MathWorks, Inc.

3

Signals and Systems

In Chapter 2, we presented singular values as a multivariable design tool for systems described by rational transfer function matrices—systems that are linear, time-invariant and finite-dimensional. However, as all physical systems are both time-varying and nonlinear to some extent, the assumption that both models and modelling errors are described by transfer function matrices is unacceptable. In particular, we need to be able to allow time-varying and nonlinear modelling errors. Fortunately, a singular value bound of the form $\overline{\sigma}\big(\boldsymbol{G}(j\omega)\big) < \gamma$ for all ω has implications beyond linear, time-invariant theory. In this chapter we review the basic definitions and properties of signals and systems required to make these generalizations. Two important results, the small gain theorem and the bounded real lemma, are the main focus of the chapter.

Sections 3.1 and 3.2 are concerned with the basic definitions and properties of signals and systems. The Lebesgue 2-spaces $\mathcal{L}_2[0,T]$ and $\mathcal{L}_2[0,\infty)$ are reviewed. The frequency domain Lebesgue space $\mathcal{L}_2$ and the Hardy space $\mathcal{H}_2$ are introduced. Definitions of causality, time-invariance, stability and linearity are given. The infinity norm is defined and the spaces $\mathcal{L}_\infty$ and $\mathcal{H}_\infty$ are introduced. The properties of adjoint and allpass systems are reviewed. These sections do not attempt to provide a definitive or comprehensive treatment of signal and system theory; we assume that the reader is familiar with most of this material through exposure to senior undergraduate or graduate level courses and texts. In particular, we assume familiarity with state-space system descriptions, controllability, observability and minimality. Our treatment does little more than introduce the terminology, notation and results that will be required for our subsequent work.

In Section 3.3, the incremental gain and the induced norm are introduced as measures of system size. In addition, the 2-norm of a system, which is the objective function of interest in LQG optimal control, is defined. Section 3.4 presents the small gain theorem. Some extensions of the basic result that can be obtained by simple loop transformations are presented in Section 3.5. Again, our treatment is reasonably terse in order to restrict its length. We excuse this on the grounds that this material is covered in several excellent texts. The small gain theorem allows us to obtain robust stability results in Section 3.6 which permit time-varying and nonlinear model errors. These results are natural generalizations of those given in Chapter 2.

The chapter concludes with the bounded real lemma, which allows us to answer the question "is $\overline{\sigma}\big(G(j\omega)\big) < \gamma$ for all ω?". The proof of this result provides a warm-up exercise for our later work on the synthesis of controllers that meet singular value objectives.

3.1 Signals

A *signal* is a (Lebesgue) measurable function that maps the real numbers $\mathbb{R}$ to $\mathbb{R}^n$. The set of signals is

$$\mathcal{S} = \{f : \mathbb{R} \mapsto \mathbb{R}^n\}.$$

Note here, once and for all, that $\mathcal{S}$ is formally being considered as a set of equivalence classes of signals—signals which differ only on sets of (Lebesgue) measure zero are formally identical. Readers not familiar with measure theory may regard $\mathcal{S}$ as a set which contains all signals that could occur in an engineering system. It also contains many functions which could not conceivably occur in any engineering system.

Signals form a natural vector space under addition and scalar multiplication, which are defined by

$$\begin{aligned} (f+g)(t) &= f(t) + g(t) \\ (\alpha f)(t) &= \alpha f(t). \end{aligned}$$

It is convenient to define the two subspaces

$$\begin{aligned} \mathcal{S}_+ &= \{f \in \mathcal{S} : f(t) = 0 \text{ for all } t < 0\} \\ \mathcal{S}_- &= \{f \in \mathcal{S} : f(t) = 0 \text{ for all } t > 0\}. \end{aligned}$$

3.1.1 The size of signals

The size of a signal will be measured by a 2-norm defined over either a finite or infinite time interval. In the sequel, $\|x\| = \sqrt{x'x}$ is the Euclidean norm.[1]

[1] We also use $\|X\|$ to denote the matrix norm $\overline{\sigma}(X)$. The use of upper-case letters for matrices and lower-case letters for vectors means that no confusion should arise.

Finite horizon

The finite-horizon 2-norm is defined by

$$\|f\|_{2,[0,T]} = \left\{ \int_0^T \|f(t)\|^2 \, dt \right\}^{\frac{1}{2}}. \tag{3.1.1}$$

The set of signals for which this norm is finite is known as the finite-horizon Lebesgue 2-space:

$$\mathcal{L}_2[0,T] = \left\{ f \in \mathcal{S}_+ : \|f\|_{2,[0,T]} < \infty \right\}. \tag{3.1.2}$$

Any signal that is continuous on $[0,T]$ is bounded and is therefore in $\mathcal{L}_2[0,T]$. Signals like $\frac{1}{|2t-T|}$ are not in $\mathcal{L}_2[0,T]$.

A signal f is in the finite-horizon 2-space $\mathcal{L}_2[t_0,T]$ if and only if the time-shifted signal $g(t) = f(t+t_0)$ is in $\mathcal{L}_2[0,T-t_0]$. The norm $\|f\|_{2,[t_0,T]}$ is defined in the obvious way.

Infinite horizon

In order to address stability issues, we must consider the behavior of signals over infinite time intervals. The infinite-horizon Lebesgue 2-space is defined by

$$\mathcal{L}_2(-\infty,\infty) = \{ f \in \mathcal{S} : \|f\|_2 < \infty \}, \tag{3.1.3}$$

in which

$$\|f\|_2 = \left\{ \int_{-\infty}^{\infty} \|f(t)\|^2 \, dt \right\}^{\frac{1}{2}}. \tag{3.1.4}$$

The spaces $\mathcal{L}_2[0,\infty)$ and $\mathcal{L}_2(-\infty,0]$ are defined by $\mathcal{L}_2[0,\infty) = \mathcal{S}_+ \cap \mathcal{L}_2(-\infty,\infty)$ and $\mathcal{L}_2(-\infty,0] = \mathcal{S}_- \cap \mathcal{L}_2(-\infty,\infty)$.

Establishing that signals are in $\mathcal{L}_2[0,\infty)$ will often be done in several steps, with each step corresponding to increasingly stringent growth conditions. For this purpose, it is convenient to introduce the extended 2-space $\mathcal{L}_{2e}$ defined by

$$\mathcal{L}_{2e} = \{ f \in \mathcal{L}_2[0,T] \text{ for all } T < \infty \}. \tag{3.1.5}$$

Note, however, that $f \in \mathcal{L}_{2e}$ does not imply $\sup_T \|f\|_{2,[0,T]} < \infty$. For example, $f(t) = t$ and $g(t) = e^t$, $t \geq 0$, are both in $\mathcal{L}_{2e}$, but are not in $\mathcal{L}_2[0,\infty)$.

Inner product

The space $\mathcal{L}_2(-\infty,\infty)$ is a Hilbert space with *inner product* defined by

$$\langle f, g \rangle = \int_{-\infty}^{\infty} g'(t) f(t) \, dt.$$

Two signals f and g are orthogonal if $\langle f, g\rangle = 0$. This is a natural extension of orthogonality in $\mathbb{R}^n$. Note that $f \in \mathcal{L}_2[0,\infty)$ and $g \in \mathcal{L}_2(-\infty,0]$ implies that $\langle f, g\rangle = 0$, which means that $\mathcal{L}_2[0,\infty)$ and $\mathcal{L}_2(-\infty,0]$ are orthogonal subspaces of $\mathcal{L}_2(-\infty,\infty)$.

The spaces $\mathcal{L}_2[0,\infty)$, $\mathcal{L}_2(-\infty,0]$ and $\mathcal{L}_2[0,T]$ are all Hilbert spaces in their own right, with the inner product integral taken over the appropriate time interval. For example, for $\mathcal{L}_2[0,T]$ we have

$$\langle f, g\rangle_{[0,T]} = \int_0^T g'(t)f(t)\,dt.$$

Note that $\|f\|_2^2 = \langle f, f\rangle$ and that the inner product satisfies the *Cauchy-Schwarz inequality*[2]

$$|\langle f, g\rangle| \leq \|f\|_2\|g\|_2.$$

The 2-norm of exponential signals

The following theorem shows that the initial condition response of a time-varying state-space system is always in $\mathcal{L}_{2e}$ and, in the time-invariant case, gives conditions under which the initial condition response is in $\mathcal{L}_2[0,\infty)$. The proof provides an elementary introduction to the techniques we will use to prove the bounded real lemma and the later results on controller synthesis.

Theorem 3.1.1 *Consider a signal z such that*

$$\begin{aligned} \dot{x}(t) &= A(t)x(t), \qquad x(0) = x_0,\\ z(t) &= C(t)x(t), \end{aligned}$$

in which $A(t)$ and $C(t)$ are continuous matrix valued functions of appropriate dimension.

1. The finite-horizon case*:*

   (a) $z \in \mathcal{L}_{2e}$ for all x_0.

   (b) $\|z\|_{2,[0,T]}^2 = x_0'Q(0)x_0$, in which $Q(t)$ is the observability gramian generated by

$$-\dot{Q}(t) = Q(t)A(t) + A'(t)Q(t) + C'(t)C(t), \quad Q(T) = 0. \tag{3.1.6}$$

2. The infinite-horizon case*: Assume that A and C are constant.*

   (a) The following are equivalent:

   (i) $z \in \mathcal{L}_2[0,\infty)$ for all x_0.

[2] Any inner product satisfies the Cauchy-Schwarz inequality.

(ii) $Ce^{At} \to 0$ *as* $t \to \infty$.

(iii) *Every observable eigenspace of* A *is asymptotically stable.*

(iv) $Q(t)$ *satisfying*

$$-\dot{Q}(t) = Q(t)A + A'Q(t) + C'C, \qquad Q(T) = 0, \tag{3.1.7}$$

is uniformly bounded on $t \leq T$.

In this case, $Q = \lim_{t \to -\infty} Q(t)$ *exists, is independent of* T *and satisfies*

$$QA + A'Q + C'C = 0. \tag{3.1.8}$$

Furthermore, $Q \geq 0$.

(v) *There exists* $Q \geq 0$ *satisfying (3.1.8).*

(Such a Q *may not be equal to* $\lim_{t \to -\infty} Q(t)$*, which is the smallest nonnegative definite solution to (3.1.8).)*

(b) *If the conditions in Item 2a hold, then* $\|z\|_2^2 = x_0'Qx_0$*, in which* $Q = \lim_{t \to -\infty} Q(t)$.

Proof.

1. The solution of the differential equation is given by $z(t) = C(t)\Phi(t,0)x_0$, in which $\Phi(t,\tau)$ denotes the transition matrix associated with the linear system:

$$\frac{d}{dt}\Phi(t,\tau) = A(t)\Phi(t,\tau), \qquad \Phi(\tau,\tau) = I.$$

Some properties of $\Phi(t,\tau)$ that are needed in the sequel are explored in Problem 3.3. Since z is continuous, $z \in \mathcal{L}_2[0,T]$ for any finite T. Furthermore,

$$\begin{aligned} \int_0^T z'(t)z(t)\,dt &= x_0' \left\{ \int_0^T \Phi'(t,0)C'(t)C(t)\Phi(t,0)\,dt \right\} x_0 \\ &= x_0' M(0) x_0, \end{aligned}$$

in which

$$M(t) = \int_t^T \Phi'(\tau,t)C'(\tau)C(\tau)\Phi(\tau,t)\,d\tau.$$

Invoking Leibniz's rule concerning the interchange of the order of integration and differentiation, we obtain

$$\begin{aligned} \frac{d}{dt}M(t) &= -C'(t)C(t) + \int_t^T \frac{d}{dt}\big(\Phi'(\tau,t)C'(\tau)C(\tau)\Phi(\tau,t)\big)\,d\tau \\ &= -C'(t)C(t) - A'(t)M(t) - M(t)A(t). \end{aligned}$$

Since $M(T) = 0$ and $Q(T) = 0$, we conclude that $M(t) = Q(t)$ as they satisfy the same differential equation.

2.

(i)⇒(ii) Follows from $z(t) = Ce^{At}x_0$.

(ii)⇒(iii) If $AW = WJ$, in which J is a Jordan block corresponding to an eigenvalue s with $R_e(s) \geq 0$, then $Ce^{At}W = CWe^{Jt}$. Hence $Ce^{At}W \to 0$ as $t \to \infty$ implies $CW = 0$.

(iii)⇒(iv) $Q(t)$ is given by the integral

$$Q(t) = \int_0^{T-t} e^{A'\sigma}C'Ce^{A\sigma}\,d\sigma. \tag{3.1.9}$$

Write A in the form

$$A = \begin{bmatrix} W_1 & W_2 \end{bmatrix} \begin{bmatrix} \Lambda_1 & 0 \\ 0 & \Lambda_2 \end{bmatrix} \begin{bmatrix} V_1 \\ V_2 \end{bmatrix},$$

in which $\mathrm{R}_e\big(\lambda_i(\Lambda_1)\big) < 0$, $\mathrm{R}_e\big(\lambda_i(\Lambda_2)\big) \geq 0$ and $V = W^{-1}$. Since every unstable mode is unobservable, $CW_2 = 0$. Therefore, $Ce^{At} = CW_1e^{\Lambda_1 t}V_1$ and $\|CW_1e^{\Lambda_1\sigma}V_1\| \leq \alpha e^{\lambda t}$ for $\lambda = \max_i \mathrm{R}_e\big(\lambda_i(\Lambda_1)\big) < 0$ and some $\alpha < \infty$. Hence

$$\begin{aligned} \|Q(t)\| &\leq \int_0^{T-t} \|CW_1e^{\Lambda_1\sigma}V_1\|^2\,d\sigma \\ &\leq \alpha^2 \int_0^{T-t} e^{2\lambda\sigma}\,d\sigma \\ &\leq \alpha^2 \int_0^{\infty} e^{2\lambda\sigma}\,d\sigma = \frac{\alpha^2}{2|\lambda|}. \end{aligned}$$

Therefore $Q(t)$ is uniformly bounded. From (3.1.9), it follows that $Q(t_1) \geq Q(t_2)$ for any $t_1 \leq t_2$, which is to say that $Q(t)$ is monotonic. Consequently, $Q(t)$ uniformly bounded implies that $\lim_{t\to-\infty} Q(t)$ exists. From (3.1.9) we see that $Q = Q(-\infty)$ is independent of t, satisfies (3.1.8) and $Q \geq 0$.

(iv)⇒(v) Set $Q = \lim_{t\to-\infty} Q(t)$.

(v)⇒(i) Let Q be any nonnegative definite solution to (3.1.8) and define $X(t) = Q - Q(t)$. Then

$$\dot{X}(t) = -X(t)A - A'X(t), \qquad X(T) = Q,$$

so that $X(t) = e^{A'(T-t)}Qe^{A(T-t)} \geq 0$ for all t, T. Hence $0 \leq Q(t) \leq Q$ for all $t \leq T$, which shows that $\lim_{t\to-\infty} Q(t)$ is the smallest nonnegative definite solution to (3.1.8). It also shows that

$$\begin{aligned} \int_0^T z'(t)z(t)\,dt &= x_0'Q(0)x_0 \\ &\leq x_0'Qx_0. \end{aligned}$$

Since this bound is independent of T, it follows that $z \in \mathcal{L}_2[0,\infty)$.

To prove Item 2(b), we note that $\|z\|_2 = \lim_{T\to\infty} \|z\|_{2,[0,T]}$. ■

3.1.2 Signals in the frequency domain

A frequency domain signal is a (measurable) function $f(j\omega)$ that has the property $(f(j\omega))^* = f'(-j\omega)$. The variable ω is the real frequency variable in radians per unit time and the superscript $(\cdot)^*$ denotes the complex conjugate transpose. The frequency domain 2-norm is defined by

$$\|f\|_2 = \left\{ \frac{1}{2\pi} \int_{-\infty}^{\infty} f^*(j\omega) f(j\omega)\, d\omega \right\}^{\frac{1}{2}}. \tag{3.1.10}$$

The frequency domain Lebesgue 2-space consists of those signals with finite norm:

$$\mathcal{L}_2 = \{f : \|f\|_2 < \infty\}. \tag{3.1.11}$$

$\mathcal{L}_2$ is a Hilbert space under the inner product

$$\langle f, g\rangle = \frac{1}{2\pi} \int_{-\infty}^{\infty} g^*(j\omega) f(j\omega)\, d\omega. \tag{3.1.12}$$

The reason we use the same symbol for the norm and the inner product in both the time and frequency domains is because the Fourier transform, which is a Hilbert space isomorphism between $\mathcal{L}_2(-\infty,\infty)$ and $\mathcal{L}_2$, preserves the inner product and the 2-norm.[3] For $f \in \mathcal{L}_2(-\infty,\infty)$, the *Fourier transform* of f is

$$\widehat{f}(j\omega) = \lim_{T\to\infty} \int_{-T}^{T} f(t) e^{-j\omega t}\, dt.$$

Here, lim denotes convergence in the $\mathcal{L}_2$ norm.[4] Furthermore,

$$\langle f, g\rangle = \langle \widehat{f}, \widehat{g}\rangle, \tag{3.1.13}$$

which is known as *Parseval's identity.* A consequence of (3.1.13) is that $\|f\|_2 = \|\widehat{f}\|_2$.

Since $\mathcal{L}_2(-\infty,\infty)$ and $\mathcal{L}_2$ are isomorphic, we will not make a notational distinction between time-domain signals and their frequency-domain counterparts—the "hat" notation is only used on the rare occasions on which some confusion might arise. Generally, the context determines whether signals are being considered as elements of $\mathcal{L}_2(-\infty,\infty)$ or $\mathcal{L}_2$.

---

[3]Isomorphism comes from the Greek for *same shape.* Two Hilbert spaces are isomorphic if there is a bijective linear mapping from one to the other that preserves the inner product.

[4]That is, $\|\widehat{f} - \int_{-T}^{T} f(t)e^{-j\omega t}\, dt\|_2 \to 0$ as $T \to \infty$.

The space $\mathcal{H}_2$

The Hardy 2-space $\mathcal{H}_2$ consists of functions of a complex variable that are analytic in the open right-half of the complex plane and such that the norm

$$\|f\|_2 = \left\{ \sup_{\alpha>0} \frac{1}{2\pi} \int_{-\infty}^{\infty} f^*(\alpha + j\omega) f(\alpha + j\omega)\, d\omega \right\}^{\frac{1}{2}} \tag{3.1.14}$$

is finite. That is,

$$\mathcal{H}_2 = \{f : f(s) \text{ is analytic in } \mathrm{R}_e(s) > 0 \text{ and } \|f\|_2 < \infty\}. \tag{3.1.15}$$

We also assume that $(f(s))^* = f'(\bar{s})$.

For any $f \in \mathcal{H}_2$, the boundary function defined by $f_b(j\omega) = \lim_{\alpha\downarrow 0} f(\alpha + j\omega)$ exists for almost all ω, which is Fatou's theorem. In addition: (1) $f_b \in \mathcal{L}_2$; (2) the mapping $f \mapsto f_b$ is linear and injective[5]; and (3) $\|f_b\|_2 = \|f\|_2$. This final property means that we may evaluate the $\mathcal{H}_2$ norm by the formula

$$\|f\|_2 = \left\{ \frac{1}{2\pi} \int_{-\infty}^{\infty} f_b(j\omega)^* f_b(j\omega)\, d\omega \right\}^{\frac{1}{2}}$$

instead of (3.1.14)—the supremum always occurs on the boundary $\alpha = 0$.

Because the mapping from $f \in \mathcal{H}_2$ to the boundary function $f_b \in \mathcal{L}_2$ is linear, injective and norm preserving, we will drop the subscript b, writing $f(j\omega)$ instead of $f_b(j\omega)$, and will regard $\mathcal{H}_2$ as a closed subspace of $\mathcal{L}_2$.[6] The *Paley-Wiener theorem* states that $\mathcal{H}_2$ is isomorphic to $\mathcal{L}_2[0,\infty)$ under the Laplace transform. For any signal $f \in \mathcal{S}$ the *Laplace transform* is defined by the integral

$$\widehat{f}(s) = \int_{-\infty}^{\infty} f(t)e^{-st}\, dt. \tag{3.1.16}$$

For any particular f, the domain of definition (allowable values of s) depends on the convergence of the integral. For $f \in \mathcal{L}_2[0,\infty)$ the domain of definition is $\mathrm{R}_e(s) > 0$ and $\widehat{f} \in \mathcal{H}_2$. The function $\widehat{f}(s)$ is often defined outside this domain of convergence by analytic continuation.

The space $\mathcal{H}_2^-$ defined by

$$\mathcal{H}_2^- = \{f : f(-s) \in \mathcal{H}_2\}$$

is isomorphic to $\mathcal{L}_2(-\infty, 0]$ under the Laplace transform. It follows that the spaces $\mathcal{H}_2$ and $\mathcal{H}_2^-$ are orthogonal.

[5] That is, the function f_b is uniquely defined by the equation $f_b(j\omega) = \lim_{\alpha\downarrow 0} f(\alpha + j\omega)$.

[6] Every $f \in \mathcal{H}_2$ is identified with its boundary function $f_b \in \mathcal{L}_2$.

Main points of the section

1. In this book, the size of a signal is its 2-norm, which is denoted by $\|\cdot\|_{2,[0,T]}$ in the case of a finite horizon and by $\|\cdot\|_2$ in the case of an infinite horizon.
2. The signals of interest to us are signals that have finite 2-norm. This property defines the time-domain 2-spaces $\mathcal{L}_2[0,T]$, $\mathcal{L}_2[0,\infty)$ and $\mathcal{L}_2(-\infty,\infty)$, which are Hilbert spaces.
3. The Cauchy-Schwartz inequality $|\langle f,g\rangle| \leq \|f\|_2\|g\|_2$ holds.
4. The Fourier transform is a Hilbert space isomorphism from the time-domain 2-space $\mathcal{L}_2(-\infty,\infty)$ to the frequency-domain 2-space $\mathcal{L}_2$.
5. The Laplace transform is a Hilbert space isomorphism from the time-domain 2-space $\mathcal{L}_2[0,\infty)$ to the frequency-domain 2-space $\mathcal{H}_2$. Signals in $\mathcal{H}_2$ are analytic in the open-right-half plane.

3.2 Systems

A system is a mapping from one signal space, the input space, to another signal space, the output space:

$$\begin{aligned} \boldsymbol{G} &: \mathcal{S}_1 \mapsto \mathcal{S}_2 \\ &: w \mapsto z = \boldsymbol{G}w. \end{aligned}$$

Systems form a linear space under addition (parallel connection) and multiplication by a scalar, which are defined by

$$\begin{aligned} (\boldsymbol{G}_1 + \boldsymbol{G}_2)w &= \boldsymbol{G}_1 w + \boldsymbol{G}_2 w \\ (\alpha \boldsymbol{G})w &= \alpha(\boldsymbol{G}w). \end{aligned}$$

A system is called *causal* if the output up to time T depends only on the input up to time T, for every T. That is, $\boldsymbol{G}$ is causal if $\boldsymbol{P}_T\boldsymbol{G}\boldsymbol{P}_T = \boldsymbol{P}_T\boldsymbol{G}$, in which $\boldsymbol{P}_T$ is the projection operator defined by the truncation operation

$$(\boldsymbol{P}_T w)(t) = \begin{cases} w(t) & t \leq T \\ 0 & t > T. \end{cases} \tag{3.2.1}$$

Let $z(t)$ be the response of a system $\boldsymbol{G}$ to input $w(t)$. If the response to the time-shifted input $w(t-T)$ is $z(t-T)$, the system is called *time-invariant*. Defining the time-shift operator $\boldsymbol{S}_T$ by

$$(\boldsymbol{S}_T w)(t) = w(t-T),$$

we see that a system is time-invariant if it commutes with the time-shift operator. That is, if $\boldsymbol{G}\boldsymbol{S}_T = \boldsymbol{S}_T\boldsymbol{G}$, for every T.

A system $\boldsymbol{G}$ is *stable* if $z = \boldsymbol{G}w$ is in $\mathcal{L}_2[0,\infty)$ whenever w is in $\mathcal{L}_2[0,\infty)$.

3.2.1 Linear systems

A system $\boldsymbol{G} : \mathcal{S}_1 \mapsto \mathcal{S}_2$ is *linear* if

$$\boldsymbol{G}(\alpha w_1 + \beta w_2) = \alpha \boldsymbol{G} w_1 + \beta \boldsymbol{G} w_2$$

for all scalars α, β and for all $w_1, w_2 \in \mathcal{S}_1$. The space of linear systems forms an algebra under addition (parallel connection) and composition (series connection). For systems $\boldsymbol{G} : \mathcal{S}_1 \mapsto \mathcal{S}_1$, this algebra has the identity $Iw = w$ for all w.

Any linear system may be represented by the integral operator

$$z(t) = \int_{-\infty}^{\infty} G(t,\tau) w(\tau)\, d\tau.$$

The matrix valued function $G(t,\tau)$ may have to be a generalized function[7]; a δ-function for example.

The system is causal if and only if $G(t,\tau) = 0$ for all $\tau > t$ and is time-invariant if $G(t,\tau) = G(t-\tau, 0)$ for all t, τ. Thus any linear, time-invariant system may be represented as a convolution integral

$$z(t) = \int_{-\infty}^{\infty} G(t-\tau) w(\tau)\, d\tau, \tag{3.2.2}$$

in which we have written $G(t-\tau)$ instead of $G(t-\tau, 0)$ to make the formula more compact.

Transfer function matrices

Taking the Laplace transform of (3.2.2), we have

$$z(s) = \boldsymbol{G}(s) w(s),$$

in which

$$\boldsymbol{G}(s) = \int_{-\infty}^{\infty} G(t) e^{-st}\, dt.$$

The function $\boldsymbol{G}$ is known as the *transfer function matrix* of the system. Note that *any system described by a transfer function matrix is linear and time-invariant.* The transfer function is called *proper* if $\lim_{s\to\infty} \boldsymbol{G}(s)$ exists and is finite.

In this book, a signal is a real vector valued function of time. It follows that the impulse response matrix $G(t)$ is a real matrix valued function and that the transfer function matrix $\boldsymbol{G}(s)$ is a complex matrix valued function of s such that

$$\boldsymbol{G}^*(s) = \boldsymbol{G}'(\bar{s}).$$

For want of a better word, we shall call such transfer function matrices real transfer function matrices—all transfer function matrices in this book are assumed to be real.

[7]That is, for each t, $G(t,\tau)d\tau$ is a measure.

State-space systems

Systems that are described by linear differential equations are our main concern. We shall assume that the design problem is governed by equations of this form and that a controller of this form is desired. These systems will invariably be written as state-space equations:

$$\begin{aligned} \dot{x}(t) &= A(t)x(t) + B(t)w(t), \qquad x(t_0) = x_0 \in \mathbb{R}^n, \\ z(t) &= C(t)x(t) + D(t)w(t). \end{aligned} \tag{3.2.3}$$

In (3.2.3), $w(t) \in \mathbb{R}^m$ is the input vector, $x(t) \in \mathbb{R}^n$ is the state vector and $z(t) \in \mathbb{R}^p$ is the output vector. We assume that $A(t)$, $B(t)$, $C(t)$ and $D(t)$ are continuous real matrix valued functions of time with appropriate dimensions.

The equations (3.2.3) define a linear system

$$\boldsymbol{G} : \mathbb{R}^n \oplus \mathcal{S}_1 \mapsto \mathcal{S}_2; \qquad \begin{bmatrix} x_0 \\ w \end{bmatrix} \mapsto z.$$

In the case that $x(t_0) = 0$, the system is said to be relaxed at time t_0 and we may write $\boldsymbol{G} : \mathcal{S}_1 \mapsto \mathcal{S}_2$. It is often convenient to assume that the system is relaxed in the infinitely remote past, *i.e.*, that $\lim_{t_0 \to -\infty} x(t_0) = 0$.

The quadruple of matrices $\big(A(t), B(t), C(t), D(t)\big)$ is called a *realization* of the system. We will also use the notation

$$\boldsymbol{G} \stackrel{s}{=} \left[\begin{array}{c|c} A(t) & B(t) \\ \hline C(t) & D(t) \end{array}\right].$$

Realizations are not unique and we assume that the reader is familiar with concepts such as controllability, observability and minimality.[8] Briefly, the realization is *observable* if the pair $\big(z(t), w(t)\big)$, $t \in [t_0, T]$, uniquely determines $x(t_0)$. This is equivalent to $Q(t_0, T) > 0$, in which $Q(t, T)$ is the observability gramian satisfying (3.1.6). Thus observability depends only on $A(t)$ and $C(t)$. In the time-invariant case, (A, C) is observable if and only if $CA^k x = 0$ for $k = 0, 1, 2, \ldots$ implies $x = 0$, which is equivalent to the condition

$$\begin{bmatrix} A - \lambda I \\ C \end{bmatrix} x = 0 \Rightarrow x = 0,$$

which is known as the Popov-Belevitch-Hautus test. The realization is *controllable* if and only if, for any $x_T \in \mathbb{R}^n$, there exists a $w(t)$, $t \in [t_0, T]$, such that $x(T) = x_T$. Controllability depends only on $A(t)$ and $B(t)$ and it can be shown that $\big(A(t), B(t)\big)$ is controllable if and only if $\big(A'(t), B'(t)\big)$ is observable. The realization is *minimal* if no other realization with the same input-output properties has a lower state dimension. It can be shown that the realization is minimal if and only if it is both controllable and observable.

[8] See, for example, [105, 33, 126].

Let $\Phi(t,\tau)$ be the *transition matrix* associated with (3.2.3), which is the solution to the array of first-order differential equations

$$\frac{d}{dt}\Phi(t,\tau) = A(t)\Phi(t,\tau), \quad \Phi(\tau,\tau) = I.$$

Then

$$z(t) = D(t)w(t) + C(t)\int_{t_0}^{t} \Phi(t,\tau)B(\tau)w(\tau)\,d\tau + C(t)\Phi(t,t_0)x_0. \tag{3.2.4}$$

Notice that $z \in \mathcal{L}_2[t_0,T]$ for any $w \in \mathcal{L}_2[t_0,T]$, so that $w \in \mathcal{L}_{2e}$ implies $z \in \mathcal{L}_{2e}$.

State-space systems are always causal on the restricted time interval $[t_0,\infty)$. That is, $\boldsymbol{P_T G P_T} = \boldsymbol{P_T G}$ for all $T \geq t_0$. State-space systems are time-invariant when the matrices $A(t)$, $B(t)$, $C(t)$ and $D(t)$ are constant. In this case, $\Phi(t,\tau) = e^{A(t-\tau)}$ and

$$z(t) = Dw(t) + C\int_{t_0}^{t} e^{A(t-\tau)}Bw(\tau)\,d\tau + Ce^{A(t-t_0)}x_0.$$

Taking Laplace transforms we obtain

$$z(s) = \big(D + C(sI-A)^{-1}B\big)w(s) + C(sI-A)^{-1}x_0.$$

The matrix valued function $\boldsymbol{G} = D + C(sI-A)^{-1}B$ is the transfer function matrix of the system. The number of poles in $\boldsymbol{G}(s)$ is known as the *McMillan degree* of $\boldsymbol{G}$. The McMillan degree of $\boldsymbol{G}$ is equal to the dimension of the state vector in a minimal realization of the system.

The transfer function matrix $\boldsymbol{G} = D + C(sI-A)^{-1}B$ has no poles in the closed-right-half plane if and only if $\boldsymbol{G}$ defines a stable system. Therefore, $\boldsymbol{G}$ is stable if and only if every unstable eigenspace of A is either uncontrollable or unobservable. We say that (A,B) is *stabilizable* if every unstable eigenspace is controllable, and we say that (A,C) is *detectable* if every unstable eigenspace is observable. Thus, if (A,B,C,D) is a stabilizable and detectable realization, $\boldsymbol{G}$ is stable if and only if A is *asymptotically stable*, which is to say its eigenvalues $\lambda_i(A)$ all have strictly negative real part $(\mathrm{R}_e\big(\lambda_i(A)\big) < 0$ for all i).

3.2.2 The space $\mathcal{L}_\infty$

Our basic infinite-horizon signal space is $\mathcal{L}_2(-\infty,\infty)$, so we will be concerned with systems $\boldsymbol{G} : \mathcal{L}_2(-\infty,\infty) \mapsto \mathcal{L}_2(-\infty,\infty)$.

Because $\mathcal{L}_2(-\infty,\infty)$ is isomorphic to $\mathcal{L}_2$, a linear time-invariant system maps $\mathcal{L}_2(-\infty,\infty)$ to $\mathcal{L}_2(-\infty,\infty)$ if and only if the transfer function matrix $\boldsymbol{G}$ is such that $\boldsymbol{G}w \in \mathcal{L}_2$ for any $w \in \mathcal{L}_2$. A sufficient condition for this is $\sup_\omega \overline{\sigma}\big(\boldsymbol{G}(j\omega)\big) < \infty$, since

$$\|\boldsymbol{G}w\|_2^2 = \frac{1}{2\pi}\int_{-\infty}^{\infty} \|\boldsymbol{G}(j\omega)w(j\omega)\|^2\,d\omega$$

$$\begin{aligned}
&\le \frac{1}{2\pi}\int_{-\infty}^{\infty} \overline{\sigma}\big(\boldsymbol{G}(j\omega)\big)^2 \|w(j\omega)\|^2\, d\omega \\
&\le \sup_{\omega} \overline{\sigma}\big(\boldsymbol{G}(j\omega)\big)^2 \frac{1}{2\pi}\int_{-\infty}^{\infty} \|w(j\omega)\|^2\, d\omega.
\end{aligned}$$

The class of systems for which the supremum is finite is known as $\mathcal{L}_\infty$:

$$\mathcal{L}_\infty = \{\boldsymbol{G} : \|\boldsymbol{G}\|_\infty < \infty\},$$

in which the $\mathcal{L}_\infty$-norm is defined by

$$\|\boldsymbol{G}\|_\infty = \sup_{\omega} \overline{\sigma}\big(\boldsymbol{G}(j\omega)\big). \tag{3.2.5}$$

It is a straightforward exercise to show that $\|\cdot\|_\infty$ is a norm. We note that

$$\|\boldsymbol{G}w\|_2 \le \|\boldsymbol{G}\|_\infty \|w\|_2 \quad \text{for all } w \in \mathcal{L}_2,$$

and also that the important submultiplicative property

$$\|\boldsymbol{G}\boldsymbol{H}\|_\infty \le \|\boldsymbol{G}\|_\infty \|\boldsymbol{H}\|_\infty$$

is satisfied.

When $\boldsymbol{G}$ is rational, $\boldsymbol{G} \in \mathcal{L}_\infty$ if and only if $\boldsymbol{G}$ has no poles on the imaginary axis. In this case $\overline{\sigma}\big(\boldsymbol{G}(j\omega)\big)$ is a continuous function of ω and

$$\|\boldsymbol{G}\|_\infty < \gamma \Leftrightarrow \overline{\sigma}\big(\boldsymbol{G}(j\omega)\big) < \gamma \text{ for all } \omega \in \mathbb{R} \cup \infty.$$

Thus bounds on $\|\boldsymbol{G}\|_\infty$ are equivalent to uniform bounds on $\overline{\sigma}\big(\boldsymbol{G}(j\omega)\big)$, thereby allowing us to write objectives of the form $\overline{\sigma}\big(\boldsymbol{G}(j\omega)\big) < \gamma$ for all ω using the more compact notation $\|\boldsymbol{G}\|_\infty < \gamma$. All the design problems discussed in Chapter 2 can be expressed in terms of bounds on the infinity norm of various closed-loop transfer function matrices.

We have shown that $\boldsymbol{G} \in \mathcal{L}_\infty$ implies that $\boldsymbol{G}\mathcal{L}_2 \subset \mathcal{L}_2$. The converse is also true. To see why, choose any $\omega_0 \in \mathbb{R}$ and let v and u be unit vectors such that

$$\boldsymbol{G}(j\omega_0)v = \overline{\sigma}\big(\boldsymbol{G}(j\omega_0)\big)u.$$

(*i.e.*, v is the right singular vector corresponding to the maximum singular value of $\boldsymbol{G}(j\omega_0)$). Considering $w(j\omega) = \sqrt{2\pi}v\delta^{\frac{1}{2}}(\omega - \omega_0)$ we have that

$$\begin{aligned}
\|\boldsymbol{G}w\|_2^2 &= \int_{-\infty}^{\infty} v^*\boldsymbol{G}^*(j\omega)\boldsymbol{G}(j\omega)v\delta(\omega-\omega_0)\, d\omega \\
&= v^*\boldsymbol{G}^*(j\omega_0)\boldsymbol{G}(j\omega_0)v \\
&= \overline{\sigma}\big(\boldsymbol{G}(j\omega_0)\big)^2 u'u \\
&= \overline{\sigma}\big(\boldsymbol{G}(j\omega_0)\big)^2.
\end{aligned}$$

The right-hand side must be finite if $Gw \in \mathcal{L}_2$ and we conclude that $G\mathcal{L}_2 \subset \mathcal{L}_2 \Rightarrow \|G\|_\infty < \infty$. The trouble with this argument is that neither the input nor the output considered are in $\mathcal{L}_2$ in the first place! However, these "functions" may be approximated to arbitrary accuracy by signals that are in $\mathcal{L}_2$ and the argument can be made rigorous.

Mathematically inclined readers may prefer the proof of this result presented in [222], page 171, which is based on a different approach.

3.2.3 The space $\mathcal{H}_\infty$

If G is the transfer function matrix of a linear, time-invariant system, then G defines a stable system if and only if $z = Gw \in \mathcal{H}_2$ whenever $w \in \mathcal{H}_2$. This is because $\mathcal{L}_2[0,\infty)$ is isomorphic to $\mathcal{H}_2$.

Since $z \in \mathcal{H}_2$ requires that z is analytic in the open-right-half plane, a necessary condition for stability is that G is analytic in the open-right-half plane. A sufficient condition for $\|z\|_2 < \infty$ is $\sup_{\alpha>0}\{\sup_\omega \overline{\sigma}(G(\alpha+j\omega))\} < \infty$, since

$$\begin{aligned}
\|Gw\|_2^2 &= \sup_{\alpha>0} \frac{1}{2\pi}\int_{-\infty}^{\infty} \|G(\alpha+j\omega)w(\alpha+j\omega)\|^2\, d\omega \\
&\leq \sup_{\alpha>0} \frac{1}{2\pi}\int_{-\infty}^{\infty} \overline{\sigma}\big(G(\alpha+j\omega)\big)^2 \|w(\alpha+j\omega)\|^2\, d\omega \\
&\leq \left\{\sup_{\alpha>0}\sup_{\omega} \overline{\sigma}\big(G(\alpha+j\omega)\big)^2\right\} \sup_{\alpha>0} \frac{1}{2\pi}\int_{-\infty}^{\infty} \|w(\alpha+j\omega)\|^2\, d\omega \\
&= \sup_{\alpha>0}\sup_{\omega} \overline{\sigma}\big(G(\alpha+j\omega)\big)^2 \|w\|_2^2.
\end{aligned}$$

The class of systems for which G is analytic in the open-right-half plane and this supremum is finite is known as $\mathcal{H}_\infty$:

$$\mathcal{H}_\infty = \{G : G \text{ is analytic in } \mathrm{R}_e(s) > 0 \text{ and } \|G\|_\infty < \infty\}, \tag{3.2.6}$$

in which

$$\|G\|_\infty = \sup_{\alpha>0}\left\{\sup_{\omega} \overline{\sigma}\big(G(\alpha+j\omega)\big)\right\}. \tag{3.2.7}$$

A system that has a transfer function matrix in $\mathcal{H}_\infty$ is a stable system. In fact, a transfer function matrix G defines a stable system if and only if $G \in \mathcal{H}_\infty$.

We use the symbol $\|\cdot\|_\infty$ for both the $\mathcal{L}_\infty$ and $\mathcal{H}_\infty$ norms because the limit $G_b(j\omega) = \lim_{\alpha\downarrow 0} G(\alpha+j\omega)$ exists for almost all ω if $G \in \mathcal{H}_\infty$. Furthermore, the mapping $G \mapsto G_b$ is linear, injective and

$$\|G\|_\infty = \sup_{\omega} \overline{\sigma}\big(G_b(j\omega)\big).$$

We therefore drop the b notation, writing $G(j\omega)$ instead of $G_b(j\omega)$, and regard $\mathcal{H}_\infty$ as a closed subspace of $\mathcal{L}_\infty$.

In the case that $\boldsymbol{G}$ is rational, $\boldsymbol{G} \in \mathcal{H}_\infty$ if and only if $\boldsymbol{G}$ has no pole in the closed-right-half plane.

The terminology "$\mathcal{H}_\infty$ control theory" derives from the fact that we would like to achieve objectives on $\|\cdot\|_\infty$ subject to closed-loop stability.

Spaces of rational transfer function matrices

As we have previously indicated, we are primarily concerned with state-space systems. In the time-invariant case, such systems have transfer function matrices that are rational functions of the Laplace transform variable s. We use the prefix $\mathcal{R}$ to denote rationality. Thus $\mathcal{RL}_\infty$ and $\mathcal{RH}_\infty$ denote the rational subspaces of $\mathcal{L}_\infty$ and $\mathcal{H}_\infty$ respectively.

3.2.4 Adjoint systems

Suppose $\boldsymbol{G} : \mathcal{S}_1 \to \mathcal{S}_2$ is a linear system and $\mathcal{S}_1$ and $\mathcal{S}_2$ are Hilbert spaces such as $\mathcal{L}_2[0,T]$ or $\mathcal{L}_2[0,\infty)$. The *adjoint system* is the linear system $\boldsymbol{G}^\sim : \mathcal{S}_2 \to \mathcal{S}_1$ that has the property

$$\langle \boldsymbol{G}w, y\rangle_{\mathcal{S}_2} = \langle w, \boldsymbol{G}^\sim y\rangle_{\mathcal{S}_1}$$

for all $w \in \mathcal{S}_1$ and all $y \in \mathcal{S}_2$. It is a standard exercise to show that $\boldsymbol{G}^\sim$ is uniquely defined by this equation and that $(\boldsymbol{G}^\sim)^\sim = \boldsymbol{G}$.

To determine the adjoint of $\boldsymbol{G}$ in the Hilbert space $\mathcal{L}_2[0,T]$, consider inputs $w \in \mathcal{L}_2[0,T]$ and represent the linear system $z = \boldsymbol{G}w$ by

$$z(t) = \int_0^T G(t,\tau)w(\tau)\,d\tau.$$

(It is assumed that $w(t) = 0$ for $t \notin [0,T]$). For any $y \in \mathcal{L}_2[0,T]$,

$$\begin{aligned}
\langle \boldsymbol{G}w, y\rangle_{[0,T]} &= \int_0^T dt \int_0^T y'(t)G(t,\tau)w(\tau)\,d\tau \\
&= \int_0^T d\tau \int_0^T \big(G'(t,\tau)y(t)\big)' w(\tau)\,dt \\
&= \langle w, \eta\rangle_{[0,T]},
\end{aligned}$$

in which

$$\eta(\tau) = \int_0^T G'(t,\tau)y(t)\,dt.$$

The $\mathcal{L}_2[0,T]$ adjoint of $\boldsymbol{G}$ is therefore the system $\boldsymbol{G}^\sim$ defined by

$$(\boldsymbol{G}^\sim y)(t) = \int_0^T G'(\tau,t)y(\tau)\,d\tau.$$

In the case of a state-space system,

$$G(t,\tau) = \begin{cases} C(t)\Phi(t,\tau)B(\tau) + D(t)\delta(t-\tau) & \text{if } t \geq \tau \\ 0 & \text{otherwise,} \end{cases}$$

and it is easily shown that $\eta(t) = \int_0^T G'(\tau,t)y(\tau)\,d\tau$ satisfies

$$\dot{p}(t) = -A'(t)p(t) - C'(t)y(t), \qquad p(T) = 0, \tag{3.2.8}$$

$$\eta(t) = B'(t)p(t) + D'(t)y(t), \tag{3.2.9}$$

which is therefore a state-space realization of the adjoint system $\boldsymbol{G}^{\sim}$. Note that a zero terminal condition is applied to the state of $\boldsymbol{G}^{\sim}$.

If $\boldsymbol{G}$ is a transfer function matrix mapping $\mathcal{L}_2$ to $\mathcal{L}_2$, which is to say $\boldsymbol{G} \in \mathcal{L}_\infty$, the adjoint system has transfer function matrix

$$\boldsymbol{G}^{\sim}(s) = \boldsymbol{G}'(-s).$$

If $\boldsymbol{G}$ has realization (A,B,C,D) then $\boldsymbol{G}^{\sim}$ has realization $(-A',-C',B',D')$.

3.2.5 Allpass systems

An *allpass system* has the property that the norm of the output is equal to the norm of the input.[9] The term "allpass" derives from the fact that, by definition, allpass systems pass all signals with unchanged magnitude, in contrast to other systems of interest such as low-pass, high-pass or band-pass systems, which attenuate the magnitude of certain signals. The term lossless is also used in the network theory literature. As we have already seen in Chapter 1, these systems play an important role in the synthesis of $\mathcal{H}_\infty$ optimal controllers.

Suppose $\mathcal{S}_1$ and $\mathcal{S}_2$ are normed signal spaces such as $\mathcal{L}_2[0,T]$ or $\mathcal{L}_2(-\infty,\infty)$, with the norms on these spaces denoted by $\|\cdot\|_{\mathcal{S}_i}$. If $\boldsymbol{G} : \mathcal{S}_1 \mapsto \mathcal{S}_2$ is linear, then $\boldsymbol{G}$ is allpass if

$$\|\boldsymbol{G}w\|_{\mathcal{S}_2} = \|w\|_{\mathcal{S}_1} \quad \text{for all } w \in \mathcal{S}_1. \tag{3.2.10}$$

Note that an allpass system is necessarily injective, since (3.2.10) gives $\|\boldsymbol{G}w\|_{\mathcal{S}_2} = 0 \Leftrightarrow \|w\|_{\mathcal{S}_1} = 0$.

In any real inner product space ($\mathcal{L}_2(-\infty,\infty)$ for example), the polarization identity

$$4\langle x,y\rangle = \|x+y\|^2 - \|x-y\|^2$$

holds. It follows that when the spaces $\mathcal{S}_i$ are Hilbert spaces, $\boldsymbol{G}$ is an allpass if and only if

$$\langle \boldsymbol{G}u, \boldsymbol{G}w\rangle_{\mathcal{S}_2} = \langle u,w\rangle_{\mathcal{S}_1}, \quad \text{for all } u,w \in \mathcal{S}_1,$$

[9] In the mathematician's terminology, these systems are isometric operators.

which means an allpass system between two Hilbert spaces preserves the inner product. Consequently, $\boldsymbol{G}$ is an allpass system between two Hilbert spaces if and only if

$$\boldsymbol{G}^{\sim}\boldsymbol{G} = I. \tag{3.2.11}$$

If an allpass system is a bijection (*i.e.*, is surjective[10] in addition to being injective), then the spaces $\mathcal{S}_i$ are necessarily of the same dimension and $\boldsymbol{G}^{\sim} = \boldsymbol{G}^{-1}$. This implies that $\boldsymbol{G}\boldsymbol{G}^{\sim} = I$.

Theorem 3.2.1 *(A characterization of allpass state-space systems)*

1. *Suppose* $\boldsymbol{G}$ *is a state-space system with realization*

$$\begin{aligned} \dot{x}(t) &= A(t)x(t) + B(t)w(t), \qquad x(0) = 0, \\ z(t) &= C(t)x(t) + D(t)w(t) \end{aligned}$$

   and let $Q(t)$ *be the observability gramian satisfying (3.1.6). If the realization satisfies*

$$\begin{aligned} D'(t)C(t) + B'(t)Q(t) &= 0 \\ D'(t)D(t) &= I \end{aligned}$$

   for all $t \in [0, T]$, *then* $\boldsymbol{G}$ *is allpass on* $\mathcal{L}_2[0, T]$.

   If the system is controllable, these conditions are also necessary.

2. *Suppose the matrices* A, B, C, D *are constant and* $\boldsymbol{G}(s) = D + C(sI - A)^{-1}B$.

   (a) *If there is a symmetric* Q *such that*

$$QA + A'Q + C'C = 0 \tag{3.2.12}$$

$$D'C + B'Q = 0 \tag{3.2.13}$$

$$D'D = I, \tag{3.2.14}$$

   then $\boldsymbol{G}^{\sim}\boldsymbol{G} = I$ *and* $\boldsymbol{G} \in \mathcal{L}_\infty$. *Consequently,* $\boldsymbol{G}$ *is allpass on* $\mathcal{L}_2$.

   (b) *If there is a* $Q \geq 0$ *such that (3.2.12), (3.2.13) and (3.2.14) hold, then* $\boldsymbol{G} \in \mathcal{H}_\infty$ *and* $\boldsymbol{G}^{\sim}\boldsymbol{G} = I$. *Consequently,* $\boldsymbol{G}$ *is allpass on* $\mathcal{H}_2$ *(and on* $\mathcal{L}_2[0, \infty)$, *with initial condition* $x(0) = 0$*).*

   If (A, B) *is controllable, then these conditions are also necessary.*

---

[10] That is, for any $z \in \mathcal{S}_2$, there exists a $w \in \mathcal{S}_1$ such that $z = \boldsymbol{G}w$.

Proof.

1.

$$\begin{aligned}\|z\|_{2,[0,T]}^2 &= \int_0^T (Cx+Dw)'(Cx+Dw) + \frac{d}{dt}(x'Qx)\,dt,\\ &\quad \text{since } x(0)=0 \text{ and } Q(T)=0,\\ &= \int_0^T w'D'Dw + 2w'(D'C+B'Q)x\,dt, \quad \text{using (3.1.6)}\\ &= \|w\|_{2,[0,T]}^2,\end{aligned}$$

when $D'C + B'Q = 0$ and $D'D = I$.

The proof that these conditions are necessary if the system is controllable is left as an exercise. (Hint: consider $w_{t^*} = \boldsymbol{P}_{t^*}w$ and note that controllability ensures that $x(t^*)$ spans $\mathbb{R}^n$ as w ranges over $\mathcal{L}_2[0,T]$.)

2. (a) If Q satisfies (3.2.12), then

$$\begin{aligned}\boldsymbol{G}^{\sim}\boldsymbol{G} &= \big(D' + B'(-sI-A')^{-1}C'\big)\big(D + C(sI-A)^{-1}B\big)\\ &= D'D + B'(-sI-A')^{-1}C'D + D'C(sI-A)^{-1}B\\ &\quad +B'(-sI-A')^{-1}C'C(sI-A)^{-1}B\\ &= D'D + B'(-sI-A')^{-1}C'D + D'C(sI-A)^{-1}B\\ &\quad +B'(-sI-A')^{-1}[Q(sI-A)+(-sI-A')Q](sI-A)^{-1}B\\ &= D'D + B'(-sI-A')^{-1}(C'D+QB)\\ &\quad +(D'C+B'Q)(sI-A)^{-1}B. \qquad (3.2.15)\\ &= I\end{aligned}$$

if (3.2.13) and (3.2.14) hold. This also implies that $\boldsymbol{G}$ has no pole on the imaginary axis, so $\boldsymbol{G} \in \mathcal{L}_\infty$ is allpass on $\mathcal{L}_2$.

(b) If $Q \geq 0$, then every eigenvalue of A in the closed-right-half plane is unobservable (see Theorem 3.1.1) and consequently $\boldsymbol{G}$ has no poles in the closed-right-half plane, so $\boldsymbol{G} \in \mathcal{H}_\infty$. The identity $\boldsymbol{G}^{\sim}\boldsymbol{G}$ follows as before and $\boldsymbol{G}$ is allpass on $\mathcal{H}_2$.

To prove necessity, we note that (A, B) controllable and $\boldsymbol{G} \in \mathcal{H}_\infty$ implies that every eigenvalue of A in the closed right-half plane is unobservable. We therefore let $Q = \lim_{t\to-\infty} Q(t)$ with $Q(t)$ the solution to (3.1.7), which satisfies (3.2.12) and $Q \geq 0$ by Theorem 3.1.1. Hence (3.2.15) holds. Setting $s = \infty$ in (3.2.15) results in $D'D = I$.

To conclude that $D'C + B'Q = 0$, we suppose (without loss of generality) that

$$A = \begin{bmatrix} A_1 & 0 \\ 0 & A_2 \end{bmatrix}, \quad B = \begin{bmatrix} B_1 \\ B_2 \end{bmatrix},$$

$$C = \begin{bmatrix} C_1 & 0 \end{bmatrix},$$

in which A_1 is asymptotically stable and A_2 has all its eigenvalues in the closed right-half plane. Since $Q = \lim_{t\to-\infty} Q(t)$ and $Q(T) = 0$, it follows that

$$Q = \begin{bmatrix} Q_1 & 0 \\ 0 & 0 \end{bmatrix}.$$

From these considerations and (3.2.15), $\boldsymbol{Z} \in \mathcal{H}_\infty$ defined by the realization $(A_1, B_1, D'C_1 + B_1'Q_1, 0)$ satisfies $\boldsymbol{Z} + \boldsymbol{Z}^\sim = 0$, which is equivalent to $\boldsymbol{Z} = 0$ because $\boldsymbol{Z}$ has all its poles in the open-left-half plane. Since (A, B) is controllable, (A_1, B_1) is also controllable and we conclude that $D'C_1 + B_1'Q_1 = 0$. It now follows that $D'C + B'Q = 0$. ■

Main points of the section

1. The basic system theoretic notions of causality, time-invariance and linearity have been reviewed. Stability has been defined to mean $w \in \mathcal{L}_2[0,\infty) \Rightarrow \boldsymbol{G}w \in \mathcal{L}_2[0,\infty)$.
2. The infinity norm of a transfer function matrix $\boldsymbol{G}$ is defined by $\|\boldsymbol{G}\|_\infty = \sup_\omega \overline{\sigma}\big(\boldsymbol{G}(j\omega)\big)$. A transfer function matrix $\boldsymbol{G}$ maps $\mathcal{L}_2$ to $\mathcal{L}_2$ if and only if $\|\boldsymbol{G}\|_\infty$ is finite; this space is known as $\mathcal{L}_\infty$.
3. A transfer function matrix $\boldsymbol{G}$ defines a stable system if and only if
   (a) $\boldsymbol{G}$ is analytic in the right-half of the complex plane;
   (b) $\|\boldsymbol{G}\|_\infty$ is finite.

   The space of transfer function matrices satisfying these properties is called $\mathcal{H}_\infty$.
4. A linear system $\boldsymbol{G}$ has adjoint system denoted by $\boldsymbol{G}^\sim$.
5. A system for which the norm of the output is equal to the norm of the input is called an allpass system. A system is allpass if and only if $\boldsymbol{G}^\sim\boldsymbol{G} = I$. A condition for a state-space system to be allpass is given in Theorem 3.2.1.

3.3 The size of a system

For a linear, time-invariant system, we may use the infinity norm of the transfer function matrix as the measure of size. This notion of system size is ideally suited to the frequency domain design ideas developed in Chapter 2, but is limited to the linear time-invariant case. Since our aim is to obtain robust stability theorems in which the systems may be time-varying and nonlinear, a generalization of the notion of size to time-varying and nonlinear systems is required. The basic theorem we need for such stability results is known as the small gain theorem and we will measure the size of systems by a quantity known as the incremental gain. For systems that are causal and stable, the incremental gain is equal to the (Lipschitz) induced norm. The incremental gain, the induced norm and the infinity norm are identical for systems that are causal, linear, stable and time-invariant.

We also introduce the 2-norm of a system, which is the norm associated with the LQG optimal control problem, although this will play only a minor role in this book.

3.3.1 The incremental gain

Suppose $\boldsymbol{G} : \mathcal{L}_{2e} \mapsto \mathcal{L}_{2e}$. The *incremental gain* of the system $\boldsymbol{G}$ is defined by

$$\begin{aligned}\gamma(\boldsymbol{G}) &= \inf\{\gamma : \|\boldsymbol{G}w - \boldsymbol{G}\tilde{w}\|_{2,[0,T]} \leq \gamma\|w - \tilde{w}\|_{2,[0,T]} \\ &\qquad \text{for all } w, \tilde{w} \in \mathcal{L}_{2e} \text{ and for all } T \geq 0\}. \end{aligned} \tag{3.3.1}$$

Since

$$\|(\boldsymbol{G}+\boldsymbol{H})w - (\boldsymbol{G}+\boldsymbol{H})\tilde{w}\|_{2,[0,T]} \leq \|\boldsymbol{G}w - \boldsymbol{G}\tilde{w}\|_{2,[0,T]} + \|\boldsymbol{H}w - \boldsymbol{H}\tilde{w}\|_{2,[0,T]},$$

it is clear that

$$\gamma(\boldsymbol{G}+\boldsymbol{H}) \leq \gamma(\boldsymbol{G}) + \gamma(\boldsymbol{H}).$$

Indeed, the incremental gain is a norm. In addition, the submultiplicative property

$$\gamma(\boldsymbol{GH}) \leq \gamma(\boldsymbol{G})\gamma(\boldsymbol{H})$$

which is vital to our work is satisfied. This follows from the inequalities

$$\begin{aligned}\|\boldsymbol{GH}w - \boldsymbol{GH}\tilde{w}\|_{2,[0,T]} &\leq \gamma(\boldsymbol{G})\|\boldsymbol{H}w - \boldsymbol{H}\tilde{w}\|_{2,[0,T]} \\ &\leq \gamma(\boldsymbol{G})\gamma(\boldsymbol{H})\|w - \tilde{w}\|_{2,[0,T]}.\end{aligned}$$

We note the following facts concerning the incremental gain:

1. Any system that has finite incremental gain is causal. To see this, suppose $\gamma(\boldsymbol{G})$ is finite. Take $\tilde{w} = \boldsymbol{P}_T w$ in the definition to obtain $\|(\boldsymbol{G} - \boldsymbol{G}\boldsymbol{P}_T)w\|_{2,[0,T]} = 0$ for all w and all T. Hence $\boldsymbol{P}_T\boldsymbol{G} = \boldsymbol{P}_T\boldsymbol{G}\boldsymbol{P}_T$ for all T, which shows $\boldsymbol{G}$ is causal.

2. Any system that has finite incremental gain is stable, since

$$\begin{aligned}\|\boldsymbol{G}w\|_{2,[0,T]} &\leq \gamma(\boldsymbol{G})\|w\|_{2,[0,T]} \\ &\leq \gamma(\boldsymbol{G})\|w\|_2.\end{aligned}$$

   The right-hand side is finite if $w \in \mathcal{L}_2[0,\infty)$ and is independent of T. Therefore $\|\boldsymbol{G}w\|_2$ is finite.

3. Any system that has finite incremental gain is continuous on $\mathcal{L}_2[0,T]$, since $\|w - \tilde{w}\|_{2,[0,T]} < \epsilon/\gamma(\boldsymbol{G})$ implies that $\|\boldsymbol{G}w - \boldsymbol{G}\tilde{w}\|_{2,[0,T]} < \epsilon$.

4. The memoryless system $(\boldsymbol{f}w)(t) = f(w(t))$ with f a differentiable real valued function of a real variable has $\gamma(\boldsymbol{f}) = \sup_w |\frac{df}{dw}|$.

3.3.2 The induced norm

Suppose $\boldsymbol{G} : \mathcal{S}_1 \mapsto \mathcal{S}_2$, where $\mathcal{S}_1$ and $\mathcal{S}_2$ are normed spaces such as $\mathcal{L}_2[0,T]$ or $\mathcal{L}_2[0,\infty)$. The (Lipschitz) *induced norm* of $\boldsymbol{G}$ is defined by

$$\|\boldsymbol{G}\| = \sup_{w-\tilde{w}\neq 0} \frac{\|\boldsymbol{G}w - \boldsymbol{G}\tilde{w}\|_{\mathcal{S}_2}}{\|w-\tilde{w}\|_{\mathcal{S}_1}}. \tag{3.3.2}$$

It follows trivially from the definition (3.3.2) that

$$\|\boldsymbol{G}w - \boldsymbol{G}\tilde{w}\|_{\mathcal{S}_2} \leq \|\boldsymbol{G}\|\|w-\tilde{w}\|_{\mathcal{S}_1} \quad \text{for all } w, \tilde{w} \in \mathcal{S}_1.$$

Notice that although we have used the symbol $\|\cdot\|$ again, no confusion should arise. $\|\boldsymbol{X}\|$ is the induced norm of a system, $\|X\| = \overline{\sigma}(X)$ is a matrix norm (which is induced by the Euclidean norm on $\mathbb{R}^n$) and $\|x\| = \sqrt{x'x}$ is the Euclidean norm on $\mathbb{R}^n$.

It is a standard exercise to show that an induced norm is indeed a norm. In addition, the induced norm has the submultiplicative property

$$\|\boldsymbol{GH}\| \leq \|\boldsymbol{G}\|\|\boldsymbol{H}\|. \tag{3.3.3}$$

For systems that are causal and stable, $\|\boldsymbol{G}\| = \gamma(\boldsymbol{G})$, in which $\|\boldsymbol{G}\|$ is the norm induced by $\mathcal{L}_2[0,\infty)$. We use $\|\cdot\|_{[0,T]}$ to denote the norm induced by $\mathcal{L}_2[0,T]$.

In the case of linear systems, we may replace (3.3.2) by

$$\|\boldsymbol{G}\| = \sup_{w\neq 0} \frac{\|\boldsymbol{G}w\|_{\mathcal{S}_2}}{\|w\|_{\mathcal{S}_1}}. \tag{3.3.4}$$

If $\boldsymbol{G}$ is a state-space system, it follows from (3.2.4) that $\|\boldsymbol{G}\|_{[0,T]}$ is finite for any finite T. To see this, we note that

$$z(t) - D(t)w(t) = \int_0^T G(t,\tau)w(\tau)\,d\tau,$$

in which $G(t,\tau) = C(t)\Phi(t,\tau)B(\tau)$ for $t \geq \tau$ and $G(t,\tau) = 0$ for $t < \tau$. By the Cauchy-Schwartz inequality,

$$\begin{aligned}\|z(t) - D(t)w(t)\|^2 &\leq \int_0^T \overline{\sigma}\big(G(t,\tau)\big)^2\,d\tau \int_0^T \|w(\tau)\|^2\,d\tau \\ &\leq M^2\|w\|_{2,[0,T]}^2,\end{aligned}$$

in which $M^2 = \max_{t\in[0,T]} \int_0^T \overline{\sigma}\big(G(t,\tau)\big)^2\,d\tau < \infty$, since $G(t,\tau)$ is continuous in t and τ. Therefore

$$\begin{aligned}\|z\|_{2,[0,T]} &\leq \|z - Dw\|_{2,[0,T]} + \|Dw\|_{2,[0,T]} \\ &\leq \left(MT^{1/2} + \max_{t\in[0,T]} \overline{\sigma}\big(D(t)\big)\right)\|w\|_{2,[0,T]}.\end{aligned}$$

As $D(t)$ is continuous, the maximum is finite and we conclude that $\|\boldsymbol{G}\|_{[0,T]}$ is finite.

When the system $\boldsymbol{G}$ is linear and time-invariant, it may be represented by a transfer function matrix $\boldsymbol{G}(s)$. Since $z(s) = \boldsymbol{G}(s)w(s)$ we may define $\|\boldsymbol{G}(s)\|$ to be the norm induced by a frequency domain signal norm such as the $\mathcal{L}_2$ norm. By Parseval's identity, this induced norm on the transfer function matrix is identical to the norm on the system induced by $\mathcal{L}_2(-\infty,\infty)$ and we may therefore write $\|\boldsymbol{G}\| = \|\boldsymbol{G}(s)\|$.

For $w \in \mathcal{L}_2$ and $z = \boldsymbol{G}w$ we have

$$\begin{aligned}
\|z\|_2^2 &= \frac{1}{2\pi}\int_{-\infty}^{\infty} \|z(j\omega)\|^2\, d\omega \\
&\leq \sup_{\omega} \overline{\sigma}\big(\boldsymbol{G}(j\omega)\big)^2 \frac{1}{2\pi}\int_{-\infty}^{\infty} \|w(j\omega)\|^2\, d\omega \\
&= \|\boldsymbol{G}\|_\infty^2 \|w\|_2^2.
\end{aligned}$$

Hence, by (3.3.4), $\|\boldsymbol{G}\| \leq \|\boldsymbol{G}\|_\infty$. In fact

$$\|\boldsymbol{G}\| = \|\boldsymbol{G}\|_\infty.$$

That is, for a linear, time-invariant system, the norm induced by the 2-norm is precisely the infinity norm of its transfer function matrix.

Induced norms and allpass systems

Suppose a system $\boldsymbol{G} : \mathcal{S}_1 \mapsto \mathcal{S}_2$ and $\boldsymbol{A} : \mathcal{S}_2 \mapsto \mathcal{S}_3$ is allpass. Since $\|\boldsymbol{AG}w\|_{\mathcal{S}_3} = \|\boldsymbol{G}w\|_{\mathcal{S}_2}$ for all $w \in \mathcal{S}_1$ it follows from (3.3.4) that

$$\|\boldsymbol{AG}\| = \|\boldsymbol{G}\|. \tag{3.3.5}$$

Considering the case $\boldsymbol{G} = I$, any allpass system $\boldsymbol{A}$ has $\|\boldsymbol{A}\| = 1$.

The induced norm of the adjoint system

Suppose $\mathcal{S}_1$ and $\mathcal{S}_2$ are Hilbert spaces and $\boldsymbol{G} : \mathcal{S}_1 \mapsto \mathcal{S}_2$ is a linear system with adjoint $\boldsymbol{G}^\sim$. Then for any $z \in \mathcal{S}_2$

$$\begin{aligned}
\|\boldsymbol{G}^\sim z\|_{\mathcal{S}_1}^2 &= \langle \boldsymbol{G}^\sim z, \boldsymbol{G}^\sim z\rangle_{\mathcal{S}_1} \\
&= \langle \boldsymbol{G}\boldsymbol{G}^\sim z, z\rangle_{\mathcal{S}_2} \\
&\leq \|\boldsymbol{G}\boldsymbol{G}^\sim z\|_{\mathcal{S}_2}\|z\|_{\mathcal{S}_2} \quad \text{by the Cauchy-Schwarz inequality} \\
&\leq \|\boldsymbol{G}\|\|\boldsymbol{G}^\sim z\|_{\mathcal{S}_1}\|z\|_{\mathcal{S}_2}.
\end{aligned}$$

Therefore, $\|\boldsymbol{G}^\sim z\|_{\mathcal{S}_1} \leq \|\boldsymbol{G}\|\|z\|_{\mathcal{S}_2}$ for all z. Consequently $\|\boldsymbol{G}^\sim\| \leq \|\boldsymbol{G}\|$. Since $(\boldsymbol{G}^\sim)^\sim = \boldsymbol{G}$, we also see that $\|\boldsymbol{G}\| = \|(\boldsymbol{G}^\sim)^\sim\| \leq \|\boldsymbol{G}^\sim\|$. Hence

$$\|\boldsymbol{G}^\sim\| = \|\boldsymbol{G}\|. \tag{3.3.6}$$

3.3.3 The 2-norm of a system

The 2-norm of the system $\boldsymbol{G}$ is the expected root-mean-square (RMS) value of the output when the input is a realization of a unit variance white noise process. That is, if the input is

$$w(t) = \begin{cases} \text{a unit variance white noise process, } t \in [0,T] \\ 0 \quad \text{otherwise.} \end{cases} \tag{3.3.7}$$

and $z = \boldsymbol{G}w$, the finite-horizon 2-norm of $\boldsymbol{G}$ is defined by

$$\|\boldsymbol{G}\|_{2,[0,T]}^2 = \mathcal{E}\left\{\frac{1}{T}\int_0^T z'(t)z(t)\,dt\right\}, \tag{3.3.8}$$

in which $\mathcal{E}(\cdot)$ is the expectation operator.

In the case of a linear system,

$$z(t) \;=\; \int_0^T G(t,\tau)w(\tau)\,d\tau$$

when w is given by (3.3.7). Substituting into (3.3.8), noting that $z'z = \operatorname{trace}(zz')$ and interchanging the order of integration and expectation we obtain

$$\begin{aligned}\|\boldsymbol{G}\|_{2,[0,T]}^2 &= \frac{1}{T}\int_0^T dt\int_0^T d\tau\int_0^T \operatorname{trace}\big(G(t,\tau)\mathcal{E}\{w(\tau)w'(\sigma)\}G'(t,\sigma)\big)\,d\sigma \\ &= \frac{1}{T}\int_0^T dt\int_0^T \operatorname{trace}\big(G(t,\tau)G'(t,\tau)\big)\,d\tau \end{aligned} \tag{3.3.9}$$

since $\mathcal{E}\big(w(\tau)w'(\sigma)\big) = I\delta(\tau-\sigma)$.

Note that the right-hand side of (3.3.9) is finite if and only if $G(\cdot,\cdot) \in \mathcal{L}_2[0,T] \times \mathcal{L}_2[0,T]$. In particular, $G(\cdot,\cdot)$ must not contain delta functions. Thus, the system defined by $w(t) \mapsto D(t)w(t)$, which we may write as

$$w(t) = \int_{-\infty}^{\infty} D(t)\delta(t-\tau)w(\tau)\,d\tau,$$

has infinite 2-norm (unless $D(t) \equiv 0$).

In the time-invariant case $G(t,\tau) = G(t-\tau,0)$. Writing $G(t-\tau)$ instead of $G(t-\tau,0)$ and setting $\sigma = t-\tau$ in (3.3.9) we obtain

$$\|\boldsymbol{G}\|_{2,[0,T]}^2 = \frac{1}{T}\int_0^T dt\int_{t-T}^{t} \operatorname{trace}\big(G(\sigma)G'(\sigma)\big)\,d\sigma.$$

Interchanging the order of integration yields

$$\begin{aligned}\|\boldsymbol{G}\|_{2,[0,T]}^2 &= \int_{-T}^{T} \operatorname{trace}\big(G(t)G'(t)\big)\,dt \\ &\quad -\frac{1}{T}\int_0^T \operatorname{trace}\big(G(t)G'(t) + G(-t)G'(-t)\big)t\,dt.\end{aligned}$$

If $\boldsymbol{G}$ is such that the integrals remain bounded[11] as $T \to \infty$ we obtain the infinite-horizon 2-norm of $\boldsymbol{G}$:

$$\|\boldsymbol{G}\|_2^2 = \int_{-\infty}^{\infty} \operatorname{trace}\big(G(t)G'(t)\big)\,dt \tag{3.3.10}$$

$$= \frac{1}{2\pi}\int_{-\infty}^{\infty} \operatorname{trace}\big(\boldsymbol{G}(j\omega)\boldsymbol{G}^*(j\omega)\big)\,d\omega. \tag{3.3.11}$$

Here $\boldsymbol{G}(j\omega)$ is the Fourier transform of $G(t)$; the final equality follows from Parseval's identity. It follows from (3.3.11) that a necessary and sufficient condition for $\|\boldsymbol{G}\|_2$ finite is that $\boldsymbol{G} \in \mathcal{L}_2$.

Although $\|\cdot\|_2$ defines a norm on systems, the submultiplicative property satisfied by the incremental gain, the induced norm and the infinity norm does not hold for $\|\cdot\|_2$. That is, $\|\boldsymbol{GH}\|_2$ may be greater than or less than $\|\boldsymbol{G}\|_2\|\boldsymbol{H}\|_2$ (an exercise requests an example of each case). This is why it is not possible to obtain stability robustness results using the 2-norm as the measure of system size.

The adjoint of $\boldsymbol{G}$ on $\mathcal{L}_2[0,T]$ has the form

$$[\boldsymbol{G}^{\sim}y](t) = \int_0^T G'(\tau,t)y(\tau)\,d\tau.$$

Since trace$[XY'] =$ trace$[Y'X]$ for any matrices X and Y of the same dimensions, it follows from (3.3.9) that $\|\boldsymbol{G}^{\sim}\|_{2,[0,T]} = \|\boldsymbol{G}\|_{2,[0,T]}$ and from (3.3.10) that $\|\boldsymbol{G}^{\sim}\|_2 = \|\boldsymbol{G}\|_2$.

The following result expresses the 2-norm of a state-space system in terms of the controllability or observability gramian of the realization.

Theorem 3.3.1 *Suppose $\boldsymbol{G}$ is a linear system described by the state-space equations*

$$\begin{aligned} \dot{x}(t) &= A(t)x(t) + B(t)u(t), \qquad x_0 = 0, \\ y(t) &= C(t)x(t) + D(t)w(t). \end{aligned}$$

1. *A necessary and sufficient condition for $\|\boldsymbol{G}\|_{2,[0,T]} < \infty$ is $D(t) \equiv 0$ for all $t \in [0,T]$.*

2. *If $D(t) \equiv 0$ for all $t \in [0,T]$, then*

$$\|\boldsymbol{G}\|_{2,[0,T]}^2 = \frac{1}{T}\int_0^T \operatorname{trace}\big(C(t)P(t)C'(t)\big)\,dt \tag{3.3.12}$$

$$= \frac{1}{T}\int_0^T \operatorname{trace}\big(B'(t)Q(t)B(t)\big)\,dt, \tag{3.3.13}$$

in which $P(t)$ is the controllability gramian satisfying

$$\dot{P}(t) = A(t)P(t) + P(t)A'(t) + B(t)B'(t), \qquad P(0) = 0,$$

[11] For example, assume that $\operatorname{trace}\big(G(t)G'(t)\big) \le \alpha e^{-\beta^2|t|}$.

and $Q(t)$ is the observability gramian satisfying

$$-\dot{Q}(t) = Q(t)A(t) + A'(t)Q(t) + C'(t)C(t), \qquad Q(T) = 0.$$

3. *If the matrices A, B and C and D are constant and A is asymptotically stable, then $\|\boldsymbol{G}\|_2$ is finite if and only if $D = 0$ and in this case*

$$\begin{aligned} \|\boldsymbol{G}\|_2^2 &= \operatorname{trace}(CPC') \\ &= \operatorname{trace}(B'QB), \end{aligned}$$

in which

$$\begin{aligned} AP + PA' + BB' &= 0 \\ QA + A'Q + C'C &= 0. \end{aligned}$$

Proof. Let $\Phi(t,\tau)$ denote the transition matrix associated with $A(t)$. Then

$$G(t,\tau) = \begin{cases} C(t)\Phi(t,\tau)B(\tau) + D(t)\delta(t-\tau) & \text{for } t \geq \tau \\ 0 & \text{otherwise.} \end{cases}$$

We see that $G(t,\tau) \in \mathcal{L}_2[0,T] \times \mathcal{L}_2[0,T]$ if and only if $D(t) \equiv 0$ for $t \in [0,T]$, and consequently $\|\boldsymbol{G}\|_{2,[0,T]}$ is finite if and only if $D(t) \equiv 0$ for $t \in [0,T]$, which we henceforth assume. Substituting $G(t,\tau)$ into (3.3.9) we obtain

$$\|\boldsymbol{G}\|_{2,[0,T]}^2 = \frac{1}{T}\int_0^T \operatorname{trace}\big(C(t)M(t)C'(t)\big)\, dt,$$

in which

$$M(t) = \int_0^t \Phi(t,\tau)B(\tau)B'(\tau)\Phi'(t,\tau)\, d\tau.$$

Invoking Leibniz's rule on interchanging the order of differentiation and integration we obtain

$$\frac{d}{dt}M(t) = B(t)B'(t) + A(t)M(t) + M(t)A'(t).$$

Since $M(0) = 0$, we see that $P(t) = M(t)$ and (3.3.12) follows.

To obtain (3.3.13), we note that

$$\begin{aligned} \frac{d}{dt}\big(P(t)Q(t)\big) &= \dot{P}(t)Q(t) + P(t)\dot{Q}(t) \\ &= APQ - PQA + BB'Q - PC'C. \end{aligned}$$

Integrating from 0 to T yields

$$\begin{aligned} &\int_0^T P(t)C'(t)C(t)\, dt \\ &= \int_0^T \big(A(t)P(t)Q(t) - P(t)Q(t)A(t) + B(t)B'(t)Q(t)\big)\, dt. \end{aligned}$$

Taking the trace of this identity, we have that

$$\int_0^T \operatorname{trace}\big(C(t)P(t)C'(t)\big)\,dt = \int_0^T \operatorname{trace}\big(B'(t)Q(t)B(t)\big)\,dt.$$

For the infinite-horizon result, since A is asymptotically stable, the controllability and observability gramians $P(t)$ and $Q(t)$ converge to constant matrices, which are the unique solutions to the stated algebraic equations. ■

Main points of the section

1. We have introduced three ways of determining the "size" of a system. These are the incremental gain, the induced norm and the 2-norm.
2. A system with finite incremental gain is causal and stable.
3. The $\mathcal{L}_2[0,T]$ induced norm of a state-space system is finite.
4. For causal, stable systems, the incremental gain and the $\mathcal{L}_2[0,\infty)$ induced norm are equal. If, in addition, the system is linear and time-invariant, the incremental gain and the induced norm are equal to the infinity norm.
5. An allpass system $\boldsymbol{A}$ has the property $\|\boldsymbol{GA}\| = \|\boldsymbol{G}\|$. In particular, $\|\boldsymbol{A}\| = 1$.
6. A linear system and its adjoint system have the same induced norm.
7. The 2-norm of a system is the expected value of the RMS power of the output when the system is driven by white noise of unit variance.
8. A linear system and its adjoint system have the same 2-norm.
9. The 2-norm of a state-space system is given by a trace formula involving either the controllability or the observability gramian of the realization.

3.4 The small gain theorem

The small gain theorem is the key result on which the robust stability analysis in this book depends. Essentially, the small gain theorem states that if a feedback loop consists of stable systems and the loop-gain product is less than unity, then the feedback loop is internally stable. Several versions of the small gain theorem are available in the literature. The version we will use is based on the incremental gain and it guarantees the existence of solutions to the loop equations as well as their stability.

The small gain theorem is based on a fixed point theorem known as the contraction mapping theorem, which we now present.

Contractive systems

A system $\boldsymbol{S} : \mathcal{S} \mapsto \mathcal{S}$ in which $\mathcal{S}$ is a Banach space (such as $\mathcal{L}_2[0,T]$ or $\mathcal{L}_2[0,\infty)$) is a contraction if its (Lipschitz) induced norm is less than 1. That is, there exists a $\gamma < 1$ such that

$$\|\boldsymbol{S}w - \boldsymbol{S}\tilde{w}\|_{\mathcal{S}} \leq \gamma \|w - \tilde{w}\|_{\mathcal{S}} \text{ for all } w, \tilde{w} \in \mathcal{S}.$$

For example, a system $\boldsymbol{S} : \mathcal{L}_{2e} \mapsto \mathcal{L}_{2e}$ with $\gamma(\boldsymbol{S}) < 1$ is a contraction on $\mathcal{L}_2[0,T]$ for any T.

A contractive system $\boldsymbol{S}$ has the property that there exists $w \in \mathcal{S}$ such that $w = \boldsymbol{S}w$. This is known as the *contraction mapping theorem.*

To see that such a w exists, choose any $w_0 \in \mathcal{S}$ and define the sequence $w_{k+1} = \boldsymbol{S}w_k$. This sequence is Cauchy, since $\|w_{k+1} - w_k\| \leq \gamma \|w_k - w_{k-1}\|$ for some $\gamma < 1$, and this implies $\lim_{k\to\infty} \|w_{k+1} - w_k\| = 0$. Since $\mathcal{S}$ is a Banach space, there is a $w \in \mathcal{S}$ such that $w = \lim_{k\to\infty} w_k$. Since $\|\boldsymbol{S}\|_{\mathcal{S}}$ is finite, $\boldsymbol{S}$ is continuous on $\mathcal{S}$. Hence $w = \lim_{k\to\infty}(\boldsymbol{S}w_{k-1}) = \boldsymbol{S}(\lim_{k\to\infty} w_{k-1}) = \boldsymbol{S}w$.

The small gain theorem

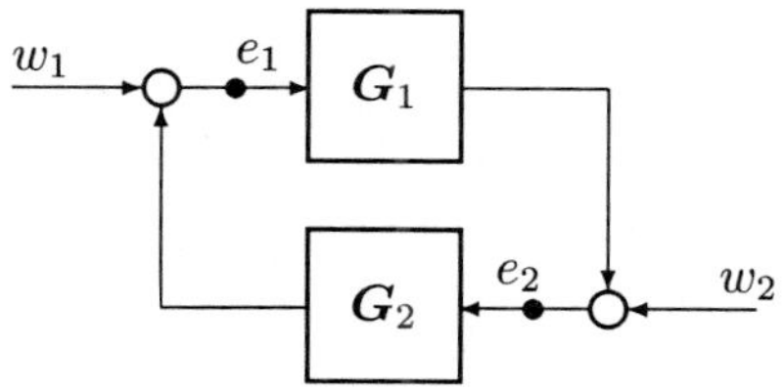

Figure 3.1: Feedback loop for the small gain theorem.

Theorem 3.4.1 *Suppose the systems $\boldsymbol{G}_1 : \mathcal{L}_{2e} \mapsto \mathcal{L}_{2e}$ and $\boldsymbol{G}_2 : \mathcal{L}_{2e} \mapsto \mathcal{L}_{2e}$ in Figure 3.1 have finite incremental gains such that $\gamma(\boldsymbol{G}_1)\gamma(\boldsymbol{G}_2) < 1$. Then:*

1. *For all w_1, $w_2 \in \mathcal{L}_{2e}$, there exist unique solutions e_1, $e_2 \in \mathcal{L}_{2e}$.*
2. *For all w_1, $w_2 \in \mathcal{L}_2[0,\infty)$, there exist unique solutions e_1, $e_2 \in \mathcal{L}_2[0,\infty)$. That is, the closed loop is internally stable.*

Proof. Let $w_{1T} = \boldsymbol{P}_T w_1$ and $w_{2T} = \boldsymbol{P}_T w_2$ and define the system $\boldsymbol{S}$ by

$$\boldsymbol{S}e_{2T} = w_{2T} + \boldsymbol{P}_T\left(\boldsymbol{G}_1\left(w_{1T} + \boldsymbol{P}_T(\boldsymbol{G}_2 e_{2T})\right)\right).$$

$\boldsymbol{S}$ is a contraction on $\mathcal{L}_2[0,T]$ since $\gamma(\boldsymbol{G}_1)\gamma(\boldsymbol{G}_2) < 1$ and

$$\begin{aligned}
&\|\boldsymbol{S}e_{2T} - \boldsymbol{S}\widehat{e}_{2T}\|_{2,[0,T]} \\
&\quad = \|\boldsymbol{G}_1\left(w_{1T} + \boldsymbol{P}_T(\boldsymbol{G}_2 e_{2T})\right) - \boldsymbol{G}_1\left(w_{1T} + \boldsymbol{P}_T(\boldsymbol{G}_2 \widehat{e}_{2T})\right)\|_{2,[0,T]} \\
&\quad \leq \gamma(\boldsymbol{G}_1)\|\boldsymbol{G}_2 e_{2T} - \boldsymbol{G}_2\widehat{e}_{2T}\|_{2,[0,T]} \\
&\quad \leq \gamma(\boldsymbol{G}_1)\gamma(\boldsymbol{G}_2)\|e_{2T} - \widehat{e}_{2T}\|_{2,[0,T]}.
\end{aligned}$$

Consequently, by the contraction mapping theorem, there is an $e_{2T} \in \mathcal{L}_2[0,T]$ such that $e_{2T} = \boldsymbol{S}e_{2T}$ for any T. That is,

$$e_{2T} = w_{2T} + \boldsymbol{P}_T\left(\boldsymbol{G}_1\left(w_{1T} + \boldsymbol{P}_T(\boldsymbol{G}_2 e_{2T})\right)\right).$$

Recalling that the finite incremental gain assumption implies that the systems $\boldsymbol{G}_i$ are causal, it follows that

$$\begin{aligned} e_{2T} &= \boldsymbol{P}_T\left(w_2 + \boldsymbol{G}_1(w_1 + \boldsymbol{G}_2 e_2)\right) \\ &= \boldsymbol{P}_T e_2, \end{aligned}$$

in which e_2 satisfies the loop equations (on $[0,T]$). Since T was arbitrary, we conclude that for any w_1 and $w_2 \in \mathcal{L}_{2e}$, there is an $e_2 \in \mathcal{L}_{2e}$ satisfying the loop equations. The same holds for e_1 by a similar argument.

When w_1 and w_2 are in $\mathcal{L}_2[0,\infty)$, we may apply the above arguments on $\mathcal{L}_2[0,\infty)$ instead of $\mathcal{L}_2[0,T]$ to obtain the result. ■

The remarkable feature of this theorem is that we can establish the internal stability of the closed loop without any precise knowledge of the systems $\boldsymbol{G}_i$ making up the loop. All we need to know is that the systems $\boldsymbol{G}_i$ have finite incremental gains such that the product of their incremental gains is smaller than 1.

Example 3.4.1. Suppose $\boldsymbol{G}_1$ is the saturation nonlinearity

$$(\boldsymbol{G}_1 e_1)(t) = \begin{cases} e_1(t) & \text{if } \|e_1(t)\| \leq M \\ M\text{sign}(e_1(t)) & \text{otherwise,} \end{cases}$$

which has $\gamma(\boldsymbol{G}_1) = 1$. Then the feedback loop will be internally stable for any system $\boldsymbol{G}_2$ for which $\gamma(\boldsymbol{G}_2) < 1$. ▽

Main point of the section

> If the product of the incremental gains of systems in a feedback loop is strictly less than unity, the feedback loop is internally stable. This is known as the small gain theorem.

3.5 Loop transformation

It is often the case that the systems comprising a feedback loop fail to satisfy the hypotheses of the small gain theorem. In such cases, it may be possible to establish the stability of the closed loop by applying the small gain theorem to a modified form of the feedback system that has the same stability properties.

Three common loop transformations will be introduced. The first is a linear multiplier or weight, the second is a linear shift and the third is the famous transformation relating passive and contractive systems. Readers familiar with classical network theory will recall this as the transformation relating the admittance description of a circuit to its scattering description. Many other loop transformations are possible—sector bounded nonlinearities, for example, may be transformed into systems that have incremental gain less than unity (see Section 4.7). These transformations have a linear fractional character that will be considered in more detail in the next chapter. Our purpose here is to show that loop transformations can extend the range of applicability of the small gain theorem.

3.5.1 Multipliers or weights

The use of "multipliers" or "weights" is common currency in control system optimization. In the case of infinity norm optimization, the introduction of weights allows the frequency dependent characteristics of signals and systems to be captured as well as their size. For example, if $\boldsymbol{G}$ is known to be low-pass, meaning that $\overline{\sigma}(\boldsymbol{G}(j\omega)) < \boldsymbol{w}(j\omega)$ for all ω and some scalar low-pass weight $\boldsymbol{w}$, then $\|\boldsymbol{w}^{-1}\boldsymbol{G}\|_\infty < 1$ contains this information in a compact way. Similarly, a low-frequency disturbance is modelled by $\|\boldsymbol{w}^{-1}d\|_2 < 1$, in preference to the model $\|d\|_2 < 1$, which does not contain the *a priori* knowledge about the low-frequency nature of the disturbance.

The following result justifies the use of weights in determining closed-loop stability.

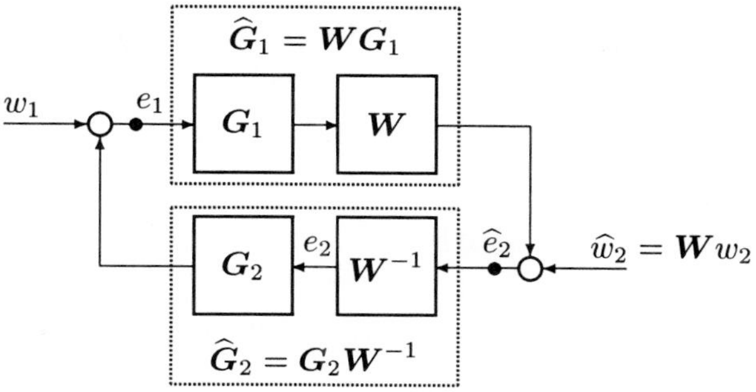

Figure 3.2: Feedback loop with weight.

Lemma 3.5.1 *Consider the two feedback loops shown in Figures 3.1 and 3.2. Suppose* $\boldsymbol{G}_1, \boldsymbol{G}_2 : \mathcal{L}_{2e} \mapsto \mathcal{L}_{2e}$ *and that* $\boldsymbol{W} : \mathcal{L}_{2e} \mapsto \mathcal{L}_{2e}$ *is a linear system such that* $\boldsymbol{W}^{-1} : \mathcal{L}_{2e} \mapsto \mathcal{L}_{2e}$.

1. *If* $w_1, w_2 \in \mathcal{L}_{2e}$ *implies* $e_1, e_2 \in \mathcal{L}_{2e}$ *in Figure 3.1, then* $w_1, \widehat{w}_2 \in \mathcal{L}_{2e}$ *implies* $e_1, \widehat{e}_2 \in \mathcal{L}_{2e}$ *in Figure 3.2.*

2. *If* w_1, $\widehat{w}_2 \in \mathcal{L}_{2e}$ *implies* e_1, $\widehat{e}_2 \in \mathcal{L}_{2e}$ *in Figure 3.2, then* w_1, $w_2 \in \mathcal{L}_{2e}$ *implies* e_1, $e_2 \in \mathcal{L}_{2e}$ *in Figure 3.1.*

If $\boldsymbol{W}$ *and* $\boldsymbol{W}^{-1}$ *are stable, then*

3. *The loop in Figure 3.1 is internally stable if and only if the loop in Figure 3.2 is internally stable.*

Proof. Since $\boldsymbol{W}^{-1}$ is linear, we have

$$\begin{aligned} e_2 &= w_2 + \boldsymbol{G}_1 e_1 \\ &= \boldsymbol{W}^{-1}(\boldsymbol{W} w_2 + \boldsymbol{W}\boldsymbol{G}_1 e_1), \end{aligned}$$

which verifies that the loop in Figure 3.2 generates the same signal as that in Figure 3.1.

1. Let w_1, $\widehat{w}_2 \in \mathcal{L}_{2e}$. Define $w_2 = \boldsymbol{W}^{-1}\widehat{w}_2 \in \mathcal{L}_{2e}$ and apply the inputs w_1 and w_2 to the loop of Figure 3.1 to obtain e_1, $e_2 \in \mathcal{L}_{2e}$. Now define $\widehat{e}_2 = \boldsymbol{W} e_2 \in \mathcal{L}_{2e}$.
2. Let w_1, $w_2 \in \mathcal{L}_{2e}$. Define $\widehat{w}_2 = \boldsymbol{W} w_2$ and apply the inputs w_1 and $\widehat{w}_2$ to the loop in Figure 3.2 to obtain e_1 and $\widehat{e}_2 \in \mathcal{L}_{2e}$. Now define $e_2 = \boldsymbol{W}^{-1}\widehat{e}_2 \in \mathcal{L}_{2e}$.
3. Repeat the above arguments with $\mathcal{L}_{2e}$ replaced by $\mathcal{L}_2[0,\infty)$. ■

Combining this with the small gain theorem we have, for example:

Corollary 3.5.2 *Suppose* $\boldsymbol{G}_1$, $\boldsymbol{G}_2$ *are stable. Then the loop in Figure 3.1 is internally stable if there exists a stable linear system* $\boldsymbol{W}$ *such that* $\boldsymbol{W}^{-1}$ *is stable and*

$$\gamma(\boldsymbol{W}\boldsymbol{G}_1)\gamma(\boldsymbol{G}_2\boldsymbol{W}^{-1}) < 1.$$

3.5.2 Linear shift

Lemma 3.5.3 *Consider the two feedback loops shown in Figures 3.1 and 3.3. Suppose* $\boldsymbol{G}_1$, $\boldsymbol{G}_2 : \mathcal{L}_{2e} \mapsto \mathcal{L}_{2e}$ *and that* $\boldsymbol{H} : \mathcal{L}_{2e} \mapsto \mathcal{L}_{2e}$ *is a linear system such that* $\boldsymbol{G}_2(I - \boldsymbol{H}\boldsymbol{G}_2)^{-1} : \mathcal{L}_{2e} \mapsto \mathcal{L}_{2e}$.

1. *If* w_1, $w_2 \in \mathcal{L}_{2e}$ *implies* e_1, $e_2 \in \mathcal{L}_{2e}$ *in Figure 3.1, then* w_1, $\widehat{w}_2 \in \mathcal{L}_{2e}$ *implies* e_1, $\widehat{e}_2 \in \mathcal{L}_{2e}$ *in Figure 3.3.*
2. *If* w_1, $\widehat{w}_2 \in \mathcal{L}_{2e}$ *implies* e_1, $\widehat{e}_2 \in \mathcal{L}_{2e}$ *in Figure 3.3, then* w_1, $w_2 \in \mathcal{L}_{2e}$ *implies* e_1, $e_2 \in \mathcal{L}_{2e}$ *in Figure 3.1.*

If $\boldsymbol{H}$ *and* $\boldsymbol{G}_2(I - \boldsymbol{H}\boldsymbol{G}_2)^{-1}$ *are stable, then*

3. *The loop in Figure 3.1 is internally stable if and only if the loop in Figure 3.3 is internally stable.*

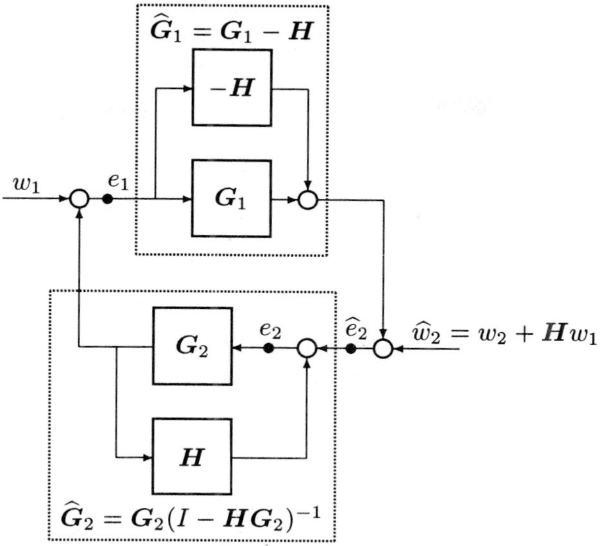

Figure 3.3: Linear shift transformation.

Proof. Since $\boldsymbol{H}$ is linear, we have

$$\begin{aligned} \boldsymbol{H}e_1 &= \boldsymbol{H}(w_1 + \boldsymbol{G}_2 e_2) \\ &= \boldsymbol{H}w_1 + \boldsymbol{H}\boldsymbol{G}_2 e_2, \end{aligned}$$

which verifies that the loop in Figure 3.3 generates the same signal as that in Figure 3.1.

1. Let $w_1, \widehat{w}_2 \in \mathcal{L}_{2e}$. Define $w_2 = \widehat{w}_2 - \boldsymbol{H}w_1 \in \mathcal{L}_{2e}$ and apply the inputs w_1 and w_2 to the loop of Figure 3.1 to obtain $e_1, e_2 \in \mathcal{L}_{2e}$. Now define $\widehat{e}_2 = (I - \boldsymbol{H}\boldsymbol{G}_2)e_2 \in \mathcal{L}_{2e}$.

2. Let $w_1, w_2 \in \mathcal{L}_{2e}$. Define $\widehat{w}_2 = w_2 + \boldsymbol{H}w_1 \in \mathcal{L}_{2e}$ and apply the inputs w_1 and $\widehat{w}_2$ to the loop in Figure 3.3 to obtain e_1 and $\widehat{e}_2 \in \mathcal{L}_{2e}$. Now define $e_2 = \big(I + \boldsymbol{H}\boldsymbol{G}_2(I - \boldsymbol{H}\boldsymbol{G}_2)^{-1}\big)\widehat{e}_2 \in \mathcal{L}_{2e}$.

3. Repeat the above arguments with $\mathcal{L}_{2e}$ replaced by $\mathcal{L}_2[0,\infty)$. Note that internal stability of the loop in Figure 3.1 implies that $\boldsymbol{G}_2 e_2 = e_1 - w_1 \in \mathcal{L}_2[0,\infty)$ for all $w_1, w_2 \in \mathcal{L}_2[0,\infty)$. ■

This linear shift together with the small gain theorem yields, for example, the following closed-loop stability result.

Corollary 3.5.4 *The loop in Figure 3.1 is internally stable if there exists a stable linear system* $\boldsymbol{H}$ *such that* $\boldsymbol{G}_2(I-\boldsymbol{H}\boldsymbol{G}_2)^{-1}$ *has finite incremental gain and*

$$\gamma(\boldsymbol{G}_1-\boldsymbol{H})\gamma(\boldsymbol{G}_2(I-\boldsymbol{H}\boldsymbol{G}_2)^{-1})<1.$$

Note that this corollary requires that we have sufficient information about $\boldsymbol{G}_2$ to determine whether $\boldsymbol{G}_2(I-\boldsymbol{H}\boldsymbol{G}_2)^{-1}$ is stable.

3.5.3 Passivity

The passivity theorem is another theorem which allows us to conclude closed-loop stability from very general properties of the systems comprising the feedback loop. Any negative feedback loop which is made up of a passive system and a strictly passive system will be stable. We now show how a version of this result may be deduced from the small gain theorem.

A system $\boldsymbol{P}:\mathcal{L}_{2e}\mapsto\mathcal{L}_{2e}$ is *incrementally strictly passive* if there exists an $\epsilon>0$ such that

$$\langle \boldsymbol{P}w-\boldsymbol{P}\tilde{w}, w-\tilde{w}\rangle_{[t_0,T]} \;\geq\; \epsilon\|w-\tilde{w}\|^2_{2,[t_0,T]} \quad \text{for all } w,\tilde{w}\in\mathcal{L}_2[t_0,T] \text{ and all } T. \tag{3.5.1}$$

It is assumed that the system is relaxed at time $t_0=0$. If $\epsilon=0$ is allowed, the system is incrementally passive, rather than incrementally strictly passive.

To motivate this definition, let $\boldsymbol{Z}$ be the impedance of a linear, passive circuit, which maps the vector of port currents i to the vector of port voltages v. Then

$$\langle \boldsymbol{Z}i, i\rangle_{[0,T]}=\int_0^T i'(t)v(t)\,dt \tag{3.5.2}$$

is the energy consumed by the circuit over the time interval $[0,T]$. Since a passive circuit never produces energy, the integral in (3.5.2) must be nonnegative. A strictly passive circuit consumes energy for any port current $i\neq 0$ and all terminal times T, so the integral in (3.5.2) must be positive for any $i\neq 0$. By evaluating the inner product in the frequency domain, one can show that the (time-invariant) circuit is incrementally strictly passive if and only if the transfer function matrix $\boldsymbol{Z}$ is in $\mathcal{H}_\infty$ and satisfies

$$\boldsymbol{Z}(j\omega)+\boldsymbol{Z}^*(j\omega)\geq 2\epsilon I.$$

A proof of this is requested as an exercise (Problem 3.15). Since this inequality is equivalent to the requirement that the real part of $\boldsymbol{Z}(j\omega)$ is larger than ϵ for all ω, such transfer function matrices are called *strictly positive real.*[12] If $\boldsymbol{z}$ is a scalar positive real transfer function, the positive real condition is equivalent to the requirement that the phase of $\boldsymbol{z}$ lies between $\pm 90°$. It is easy to see that if a positive real transfer function $\boldsymbol{z}_1$ and a strictly positive real transfer function $\boldsymbol{z}_2$ are

[12] The transfer function matrix is positive real if $\epsilon=0$ is allowed.

connected in a negative feedback configuration, then the Nyquist diagram of $z_1 z_2$ can never encircle the -1 point. Therefore, the feedback loop must be stable by the Nyquist criterion.

To derive the passivity theorem from the small gain theorem, we will need the following properties of passive systems.

Lemma 3.5.5 *Suppose $\boldsymbol{P} : \mathcal{L}_{2e} \mapsto \mathcal{L}_{2e}$ is incrementally strictly passive and has finite incremental gain. Then*

1. $\boldsymbol{P}^{-1} : \mathcal{L}_{2e} \mapsto \mathcal{L}_{2e}$ *exists, is incrementally strictly passive and* $\gamma(\boldsymbol{P}^{-1}) \leq 1/\epsilon$.
2. $(I + \boldsymbol{P})^{-1} : \mathcal{L}_{2e} \mapsto \mathcal{L}_{2e}$ *exists, is incrementally strictly passive and* $\gamma\big((I + \boldsymbol{P})^{-1}\big) < 1$.

Proof.

1. Note that $z = \boldsymbol{P}w$ is equivalent to $w = w + \alpha(z - \boldsymbol{P}w)$, for $\alpha \neq 0$. Choose $z \in \mathcal{L}_{2e}$ and set $\alpha = \epsilon/\gamma^2$, where ϵ is such that (3.5.1) is satisfied and $\gamma = \gamma(\boldsymbol{P})$. Define the system $\boldsymbol{S}$ by $\boldsymbol{S}w = w + \alpha(z - \boldsymbol{P}w)$. Then $\boldsymbol{S}$ is a contraction, since

$$\begin{aligned} \|\boldsymbol{S}w - \boldsymbol{S}\tilde{w}\|_{2,[0,T]}^2 &= \|w - \tilde{w} - \alpha(\boldsymbol{P}w - \boldsymbol{P}\tilde{w})\|_{2,[0,T]}^2 \\ &= \|w - \tilde{w}\|_{2,[0,T]}^2 + \alpha^2\|\boldsymbol{P}w - \boldsymbol{P}\tilde{w}\|_{2,[0,T]}^2 \\ &\quad -2\alpha\langle \boldsymbol{P}w - \boldsymbol{P}\tilde{w}, w - \tilde{w}\rangle_{[0,T]} \\ &\leq \|w - \tilde{w}\|_{2,[0,T]}^2 \left(\alpha^2\gamma^2 - 2\epsilon\alpha + 1\right) \\ &= \left(1 - (\epsilon/\gamma)^2\right) \|w - \tilde{w}\|_{2,[0,T]}^2. \end{aligned}$$

Hence, there exists a unique $w \in \mathcal{L}_{2e}$ such that $w = \boldsymbol{S}w$. That is, for any $z \in \mathcal{L}_{2e}$, there is a unique $w \in \mathcal{L}_{2e}$ such that $\boldsymbol{P}w = z$. Thus $\boldsymbol{P}^{-1}$ exists.

Notice that

$$\begin{aligned} \|w - \tilde{w}\|_{2,[0,T]} &= \|\boldsymbol{P}\boldsymbol{P}^{-1}w - \boldsymbol{P}\boldsymbol{P}^{-1}\tilde{w}\|_{2,[0,T]} \\ &\leq \gamma(\boldsymbol{P})\|\boldsymbol{P}^{-1}w - \boldsymbol{P}^{-1}\tilde{w}\|_{2,[0,T]}. \end{aligned}$$

Therefore

$$\begin{aligned} &\langle \boldsymbol{P}^{-1}w - \boldsymbol{P}^{-1}\tilde{w}, w - \tilde{w}\rangle_{2,[0,T]} \\ &\quad = \langle \boldsymbol{P}^{-1}w - \boldsymbol{P}^{-1}\tilde{w}, \boldsymbol{P}\boldsymbol{P}^{-1}w - \boldsymbol{P}\boldsymbol{P}^{-1}\tilde{w}\rangle_{2,[0,T]} \\ &\quad \geq \epsilon\|\boldsymbol{P}^{-1}w - \boldsymbol{P}^{-1}\tilde{w}\|_{2,[0,T]}^2 \\ &\quad \geq \frac{\epsilon}{\gamma(\boldsymbol{P})^2}\|w - \tilde{w}\|_{2,[0,T]}^2, \end{aligned}$$

which shows that $\boldsymbol{P}^{-1}$ is incrementally strictly passive.

Also,

$$\begin{aligned}
&\|\boldsymbol{P}^{-1}w - \boldsymbol{P}^{-1}\tilde{w}\|^2_{2,[0,T]} \\
&\leq \frac{1}{\epsilon}\langle \boldsymbol{P}\boldsymbol{P}^{-1}w - \boldsymbol{P}\boldsymbol{P}^{-1}\tilde{w}, \boldsymbol{P}^{-1}w - \boldsymbol{P}^{-1}\tilde{w}\rangle_{2,[0,T]} \\
&= \frac{1}{\epsilon}\langle w - \tilde{w}, \boldsymbol{P}^{-1}w - \boldsymbol{P}^{-1}\tilde{w}\rangle_{2,[0,T]} \\
&\leq \frac{1}{\epsilon}\|w - \tilde{w}\|_{2,[0,T]}\|\boldsymbol{P}^{-1}w - \boldsymbol{P}^{-1}\tilde{w}\|_{2,[0,T]}
\end{aligned}$$

by Cauchy-Schwartz. Hence

$$\|\boldsymbol{P}^{-1}w - \boldsymbol{P}^{-1}\tilde{w}\|_{2,[0,T]} \leq \frac{1}{\epsilon}\|w - \tilde{w}\|^2_{2,[0,T]},$$

which shows that $\gamma(\boldsymbol{P}^{-1}) \leq 1/\epsilon$.

2. Since $\boldsymbol{P}$ is incrementally strictly passive, the system $I+\boldsymbol{P}$ is also incrementally strictly passive:

$$\begin{aligned}
&\langle (I+\boldsymbol{P})w - (I+\boldsymbol{P})\tilde{w}, w - \tilde{w}\rangle_{[0,T]} \\
&= \|w - \tilde{w}\|^2_{2,[0,T]} + \langle \boldsymbol{P}w - \boldsymbol{P}\tilde{w}, w - \tilde{w}\rangle_{[0,T]} \\
&\geq (1+\epsilon)\|w - \tilde{w}\|^2_{2,[0,T]}.
\end{aligned}$$

The result now follows from Item 1. ■

This result implies that the closed-loop system of Figure 3.1 with $\boldsymbol{G}_2 = -I$ is internally stable provided $\boldsymbol{G}_1$ has finite incremental gain and is incrementally strictly passive. Item 2, however, does not provide a complete connection between passive and "small gain" systems, since $\gamma(\boldsymbol{S}) < 1$ does *not* imply $\boldsymbol{P} = \boldsymbol{S}^{-1} - I$ is incrementally strictly passive.

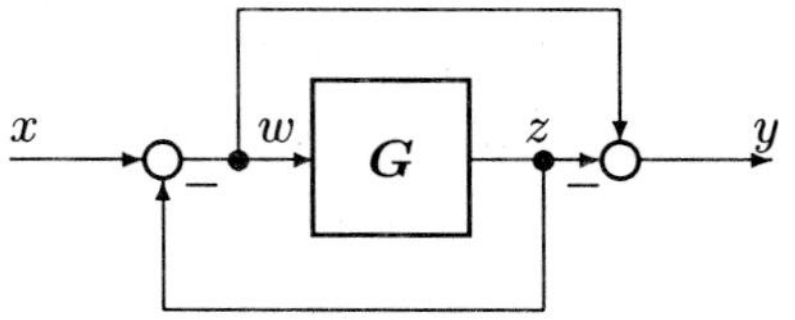

Figure 3.4: Transformation between passive and contractive systems.

Lemma 3.5.6

1. *If $\boldsymbol{S} : \mathcal{L}_{2e} \mapsto \mathcal{L}_{2e}$ and $\gamma(\boldsymbol{S}) < 1$, then $\boldsymbol{P} = (I - \boldsymbol{S})(I + \boldsymbol{S})^{-1} : \mathcal{L}_{2e} \mapsto \mathcal{L}_{2e}$ is incrementally strictly passive and has finite incremental gain.*

2. *If $\boldsymbol{P} : \mathcal{L}_{2e} \mapsto \mathcal{L}_{2e}$ is incrementally strictly passive and has finite incremental gain, then the system $\boldsymbol{S} = (I - \boldsymbol{P})(I + \boldsymbol{P})^{-1} : \mathcal{L}_{2e} \mapsto \mathcal{L}_{2e}$ and $\gamma(\boldsymbol{S}) < 1$.*

Proof.

1. If $\boldsymbol{S} : \mathcal{L}_{2e} \mapsto \mathcal{L}_{2e}$ and $\gamma(\boldsymbol{S}) < 1$, then $(I + \boldsymbol{S})^{-1} : \mathcal{L}_{2e} \mapsto \mathcal{L}_{2e}$ by the small gain theorem (Theorem 3.4.1). Furthermore (exercise),

$$\gamma\big((I + \boldsymbol{S})^{-1}\big) \leq \frac{1}{1 - \gamma(\boldsymbol{S})},$$

giving

$$\gamma(\boldsymbol{P}) \leq \frac{1 + \gamma(\boldsymbol{S})}{1 - \gamma(\boldsymbol{S})} < \infty.$$

It remains to show that $\boldsymbol{P}$ is incrementally strictly passive.

Consider two signals x and $\tilde{x}$ entering the loop of Figure 3.4 in which we set $\boldsymbol{G} = \boldsymbol{S}$. Let y and $\tilde{y}$ be the corresponding outputs and let w, $\tilde{w}$ and z, $\tilde{z}$ be the intermediate signals. Note that these signals are all in $\mathcal{L}_{2e}$ by the small gain theorem.

$$\begin{aligned}
\langle y - \tilde{y}, x - \tilde{x}\rangle_{[0,T]} &= \langle w - z - (\tilde{w} - \tilde{z}), w + z - (\tilde{w} + \tilde{z})\rangle_{[0,T]} \\
&= \|w - \tilde{w}\|^2_{2,[0,T]} - \|z - \tilde{z}\|^2_{2,[0,T]} \\
&\geq (1 - \gamma(\boldsymbol{S})^2)\|w - \tilde{w}\|^2_{2,[0,T]} \\
&\geq \frac{1 - \gamma(\boldsymbol{S})}{1 + \gamma(\boldsymbol{S})}\|x - \tilde{x}\|^2_{2,[0,T]}.
\end{aligned}$$

The last inequality follows from $x - \tilde{x} = (I + \boldsymbol{S})w - (I + \boldsymbol{S})\tilde{w}$, which implies that $\|x - \tilde{x}\|_{2,[0,T]} \leq (1 + \gamma(\boldsymbol{S}))\|w - \tilde{w}\|_{2,[0,T]}$. Hence $\boldsymbol{P}$ is incrementally strictly passive.

2. If $\boldsymbol{P} : \mathcal{L}_{2e} \mapsto \mathcal{L}_{2e}$ is incrementally strictly passive and has finite incremental gain, then $(I + \boldsymbol{P})^{-1} : \mathcal{L}_{2e} \mapsto \mathcal{L}_{2e}$ by Lemma 3.5.5. It remains to show that $\gamma(\boldsymbol{S}) < 1$.

Consider two signals x and $\tilde{x}$ entering the loop of Figure 3.4 in which we set $\boldsymbol{G} = \boldsymbol{P}$. Let y and $\tilde{y}$ be the corresponding outputs and let w, $\tilde{w}$ and z, $\tilde{z}$ be the intermediate signals. Note that these signals are all in $\mathcal{L}_{2e}$ by Lemma 3.5.5.

$$\begin{aligned}
&\|y - \tilde{y}\|^2_{2,[0,T]} \\
&= \langle w - z - (\tilde{w} - \tilde{z}), w - z - (\tilde{w} - \tilde{z})\rangle_{[0,T]} \\
&= \|w - \tilde{w}\|^2_{2,[0,T]} + \|z - \tilde{z}\|^2_{2,[0,T]} - 2\langle z - \tilde{z}, w - \tilde{w}\rangle_{[0,T]} \\
&\leq \langle w - \tilde{w} + (z - \tilde{z}), w - \tilde{w} + (z - \tilde{z})\rangle_{[0,T]} - 4\epsilon\|w - \tilde{w}\|^2_{2,[0,T]} \\
&= \|x - \tilde{x}\|^2_{2,[0,T]} - 4\epsilon\|w - \tilde{w}\|^2_{2,[0,T]} \\
&\leq \left(1 - \frac{4\epsilon}{(1 + \gamma(\boldsymbol{P}))^2}\right)\|x - \tilde{x}\|^2_{2,[0,T]}.
\end{aligned}$$

The last inequality follows from $x - \tilde{x} = (I + \boldsymbol{P})w - (I + \boldsymbol{P})\tilde{w}$ as before. ■

Using this transformation and the small gain theorem, we obtain the passivity theorem:

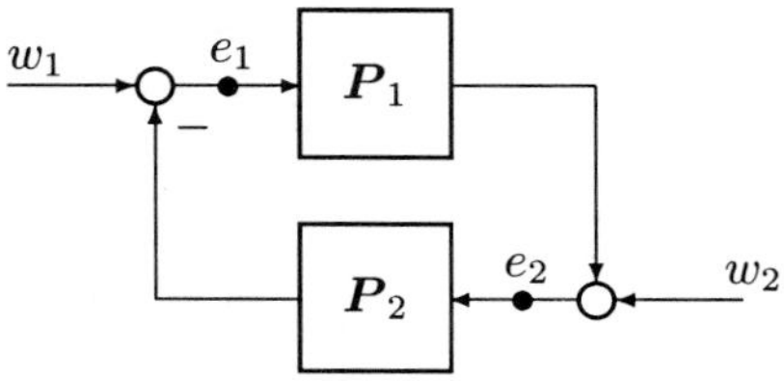

Figure 3.5: Feedback loop for passivity theorem.

Theorem 3.5.7 *Suppose that in Figure 3.5 the systems* $\boldsymbol{P}_1$, $\boldsymbol{P}_2 : \mathcal{L}_{2e} \mapsto \mathcal{L}_{2e}$ *have finite incremental gain and are incrementally strictly passive. Then*

1. *For all* w_1, $w_2 \in \mathcal{L}_{2e}$ *there exist unique solutions* e_1, $e_2 \in \mathcal{L}_{2e}$.
2. *For all* w_1, $w_2 \in \mathcal{L}_2[0, \infty)$, *there exist unique solutions* e_1, $e_2 \in \mathcal{L}_2[0, \infty)$. *That is, the loop is internally stable.*

Proof. Redraw the loop of Figure 3.1 as shown in Figure 3.6. The results follow immediately from Lemma 3.5.6 and the small gain theorem (Theorem 3.4.1). ■

Main points of the section

1. Loop transformations may be introduced before applying the small gain theorem.
2. Multipliers or weights must be stable, linear systems with stable inverses if stability properties are to be preserved.
3. By introducing a simple loop transformation, a passivity condition may be converted into a small gain condition.
4. Two incrementally strictly passive systems may be connected to form a stable negative feedback loop.

3.6 Robust stability revisited

By using the small gain theorem, the robust stability results of Chapter 2 may be extended to encompass systems that may be time-varying and nonlinear. The general situation is depicted in Figure 3.7.

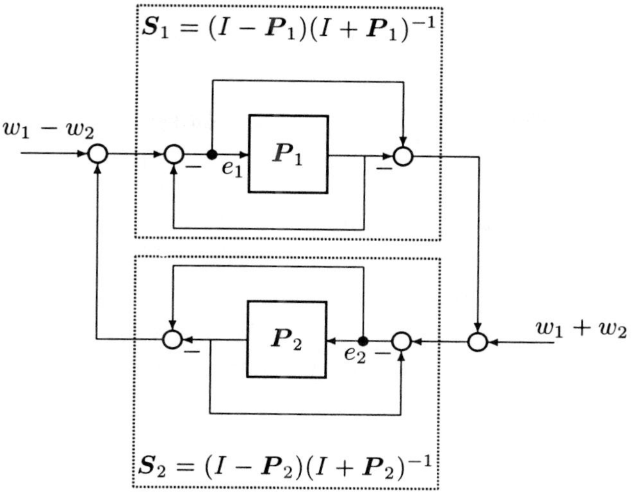

Figure 3.6: Loop shifting transformation for passivity theorem.

Theorem 3.6.1 *Consider the system shown in Figure 3.7. Suppose that* $\boldsymbol{\Delta} : \mathcal{L}_{2e} \mapsto \mathcal{L}_{2e}$ *and that* $\boldsymbol{P} : \mathcal{L}_{2e} \mapsto \mathcal{L}_{2e}$ *is causal and linearly connected in the sense that*

$$\begin{aligned} z_1 &= \boldsymbol{P}_{11} w_1 + \boldsymbol{P}_{12} w_2 \\ z_2 &= \boldsymbol{P}_{21} w_1 + \boldsymbol{P}_{22} w_2. \end{aligned}$$

Suppose also that $\boldsymbol{P}_{11}$ *has finite incremental gain. Then*

$$\gamma(\boldsymbol{P}_{11})\gamma(\boldsymbol{\Delta}) < 1 \tag{3.6.1}$$

implies that for any $w_2 \in \mathcal{L}_{2e}$*, there exist unique solutions* w_1*,* z_1*,* $z_2 \in \mathcal{L}_{2e}$*.*

If, in addition, $\boldsymbol{P}$ *is stable, then* $w_2 \in \mathcal{L}_2[0, \infty)$ *implies* w_1*,* z_1*,* $z_2 \in \mathcal{L}_2[0, \infty)$*. That is, the closed loop is stable.*

Proof. Write the loop equations as

$$\begin{aligned} z_1 &= \boldsymbol{P}_{11} w_1 + (\boldsymbol{P}_{12} w_2) \\ w_1 &= \boldsymbol{\Delta} z_1. \end{aligned}$$

Noting that $[\boldsymbol{P}_{12} w_2] \in \mathcal{L}_{2e}$ for any $w_2 \in \mathcal{L}_{2e}$, the result follows from the small gain theorem (Theorem 3.4.1). When $\boldsymbol{P}$ is stable, replace $\mathcal{L}_{2e}$ with $\mathcal{L}_2[0, \infty)$. ■

As an example of the application of this theorem, we consider the analysis of robustness with respect to an additive model error. The situation is shown in Figure 3.8, in which $\boldsymbol{G}$ and $\boldsymbol{K}$ are assumed to be causal and linear.

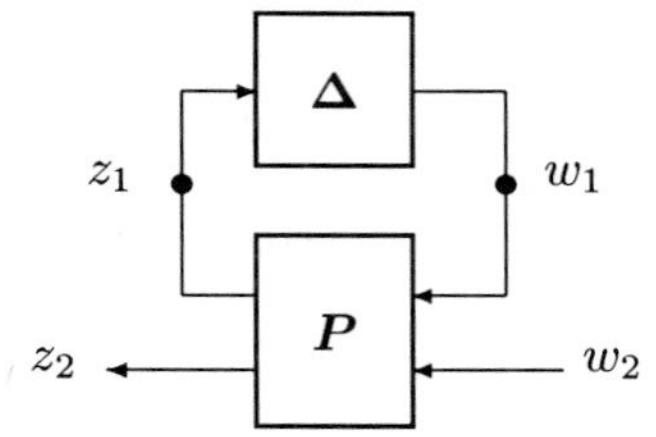

Figure 3.7: Figure for robust stability considerations.

The loop may be redrawn in the form of Figure 3.7 by choosing z_1, z_2 and w_1 as shown in Figure 3.8 and setting

$$w_2 = \begin{bmatrix} w_{21} \\ w_{22} \end{bmatrix}.$$

A routine calculation reveals that $\boldsymbol{P}$ is given by

$$\boldsymbol{P} = \left[\begin{array}{c|cc} \boldsymbol{K}(I-\boldsymbol{GK})^{-1} & (I-\boldsymbol{GK})^{-1} & \boldsymbol{K}(I-\boldsymbol{GK})^{-1} \\ \hline (I-\boldsymbol{GK})^{-1} & (I-\boldsymbol{GK})^{-1}\boldsymbol{G} & (I-\boldsymbol{GK})^{-1} \end{array}\right].$$

If $\boldsymbol{P}$ is stable and $\gamma\big(\boldsymbol{K}(I-\boldsymbol{GK})^{-1}\big) < \infty$, the closed-loop system will map inputs $w_2 \in \mathcal{L}_2[0,\infty)$ to "outputs" z_1, $z_2 \in \mathcal{L}_2[0,\infty)$ provided

$$\gamma(\boldsymbol{A}) < \frac{1}{\gamma\big(\boldsymbol{K}(I-\boldsymbol{GK})^{-1}\big)}. \tag{3.6.2}$$

The stability of the system $\boldsymbol{P}$ is (by definition) equivalent to the internal stability of the nominal ($\boldsymbol{A} = 0$) closed loop. Therefore, provided $\boldsymbol{K}$ stabilizes the nominal loop, the closed-loop system will be internally stable for any model error $\boldsymbol{A}$ that satisfies (3.6.2).

Main points of the section

1. The feedback loop of Figure 3.7 is stable provided $\boldsymbol{P}$ is a stable linearly connected system with $\gamma(\boldsymbol{P}_{11})$ finite and $\gamma(\boldsymbol{P}_{11})\gamma(\boldsymbol{\Delta}) < 1$.
2. The stability robustness theorems of Chapter 2 can be extended to time-varying, nonlinear model errors by replacing conditions of the form $\overline{\sigma}\big(\boldsymbol{\Delta}(j\omega)\big) < \delta$ for all ω with $\gamma(\boldsymbol{\Delta}) < \delta$.

3.7 The bounded real lemma

In Chapter 2, we argued that performance and robustness issues in feedback system design could be posed as objectives for certain closed-loop transfer matrices of the

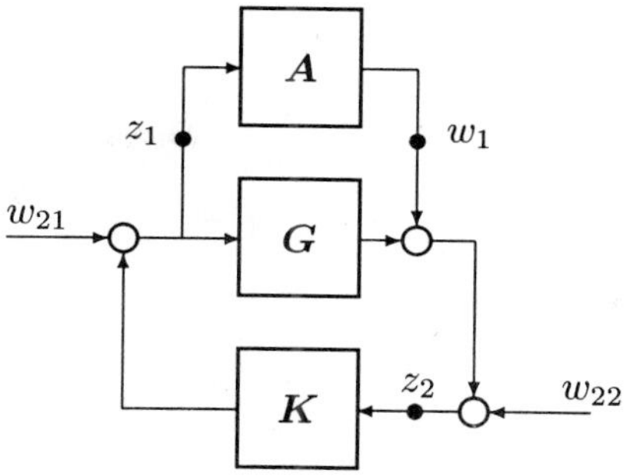

Figure 3.8: Feedback system with additive uncertainty.

form $\overline{\sigma}(\boldsymbol{G}(j\omega)) < \gamma$ for all ω. These objectives may be written as infinity norm objectives of the form $\|\boldsymbol{G}\|_\infty < \gamma$, since $\sup_\omega \overline{\sigma}(\boldsymbol{G}(j\omega)) = \|\boldsymbol{G}\|_\infty$. It is therefore important that we are able to determine whether $\|\boldsymbol{G}\|_\infty < \gamma$.

One approach is to plot $\overline{\sigma}(\boldsymbol{G}(j\omega))$ as a function of ω and determine the maximum by inspection. A more sophisticated version of this approach might involve a search over ω performed by a computer. Such an approach cannot determine whether $\|\boldsymbol{G}\|_\infty < \gamma$ because for any ω_0, the evaluation of $\overline{\sigma}(\boldsymbol{G}(j\omega_0))$ merely informs us that $\|\boldsymbol{G}\|_\infty \geq \overline{\sigma}(\boldsymbol{G}(j\omega_0))$. If we have smoothness information about $\overline{\sigma}(\boldsymbol{G}(j\omega))$, we can determine $\|\boldsymbol{G}\|_\infty$ from such an approach to any desired accuracy.

Alternatively, if we have a method of determining whether $\|\boldsymbol{G}\|_\infty < \gamma$, then $\|\boldsymbol{G}\|_\infty$ may be found from

$$\|\boldsymbol{G}\|_\infty = \inf_\gamma\{\|\boldsymbol{G}\|_\infty < \gamma\}.$$

This technique of finding $\|\boldsymbol{G}\|_\infty$ involves a search over $\gamma > 0$. For each γ, we test whether $\|\boldsymbol{G}\|_\infty < \gamma$ and then decrease or increase γ accordingly. The algorithm may be designed so that at any time we can stop and conclude that $\gamma_{low} < \|\boldsymbol{G}\|_\infty < \gamma_{high}$.

If $\boldsymbol{G}$ is a state-space system, determining whether $\|\boldsymbol{G}\|_\infty < \gamma$ is an algebraic problem: find conditions on a realization (A, B, C, D) of $\boldsymbol{G}$ that are equivalent to $\|\boldsymbol{G}\|_\infty < \gamma$. The bounded real lemma provides this characterization.[13]

Theorem 3.7.1 *Suppose $\boldsymbol{G} = D + C(sI - A)^{-1}B$ with A asymptotically stable. Then $\|\boldsymbol{G}\|_\infty < \gamma$ if and only if*

1. $\|D\| < \gamma$ *(equivalently $R = \gamma^2 I - D'D > 0$);*

2. *There exists $P = P'$ satisfying the Riccati equation*

$$P(A + BR^{-1}D'C) + (A + BR^{-1}D'C)'P \\ + PBR^{-1}B'P + C'(I + DR^{-1}D')C = 0 \qquad (3.7.1)$$

[13]In network theory, matrices $\boldsymbol{S} \in \mathcal{H}_\infty$ satisfying $\|\boldsymbol{S}\|_\infty < 1$ are called strictly bounded real.

such that $A + BR^{-1}(D'C + B'P)$ is asymptotically stable.

Furthermore, when such a P exists, $P \geq 0$.

Example 3.7.1. Consider the system $\boldsymbol{g} = \frac{1}{s-a}$, with $a < 0$ and realization $(a, 1, 1, 0)$. The Riccati equation (3.7.1) is

$$2ap + p^2/\gamma^2 + 1 = 0,$$

which has solutions $p = \gamma^2(-a \pm \sqrt{a^2 - \gamma^{-2}})$. Now $a + p/\gamma^2 = \pm\sqrt{a^2 - \gamma^{-2}}$ is either pure imaginary or real and therefore can be asymptotically stable only if real. In this case, the solution with the minus sign is asymptotically stable. Thus $\|\boldsymbol{g}\|_\infty < \gamma$ if and only if $\gamma > 1/|a|$. Hence,

$$\|\boldsymbol{g}\|_\infty = \inf_\gamma [\gamma > \|\boldsymbol{g}\|_\infty] = 1/|a|. \qquad \nabla$$

Two proofs of the bounded real lemma will be given. The first is based on purely algebraic arguments, while the second is based on an optimization problem. The first proof shows that the question of whether P exists may be settled by an eigenvalue calculation and provides an algebraic procedure for determining P. The second proof shows that P may be determined, when it exists, as the steady-state solution to a matrix Riccati differential equation. It is also applicable to time-varying systems—we can determine whether $\|\boldsymbol{G}\|_{[0,T]} < \gamma$ and whether $\gamma(\boldsymbol{G}) < \gamma$. The optimal control proof also provides a preview of the approach we will use to solve the controller synthesis problem.

Before proceeding to these complete proofs, we present an sufficiency argument based on spectral factorization.

Spectral factorization proof of sufficiency

Suppose there is a transfer function matrix $\boldsymbol{W} \in \mathcal{RH}_\infty$ such that $\boldsymbol{W}^{-1} \in \mathcal{RH}_\infty$ and

$$\gamma^2 I - \boldsymbol{G}^\sim(j\omega)\boldsymbol{G}(j\omega) = \boldsymbol{W}^\sim(j\omega)\boldsymbol{W}(j\omega). \qquad (3.7.2)$$

Any such transfer function matrix $\boldsymbol{W}$ is called a *spectral factor* of $\gamma^2 I - \boldsymbol{G}^\sim\boldsymbol{G}$. Since $\boldsymbol{W}^{-1} \in \mathcal{RH}_\infty$, the right-hand side of (3.7.2) is strictly positive for all real ω. Therefore, if a spectral factor $\boldsymbol{W}$ exists, $\|\boldsymbol{G}\|_\infty < \gamma$.

Conditions 1 and 2 of the bounded real lemma, namely that $R > 0$ and that P exists, enable us to construct a spectral factor of $\gamma^2 I - \boldsymbol{G}^\sim\boldsymbol{G}$. Let W be any nonsingular matrix such that $W'W = \gamma^2 I - D'D$, define $L = -(W')^{-1}(D'C + B'P)$ and define

$$\boldsymbol{W} = W + L(sI - A)^{-1}B. \qquad (3.7.3)$$

Note that $\boldsymbol{W}^{-1}$ has realization $(A - BW^{-1}L, BW^{-1}, -W^{-1}L, W^{-1})$. Since A and $A - BW^{-1}L$ are asymptotically stable, $\boldsymbol{W}$ and $\boldsymbol{W}^{-1}$ are in $\mathcal{RH}_\infty$. From (3.7.1) and the definition of W and L, we obtain

$$\begin{aligned} PA + A'P + \begin{bmatrix} C' & L' \end{bmatrix}\begin{bmatrix} C \\ L \end{bmatrix} &= 0 \\ \begin{bmatrix} \gamma^{-1}D' & \gamma^{-1}W' \end{bmatrix}\begin{bmatrix} C \\ L \end{bmatrix} + \gamma^{-1}B'P &= 0 \\ \begin{bmatrix} \gamma^{-1}D' & \gamma^{-1}W' \end{bmatrix}\begin{bmatrix} \gamma^{-1}D \\ \gamma^{-1}W \end{bmatrix} &= I. \end{aligned}$$

By Theorem 3.2.1, the transfer function matrix

$$\gamma^{-1}\begin{bmatrix} \boldsymbol{G} \\ \boldsymbol{W} \end{bmatrix} \stackrel{s}{=} \left[\begin{array}{c|c} A & \gamma^{-1}B \\ \hline C & \gamma^{-1}D \\ L & \gamma^{-1}W \end{array}\right]$$

is allpass. Hence $\boldsymbol{G}^{\sim}\boldsymbol{G} + \boldsymbol{W}^{\sim}\boldsymbol{W} = \gamma^2 I$ and we conclude that $\boldsymbol{W}$ is the desired spectral factor.

Note

Theorem 3.7.1 characterizes state-space systems that satisfy $\|\boldsymbol{G}\|_\infty < \gamma$. The term "bounded real lemma" generally refers to the characterization of state-space systems that satisfy $\|\boldsymbol{G}\|_\infty \leq \gamma$:

> If A is asymptotically stable, then $\|\boldsymbol{G}\|_\infty \leq \gamma$ if and only if there exist real matrices $P \geq 0$, L and W satisfying
>
> $$\begin{aligned} PA + A'P + C'C &= -L'L \\ D'C + B'P &= -W'L \\ \gamma^2 I - D'D &= W'W. \end{aligned}$$

The sufficiency proof follows by the spectral factorization argument above. When $\|\boldsymbol{G}\|_\infty = \gamma$, the spectral factor $\boldsymbol{W} = W + L(sI - A)^{-1}B$ will have zeros on the imaginary axis. The strict inequality case is technically easier and is all we require.

3.7.1 An algebraic proof

The question of whether $\|\boldsymbol{G}\|_\infty < \gamma$ may be settled by determining whether some object has imaginary axis roots. To see this, choose any $\omega_0 \in \mathbb{R} \cup \infty$. If $\overline{\sigma}(\boldsymbol{G}(j\omega_0)) \geq \gamma$, then $\|\boldsymbol{G}\|_\infty \geq \gamma$. If, on the other hand, $\overline{\sigma}(\boldsymbol{G}(j\omega_0)) < \gamma$, then $\overline{\sigma}(\boldsymbol{G}(j\omega)) < \gamma$ for all ω if and only if $\gamma - \overline{\sigma}(\boldsymbol{G}(j\omega))$ is never zero. It is convenient to take $w_0 = \infty$, which yields the following lemma. It is worth noting that this result has the added advantage of not requiring that A be asymptotically stable.

Lemma 3.7.2 *Suppose $\boldsymbol{G} = D + C(sI - A)^{-1}B$ in which A has no imaginary axis eigenvalue. Then*

$$\sup_{\omega} \overline{\sigma}\big(\boldsymbol{G}(j\omega)\big) < \gamma \tag{3.7.4}$$

if and only if:

1. $\|D\| < \gamma$ *(equivalently $R = \gamma^2 I - D'D > 0$);*

2. $$H = \begin{bmatrix} A & 0 \\ -C'C & -A' \end{bmatrix} - \begin{bmatrix} -B \\ C'D \end{bmatrix} R^{-1} \begin{bmatrix} D'C & B' \end{bmatrix} \tag{3.7.5}$$

   has no eigenvalue on the imaginary axis.

Proof. Condition 1 is obtained from $\|D\| = \overline{\sigma}\big(\boldsymbol{G}(\infty)\big) \leq \sup_\omega \overline{\sigma}\big(\boldsymbol{G}(j\omega)\big) < \gamma$. Assuming now that $\|D\| < \gamma$,

$$\begin{aligned} \sup_{\omega} \overline{\sigma}\big(\boldsymbol{G}(j\omega)\big) < \gamma \quad &\Leftrightarrow \quad \gamma^2 I - \boldsymbol{G}^{\sim}(j\omega)\boldsymbol{G}(j\omega) > 0 \quad \text{for all } \omega \\ &\Leftrightarrow \quad det\big(\gamma^2 I - \boldsymbol{G}^{\sim}(j\omega)\boldsymbol{G}(j\omega)\big) \neq 0 \quad \text{for any } \omega. \end{aligned}$$

Now

$$\gamma^2 I - \boldsymbol{G}^{\sim}\boldsymbol{G} \stackrel{s}{=} \left[\begin{array}{cc|c} A & 0 & -B \\ -C'C & -A' & C'D \\ \hline D'C & B' & \gamma^2 I - D'D \end{array}\right]. \tag{3.7.6}$$

Since A has no eigenvalue on the imaginary axis, the realization in (3.7.6) has no uncontrollable or unobservable mode on the imaginary axis. Therefore, $\gamma^2 I - \boldsymbol{G}^{\sim}\boldsymbol{G}$ has no zero on the imaginary axis if and only if H has no eigenvalue on the imaginary axis. ■

Example 3.7.2. Consider $\boldsymbol{g} = \frac{1}{s-a}$ again. Then

$$H = \begin{bmatrix} a & \gamma^{-2} \\ -1 & -a \end{bmatrix} \tag{3.7.7}$$

has eigenvalues $\pm\sqrt{a^2 - \gamma^{-2}}$. Clearly H has no imaginary axis eigenvalue if and only if $\gamma > 1/|a| = \|\boldsymbol{g}\|_\infty$. ▽

The next result links the spectral condition on the Hamiltonian matrix (3.7.5) with the existence of a stabilizing solution to the Riccati equation (3.7.1).

Lemma 3.7.3 *Suppose A is asymptotically stable, $\|D\| < \gamma$ and H is as in (3.7.5). Then H has no imaginary axis eigenvalue if and only if there exists a matrix P satisfying Condition 2 of Theorem 3.7.1. Furthermore, $P \geq 0$.*

Proof. Suppose P satisfying Condition 2 exists. Then

$$\begin{bmatrix} I & 0 \\ -P & I \end{bmatrix} H \begin{bmatrix} I & 0 \\ P & I \end{bmatrix} = \begin{bmatrix} \widehat{A} & BR^{-1}B' \\ 0 & -\widehat{A}' \end{bmatrix},$$

in which $\widehat{A} = A + BR^{-1}(D'C + B'P)$. Since $\widehat{A}$ is asymptotically stable, it follows that H has no imaginary axis eigenvalue.

Now suppose H has no imaginary axis eigenvalue. Since H is Hamiltonian, its eigenvalues are symmetric with respect to the imaginary axis (see Problem 3.21) and since none are on the axis, H has n eigenvalues with strictly negative real part. Let

$$H \begin{bmatrix} X_1 \\ X_2 \end{bmatrix} = \begin{bmatrix} X_1 \\ X_2 \end{bmatrix} \Lambda, \tag{3.7.8}$$

in which Λ is an $n \times n$, asymptotically stable and real matrix, and $\begin{bmatrix} X_1 \\ X_2 \end{bmatrix}$ is a $2n \times n$ real matrix with full column rank, in which n is the dimension of A. From the properties of Hamiltonian matrices, $X_2'X_1 = X_1'X_2$ (see Problem 3.21).

Claim X_1 is nonsingular. Suppose, to the contrary, that $X_1 z = 0$, $z \neq 0$. From (3.7.8), we have

$$(A + BR^{-1}D'C)X_1 + BR^{-1}B'X_2 = X_1\Lambda. \tag{3.7.9}$$

Hence

$$X_2'(A + BR^{-1}D'C)X_1 + X_2'BR^{-1}B'X_2 = X_2'X_1\Lambda = X_1'X_2\Lambda.$$

Multiplying by z' on the left and by z on the right, and noting that $R^{-1} > 0$ by assumption, we obtain $B'X_2 z = 0$. Now multiply (3.7.9) by z to obtain $X_1\Lambda z = 0$. Iterating this argument yields

$$\begin{aligned} X_1 z = 0 \quad &\Rightarrow \quad \begin{bmatrix} X_1 \\ B'X_2 \end{bmatrix} \Lambda^k z = 0 \text{ for } k = 0, 1, 2, \ldots \\ &\Rightarrow \quad (\Lambda, \begin{bmatrix} X_1 \\ B'X_2 \end{bmatrix}) \text{ is not observable.} \end{aligned}$$

Consequently, by the Popov-Belevich-Hautus observability test (see Kailath [105], for example), there exists $y \neq 0$ and λ such that

$$\begin{bmatrix} \Lambda - \lambda I \\ X_1 \\ B'X_2 \end{bmatrix} y = 0.$$

Note that $\mathrm{R}_e(\lambda) < 0$ because Λ is asymptotically stable. From (3.7.8) we have that

$$-C'(I + DR^{-1}D')CX_1 - (A' + C'DR^{-1}B')X_2 = X_2\Lambda.$$

Multiplying by y we get $-A'X_2y = \lambda X_2y$, which we may rearrange to obtain $(\lambda I + A')X_2y = 0$. Because A is asymptotically stable and $\mathrm{R}_e(\lambda) < 0$, $\lambda I + A'$ is nonsingular and therefore $X_2y = 0$. We now have $X_1y = 0$ and $X_2y = 0$, which contradicts the full rank property of $\begin{bmatrix} X_1 \\ X_2 \end{bmatrix}$. We conclude that X_1 is nonsingular.

To obtain P, set $P = X_2X_1^{-1}$. It is easy to show that (3.7.1) is satisfied and that

$$A + BR^{-1}(D'C + B'P) = X_1\Lambda X_1^{-1},$$

which is asymptotically stable. (The required calculations are requested in Problem 3.21.)

To show that $P \geq 0$, write the Riccati equation (3.7.1) as

$$PA + A'P + (D'C + B'P)'R^{-1}(D'C + B'P) + C'C = 0. \tag{3.7.10}$$

This, together with A stable and $R^{-1} > 0$, implies $P \geq 0$, since P is the observability gramian of $\left(A, \begin{bmatrix} C \\ R^{-\frac{1}{2}}(D'C + B'P) \end{bmatrix}\right)$. ■

The bounded real lemma is obtained by combining these two results.

3.7.2 An optimal control proof

Instead of using the property $\|\boldsymbol{G}\|_\infty = \sup_\omega \overline{\sigma}\big(\boldsymbol{G}(j\omega)\big)$, we now use the property that, for a stable system,

$$\|\boldsymbol{G}\|_\infty = \sup_{w \in \mathcal{L}_2[0,\infty)} \frac{\|z\|_2}{\|w\|_2},$$

in which $z = \boldsymbol{G}w$. Hence $\|\boldsymbol{G}\|_\infty < \gamma$ if and only if there is an $\epsilon > 0$ such that $\|z\|_2^2 - \gamma^2\|w\|_2^2 \leq -\epsilon\|w\|_2^2$ for all $w \in \mathcal{L}_2[0,\infty)$. The optimal control problem

$$\max_{w \in \mathcal{L}_2[0,\infty)} \left\{ J(w) = \int_0^\infty \big(z'(t)z(t) - \gamma^2 w'(t)w(t)\big)\, dt \right\}$$

is therefore intimately related to the question at hand.

Initially, we consider the optimization problem on the finite time interval $[0, T]$; this determines whether the $\mathcal{L}_2[0, T]$ induced norm is strictly less than γ. For this work, there is no advantage in assuming that the system is time-invariant. By allowing the horizon length T to be arbitrary, we may determine whether the incremental gain $\gamma(\boldsymbol{G})$ is strictly less than γ. For the infinite-horizon problem, the main technical issue is to show that the maximizing w is actually in $\mathcal{L}_2[0,\infty)$ rather than $\mathcal{L}_{2e}$. For this work we restrict our attention to the time-invariant case.

The finite-horizon case

Consider the state-space system

$$\dot{x}(t) = A(t)x + B(t)w(t), \qquad x(0) = 0, \tag{3.7.11}$$
$$z(t) = C(t)x(t). \tag{3.7.12}$$

To simplify the expressions, we have assumed that $D(t) = 0$, since this assumption results in no loss of generality (see Problem 4.16). In the following, the time dependence is not shown explicitly. Define the performance index

$$J_T(w) = \int_0^T (z'z - \gamma^2 w'w)\,dt. \tag{3.7.13}$$

Theorem 3.7.4 *There exists an $\epsilon > 0$ such that $J_T(w) \leq -\epsilon\|w\|^2_{2,[0,T]}$ for all $w \in \mathcal{L}_2[0,T]$ if and only if the Riccati differential equation*

$$-\dot{P} = PA + A'P + \gamma^{-2}PBB'P + C'C, \qquad P(T) = 0 \tag{3.7.14}$$

has a solution on $[0,T]$.

If the solution $P(t)$ exists on $[0,T]$, then $P(t) \geq 0$ for any $t \in [0,T]$.

An alternative statement of the result is that $\|\boldsymbol{G}\|_{[0,T]} < \gamma$ if and only if (3.7.14) has a solution on $[0,T]$.

Recall that for a linear system the incremental gain is given by

$$\gamma(\boldsymbol{G}) = \inf\{\gamma : \|\boldsymbol{G}w\|_{2,[0,T]} \leq \gamma\|w\|_{2,[0,T]} \text{ for all } w \in \mathcal{L}_{2e} \text{ and for all } T\}.$$

Hence $\gamma(\boldsymbol{G}) < \gamma$ if and only if the Riccati differential equation (3.7.14) has a solution on $[0,T]$ for all finite T.

Example 3.7.3. We return to the system $\boldsymbol{g} = \frac{1}{s-a}$, $a < 0$, once more. Let $\tau = T - t$, $\lambda = \sqrt{a^2 - \gamma^{-2}}$, and note that $\pm\lambda$ are the eigenvalues of H in (3.7.7).

When λ is imaginary (*i.e.*, $\gamma \leq 1/|a|$) let $\lambda = j\omega$. The solution to the Riccati equation is then given by

$$p(t) = \frac{1}{\omega\cot(\omega\tau) - a}.$$

Hence $p(t)$ exists only for $T - t < \frac{\tan^{-1}(\omega/a)}{\omega}$, so that $\|\boldsymbol{g}\|_{[0,T]} < \gamma$ if and only if $T < \frac{\tan^{-1}(\omega/a)}{\omega}$.

In the case when λ is real,

$$p(t) = \frac{1}{\lambda\coth(\lambda\tau) - a},$$

which exists for all $t \leq T$, since the denominator can never be zero for $\tau \geq 0$. Evaluating $p(0)$ in the limit as $T \to \infty$ gives

$$\lim_{T\to\infty} p(0) = \frac{1}{\lambda - a} = -\gamma^2(a + \sqrt{a^2 - \gamma^{-2}}).$$

Thus, when $\gamma > \|\boldsymbol{g}\|_\infty$, the solution to the Riccati differential equation converges to the stabilizing solution to the algebraic Riccati equation. ∇

Proof of sufficiency

We prove sufficiency using a time-varying, finite-horizon version of the spectral factorization argument.

Suppose the solution $P(t)$ exists and define

$$\boldsymbol{W} \stackrel{s}{=} \left[\begin{array}{c|c} A & B \\ \hline -\gamma^{-1}B'P & \gamma I \end{array}\right].$$

Then

$$\gamma^{-1}\begin{bmatrix} \boldsymbol{G} \\ \boldsymbol{W} \end{bmatrix} \stackrel{s}{=} \left[\begin{array}{c|c} A & \gamma^{-1}B \\ \hline C & 0 \\ -\gamma^{-1}B'P & I \end{array}\right]$$

is allpass on $\mathcal{L}_2[0,T]$ by Theorem 3.2.1. Hence $\|z\|_{2,[0,T]}^2 + \|\eta\|_{2,[0,T]}^2 = \|\gamma w\|_{2,[0,T]}^2$, in which $\eta = \boldsymbol{W}w$, for all $w \in \mathcal{L}_2[0,T]$. Since $\boldsymbol{W}$ has a nonsingular D-matrix, $\boldsymbol{W}^{-1}$ exists and $\|\boldsymbol{W}^{-1}\|_{[0,T]} < \infty$. Setting $\epsilon = 1/\|\boldsymbol{W}^{-1}\|_{[0,T]}^2$, we have

$$\|z\|_{2,[0,T]}^2 - \|\gamma w\|_{2,[0,T]}^2 = -\|\eta\|_{2,[0,T]}^2 \le -\epsilon\|w\|_{2,[0,T]}^2,$$

which is equivalent to $J_T(w) \le -\epsilon\|w\|_2^2$, for all $w \in \mathcal{L}_2[0,T]$.

Proof of necessity

We prove necessity using a conjugate point argument frequently used in the calculus of variations and optimal control.

Conjugate points:

> Two times t_0 and t_f, with $t_0 \le t_f$, are conjugate points of the two-point-boundary-value problem (TPBVP)
>
> $$\begin{bmatrix} \dot{x}^*(t) \\ \dot{\lambda}(t) \end{bmatrix} = \begin{bmatrix} A & \gamma^{-2}BB' \\ -C'C & -A' \end{bmatrix}\begin{bmatrix} x^*(t) \\ \lambda(t) \end{bmatrix}, \quad \begin{bmatrix} x^*(t_0) \\ \lambda(t_f) \end{bmatrix} = \begin{bmatrix} 0 \\ 0 \end{bmatrix} \tag{3.7.15}$$
>
> if (3.7.15) has a *nontrivial* solution.[14]

Equation (3.7.15) is a two-point-boundary-value problem because there is an initial condition on x^* and a terminal condition on λ.

[14]The trivial solution is the solution $x^* \equiv 0$ and $\lambda \equiv 0$.

Example 3.7.4. If $a^2 - \gamma^{-2} < 0$, then the TPBVP

$$\frac{d}{dt}\begin{bmatrix} x^* \\ \lambda \end{bmatrix} = \begin{bmatrix} a & \gamma^{-2} \\ -1 & -a \end{bmatrix}\begin{bmatrix} x^* \\ \lambda \end{bmatrix}, \qquad \begin{bmatrix} x^*(t_0) \\ \lambda(t_f) \end{bmatrix} = \begin{bmatrix} 0 \\ 0 \end{bmatrix}$$

has the nontrivial solution

$$\begin{bmatrix} x^*(t) \\ \lambda(t) \end{bmatrix} = \begin{bmatrix} \sin\big(\omega_0(t-t_0)\big) \\ \gamma^2\omega_0\cos\big(\omega_0(t-t_0)\big) - \gamma^2 a\sin\big(w_0(t-t_0)\big) \end{bmatrix}$$

whenever

$$\cot\big(\omega_0(t_f-t_0)\big) = \frac{a}{\omega_0}.$$

In the above, $\omega_0 = \sqrt{\gamma^{-2}-a^2}$. ▽

We now have the following result, which can be thought of as a finite-horizon version of Lemma 3.7.2

Lemma 3.7.5 *Suppose $t^* \in [0,T]$ and that there exists an $\epsilon > 0$ such that $J_T(w) \le -\epsilon\|w\|^2_{2,[0,T]}$ for all $w \in \mathcal{L}_2[0,T]$. Then t^* and T are not conjugate points of the TPBVP (3.7.15).*

Proof. For $t^* = T$, the result is trivial. Now consider $0 \le t^* < T$ and let x^*, λ be *any* solution to (3.7.15). Define

$$\bar{w}(t) = \begin{cases} \gamma^{-2}B'\lambda(t) & t > t^* \\ 0 & t \le t^*. \end{cases}$$

Apply $\bar{w}$ to the system (3.7.11) and note that $x(t) = 0$ for $t \le t^*$ and $x(t) = x^*(t)$ for $t \ge t^*$. This gives

$$\begin{aligned} J_T(\bar{w}) &= \int_0^T (z'z - \gamma^2\bar{w}'\bar{w})\,dt \\ &= \int_{t^*}^T (x^{*\prime}C'Cx^* - \gamma^{-2}\lambda'BB'\lambda)\,dt \qquad \text{as } \bar{w}(t) = 0 \text{ for } t \le t^* \\ &= \int_{t^*}^T \big(-x^{*\prime}(\dot\lambda + A'\lambda) + (Ax^* - \dot{x}^*)'\lambda\big)\,dt \\ &= -\int_{t^*}^T \frac{d}{dt}(x^{*\prime}\lambda)\,dt \\ &= (x^{*\prime}\lambda)(t^*) - (x^{*\prime}\lambda)(T) = 0. \end{aligned}$$

Since $J_T(w) \le -\epsilon\|w\|^2_{2,[0,T]}$ for all w, we must have $\|\bar{w}\|^2_{2,[0,T]} = 0$, giving $B'\lambda(t) = 0$ on $[t^*, T]$. This reduces the TPBVP to

$$\begin{bmatrix} \dot{x}^* \\ \dot\lambda \end{bmatrix}(t) = \begin{bmatrix} A & 0 \\ -C'C & -A' \end{bmatrix}\begin{bmatrix} x^* \\ \lambda \end{bmatrix}(t), \qquad \begin{bmatrix} x^*(t^*) \\ \lambda(T) \end{bmatrix} = \begin{bmatrix} 0 \\ 0 \end{bmatrix}$$

and we conclude that $x^* \equiv 0$ and $\lambda \equiv 0$. That is, t^* and T are not conjugate points, since any solution to the TPBVP has been shown to be trivial. ■

Lemma 3.7.6 *If there exists an* $\epsilon > 0$ *such that* $J_T(w) \leq -\epsilon\|w\|^2_{2,[0,T]}$ *for all* $w \in \mathcal{L}_2[0,T]$*, then the Riccati equation (3.7.14) has a solution on* $[0,T]$ *and* $P(t) \geq 0$.

Proof. Let $\Phi(t,T)$ be the transition matrix associated with the differential equation (3.7.15). Imposing the boundary condition $\lambda(T) = 0$, we have that

$$\begin{bmatrix} x^* \\ \lambda \end{bmatrix}(t) = \begin{bmatrix} \Phi_{11} \\ \Phi_{21} \end{bmatrix}(t,T)x^*(T).$$

Since the transition matrix $\Phi(t,T)$ is nonsingular for all t, T,

$$\begin{bmatrix} x^*(t) \\ \lambda(t) \end{bmatrix} = 0 \Leftrightarrow x^*(T) = 0. \tag{3.7.16}$$

We now show that $\Phi_{11}(t,T)$ is nonsingular for all $t \in [0,T]$. We do this by showing that if $\Phi_{11}(t^*,T)v = 0$ for some t^* and some v, then $v = 0$. Choose $t^* \in [0,T]$ and let v be *any* vector such that $\Phi_{11}(t^*,T)v = 0$. Setting $t_f = T$, $t_0 = t^*$ and imposing the boundary condition $x^*(T) = v$ results in a solution to (3.7.15). By Lemma 3.7.5, t^* and T cannot be conjugate points and we conclude that $x^*(t) = 0$ and $\lambda(t) = 0$ on $[t^*,T]$. It now follows from (3.7.16) that $v = x^*(T) = 0$, which means that $\Phi_{11}(t^*,T)$ is nonsingular. Since t^* was arbitrary, the claim that $\Phi_{11}(t,T)$ is nonsingular for any $t \in [0,T]$ is established.

It can be verified (Problem 3.22) that $P(t) = \Phi_{21}(t,T)\Phi_{11}^{-1}(t,T)$ is the solution to the Riccati equation (3.7.14).

To see that $P(t) \geq 0$, note that $X(t) = P(t) - Q(t)$, in which $Q(t)$ is the observability gramian (see (3.1.6)), satisfies

$$-\dot{X} = XA + A'X + \gamma^{-2}PBB'P, \qquad X(T) = 0.$$

That is, X is the observability gramian of $(A, \gamma^{-1}B'P)$. Hence $P - Q \geq 0$ and we conclude that $P \geq 0$. ∎

Example 3.7.5. The solution to

$$\frac{d}{dt}\begin{bmatrix} \phi_{11} \\ \phi_{21} \end{bmatrix}(t,T) = \begin{bmatrix} a & \gamma^{-2} \\ -1 & -a \end{bmatrix}\begin{bmatrix} \phi_{11} \\ \phi_{21} \end{bmatrix}(t,T), \quad \begin{bmatrix} \phi_{11} \\ \phi_{21} \end{bmatrix}(T,T) = \begin{bmatrix} I \\ 0 \end{bmatrix}$$

is given by

$$\begin{bmatrix} \phi_{11} \\ \phi_{21} \end{bmatrix}(t,T) = \frac{1}{2\lambda}\begin{bmatrix} \lambda(e^{\lambda\tau} + e^{-\lambda\tau}) - a(e^{\lambda\tau} - e^{-\lambda\tau}) \\ e^{\lambda\tau} - e^{-\lambda\tau} \end{bmatrix},$$

in which $\tau = T - t$ and $\lambda = \sqrt{a^2 - \gamma^{-2}}$. It can be verified that $\phi_{21}(t,T)\phi_{11}^{-1}(t,T)$ yields the solutions to the Riccati equation that are given in Example 3.7.3. ▽

The infinite-horizon case

We now turn our attention to the case when the time horizon T is infinite and the matrices A, B and C are constant. Our aim is to show that if $\|\boldsymbol{G}\|_\infty < \gamma$, the algebraic Riccati equation

$$0 = \Pi A + A'\Pi + \gamma^{-2}\Pi BB'\Pi + C'C \tag{3.7.17}$$

has a solution such that $A + \gamma^{-2}BB'\Pi$ is asymptotically stable and that such a solution is nonnegative definite. Our approach is to examine the behavior of the solution to the Riccati differential equation in the limit as $T \to \infty$.

The argument we use to show that $P(t)$ converges to the desired solution Π (when $\|\boldsymbol{G}\|_\infty < \gamma$) depends on a monotonicity property of the solution $P(t)$. Specifically, the solution $P(t)$ to (3.7.14) is monotonically nonincreasing as a function of t when the matrices A, B and C are constant. To see this, differentiate (3.7.14) to obtain

$$-\ddot{P} = \dot{P}(A + \gamma^{-2}BB'P) + (A + \gamma^{-2}BB'P)'\dot{P}, \quad \dot{P}(T) = -C'C.$$

If Φ is the transition matrix associated with $(A + \gamma^{-2}BB'P)'$, then

$$\dot{P}(t) = -\Phi(t,T)C'C\Phi'(t,T) \leq 0,$$

which establishes the desired monotonicity property.

Lemma 3.7.7 *Suppose the matrices A, B and C are constant, that A is asymptotically stable and that*

$$\begin{aligned} \dot{x}(t) &= Ax(t) + Bw(t), \quad x(0) = 0 \\ z(t) &= Cx(t). \end{aligned}$$

Define the cost function

$$J(w) = \int_0^\infty (z'z - \gamma^2 w'w)\, dt. \tag{3.7.18}$$

If there exists an $\epsilon > 0$ such that $J(w) \leq -\epsilon\|w\|_2^2$ for all $w \in \mathcal{L}_2[0,\infty)$, then:

1. *The Riccati differential equation (3.7.14) has a solution $P(t,T)$ on $[0,T]$ for all finite T.*

2. *There exists a constant β such that $P(t,T) \leq \beta I$ for all $t \in [0,T]$ and all finite T.*

3. *$\Pi = \lim_{T\to\infty} P(t,T)$ exists and satisfies (3.7.17). Furthermore, $\Pi \geq 0$ and $A + \gamma^{-2}BB'\Pi$ has no eigenvalue on the imaginary axis.*

4. *$A + \gamma^{-2}BB'\Pi$ is asymptotically stable.*

Proof.

1. Let $T \geq 0$ be arbitrary, let $\bar{w}$ be an arbitrary $\mathcal{L}_2[0,T]$ signal and define the $\mathcal{L}_2[0,\infty)$ signal w by $\boldsymbol{P}_T w = \bar{w}$ and $w(t) = 0$ for $t > T$. Then $J_T(\bar{w}) \leq J(w) \leq -\epsilon\|w\|_2^2 = -\epsilon\|\bar{w}\|_{2,[0,T]}^2$. Hence $P(t,T)$ exists.

2. Consider the dynamics

$$\begin{aligned} \dot{x} &= Ax + Bw, \qquad x(0) = x_0 \\ z &= Cx, \end{aligned}$$

in which $w \in \mathcal{L}_2[0,\infty)$ is arbitrary and x_0 is arbitrary. Write $z = z_{x0} + z_w$, in which z_{x_0} is that part of the response due to x_0, and z_w is that part of the response due to w. Note that $\|z\|_2^2 \leq \|z_{x_0}\|_2^2 + \|z_w\|_2^2 + 2\|z_{x_0}\|_2\|z_w\|_2$. Since A is asymptotically stable, $\|z_{x_0}\|_2 \leq \alpha\|x_0\|$ for some $\alpha > 0$. Thus

$$\begin{aligned} J(w) &\leq \int_0^\infty (z_w' z_w - \gamma^2 w'w)\,dt + \alpha\|x_0\|(\alpha\|x_0\| + 2\|z_w\|_2) \\ &\leq -\epsilon\|w\|_2^2 + \alpha\|x_0\|(\alpha\|x_0\| + 2\gamma\|w\|_2) \\ &= -\epsilon(\|w\|_2 - \frac{\alpha\gamma}{\epsilon}\|x_0\|)^2 + \alpha^2(1 + \frac{\gamma^2}{\epsilon})\|x_0\|^2 \\ &\leq \alpha^2\left(1 + \frac{\gamma^2}{\epsilon}\right)\|x_0\|^2. \end{aligned}$$

The particular input

$$w(t) = \begin{cases} \gamma^{-2}B'P(t)x(t) & t \in [0,T] \\ 0 & t > T \end{cases}$$

gives

$$\begin{aligned} J(w) &\geq \int_0^T (z'z - \gamma^2 w'w)\,dt \quad \text{since } w(t) = 0 \text{ for } t > T \\ &= -\int_0^T \frac{d}{dt}(x'Px)\,dt \\ &= x_0' P(0,T) x_0. \end{aligned}$$

on substituting for w and P. Hence

$$x_0'P(0,T)x_0 \leq \alpha^2\left(1 + \frac{\gamma^2}{\epsilon}\right)\|x_0\|^2 \text{ for all } x_0 \text{ and all } T.$$

The monotonicity of $P(t,T)$ ensures that $P(t,T) \leq \alpha^2(1 + \frac{\gamma^2}{\epsilon})I$ for $t \in [0,T]$.

3. Since $0 \leq P(t,T) \leq \beta I$ and $P(t,T)$ is monotonic, $\Pi(t) = \lim_{T\to\infty} P(t,T)$ exists for all t. To see that $\Pi(t)$ is constant, we observe that

$$\begin{aligned}\Pi(t_1) &= \lim_{T\to\infty} P(t_1,T)\\ &= \lim_{T\to\infty} P(t_2, T+t_2-t_1) \quad \text{by time-invariance}\\ &= \lim_{T\to\infty} P(t_2,T)\\ &= \Pi(t_2).\end{aligned}$$

To see that Π satisfies (3.7.17), we make use of the fact that a solution of the differential equation (3.7.14) depends continuously on the terminal condition (see Problem 3.22). That is, if $P(t,T,\Sigma)$ denotes the solution to (3.7.14) with terminal condition $P(T) = \Sigma$, then $P(t,T,\Sigma)$ is continuous in Σ. Note also that, by definition, $P(t,T,\Sigma) = P\big(t,T_1,P(T_1,T,\Sigma)\big)$, for any $t \leq T_1 \leq T$. Therefore

$$\begin{aligned}\Pi &= \lim_{T\to\infty} P(t,T,0)\\ &= \lim_{T\to\infty} P\big(t,T_1,P(T_1,T,0)\big)\\ &= P\big(t,T_1,\lim_{T\to\infty} P(T_1,T,0)\big) \quad \text{by continuity}\\ &= P(t,T_1,\Pi).\end{aligned}$$

That is, Π is a solution to the Riccati equation (3.7.14) with terminal condition Π. Noting that $\dot{\Pi} = 0$, we see that Π satisfies (3.7.17). $\Pi \geq 0$ because $P(t) \geq 0$.

To show that $A+\gamma^{-2}BB'\Pi$ has no imaginary axis eigenvalue, we observe that $\|z\|_2^2 - \gamma^2\|w\|_2^2 = -\gamma^2\|w-w^*\|_2^2$ has the transfer function matrix form

$$\gamma^2 I - \boldsymbol{G}^\sim \boldsymbol{G} = \boldsymbol{W}^\sim \boldsymbol{W}, \tag{3.7.19}$$

in which $\boldsymbol{G} = C(sI-A)^{-1}B$ and

$$\boldsymbol{W} = \gamma I - \gamma^{-1}B'\Pi(sI-A)^{-1}B. \tag{3.7.20}$$

(This follows by observing that $\boldsymbol{W}w = \gamma(w-w^*)$, or by direct calculation, or by Theorem 3.2.1). Since $\|\boldsymbol{G}\|_\infty < \gamma$, we have $\boldsymbol{W}'(j\omega)\boldsymbol{W}(j\omega) > 0$, so $\boldsymbol{W}$ has no zeros on the imaginary axis. Since A is asymptotically stable, the realization (3.7.20) has no uncontrollable or unobservable modes on the imaginary axis and we conclude that $A+\gamma^{-2}BB'\Pi$ has no eigenvalue on the imaginary axis.

4. To show that Π is the stabilizing solution, subtract (3.7.14) from (3.7.17) and rearrange to obtain

$$\begin{aligned}\dot{P} &= (\Pi-P)(A+\gamma^{-2}BB'\Pi) + (A+\gamma^{-2}BB'\Pi)'(\Pi-P)\\ &\quad -\gamma^{-2}(\Pi-P)BB'(\Pi-P), \qquad P(T)=0.\end{aligned} \tag{3.7.21}$$

We now make the assumption that $(\Pi - P)(t)$ is nonsingular for all finite t. The extension to the case when this is not necessarily true is called for in Problem 3.24. Let $V(t) = \big(\Pi - P(T-t)\big)^{-1}$. Since $\dot{V}(t) = V(t)\frac{d}{dt}\big(P(T-t)\big)V(t)$, we have from (3.7.21) that

$$\dot{V}(t) = -(A+\gamma^{-2}BB'\Pi)V(t) - V(t)(A+\gamma^{-2}BB'\Pi)' + \gamma^{-2}BB'. \quad (3.7.22)$$

If $y \neq 0$ is such that $(A+\gamma^{-2}BB'\Pi)'y = \lambda y$, then

$$\frac{d}{dt}y^*V(t)y = -(\lambda+\bar{\lambda})y^*V(t)y + \gamma^{-2}y^*BB'y.$$

But $y^*V(t)y$ is unbounded on $t \geq 0$, since $\overline{\sigma}\big(\Pi - P(T-t)\big) \to 0$ as $t \to \infty$ and $\underline{\sigma}\big((V(t)\big) = 1/\overline{\sigma}\big(\Pi - P(T-t)\big)$. Consequently $-(\lambda+\bar{\lambda}) \geq 0$, and (since $A+\gamma^{-2}BB'\Pi$ has no eigenvalue on the imaginary axis) we conclude that $A+\gamma^{-2}BB'\Pi$ is asymptotically stable. ■

Main points of the section

1. The infinity norm of a transfer function matrix $\boldsymbol{G} \in \mathcal{RH}_\infty$ is bounded by a given number γ if and only if (a) $\overline{\sigma}\big(\boldsymbol{G}(\infty)\big) < \gamma$ and (b) the algebraic Riccati equation (3.7.1) has a stabilizing solution. This is known as the bounded real lemma.
2. The solution of the algebraic Riccati equation, when it exists, may be determined either by an eigenvalue calculation on the Hamiltonian matrix (3.7.5) constructed from a realization of $\boldsymbol{G}$ and γ, or as the limiting (steady-state) solution to the Riccati differential equation (3.7.14), generalized to the $D \neq 0$ case.
3. In the case of a transfer function matrix $\boldsymbol{G} \in \mathcal{RL}_\infty$, an eigenvalue calculation on the Hamiltonian matrix (3.7.5) determines whether $\|\boldsymbol{G}\|_\infty < \gamma$.
4. The incremental gain of a time-varying, state-space system with realization $(A, B, C, 0)$ is bounded by a given number γ if and only if the Riccati differential equation (3.7.14) has a solution on $[0, T]$ for all finite T.

3.8 Notes and References

The material presented in this chapter is standard and is covered in several excellent texts.

The signals and systems text by Kwakernaak and Sivan [126] provides an introduction to the mathematical properties of signals and systems. Lebesgue 2-spaces, the Fourier transform and Parseval's identity are treated in many books on signal and systems theory ([126] or example) and in many books on integration, analysis or Hilbert space. See Rudin [174] and Young [222], for example. Hardy spaces and the Paley-Wiener theorem are treated in detail in Hoffman [93] and Duren [56], and there is a chapter on this topic in Rudin [174] and in Young [222]. State-space systems are widely used in control and system theory and are covered in many modern texts on these subjects. Brockett [33] is still amongst the best treatments of the general time-varying case. Linear systems driven by white noise processes are analyzed in Kwakernaak and Sivan [125] and other texts on stochastic optimal control—Davis [40] contains a reasonably accessible treatment and a good introduction to the stochastic process literature.

There was a great deal of interest in the late 1950s and early 1960s in the stability of feedback systems containing nonlinear elements. These problems were approached using frequency domain (function analytic) methods, Lyapunov stability theory and input-output (operator theoretic) analysis. The papers of Sandberg [187, 186, 188, 189] and Zames [224, 225, 226] are regarded as providing the general framework for the small gain theorem and in developing its application to specific problems of interest in the literature. Of these, Zames provides the more accessible account. The book by Willems [210] also considers the stability of feedback systems. Our treatment of nonlinear system stability follows the text by Desoer and Vidyasagar [47], in which a unified approach to the input-output stability of nonlinear feedback systems based on the small gain theorem is presented. The relationships between the small gain theorem, the passivity theorem, the Popov criterion and the circle criterion are explored in detail.

The book by Safonov [177] develops a general framework for considering the stability of feedback loops containing sector bounded relations, which includes passive and small gain systems, and does not require that the exogenous signals enter the loop in a linear manner. Stability theorems that allow structural and size constraints to be imposed on the systems comprising the closed loop have been developed by Doyle [51] and Safonov [178].

The positive real lemma (see Problem 3.25), which is equivalent to the bounded real lemma, originates from the Problem of Lur'e, which concerns a feedback loop containing a linear time-invariant system and a memoryless nonlinearity. Popov [165] provided a frequency domain criterion for the stability of the closed loop—the closed loop is globally asymptotically stable if a certain transfer function is positive real. He also showed that the existence of a Lyapunov function that was "a quadratic form plus an integral of the nonlinearity" and which ensured the global asymptotic stability of the closed loop implied his positive real condition. The questions which remained were (a) does Popov's positive real condition imply the existence of a Lyapunov function of the desired form? (b) how can the Lyapunov function be constructed? Yakubovič [219] and Kalman [107] solved these problems by developing a state-space characterization of positive real transfer functions, which is known as the positive real lemma—the term "lemma" derives from Kalman, who called the result the *Main Lemma*. The positive real lemma showed that the frequency domain criterion of Popov was equivalent to the existence of a Lyapunov function of the desired form and provided an "effective procedure" for computing the Lyapunov function. This work was the first example of an approach to feedback synthesis that is now known as "$\mathcal{H}_\infty$ control". The design specification (global asymptotic stability) was converted into a frequency response criterion (Popov's positive real criterion) and a state-space synthesis procedure (the positive real lemma) was developed.

The multivariable extension of the positive real lemma was stated without proof by Kalman [108], and was established in its full generality by Anderson [9]. The most complete treatment of the positive real lemma, the bounded real lemma and also the characterization of allpass systems (the lossless bounded real lemma) can be found in the text on network analysis and synthesis by Anderson and Vongpanitlerd [14].

3.9 Problems

Problem 3.1.

1. Show that $f(t) = t^\alpha$, $t > 0$, is in $\mathcal{L}_2[0,T]$ if and only if $\alpha > -\frac{1}{2}$. Show that f is not in $\mathcal{L}_2[0,\infty)$ for any α.
2. Show that $g(t) = (t+1)^\alpha$, $t > 0$, is in $\mathcal{L}_{2e}$ for any α. Show that g is in $\mathcal{L}_2[0,\infty)$ if and only if $\alpha < -\frac{1}{2}$.

Problem 3.2. Show that for any differentiable matrix function $X(t)$,

$$\frac{d}{dt}X^{-1}(t) = -X^{-1}(t)\big(\frac{d}{dt}X(t)\big)X^{-1}(t)$$

for all t for which the inverse exists.

Problem 3.3. Suppose $\Phi(t,\tau)$ is the transition matrix associated with $A(t)$. That is,

$$\frac{d}{dt}\Phi(t,\tau) = A(t)\Phi(t,\tau), \qquad \Phi(\tau,\tau) = I.$$

1. Show that Φ satisfies the functional equation $\Phi(t_2,t_1) = \Phi(t_2,\tau)\Phi(\tau,t_1)$ for any t_1, t_2 and τ.
2. Show that $\Phi(t,\tau)$ is nonsingular and that $\Phi(\tau,t) = \Phi^{-1}(t,\tau)$.
3. Show that
$$\frac{d}{d\tau}\Phi(t,\tau) = -\Phi(t,\tau)A(\tau).$$

Problem 3.4.

1. Consider the frequency domain signal $f(s) = \frac{1}{s-a}$, $a < 0$. Show that, for $\alpha \geq 0$,
$$\frac{1}{2\pi}\int_{-\infty}^{\infty} f^*(\alpha + j\omega)f(\alpha + j\omega)\,d\omega = \frac{1}{2(\alpha - a)}.$$
Conclude that $\|f\|_2 = \frac{1}{\sqrt{-2a}}$.

2. Consider the time-domain signal $f(t) = e^{at}$, $t \geq 0$ and $a < 0$. Use Theorem 3.1.1 to show that $f \in \mathcal{L}_2[0,\infty)$ and $\|f\|_2 = \frac{1}{\sqrt{-2a}}$.

Problem 3.5. Suppose $QA + A'Q + C'C = 0$.

1. Show that A asymptotically stable implies that $Q \geq 0$.
2. Show that $Q \geq 0$ implies that every unstable mode of A is unobservable.

Problem 3.6. Consider two systems $\boldsymbol{G}_1$ and $\boldsymbol{G}_2$ defined by

$$\begin{aligned} \dot{x}_i(t) &= A_i(t)x_i(t) + B_i(t)w_i(t) \\ z_i(t) &= C_i(t)x_i(t) + D_i(t)w_i(t) \end{aligned}$$

for $i = 1, 2$. In the following, the time dependence of the matrices is not shown explicitly.

1. Assuming that the dimensions of w_1 and w_2 and the dimensions of z_1 and z_2 are equal, show that the system $z = (\boldsymbol{G}_1 + \boldsymbol{G}_2)w$ has realization

$$\left[\begin{array}{cc|c} A_1 & 0 & B_1 \\ 0 & A_2 & B_2 \\ \hline C_1 & C_2 & D_1 + D_2 \end{array}\right].$$

2. Assuming the dimension of z_1 is equal to the dimension of w_2, show that the system $z = (\boldsymbol{G}_2\boldsymbol{G}_1)w$ has realization

$$\left[\begin{array}{cc|c} A_1 & 0 & B_1 \\ B_2C_1 & A_2 & B_2D_1 \\ \hline D_2C_1 & C_2 & D_2D_1 \end{array}\right].$$

3. Show that if $D_1(t)$ is nonsingular on the time interval of interest, then the inverse system $\boldsymbol{G}_1^{-1}$ has realization

$$\left[\begin{array}{c|c} A_1 - B_1D_1^{-1}C_1 & B_1D_1^{-1} \\ \hline -D_1^{-1}C_1 & D_1^{-1} \end{array}\right] = \left[\begin{array}{cc} A_1 & B_1 \\ 0 & I \end{array}\right]\left[\begin{array}{cc} I & 0 \\ C_1 & D_1 \end{array}\right]^{-1}.$$

4. Suppose

$$\left[\begin{array}{c} \boldsymbol{G}_1 \\ \boldsymbol{G}_2 \end{array}\right] \stackrel{s}{=} \left[\begin{array}{c|c} A & B \\ \hline C_1 & D_1 \\ C_2 & D_2 \end{array}\right]$$

with D_1 nonsingular on the time interval of interest. Show that the system $\boldsymbol{G}_2\boldsymbol{G}_1^{-1}$ has realization

$$\left[\begin{array}{c|c} A - BD_1^{-1}C_1 & BD_1^{-1} \\ \hline C_2 - D_2D_1^{-1}C_1 & D_2D_1^{-1} \end{array}\right] = \left[\begin{array}{cc} A & B \\ C_2 & D_2 \end{array}\right]\left[\begin{array}{cc} I & 0 \\ C_1 & D_1 \end{array}\right]^{-1}.$$

Problem 3.7. Let $\boldsymbol{G}$ have realization $\big(A(t), B(t), C(t), D(t)\big)$.

1. Show that if $D(t)$ is nonsingular on $[0, T]$ then there exist constants $\epsilon_1 > 0$ and $\epsilon_2 > 0$ such that

$$\epsilon_1 \|w\|_{2,[0,T]} \leq \|z\|_{2,[0,T]} \leq \epsilon_2 \|w\|_{2,[0.T]},$$

in which $z = \boldsymbol{G}w$, for all $w \in \mathcal{L}_2[0, T]$.
2. Show that when the system is time-invariant, the result holds for the space $\mathcal{L}_2[0, \infty)$ if the transfer function matrix is such that $\boldsymbol{G}$ and $\boldsymbol{G}^{-1} \in \mathcal{H}_\infty$.

Problem 3.8. Let $\boldsymbol{G}$ be a time-invariant system with realization (A, B, C, D). Suppose that D satisfies (3.2.14) and that there is a Q such that (3.2.12) and (3.2.13) hold.

1. Show that

$$\boldsymbol{G}(s)^*\boldsymbol{G}(s) = I - (s + \bar{s})B'(\bar{s}I - A')^{-1}Q(sI - A)^{-1}B.$$

Conclude that if $Q \geq 0$, then $\boldsymbol{G}(s)^*\boldsymbol{G}(s) \leq I$ for all $\mathrm{R}_e(s) \geq 0$.
2. Show that there exist matrices B_e and D_e such that the system $\boldsymbol{G}_e$ with realization

$$\boldsymbol{G}_e \stackrel{s}{=} \left[\begin{array}{c|cc} A & B & B_e \\ \hline C & D & D_e \end{array}\right]$$

is square and allpass. Do not assume that Q is nonsingular.

Problem 3.9. For a given pair (A, C), suppose every purely imaginary mode of A is unobservable through C. If V is a basis for the space spanned by the imaginary axis modes of A, show that there exists a $Q = Q'$ such that $QV = 0$ and

$$QA + A'Q + C'C = 0.$$

Problem 3.10. Consider the memoryless system $(\boldsymbol{f}w)(t) = f(w(t))$, in which f is a real valued function of a real variable.

1. Find a function f that is not differentiable everywhere for which $\gamma(\boldsymbol{f})$ is finite.
2. Show that if f is differentiable, then $\gamma(\boldsymbol{f}) = \sup_x |\frac{df}{dx}|$. What can you say if f is differentiable except at isolated points?
3. Suppose $\gamma(\boldsymbol{f}) < 1$. Graphically explain why the equation $w = \boldsymbol{f}w$ always has a solution.

Problem 3.11.

1. Show that $\operatorname{trace}(XY') = \operatorname{trace}(Y'X)$ for any matrices X and Y of the same dimension.
2. Show that

$$\operatorname{trace}(XX') = \sum_{i,j} x_{ij}^2,$$

in which x_{ij} is the i, j element of X.
3. Show that $\sqrt{\operatorname{trace}(XX')}$ defines a norm on the space of matrices.

Problem 3.12. Find transfer functions g and h such that $\|hg\|_2 > \|g\|_2\|h\|_2$.

Problem 3.13.

1. Suppose that $B : \mathcal{S} \mapsto \mathcal{S}$ is allpass. Show that $\|GB\| = \|G\|$, in which $\|\cdot\|$ is the appropriate induced norm.
2. Suppose that A is allpass. Show that $\|AG\|_2 = \|G\|_2$ for any system G.

Problem 3.14. Show that a transfer function matrix Z defines an incrementally strictly passive system with finite incremental gain if and only if $Z \in \mathcal{H}_\infty$ and

$$Z(s) + Z^*(s) \geq 2\epsilon I > 0 \quad \text{for all } \mathrm{R}_e(s) > 0. \tag{3.9.1}$$

Transfer function matrices that are analytic in $\mathrm{R}_e(s) > 0$ and satisfy (3.9.1) are called strictly positive real.[15]

Problem 3.15. Suppose $Z \in \mathcal{H}_\infty$. Show that Z is strictly positive real if and only if

$$Z(j\omega) + Z^*(j\omega) \geq 2\epsilon I > 0 \quad \text{for all } \omega.$$

Problem 3.16.

1. Suppose Z is strictly positive real. Show that $Z(s)$ is nonsingular for any $\mathrm{R}_e(s) \geq 0$
2. Suppose $Z = D + C(sI - A)^{-1}B$ in which A is asymptotically stable. Show that if Z is strictly positive real then $A - BD^{-1}C$ is asymptotically stable.

Problem 3.17. Consider a system G with realization $\big(A(t), B(t), C(t), D(t)\big)$. Show that if $\big(I + D(t)\big)$ is nonsingular on the time interval of interest, then the system $(I - G)(I + G)^{-1}$ has realization

$$\left[\begin{array}{c|c} A - B(I+D)^{-1}C & B(I+D)^{-1} \\ \hline -2(I+D)^{-1}C & (I-D)(I+D)^{-1} \end{array}\right].$$

Problem 3.18. Consider the feedback loop of Figure 2.8. Assume that G and K are linear, that the nominal ($\Delta_1 = 0$) closed loop is internally stable and that $\gamma\big(GK(I - GK)^{-1}\big) < \infty$.

1. Show that the actual closed loop is stable if

$$\gamma(\Delta_1)\gamma\big(GK(I - GK)^{-1}\big) < 1.$$

2. Suppose now that Δ_1 is incrementally strictly passive and has finite incremental gain. Determine an incremental gain condition that ensures the actual closed loop is internally stable.

Problem 3.19. (Structured uncertainty) Consider the feedback loop in Figure 3.9.

[15] The condition that Z is real is assumed—only real systems are considered in this book.

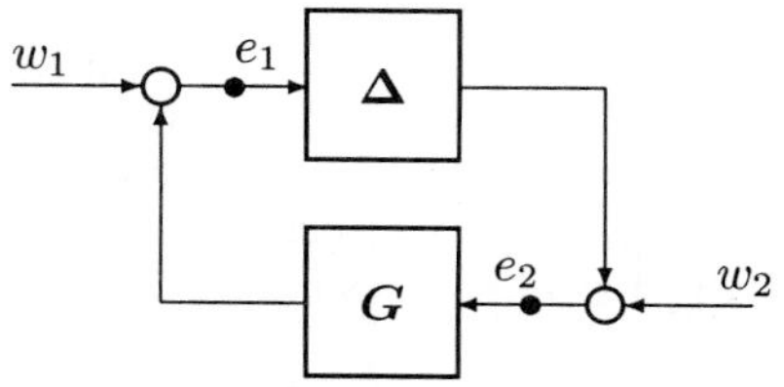

Figure 3.9: Feedback system.

Suppose that Δ is stable and block diagonal:

$$\Delta_1 = \begin{bmatrix} \Delta_1 & 0 & 0 \\ 0 & \ddots & 0 \\ 0 & 0 & \Delta_n \end{bmatrix},$$

and denote this set of stable block-diagonal Δ's by $\mathcal{U}$.

1. Show that the feedback system is internally stable if G is stable and

$$\gamma(\Delta) \min_{D} \gamma(DGD^{-1}) < 1, \tag{3.9.2}$$

in which the minimum is taken over the set $\mathcal{D}$ defined by

$$\mathcal{D} = \left\{ D : D \text{ and } D^{-1} \text{ are linear, stable and } D\Delta = \Delta D \text{ for all } \Delta \in \mathcal{U} \right\}.$$

2. Suppose the $\Delta \in \mathcal{U}$ are linear, in addition to being stable and block diagonal, and that each Δ_i is square. Determine the set $\mathcal{D}$.
(Hint: $DX = XD$ for all $p \times p$ matrices X with $p \geq 2$ if and only if $D = \alpha I$.)

Problem 3.20. Show that the equation

$$QA + A'Q + C'C = 0$$

has a unique solution if and only if $\lambda_i(A) + \lambda_j(A) \neq 0$ for any i, j.

Problem 3.21. A *Hamiltonian matrix* is any real $2n \times 2n$ matrix

$$H = \begin{bmatrix} H_{11} & H_{12} \\ H_{21} & H_{22} \end{bmatrix}$$

such that SH is symmetric, in which $S = \begin{bmatrix} 0 & -I_n \\ I_n & 0 \end{bmatrix}$.

1. Show that the eigenvalues of H are symmetric about the imaginary axis.

2. Suppose X is a $2n \times n$ real matrix such that

$$HX = X\Lambda, \tag{3.9.3}$$

in which Λ is an $n \times n$ real matrix with $\mathrm{R}_e\big(\lambda_i(\Lambda)\big) < 0$ for all i. Show that $X'SX = 0$.

3. Suppose $X = \begin{bmatrix} X_1' & X_2' \end{bmatrix}'$ is a $2n \times n$ real matrix satisfying (3.9.3), with $\mathrm{R}_e\lambda_i(\Lambda) < 0$ for all i, such that X_1 is nonsingular. Show that $P = X_2X_1^{-1}$ is symmetric and satisfies

$$\begin{aligned} PH_{11} + H_{11}'P + PH_{12}P - H_{21} &= 0 \\ H_{11} + H_{12}P &= X_1\Lambda X_1^{-1}. \end{aligned}$$

Problem 3.22. Suppose $H(t)$ is a (time-varying) Hamiltonian matrix (see Problem 3.21) and that $\Phi(t,\tau)$ is the transition matrix associated with $H(t)$. That is

$$\frac{d}{dt}\Phi(t,\tau) = H(t)\Phi(t,\tau), \qquad \Phi(\tau,\tau) = I.$$

Let Σ be any $n \times n$ matrix such that $X_1(t) = \Phi_{11}(t,T) + \Phi_{12}(t,T)\Sigma$ is nonsingular for $t \in [0,T]$ and define

$$P(t) = X_2(t)X_1^{-1}(t),$$

in which $X_2(t) = \Phi_{21}(t,T) + \Phi_{22}(t,T)\Sigma$.

1. Show that

$$-\dot{P} = PH_{11} + H_{11}'P + PH_{12}P - H_{21}, \qquad P(T) = \Sigma.$$

2. Show that $P(t)$ is a continuous function of Σ.

Problem 3.23. Suppose A is asymptotically stable and Π is any solution to (3.7.17).

1. If (A, C) is observable, show that Π is nonsingular.
2. Suppose $A + \gamma^{-1}BB'\Pi$ is asymptotically stable. Show that $\ker \Pi$ is the unobservable subspace of (A, C).
3. Conclude that if $A + \gamma^{-1}BB'\Pi$ is asymptotically stable, then Π is nonsingular if and only if (A, C) is observable.

Problem 3.24. Suppose $P(t)$ is a solution to the Riccati differential equation (3.7.14) and that $\Pi = \lim_{t \to -\infty} P(t)$ exists.

1. Show that $\big(\Pi - P(t)\big)x = 0$ for some $t \le T$ if and only if $\big(\Pi - P(t)\big)x = 0$ for *all* $t \le T$.
2. Show that there exists a constant nonsingular matrix M such that

$$M'\big(\Pi - P(t)\big)M = \begin{bmatrix} \Pi_1 - P_1(t) & 0 \\ 0 & 0 \end{bmatrix},$$

in which $\Pi_1 - P_1(t)$ is nonsingular.

3. Show that $A + \gamma^{-2}BB\Pi$ is asymptotically stable.

Problem 3.25. (The positive real lemma) Suppose $\boldsymbol{Z} = D + C(sI - A)^{-1}B$ in which A is asymptotically stable. Show that $\boldsymbol{Z}$ is strictly positive real (see Problem 3.14) if and only if $R = D + D' > 0$ and there exists a P satisfying

$$P(A - BR^{-1}C) + (A - BR^{-1}C)'P + PBR^{-1}B'P + C'R^{-1}C = 0 \qquad (3.9.4)$$

such that $A - BR^{-1}(C - B'P)$ is asymptotically stable and $P \geq 0$.

(Hint: If $\boldsymbol{Z}$ is strictly positive real, then $\|(I - \boldsymbol{Z})(I + \boldsymbol{Z})^{-1}\|_\infty < 1$. Apply the bounded real lemma to obtain P. The identity

$$I - (I + D')^{-1}(I - D')(I - D)(I + D)^{-1} = 2(I + D')^{-1}(D + D')(I + D)^{-1}$$

makes the calculations fairly easy.)

Problem 3.26. (Spectral factorization) Consider a transfer function matrix $\boldsymbol{\Phi} \in \mathcal{RL}_\infty$.

1. Show that if

$$\boldsymbol{\Phi} = \boldsymbol{W}^\sim \boldsymbol{W}, \qquad (3.9.5)$$

in which $\boldsymbol{W}$ and $\boldsymbol{W}^{-1}$ are elements of $\mathcal{RH}_\infty$, then $\boldsymbol{\Phi} = \boldsymbol{\Phi}^\sim$ and $\boldsymbol{\Phi}(j\omega) > 0$ for all ω. Show that when $\boldsymbol{W}$ exists, it is unique up to multiplication by an orthogonal matrix.

2. Show that $\boldsymbol{\Phi} = \boldsymbol{\Phi}^\sim$ and $\boldsymbol{\Phi}(j\omega) > 0$ for all ω if and only if

$$\boldsymbol{\Phi} = \boldsymbol{Z} + \boldsymbol{Z}^\sim$$

for some strictly positive real transfer function matrix $\boldsymbol{Z}$.
(Hint: consider a partial fraction expansion of $\boldsymbol{\Phi}$.)

3. Suppose that $\boldsymbol{\Phi} = \boldsymbol{Z} + \boldsymbol{Z}^\sim$, in which $\boldsymbol{Z}$ is strictly positive real. Let $\boldsymbol{Z} = D + C(sI - A)^{-1}B$ in which A is asymptotically stable. Show that a solution to (3.9.5) such that $\boldsymbol{W}$ and $\boldsymbol{W}^{-1} \in \mathcal{RH}_\infty$ is given by

$$\boldsymbol{W} = W + L(sI - A)^{-1}B, \qquad (3.9.6)$$

in which W is nonsingular and

$$\begin{aligned} W'W &= D + D' \\ W'L &= C - B'P \end{aligned}$$

and P is the stabilizing solution to (3.9.4).

4

Linear Fractional Transformations

4.1 Introduction

Linear fractional transformations (LFTs) occur in many areas of network and system theory.[1] Several examples relevant to $\mathcal{H}_\infty$ optimal control and model reduction spring to mind: (1) The transformation $z = \frac{1+s}{1-s}$, which maps the left-half plane into the unit disc, is used in the study of discrete time systems and is frequently referred to as *the bilinear transformation.* (2) The closely related transformation $\boldsymbol{P} = (I - \boldsymbol{S})(I + \boldsymbol{S})^{-1}$, which relates a positive real transfer function matrix $\boldsymbol{P}$ and a bounded real transfer function matrix $\boldsymbol{S}$, is used in passive circuit theory. (3) The transfer function $\boldsymbol{g} = \frac{as+b}{cs+d}$ represents a first-order system such as a phase-lead or phase-lag controller. First-order systems of this type are often used as weighting functions in $\mathcal{H}_\infty$ control system design. (4) Every stabilizing controller for a stable plant may be parametrized by the formula $\boldsymbol{K} = \boldsymbol{Q}(I + \boldsymbol{GQ})^{-1}$, in which $\boldsymbol{Q}$ is stable, but otherwise arbitrary. This formula is a linear fractional transformation between stable transfer function matrices and stabilizing controllers. (5) Closed-loop operators that are important in the design of control systems, such as the sensitivity operator $(I - \boldsymbol{GK})^{-1}$ and and the complementary sensitivity operator $\boldsymbol{GK}(I - \boldsymbol{GK})^{-1}$, are linear fractional in character. (6) We will show that all solutions to the $\mathcal{H}_\infty$ control problem and all solutions to the optimal Hankel norm model reduction problem are described by linear fractional transformations.

To set the scene for our study of LFTs, we will briefly review some of the

[1] Linear fractional transformations are also known as bilinear transformations.

properties of the first order rational fraction

$$\xi = \frac{as+b}{cs+d}. \tag{4.1.1}$$

Each of the coefficients is a complex number, and s and ξ are complex variables.

1. Under the assumption that $ad - bc \neq 0$, it is well known that (4.1.1) maps circles or straight lines in the s-plane into circles or straight lines in the ξ-plane.

2. By writing $\xi = \xi_1/\xi_2$, with ξ_1 and ξ_2 defined by

$$\begin{bmatrix} \xi_1 \\ \xi_2 \end{bmatrix} = \begin{bmatrix} a & b \\ c & d \end{bmatrix} \begin{bmatrix} s \\ 1 \end{bmatrix},$$

   we may represent (4.1.1) in terms of a matrix of coefficients. The coefficient matrix is unique up to multiplication by a complex number.

3. The composition of two LFTs is another LFT. Suppose that $w = w_1/w_2$ where

$$\begin{bmatrix} w_1 \\ w_2 \end{bmatrix} = \begin{bmatrix} a & b \\ c & d \end{bmatrix} \begin{bmatrix} z_1 \\ z_2 \end{bmatrix}$$

   and that $z = z_1/z_2$ where

$$\begin{bmatrix} z_1 \\ z_2 \end{bmatrix} = \begin{bmatrix} \alpha & \beta \\ \gamma & \delta \end{bmatrix} \begin{bmatrix} s \\ 1 \end{bmatrix}.$$

   Then w is given in terms of s by

$$\begin{bmatrix} w_1 \\ w_2 \end{bmatrix} = \begin{bmatrix} a & b \\ c & d \end{bmatrix} \begin{bmatrix} \alpha & \beta \\ \gamma & \delta \end{bmatrix} \begin{bmatrix} s \\ 1 \end{bmatrix}.$$

   This shows that the set of LFTs of the type given in (4.1.1) is closed under the composition operation and that compositions of LFTs may be constructed from the product of their coefficient matrices.

4. Compositions of LFTs are associative because matrix multiplication is.

5. The identity transformation exists and its coefficient matrix is the identity matrix.

6. The inverse transformation exists if the coefficient matrix is nonsingular and is given by

$$\frac{1}{ad-bc} \begin{bmatrix} d & -b \\ -c & a \end{bmatrix},$$

   which is the inverse of the coefficient matrix associated with (4.1.1).

7. It follows from Items 3, 4, 5 and 6 that nonsingular LFTs form a group under composition.

Alternative forms of LFT

The LFT given in (4.1.1) has a useful alternative representation. In the case that $d \neq 0$, we have that

$$\begin{aligned} \xi &= \frac{as+b}{cs+d} \\ &= bd^{-1} + (a - bd^{-1}c)s(1 + d^{-1}cs)^{-1}d^{-1}. \end{aligned} \tag{4.1.2}$$

This is the form we will usually use for LFTs, because it corresponds naturally to input-output block diagram representations of control systems. To see this, consider

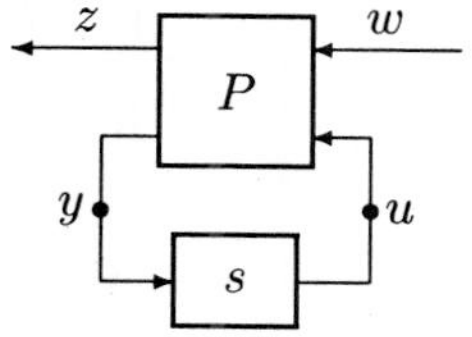

Figure 4.1: Lower linear fractional transformation.

the feedback configuration in Figure 4.1, which is defined by the equations

$$\begin{bmatrix} z \\ y \end{bmatrix} = P \begin{bmatrix} w \\ u \end{bmatrix} = \begin{bmatrix} p_{11} & p_{12} \\ p_{21} & p_{22} \end{bmatrix} \begin{bmatrix} w \\ u \end{bmatrix} \tag{4.1.3}$$

$$u = sy. \tag{4.1.4}$$

Eliminating u and y we obtain the relationship

$$\frac{z}{w} = p_{11} + p_{12}s(1 - p_{22}s)^{-1}p_{21}$$

between w and z. Comparing this with (4.1.2), we see that the ratio $\xi = (z/w)$ in Figure 4.1 is a linear fractional transformation of the variable s. The correspondence between the coefficients a, b, c, d and P is given by

$$P = \begin{bmatrix} bd^{-1} & a - bd^{-1}c \\ d^{-1} & -d^{-1}c \end{bmatrix}. \tag{4.1.5}$$

We will use the notation

$$\mathcal{F}_\ell(P, s) = p_{11} + p_{12}s(1 - p_{22}s)^{-1}p_{21} \tag{4.1.6}$$

for this form of LFT.

In the sequel, we will need generalizations of (4.1.6) of the form

$$\mathcal{F}_\ell(\boldsymbol{P}, \boldsymbol{K}) = \boldsymbol{P}_{11} + \boldsymbol{P}_{12}\boldsymbol{K}(I - \boldsymbol{P}_{22}\boldsymbol{K})^{-1}\boldsymbol{P}_{21}, \tag{4.1.7}$$

in which the $\boldsymbol{P}_{ij}$'s and $\boldsymbol{K}$ are transfer function matrices or systems. The LFT is called *well-posed* if the inverse $(I - \boldsymbol{P}_{22}\boldsymbol{K})^{-1}$ exists.[2]

By eliminating y and u from the feedback system defined by

$$\begin{aligned} \begin{bmatrix} z \\ y \end{bmatrix} &= \begin{bmatrix} \boldsymbol{P}_{11} & \boldsymbol{P}_{12} \\ \boldsymbol{P}_{21} & \boldsymbol{P}_{22} \end{bmatrix} \begin{bmatrix} w \\ u \end{bmatrix} \\ u &= \boldsymbol{K}y, \end{aligned}$$

which is illustrated in Figure 4.2, it is easily seen that $z = \mathcal{F}_\ell(\boldsymbol{P}, \boldsymbol{K})w$.

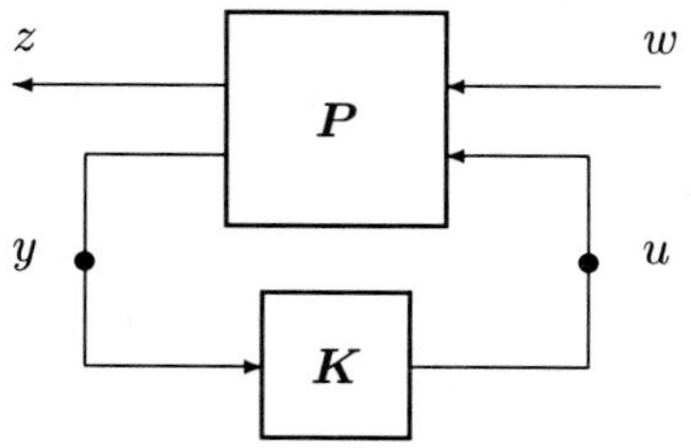

Figure 4.2: Linear fractional transformation on systems.

Most of the properties of LFTs of interest to us follow from routine applications of the definition (4.1.7). These properties are explored in the exercises at the end of the chapter which should, as always, be read as an integral part of the text.

4.1.1 The composition formula

The purpose of this section is to give a composition formula for the interconnection of two LFTs in the framework of Figure 4.3. This formula will be extensively used in what follows.

The interconnection given in Figure 4.3 is defined by the equations

$$\begin{aligned} \begin{bmatrix} z \\ y \end{bmatrix} &= \begin{bmatrix} \boldsymbol{P}_{11} & \boldsymbol{P}_{12} \\ \boldsymbol{P}_{21} & \boldsymbol{P}_{22} \end{bmatrix} \begin{bmatrix} w \\ u \end{bmatrix} \\ \begin{bmatrix} u \\ r \end{bmatrix} &= \begin{bmatrix} \boldsymbol{K}_{11} & \boldsymbol{K}_{12} \\ \boldsymbol{K}_{21} & \boldsymbol{K}_{22} \end{bmatrix} \begin{bmatrix} y \\ v \end{bmatrix}. \end{aligned}$$

Eliminating y and u, we obtain

$$\begin{bmatrix} z \\ r \end{bmatrix} = \mathcal{C}_\ell(\boldsymbol{P}, \boldsymbol{K}) \begin{bmatrix} w \\ v \end{bmatrix}, \tag{4.1.8}$$

[2] The sense in which the inverse is required to exist is context dependent. In the case of state-space systems, the LFT is well-posed if $(I - \boldsymbol{P}_{22}\boldsymbol{K})^{-1}$ can be represented as a state-space system. If we suppose that $\boldsymbol{P}$ and $\boldsymbol{K}$ are the transfer function matrices of (time-invariant) state-space systems, well-posedness is equivalent to $\det\big(I - \boldsymbol{P}_{22}(\infty)\boldsymbol{K}(\infty)\big) \neq 0$.

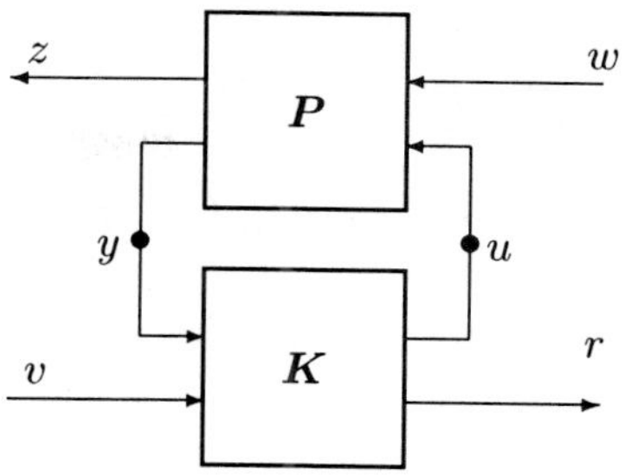

Figure 4.3: The interconnection of two LFTs.

in which the *composition operator* $\mathcal{C}_\ell(\cdot,\cdot)$ is

$$\mathcal{C}_\ell(\boldsymbol{P},\boldsymbol{K}) = \begin{bmatrix} \mathcal{F}_\ell(\boldsymbol{P},\boldsymbol{K}_{11}) & \boldsymbol{P}_{12}\widehat{\boldsymbol{S}}\boldsymbol{K}_{12} \\ \boldsymbol{K}_{21}\boldsymbol{S}\boldsymbol{P}_{21} & \boldsymbol{K}_{22}+\boldsymbol{K}_{21}\boldsymbol{P}_{22}\widehat{\boldsymbol{S}}\boldsymbol{K}_{12} \end{bmatrix}, \qquad (4.1.9)$$

with $\boldsymbol{S} = (I - \boldsymbol{P}_{22}\boldsymbol{K}_{11})^{-1}$ and $\widehat{\boldsymbol{S}} = (I - \boldsymbol{K}_{11}\boldsymbol{P}_{22})^{-1}$.

Now suppose we close the loop between r and v in Figure 4.3 by $v = \boldsymbol{F}r$. Then we see that $u = \mathcal{F}_\ell(\boldsymbol{K},\boldsymbol{F})y$ and that $z = \mathcal{F}_\ell\big(\boldsymbol{P},\mathcal{F}_\ell(\boldsymbol{K},\boldsymbol{F})\big)w$. By (4.1.8), we also have $z = \mathcal{F}_\ell(\mathcal{C}_\ell(\boldsymbol{P},\boldsymbol{K}),\boldsymbol{F})w$. That is,

$$\mathcal{F}_\ell\big(\boldsymbol{P},\mathcal{F}_\ell(\boldsymbol{K},\boldsymbol{F})\big) = \mathcal{F}_\ell\big(\mathcal{C}_\ell(\boldsymbol{P},\boldsymbol{K}),\boldsymbol{F}\big). \qquad (4.1.10)$$

The cascade of two LFTs is another LFT involving the composition operator $\mathcal{C}_\ell(\cdot,\cdot)$.

By augmenting $\boldsymbol{P}$, we may write the composition operator as a LFT, since

$$\mathcal{C}_\ell(\boldsymbol{P},\boldsymbol{K}) = \mathcal{F}_\ell\left(\left[\begin{array}{cc|cc} \boldsymbol{P}_{11} & 0 & \boldsymbol{P}_{12} & 0 \\ 0 & 0 & 0 & I \\ \hline \boldsymbol{P}_{21} & 0 & \boldsymbol{P}_{22} & 0 \\ 0 & I & 0 & 0 \end{array}\right], \begin{bmatrix} \boldsymbol{K}_{11} & \boldsymbol{K}_{12} \\ \boldsymbol{K}_{21} & \boldsymbol{K}_{22} \end{bmatrix}\right). \qquad (4.1.11)$$

(The verification of this identity is left as an exercise). This means that the properties of LFTs carry over to the composition operator.

4.1.2 Interconnections of state-space LFTs

This section provides a state-space realization for interconnections of LFTs defined by state-space realizations and considers some cancellation properties. We will need these results during our development of a representation formula for all $\mathcal{H}_\infty$ controllers in the output feedback case.

Lemma 4.1.1 *Consider the composition interconnection shown in Figure 4.3, in which*

$$\boldsymbol{P} \stackrel{s}{=} \left[\begin{array}{c|cc} A & B_1 & B_2 \\ \hline C_1 & 0 & D_{12} \\ C_2 & D_{21} & 0 \end{array}\right] \quad \text{and} \quad \boldsymbol{K} \stackrel{s}{=} \left[\begin{array}{c|cc} \tilde{A} & \tilde{B}_1 & \tilde{B}_2 \\ \hline \tilde{C}_1 & 0 & I \\ \tilde{C}_2 & I & 0 \end{array}\right].$$

Then a state-space realization for the system $\boldsymbol{R} = \mathcal{C}_\ell(\boldsymbol{P}, \boldsymbol{K}) : \begin{bmatrix} w \\ v \end{bmatrix} \mapsto \begin{bmatrix} z \\ r \end{bmatrix}$ *is*

$$\boldsymbol{R} \stackrel{s}{=} \left[\begin{array}{cc|cc} A + B_2\tilde{C}_1 & B_2\tilde{C}_1 & B_1 & B_2 \\ \tilde{A} + \tilde{B}_1 C_2 - A - B_2\tilde{C}_1 & \tilde{A} - B_2\tilde{C}_1 & \tilde{B}_1 D_{21} - B_1 & \tilde{B}_2 - B_2 \\ \hline C_1 + D_{12}\tilde{C}_1 & D_{12}\tilde{C}_1 & 0 & D_{12} \\ C_2 + \tilde{C}_2 & \tilde{C}_2 & D_{21} & 0 \end{array}\right].$$

Proof. To begin, we note that

$$\begin{aligned} \dot{x} &= Ax + B_1 w + B_2 u \\ z &= C_1 x + D_{12} u \\ y &= C_2 x + D_{21} w \\ \dot{\tilde{x}} &= \tilde{A}\tilde{x} + \tilde{B}_1 y + \tilde{B}_2 v \\ u &= \tilde{C}_1 \tilde{x} + v \\ r &= \tilde{C}_2 \tilde{x} + y. \end{aligned}$$

Eliminating u and y from these equations gives

$$\begin{aligned} \begin{bmatrix} \dot{x} \\ \dot{\tilde{x}} \end{bmatrix} &= \begin{bmatrix} A & B_2\tilde{C}_1 \\ \tilde{B}_1 C_2 & \tilde{A} \end{bmatrix} \begin{bmatrix} x \\ \tilde{x} \end{bmatrix} + \begin{bmatrix} B_1 & B_2 \\ \tilde{B}_1 D_{21} & \tilde{B}_2 \end{bmatrix} \begin{bmatrix} w \\ v \end{bmatrix} \\ \begin{bmatrix} z \\ r \end{bmatrix} &= \begin{bmatrix} C_1 & D_{12}\tilde{C}_1 \\ C_2 & \tilde{C}_2 \end{bmatrix} \begin{bmatrix} x \\ \tilde{x} \end{bmatrix} + \begin{bmatrix} 0 & D_{12} \\ D_{21} & 0 \end{bmatrix} \begin{bmatrix} w \\ v \end{bmatrix}. \end{aligned}$$

Changing variables we get

$$\begin{aligned} \begin{bmatrix} \dot{x} \\ \dot{\tilde{x}} - \dot{x} \end{bmatrix} &= \begin{bmatrix} A + B_2\tilde{C}_1 & B_2\tilde{C}_1 \\ \tilde{A} + \tilde{B}_1 C_2 - A - B_2\tilde{C}_1 & \tilde{A} - B_2\tilde{C}_1 \end{bmatrix} \begin{bmatrix} x \\ \tilde{x} - x \end{bmatrix} \\ &\quad + \begin{bmatrix} B_1 & B_2 \\ \tilde{B}_1 D_{21} - B_1 & \tilde{B}_2 - B_2 \end{bmatrix} \begin{bmatrix} w \\ v \end{bmatrix} \\ \begin{bmatrix} z \\ r \end{bmatrix} &= \begin{bmatrix} C_1 + D_{12}\tilde{C}_1 & D_{12}\tilde{C}_1 \\ C_2 + \tilde{C}_2 & \tilde{C}_2 \end{bmatrix} \begin{bmatrix} x \\ \tilde{x} - x \end{bmatrix} \\ &\quad + \begin{bmatrix} 0 & D_{12} \\ D_{21} & 0 \end{bmatrix} \begin{bmatrix} w \\ v \end{bmatrix}, \end{aligned}$$

which completes the proof. ■

The next result pins down the exact locations of any pole-zero cancellations that may occur in LFTs involving time-invariant state-space systems.

Lemma 4.1.2 *Let the* $(p_1+p_2)\times(m_1+m_2)$ *transfer function matrix* $\boldsymbol{P}$ *that maps* $\begin{bmatrix} w \\ u \end{bmatrix}$ *to* $\begin{bmatrix} z \\ y \end{bmatrix}$ *be given by*

$$\begin{bmatrix} \boldsymbol{P}_{11} & \boldsymbol{P}_{12} \\ \boldsymbol{P}_{21} & \boldsymbol{P}_{22} \end{bmatrix} \stackrel{s}{=} \left[\begin{array}{c|cc} A & B_1 & B_2 \\ \hline C_1 & D_{11} & D_{12} \\ C_2 & D_{21} & D_{22} \end{array}\right],$$

in which $m_2 \le p_1$ *and* $p_2 \le m_1$. *Suppose that* $\boldsymbol{K}$ *maps* y *to* u *and that it has a minimal realization*

$$\boldsymbol{K} \stackrel{s}{=} \left[\begin{array}{c|c} \tilde{A} & \tilde{B} \\ \hline \tilde{C} & \tilde{D} \end{array}\right]$$

satisfying the condition $\det(I - D_{22}\tilde{D}) \ne 0$ *for a well-posed closed loop. Then*

(a)

$$\mathcal{F}_\ell(\boldsymbol{P}, \boldsymbol{K}) \stackrel{s}{=} \left[\begin{array}{cc|c} A + B_2\tilde{D}MC_2 & B_2(I+\tilde{D}MD_{22})\tilde{C} & B_1 + B_2\tilde{D}MD_{21} \\ \tilde{B}MC_2 & \tilde{A} + \tilde{B}MD_{22}\tilde{C} & \tilde{B}MD_{21} \\ \hline C_1 + D_{12}\tilde{D}MC_2 & D_{12}(I+\tilde{D}MD_{22})\tilde{C} & D_{11} + D_{12}\tilde{D}MD_{21} \end{array}\right],$$

in which $M = (I - D_{22}\tilde{D})^{-1}$. *This is referred to as the natural realization of the LFT, since it results from the elimination of* u *and* y.

(b) Every unobservable mode of the realization in (a) is a value of λ *such that* $\begin{bmatrix} A-\lambda I & B_2 \\ C_1 & D_{12} \end{bmatrix}$ *has less than full column rank.*

(c) Every uncontrollable mode of the realization in (a) is a value of λ *such that* $\begin{bmatrix} A-\lambda I & B_1 \\ C_2 & D_{21} \end{bmatrix}$ *has less than full row rank.*

Proof. The equations describing $\boldsymbol{R}_{zw}$, the closed-loop system mapping w to z, are

$$\begin{aligned} \dot{x} &= Ax + B_1 w + B_2 u \\ z &= C_1 x + D_{11} w + D_{12} u \\ y &= C_2 x + D_{21} w + D_{22} u \\ \dot{\tilde{x}} &= \tilde{A}\tilde{x} + \tilde{B}y \\ u &= \tilde{C}\tilde{x} + \tilde{D}y. \end{aligned}$$

Eliminating u and y from the above equations establishes the (a) part.

If λ is an unobservable mode of the closed-loop state-space model, there exists a vector $\begin{bmatrix} w^* & u^* \end{bmatrix}^* \neq 0$ such that

$$\begin{bmatrix} A + B_2\tilde{D}MC_2 - \lambda I & B_2(I + \tilde{D}MD_{22})\tilde{C} \\ \tilde{B}MC_2 & \tilde{A} + \tilde{B}MD_{22}\tilde{C} - \lambda I \\ C_1 + D_{12}\tilde{D}MC_2 & D_{12}(I + \tilde{D}MD_{22})\tilde{C} \end{bmatrix} \begin{bmatrix} w \\ u \end{bmatrix} = 0. \tag{4.1.12}$$

Defining

$$y = \tilde{D}MC_2w + (I + \tilde{D}MD_{22})\tilde{C}u$$

gives

$$\begin{bmatrix} A - \lambda I & B_2 \\ C_1 & D_{12} \end{bmatrix} \begin{bmatrix} w \\ y \end{bmatrix} = 0.$$

The proof of the (b) part is completed by noting that $\begin{bmatrix} w^* & u^* \end{bmatrix}^* \neq 0$ implies that $\begin{bmatrix} w^* & y^* \end{bmatrix}^* \neq 0$. Suppose for contradiction that $\begin{bmatrix} w^* & y^* \end{bmatrix}^* = 0$. This gives

$$\begin{aligned} (I + \tilde{D}MD_{22})\tilde{C}u &= 0 \\ \Rightarrow \tilde{C}u &= 0, \end{aligned}$$

since the nonsingularity of M implies the nonsingularity of $(I + \tilde{D}MD_{22})$. We also get from (4.1.12) that

$$(\tilde{A} - \lambda I)u = 0.$$

Taken together, these two conditions contradict the assumed minimality of the realization of $\boldsymbol{K}$. The validity of part (c) may be established by a dual sequence of arguments. ■

4.2 LFTs in controller synthesis

Each of the controller synthesis problems considered in this book may be described in the language of LFTs. The value of this observation lies in the fact that a single theoretical framework may be used to solve a variety of optimization problems. We illustrate this with an example of robust stability optimization.

Suppose a plant is described by a given transfer function matrix $\boldsymbol{G}$ and suppose we seek a controller that stabilizes $(\boldsymbol{G} + \boldsymbol{A})$ for all model errors $\boldsymbol{A} : \mathcal{L}_2[0, \infty) \mapsto \mathcal{L}_2[0, \infty)$ satisfying

$$\gamma(\boldsymbol{W}_2^{-1}\boldsymbol{A}\boldsymbol{W}_1^{-1}) \leq 1,$$

in which $\gamma(\cdot)$ denotes the incremental gain. The weights $\boldsymbol{W}_1$ and $\boldsymbol{W}_2$ are transfer function matrices that reflect *a priori* information about the modelling error.

If the weights $\boldsymbol{W}_1$ and $\boldsymbol{W}_2$ and their inverses are stable (*i.e.*, $\boldsymbol{W}_{1,2}^{\pm 1} \in \mathcal{H}_\infty$), we conclude from Figure 4.4 and small gain considerations (see Theorem 3.6.1) that a sufficient condition for the internal stability of the closed-loop system is that $\boldsymbol{K}$ stabilizes the nominal loop and that

$$\|\boldsymbol{W}_1\boldsymbol{K}(I-\boldsymbol{G}\boldsymbol{K})^{-1}\boldsymbol{W}_2\|_\infty < 1.$$

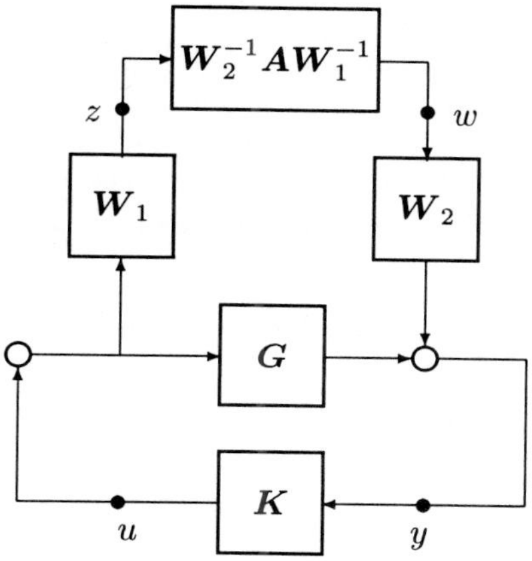

Figure 4.4: A frequency weighted robust stabilization problem.

To set this problem up in a LFT framework, we observe that

$$\begin{bmatrix} z \\ y \end{bmatrix} = \begin{bmatrix} 0 & \boldsymbol{W}_1 \\ \boldsymbol{W}_2 & \boldsymbol{G} \end{bmatrix} \begin{bmatrix} w \\ u \end{bmatrix}$$

and that

$$u = \boldsymbol{K}y.$$

Hence, setting

$$\boldsymbol{P} = \begin{bmatrix} 0 & \boldsymbol{W}_1 \\ \boldsymbol{W}_2 & \boldsymbol{G} \end{bmatrix},$$

we obtain

$$\mathcal{F}_\ell(\boldsymbol{P},\boldsymbol{K}) = \boldsymbol{W}_1\boldsymbol{K}(I-\boldsymbol{G}\boldsymbol{K})^{-1}\boldsymbol{W}_2.$$

The synthesis problem is to find a controller $\boldsymbol{K}$ that stabilizes $\mathcal{F}_\ell(\boldsymbol{P},\boldsymbol{K})$ and satisfies $\|\mathcal{F}_\ell(\boldsymbol{P},\boldsymbol{K})\|_\infty < 1$.

When solving these problems using a computer, we suppose that a state-space realization of $\boldsymbol{P}$ will be supplied as data. The computer program will return a state-space realization of the controller. If

$$\boldsymbol{G} \stackrel{s}{=} \left[\begin{array}{c|c} A & B \\ \hline C & D \end{array}\right], \quad \boldsymbol{W}_1 \stackrel{s}{=} \left[\begin{array}{c|c} A_1 & B_1 \\ \hline C_1 & D_1 \end{array}\right], \quad \boldsymbol{W}_2 \stackrel{s}{=} \left[\begin{array}{c|c} A_2 & B_2 \\ \hline C_2 & D_2 \end{array}\right],$$

are state-space models of the plant and weights, then

$$\boldsymbol{P} \stackrel{s}{=} \left[\begin{array}{ccc|cc} A & 0 & 0 & 0 & B \\ 0 & A_1 & 0 & 0 & B_1 \\ 0 & 0 & A_2 & B_2 & 0 \\ \hline 0 & C_1 & 0 & 0 & D_1 \\ C & 0 & C_2 & D_2 & D \end{array}\right]$$

is a state-space realization of $\boldsymbol{P}$.

The robust stability problem is an example of a single-target problem, because the aim is to find a controller that satisfies the single norm constraint $\|\boldsymbol{W}_1\boldsymbol{K}(I - \boldsymbol{G}\boldsymbol{K})^{-1}\boldsymbol{W}_2\|_\infty < 1$. Realistic design exercises will be more complex than this and may require a stabilizing controller that satisfies multitarget objectives such as

$$\left\| \begin{bmatrix} \boldsymbol{K} \\ I \end{bmatrix} \boldsymbol{S} \begin{bmatrix} \boldsymbol{G} & I \end{bmatrix} \right\|_\infty < 1,$$

in which $\boldsymbol{S} = (I - \boldsymbol{G}\boldsymbol{K})^{-1}$. To set this problem up in an LFT framework, we use the identity $\boldsymbol{S} = I + \boldsymbol{G}\boldsymbol{K}\boldsymbol{S}$ to obtain

$$\begin{bmatrix} \boldsymbol{K} \\ I \end{bmatrix} \boldsymbol{S} \begin{bmatrix} \boldsymbol{G} & I \end{bmatrix} = \begin{bmatrix} 0 & 0 \\ \boldsymbol{G} & I \end{bmatrix} + \begin{bmatrix} I \\ \boldsymbol{G} \end{bmatrix} \boldsymbol{K}\boldsymbol{S} \begin{bmatrix} \boldsymbol{G} & I \end{bmatrix}.$$

Comparing terms with

$$\mathcal{F}_\ell(\boldsymbol{P}, \boldsymbol{K}) = \boldsymbol{P}_{11} + \boldsymbol{P}_{12}\boldsymbol{K}(I - \boldsymbol{P}_{22}\boldsymbol{K})^{-1}\boldsymbol{P}_{21},$$

we see that

$$\begin{aligned} \boldsymbol{P}_{11} &= \begin{bmatrix} 0 & 0 \\ \boldsymbol{G} & I \end{bmatrix}, & \boldsymbol{P}_{12} &= \begin{bmatrix} I \\ \boldsymbol{G} \end{bmatrix}, \\ \boldsymbol{P}_{21} &= \begin{bmatrix} \boldsymbol{G} & I \end{bmatrix}, & \boldsymbol{P}_{22} &= \boldsymbol{G}. \end{aligned}$$

Thus, if $\boldsymbol{G} = D + C(sI - A)^{-1}B$, we have

$$\boldsymbol{P} \stackrel{s}{=} \left[\begin{array}{c|cc} A & \begin{bmatrix} B & 0 \end{bmatrix} & B \\ \hline \begin{bmatrix} 0 \\ C \end{bmatrix} & \begin{bmatrix} 0 & 0 \\ D & I \end{bmatrix} & \begin{bmatrix} I \\ D \end{bmatrix} \\ C & \begin{bmatrix} D & I \end{bmatrix} & D \end{array}\right].$$

Setting up design problems in the LFT framework is routine and the exercises at the end of the chapter should provide the reader with sufficient practise.

4.2.1 The generalized regulator problem

Consider the closed-loop system shown in Figure 4.5, in which $\boldsymbol{P} : \mathcal{L}_{2e} \mapsto \mathcal{L}_{2e}$ is causal and linearly connected in the sense that

$$\begin{bmatrix} z \\ y \end{bmatrix} = \begin{bmatrix} \boldsymbol{P}_{11} & \boldsymbol{P}_{12} \\ \boldsymbol{P}_{21} & \boldsymbol{P}_{22} \end{bmatrix} \begin{bmatrix} w \\ u \end{bmatrix},$$

and $\boldsymbol{K} : \mathcal{L}_{2e} \mapsto \mathcal{L}_{2e}$, $u = \boldsymbol{K}y$, is a causal linear controller.

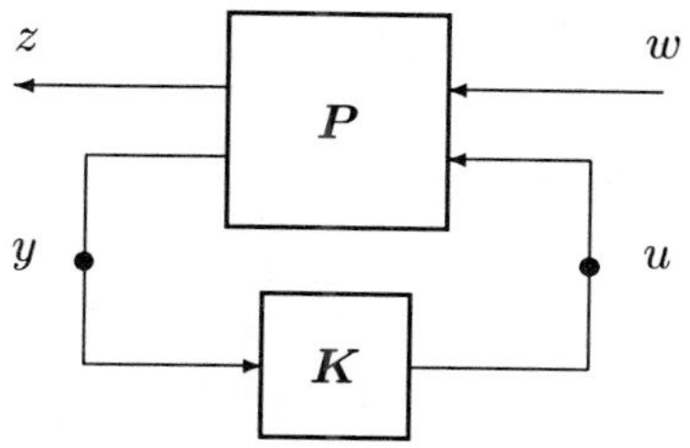

Figure 4.5: The generalized regulator configuration.

The signal w of dimension l contains all exogenous inputs and model-error outputs[3], the signal u of dimension m is the controller output (the manipulated variables) and the signal y of dimension q is the controller input signal (the measurements, references and other signals that are available for on-line control purposes). The signal z of dimension p is the objective.

We aim to select $\boldsymbol{K}$ so that the closed-loop system $\mathcal{F}_\ell(\boldsymbol{P}, \boldsymbol{K})$ mapping w to z is small in a suitable norm, subject to the constraint that the closed loop is internally stable. *Internal stability* in this case (and in all cases involving LFTs) means that z, u and y are in $\mathcal{L}_2[0,\infty)$ whenever w, v_1 and v_2 are in $\mathcal{L}_2[0,\infty)$ in Figure 4.6. (The additional inputs v_1 and v_2 are needed to ensure that no unstable cancellations occur.) Since the objective is to make z small, this problem is known as the *generalized regulator problem.* The system $\boldsymbol{P}$ is known as the *generalized plant.*

Although we have posed the problem in terms of a general linearly connected system $\boldsymbol{P}$, our main interest is focused on the case in which $\boldsymbol{P}$ is a state-space system:

$$\boldsymbol{P} \stackrel{s}{=} \left[\begin{array}{c|cc} A & B_1 & B_2 \\ \hline C_1 & D_{11} & D_{12} \\ C_2 & D_{21} & D_{22} \end{array} \right]. \tag{4.2.1}$$

That is, z and y are the solutions of ordinary linear differential equations driven by

[3]In the robust stability example, the signal w is the output of the the model error $\boldsymbol{A}$, not an exogenous input.

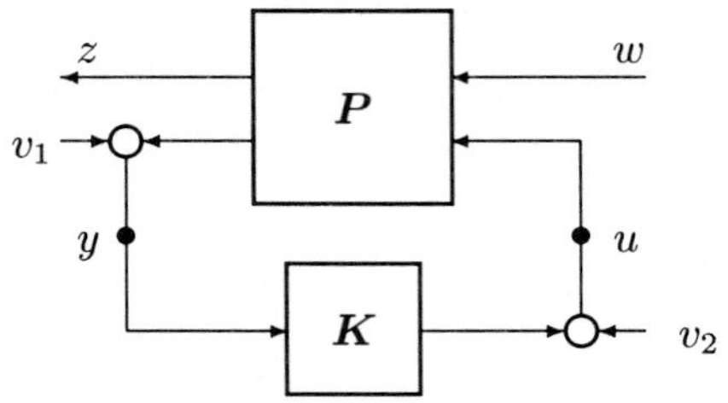

Figure 4.6: Generalized regulator: Internal stability.

w and u:

$$\begin{bmatrix} \dot{x} \\ z \\ y \end{bmatrix} = \begin{bmatrix} A & B_1 & B_2 \\ C_1 & D_{11} & D_{12} \\ C_2 & D_{21} & D_{22} \end{bmatrix} \begin{bmatrix} x \\ w \\ u \end{bmatrix}.$$

The dimension of the state vector x is n and the matrices in the realization (4.2.1) have dimensions compatible with the appropriate signals w, u, z, y and x.[4]

The controller synthesis problem is to find a causal linear controller $\boldsymbol{K} : \mathcal{L}_{2e} \mapsto \mathcal{L}_{2e}$ (if one exists) that:

1. Stabilizes the closed-loop operator $\mathcal{F}_\ell(\boldsymbol{P}, \boldsymbol{K})$.
2. Enforces the norm bound
   (a) $\|\mathcal{F}_\ell(\boldsymbol{P}, \boldsymbol{K})\|_2 < \gamma$ or
   (b) $\|\mathcal{F}_\ell(\boldsymbol{P}, \boldsymbol{K})\|_\infty < \gamma$.

The internal stability properties of the generalized regulator, including necessary and sufficient conditions for the existence of a stabilizing controller, and a LFT parametrizing all such controllers (when they exist), are given in Appendix A.

It is often convenient to assume that $\gamma = 1$ in the generalized regulator problem. This may be done by considering the scaled problem $\mathcal{F}_\ell(\widehat{\boldsymbol{P}}, \boldsymbol{K})$, in which

$$\widehat{\boldsymbol{P}} = \begin{bmatrix} \gamma^{-1}\boldsymbol{P}_{11} & \gamma^{-1}\boldsymbol{P}_{12} \\ \boldsymbol{P}_{21} & \boldsymbol{P}_{22} \end{bmatrix}.$$

In the case of the 2-norm objective in Item 2a, the signal w is a realization of a unit variance white noise process and attainment of the objective ensures that the average RMS power of z is less than γ. In general, no robust stability interpretation is possible. The *LQG problem* is the optimal version of this problem—find a stabilizing $\boldsymbol{K}$ such that $\|\mathcal{F}_\ell(\boldsymbol{P}, \boldsymbol{K})\|_2$ is minimized. The term $\mathcal{H}_2$ control is used by some authors for deterministic formulations of this problem.

[4] A is $n \times n$, B_1 is $n \times l$, B_2 is $n \times m$, C_1 is $p \times n$, C_2 is $q \times n$, D_{11} is $p \times l$, D_{12} is $p \times m$, D_{21} is $q \times l$ and D_{22} is $q \times m$.

In the case of the objective $\|\mathcal{F}_\ell(\boldsymbol{P}, \boldsymbol{K})\|_\infty < \gamma$, we have that

$$\|z\|_2 \leq \gamma \|w\|_2$$

for all $w \in \mathcal{L}_2[0, \infty)$, which corresponds to the interpretation of w as an exogenous input. We also know that the closed-loop system in Figure 4.7, defined by

$$\begin{aligned} w &= \boldsymbol{\Delta} z \\ z &= \mathcal{F}_\ell(\boldsymbol{P}, \boldsymbol{K}) w, \end{aligned}$$

is internally stable for all $\boldsymbol{\Delta} : \mathcal{L}_2[0, \infty) \mapsto \mathcal{L}_2[0, \infty)$ such that $\gamma(\boldsymbol{\Delta}) < \gamma^{-1}$.

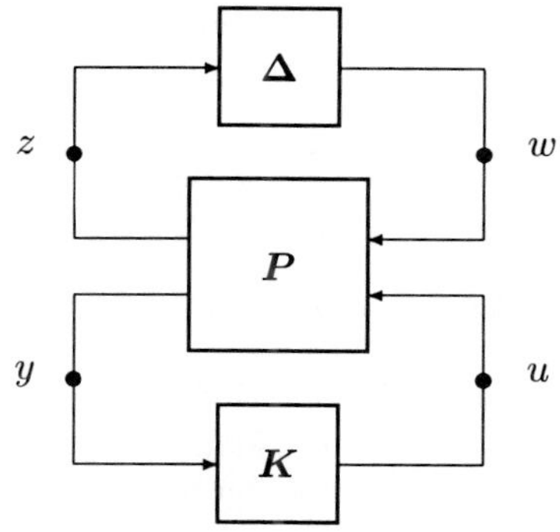

Figure 4.7: Generalized regulator with robustness interpretation.

Assumptions

In solving the generalized regulator problem, we shall make the following assumptions concerning the generalized plant in (4.2.1):

1. (A, B_2, C_2) is stabilizable and detectable.
2. $\operatorname{rank}(D_{12}) = m$ and $\operatorname{rank}(D_{21}) = q$.
3. $\operatorname{rank} \begin{bmatrix} j\omega I - A & -B_2 \\ C_1 & D_{12} \end{bmatrix} = m + n$ for all real ω.
4. $\operatorname{rank} \begin{bmatrix} j\omega I - A & -B_1 \\ C_2 & D_{21} \end{bmatrix} = q + n$ for all real ω.

These four assumptions are standard technical requirements on the data. As we proceed through the book, we will explain in detail why they are needed. Briefly, Assumption 1 is necessary and sufficient for the existence of stabilizing controllers.

Assumption 2 eliminates the possibility of singular problems. It is clear from Figure 4.5 that this assumption requires the dimension of z to be at least that of u, while the dimension of w must be at least that of y. Put another way, we assume that there are at least as many objectives as controls, and at least as many exogenous inputs as measurements. Since no measurement is error free, and no control action is costless, these are reasonable assumptions. Assumptions 3 and 4 are necessary for the existence of stabilizing solutions to the Riccati equations that are involved in the solution of the synthesis problem.

The solution of the synthesis problem for LFTs of this generality is intricate. A particular concern is that the direct feedthrough terms D_{11} and D_{22} complicate the calculations and formulas, distracting attention from the central ideas. Fortunately, these terms may be eliminated by transforming the general problem description of (4.2.1) into an equivalent problem of the form

$$\boldsymbol{P} \stackrel{s}{=} \left[\begin{array}{c|cc} * & * & * \\ \hline * & 0 & \widehat{D}_{12} \\ * & \widehat{D}_{21} & 0 \end{array}\right]. \tag{4.2.2}$$

A further simplification comes about if we scale the D_{12} and D_{21} entries so that $\widehat{D}_{12}^*\widehat{D}_{12} = I_m$ and $\widehat{D}_{21}\widehat{D}_{21}^* = I_q$.

The transformations that reduce the problem description in (4.2.1) to one of the form (4.2.2) involve LFTs with constant (nondynamic) coefficient matrices. Essentially, the reduction involves solving a nondynamic generalized regulator problem. Although this exercise provides some insights into the solution of the general problem, it may be skipped on a first reading. The full dynamical implications of the transformations will be picked up towards the end of this chapter.

Finite horizon synthesis problem

Although our main interest is in the infinite-horizon system norms $\|\mathcal{F}_\ell(\boldsymbol{P},\boldsymbol{K})\|_{2,\infty}$, we shall also consider the finite-horizon controller synthesis problem, in which we seek a causal, linear controller $\boldsymbol{K} : \mathcal{L}_2[0,T] \mapsto \mathcal{L}_2[0,T]$ (if one exists) such that

1. $\|\mathcal{F}_\ell(\boldsymbol{P},\boldsymbol{K})\|_{2,[0,T]} < \gamma$ or
2. $\|\mathcal{F}_\ell(\boldsymbol{P},\boldsymbol{K})\|_{[0,T]} < \gamma$.

Consideration of these finite-horizon objectives allows the synthesis equations and ideas to be developed in an environment in which stability issues do not arise. For the finite-horizon synthesis problem, we allow the matrices in the state-space realization of the generalized plant $\boldsymbol{P}$ to be arbitrary continuous matrix valued functions of appropriate dimensions, with $D_{12}(t)$ and $D_{21}(t)$ full column rank and full row rank respectively for all times of interest.

4.2.2 The full-information problem

The synthesis theory for the generalized regulator problem, even with the simplified D-matrix in (4.2.2), is complex. In particular, the requirement that the controller achieves the regulation objective on z while only having access to the measurement y is a significant complication. In order to tackle the generalized regulator problem in manageable steps, it is fruitful to assume that the controller has access to full information rather than just the measurable outputs, enabling us to concentrate on the conditions required to achieve the regulation objective on z. As we will show, the process of reconstructing full information from the available output measurement information is a dual problem that can then be dealt with separately. In the case of the LQG problem, full information may be constructed using a Kalman filter, while in the case of $\mathcal{H}_\infty$ control an $\mathcal{H}_\infty$ filter is required.

The configuration associated with the full-information problem is shown in Figure 4.8. In this diagram, the control signal is generated from both the state x and the disturbance w by

$$u = \begin{bmatrix} \boldsymbol{K}_1 & \boldsymbol{K}_2 \end{bmatrix} \begin{bmatrix} x \\ w \end{bmatrix}. \tag{4.2.3}$$

We assume that $\boldsymbol{K}_1$ and $\boldsymbol{K}_2$ are causal and linear.

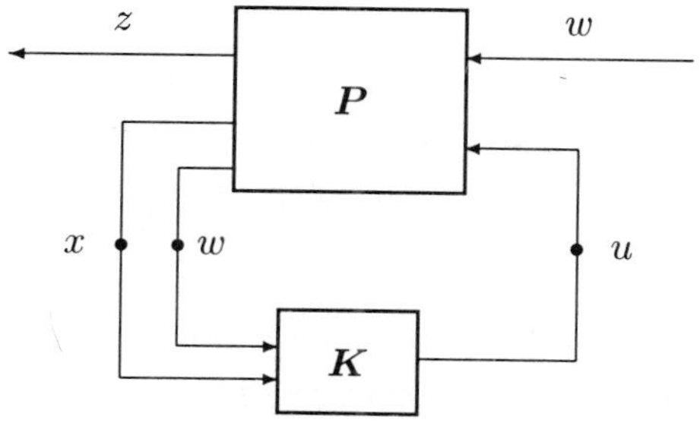

Figure 4.8: The full-information configuration.

The full-information controller structure defines a LFT with special features we will now study. Let us write down the equations that describe the situation so far. As before, the state x of the generalized plant and the objective z are related to the inputs w and u by

$$\dot{x}(t) = A(t)x(t) + B_1(t)w(t) + B_2(t)u(t), \qquad x(0) = 0, \tag{4.2.4}$$
$$z(t) = C_1(t)x(t) + D_{11}(t)w(t) + D_{12}(t)u(t). \tag{4.2.5}$$

In the sequel, the time-dependence will not be shown explicitly. The controller input is

$$y_{FI} = \begin{bmatrix} x \\ w \end{bmatrix} \tag{4.2.6}$$

instead of

$$y = C_2 x + D_{21} w + D_{22} u. \tag{4.2.7}$$

Clearly, (4.2.6) is a special case of (4.2.7), since we obtain (4.2.6) by setting

$$C_2 = \begin{bmatrix} I \\ 0 \end{bmatrix}, \qquad D_{21} = \begin{bmatrix} 0 \\ I \end{bmatrix}, \qquad D_{22} = \begin{bmatrix} 0 \\ 0 \end{bmatrix}.$$

Because D_{21} does not have full row rank, the full-information problem does not satisfy the assumptions required of the generalized plant in Section 4.2.1.

If the plant is open-loop stable, measuring the state is unnecessary, because by exploiting state reconstruction within the controller via (4.2.4), any control signal that can be generated by a full-information controller can also be generated by an open-loop controller acting on w alone. To see how this idea generalizes to the unstable plant case, we set

$$u = -Fx + \widehat{u}, \tag{4.2.8}$$

in which F is an arbitrary state feedback law that stabilizes the system. This gives

$$\dot{x} = (A - B_2 F)x + B_1 w + B_2 \widehat{u}, \qquad x(0) = 0, \tag{4.2.9}$$

together with

$$\widehat{u} = \begin{bmatrix} \widehat{\boldsymbol{K}}_1 & \boldsymbol{K}_2 \end{bmatrix} \begin{bmatrix} x \\ w \end{bmatrix}, \tag{4.2.10}$$

where $\widehat{\boldsymbol{K}}_1 = \boldsymbol{K}_1 + F$. Since (4.2.9) describes a stable system, we can always replace (4.2.10) with an equivalent open-loop control acting on w—this means that we can set $\widehat{\boldsymbol{K}}_1 \equiv 0$ without loss of generality. This information redundancy has a number of interesting consequences, which we will now investigate.

A parametrization of all control signals

In light of the redundant information structure of the full-information configuration, we expect to be able to generate all possible control signals that could result from

$$u_L = \boldsymbol{L}_1 x + \boldsymbol{L}_2 w \tag{4.2.11}$$

by considering

$$u = \boldsymbol{K}_1 x + (\boldsymbol{K}_2 + \boldsymbol{U}) w, \tag{4.2.12}$$

in which $\boldsymbol{K} = \begin{bmatrix} \boldsymbol{K}_1 & \boldsymbol{K}_2 \end{bmatrix}$ as any given full-information controller and $\boldsymbol{U}$ ranges over the class of causal linear systems.

To see that this is indeed the case, suppose (4.2.11) is implemented, giving

$$\dot{x}_L = (A + B_2\boldsymbol{L}_1)x_L + (B_1 + B_2\boldsymbol{L}_2)w, \qquad x(0) = 0.$$

This differential equation describes a causal linear system $\boldsymbol{W}_L$ mapping $w \mapsto x_L$. Hence

$$u_L = (\boldsymbol{L}_1\boldsymbol{W}_L + \boldsymbol{L}_2)w.$$

Setting $x = x_L$ in (4.2.12) gives

$$u = (\boldsymbol{K}_1\boldsymbol{W}_L + \boldsymbol{K}_2 + \boldsymbol{U})w.$$

In order to generate the control signal u_L from (4.2.12), we simply set

$$\boldsymbol{U} = (\boldsymbol{L}_1 - \boldsymbol{K}_1)\boldsymbol{W}_L + \boldsymbol{L}_2 - \boldsymbol{K}_2.$$

We conclude that all control signals that can be generated by full-information control laws can also be generated by

$$\begin{bmatrix} \boldsymbol{K}_1 & \boldsymbol{K}_2 + \boldsymbol{U} \end{bmatrix} = \mathcal{F}_\ell\left(\left[\begin{array}{cc|c} \boldsymbol{K}_1 & \boldsymbol{K}_2 & I \\ \hline 0 & I & 0 \end{array}\right], \boldsymbol{U}\right),$$

with $\boldsymbol{U}$ ranging over all causal linear systems.

A parametrization of a particular control signal

Suppose we have a full-information controller $\boldsymbol{K} = \begin{bmatrix} \boldsymbol{K}_1 & \boldsymbol{K}_2 \end{bmatrix}$ that generates the control signal

$$u = \begin{bmatrix} \boldsymbol{K}_1 & \boldsymbol{K}_2 \end{bmatrix}\begin{bmatrix} x \\ w \end{bmatrix}. \tag{4.2.13}$$

We would like to find every other full-information controller that generates the same control signal. Since any two controllers that generate the same control signal must generate the same closed-loop system $w \mapsto z$, this will also provide a parametrization of all controllers that generate a given closed-loop.

Let $\widehat{x}$ be the solution to the differential equation

$$\dot{\widehat{x}} = (A + B_2\boldsymbol{K}_1)\widehat{x} + (B_1 + B_2\boldsymbol{K}_2)w + B_2 r, \qquad \widehat{x}(0) = 0, \tag{4.2.14}$$

in which r is given by

$$r = \boldsymbol{V}(x - \widehat{x}),$$

with $\boldsymbol{V}$ an arbitrary causal linear system.

Since $\widehat{x}(0) = x(0)$, we have $r(0) = 0$ for any $\boldsymbol{V}$. As a consequence, $\widehat{x} \equiv x$ and $r \equiv 0$ for all $t \geq 0$. Therefore

$$u = \boldsymbol{K}_1 x + \boldsymbol{K}_2 w + r$$

for all $t \geq 0$. This gives

$$\begin{bmatrix} u \\ x - \widehat{x} \end{bmatrix} = \begin{bmatrix} \boldsymbol{K}_1 & \boldsymbol{K}_2 & I \\ I & -\boldsymbol{W}_1 & -\boldsymbol{W}_2 \end{bmatrix} \begin{bmatrix} x \\ w \\ r \end{bmatrix} \tag{4.2.15}$$

$$r = \boldsymbol{V}(x - \widehat{x}), \tag{4.2.16}$$

in which $\boldsymbol{W}_1$ is described by

$$\dot{\widehat{x}} = (A + B_2\boldsymbol{K}_1)\widehat{x} + (B_1 + B_2\boldsymbol{K}_2)w,$$

while $\boldsymbol{W}_2$ is described by

$$\dot{\widehat{x}} = (A + B_2\boldsymbol{K}_1)\widehat{x} + B_2 r.$$

Setting

$$\boldsymbol{K}_a = \left[\begin{array}{cc|c} \boldsymbol{K}_1 & \boldsymbol{K}_2 & I \\ \hline I & -\boldsymbol{W}_1 & -\boldsymbol{W}_2 \end{array}\right] \tag{4.2.17}$$

gives

$$u = \mathcal{F}_\ell(\boldsymbol{K}_a, \boldsymbol{V}) \begin{bmatrix} x \\ w \end{bmatrix} \tag{4.2.18}$$

$$= \begin{bmatrix} \boldsymbol{K}_1 + \boldsymbol{Z} & \boldsymbol{K}_2 - \boldsymbol{Z}\boldsymbol{W}_1 \end{bmatrix} \begin{bmatrix} x \\ w \end{bmatrix}, \tag{4.2.19}$$

in which

$$\boldsymbol{Z} = \boldsymbol{V}(I + \boldsymbol{W}_2\boldsymbol{V})^{-1}. \tag{4.2.20}$$

The control signal u in (4.2.19) is identical to that resulting from (4.2.13) because $x = \boldsymbol{W}_1 w$. Hence (4.2.18) generates a class of controllers that produce the same control signal as (4.2.13). To see that this LFT actually captures them all as $\boldsymbol{V}$ ranges over all causal linear systems, we observe that there is a one-to-one correspondence between $\boldsymbol{Z}$ and $\boldsymbol{V}$ in (4.2.20). Thus, given an arbitrary $\boldsymbol{Z}$, we can always find a $\boldsymbol{V}$ that generates it. This shows that $\boldsymbol{K}_1 + \boldsymbol{Z}$ is arbitrary in (4.2.19) as $\boldsymbol{V}$ varies, and we conclude that all the control laws that have the same control signal as (4.2.13) are generated by (4.2.18).

A parametrization of all controllers

We will now find a representation formula for all full-information controllers by combining the parametrization of all control signals with the parametrization of all controllers that give rise to the same control signal. To carry out this concatenation, we combine (4.2.15) with

$$r = \boldsymbol{V}(x - \widehat{x}) + \boldsymbol{U}w.$$

This gives

$$u = \mathcal{F}_\ell(\boldsymbol{K}_{aa}, \begin{bmatrix} \boldsymbol{V} & \boldsymbol{U} \end{bmatrix}), \tag{4.2.21}$$

where

$$K_{aa} = \left[\begin{array}{cc|c} K_1 & K_2 & I \\ \hline I & -W_1 & -W_2 \\ 0 & I & 0 \end{array}\right].$$

To see that

$$\left[\begin{array}{cc} L_1 & L_2 \end{array}\right] = \mathcal{F}_\ell(K_{aa}, \left[\begin{array}{cc} V & U \end{array}\right]) \qquad (4.2.22)$$

generates all full-information control laws, we note that (4.2.22) can always be solved for V and U because the $(1,2)$- and $(2,1)$-blocks of K_{aa} have causal inverses. That is, there is a one-to-one correspondence between L_1, L_2 and V, U in (4.2.22).

Internal stability

We conclude this section by briefly mentioning the necessary and sufficient conditions on V and U in (4.2.22) for an internally-stable closed loop. We suppose now that all the systems involved are time-invariant in addition to being causal and linear.

Suppose that $K = \left[\begin{array}{cc} K_1 & K_2 \end{array}\right]$ is a fixed internally-stabilizing controller. Since the internal dynamics of V are unobservable at the output of the controller (any V generates the same control signal!), it is necessary that V be stable in order that the closed loop be internally stable. Since the parameter U defines an open-loop map from w to r, it too must be stable if the closed loop is to be internally stable. To see that the stability of V and U is sufficient for internal stability, one needs to verify that the nine closed-loop transfer function matrices in mapping w, v_1 and v_2 to u, z and $y = \left[\begin{array}{cc} x' & w' \end{array}\right]'$ in Figure 4.6 are stable for any stable $\left[\begin{array}{cc} V & U \end{array}\right]$ pair. These matters are considered in more detail in Appendix A.

Main points of the section

1. A large class of controller synthesis problems may be described in terms of linear fractional transformations involving the controller K and a generalized plant P.
2. The generalized plant is assumed to have a known state-space realization and the aim is to synthesize an internally-stabilizing controller that satisfies a norm constraint on the closed-loop operator. We shall require either $\|\mathcal{F}_\ell(P, K)\|_2 < \gamma$ or $\|\mathcal{F}_\ell(P, K)\|_\infty < \gamma$. By dividing P_{11} and P_{12} by γ, these problems can always be scaled so that $\gamma = 1$.
3. A number of technical assumptions concerning the state-space realization of the generalized plant P are imposed.
4. The problem may be transformed to an equivalent problem in which $D_{11} = 0$, $D_{22} = 0$ and $D_{21}D_{21}' = I$ and $D_{12}'D_{12} = I$. This simplification is made using certain constant matrix LFTs, which are explained in Section 4.6.

5. The full-information problem is a feedback problem in which the controller has access to the state x and to the exogenous input w. This is a redundant information structure, because we can always construct a copy of the state from the exogenous input, provided we know the initial state. A consequence of this redundancy is that any given control signal (and hence any given closed loop) can be generated by many controllers.
6. All full-information controllers may be described in terms of a pair of parameters. The $\boldsymbol{U}$ parameter is used to generate all full-information control signals, while the $\boldsymbol{V}$ parameter is used to generate every controller that gives rise to the same control signal (and consequently the same closed-loop operator). The closed loop will be internally stable if and only if: (a) $\boldsymbol{K}$ is stabilizing; (b) $\boldsymbol{U}$ is stable; and (c) $\boldsymbol{V}$ is stable.

4.3 Contractive LFTs

Contractive systems play an important role in the synthesis of controllers that meet closed-loop norm objectives. The properties of these systems will be used throughout the remainder of the book.

To begin our analysis of LFTs involving contractive systems, we deduce conditions on the coefficients in the simple first-order fraction

$$\xi = \frac{\xi_1}{\xi_2} = \frac{as+b}{cs+d} \tag{4.3.1}$$

such that the origin-centered unit disc is mapped into itself. If $|s| \leq 1$, we seek conditions on the coefficient set (a, b, c, d) such that $|\xi| \leq 1$. Suppose

$$\begin{bmatrix} \xi_1 \\ \xi_2 \end{bmatrix} = \begin{bmatrix} a & b \\ c & d \end{bmatrix} \begin{bmatrix} s \\ 1 \end{bmatrix}.$$

Then

$$\begin{aligned} \bar{\xi}_2(|\xi|^2 - 1)\xi_2 &= \begin{bmatrix} \bar{\xi}_1 & \bar{\xi}_2 \end{bmatrix} \begin{bmatrix} 1 & 0 \\ 0 & -1 \end{bmatrix} \begin{bmatrix} \xi_1 \\ \xi_2 \end{bmatrix} \\ &= \begin{bmatrix} \bar{s} & 1 \end{bmatrix} S^*JS \begin{bmatrix} s \\ 1 \end{bmatrix}, \end{aligned}$$

in which

$$S = \begin{bmatrix} a & b \\ c & d \end{bmatrix} \quad \text{and} \quad J = \begin{bmatrix} 1 & 0 \\ 0 & -1 \end{bmatrix}.$$

If the coefficient matrix S has the J-contractive property

$$S^*JS \leq J, \tag{4.3.2}$$

we see that

$$\bar{\xi}_2(|\xi|^2 - 1)\xi_2 \le |s|^2 - 1.$$

Thus $|s| \le 1$ implies $|\xi| \le 1$. The J-contractive property given in (4.3.2) therefore implies that the LFT given in (4.3.1) maps the unit disc into itself.

The J-contractive property of S in (4.3.2) induces a similar contractive property on the P matrix defined in (4.1.5). It follows by direct calculation that

$$\begin{aligned} S^*JS - J &= \begin{bmatrix} |a|^2 - |c|^2 - 1 & \bar{a}b - \bar{c}d \\ \bar{b}a - \bar{d}c & |b|^2 + 1 - |d|^2 \end{bmatrix} \\ &= \begin{bmatrix} \bar{a} & 0 \\ \bar{b} & 1 \end{bmatrix}\begin{bmatrix} a & b \\ 0 & 1 \end{bmatrix} - \begin{bmatrix} \bar{c} & 1 \\ \bar{d} & 0 \end{bmatrix}\begin{bmatrix} c & d \\ 1 & 0 \end{bmatrix} \\ &= \begin{bmatrix} \bar{c} & 1 \\ \bar{d} & 0 \end{bmatrix}(P^*P - I)\begin{bmatrix} c & d \\ 1 & 0 \end{bmatrix}, \end{aligned}$$

since

$$P = \begin{bmatrix} a & b \\ 0 & 1 \end{bmatrix}\begin{bmatrix} c & d \\ 1 & 0 \end{bmatrix}^{-1}$$

and $d \ne 0$ is assumed. This shows that

$$S^*JS \le J \quad \Leftrightarrow \quad P^*P \le I.$$

If $P^*P \le I$ in Figure 4.1, it follows that

$$\begin{bmatrix} \bar{w} & \bar{u} \end{bmatrix}(P^*P - I)\begin{bmatrix} w \\ u \end{bmatrix} \le 0$$

for all w and u. This gives the inequality

$$|z|^2 - |w|^2 \le |u|^2 - |y|^2,$$

which can be thought of as a dissipation or passivity property.

These ideas can be generalized to include matrix and operator valued LFTs. We first consider LFTs defined by constant matrices, in which stability is not an issue. The case of LFTs defined by transfer function matrices will then be tackled.

4.3.1 Constant matrix case

The following theorem considers constant matrix LFTs of the form

$$\mathcal{F}_\ell\left(\begin{bmatrix} D_{11} & D_{12} \\ D_{21} & D_{22} \end{bmatrix}, F\right) = D_{11} + D_{12}F(I - D_{22}F)^{-1}D_{21}, \qquad (4.3.3)$$

in which F and the D_{ij}'s are complex constant matrices with $D^*D \le I$.

Theorem 4.3.1 *Suppose D and F are complex matrices such that* $\det(I - D_{22}F) \ne 0$.

(a) If $\|D\| \leq 1$*, then* $\|F\| \leq 1$ *implies* $\|\mathcal{F}_\ell(D,F)\| \leq 1$.

(b) If $D^*D = I$*, then* $F^*F = I$ *implies* $\mathcal{F}_\ell^*(D,F)\mathcal{F}_\ell(D,F) = I$.

(c) If $D^*D = I$ *and* $\|\mathcal{F}_\ell(D,F)\| < 1$*, then* D_{21} *has full column rank.*

(d) Suppose $D^*D = I$ *with* D_{21} *full row rank.*

- *(i)* $\|\mathcal{F}_\ell(D,F)\| \leq 1$ *if and only if* $\|F\| \leq 1$.
- *(ii) If* $\|\mathcal{F}_\ell(D,F)\| < 1$ *then* $\|F\| < 1$ *and* D_{21} *is nonsingular; if* D_{21} *is nonsingular and* $\|F\| < 1$*, then* $\|\mathcal{F}_\ell(D,F)\| < 1$.
- *(iii)* $F^*F = I$ *if and only if* $\mathcal{F}_\ell^*(D,F)\mathcal{F}_\ell(D,F) = I$.
- *(iv)* $\|F\| > 1$ *if and only if* $\|\mathcal{F}_\ell(D,F)\| > 1$.

Remark 4.3.1. Duals for the results in parts (b) and (c) may be found by noting that

$$\begin{aligned} \mathcal{F}_\ell^*(D,F) &= D_{11}^* + D_{21}^*F^*(I - D_{22}^*F^*)^{-1}D_{12}^* \\ &= \mathcal{F}_\ell(D^*,F^*), \end{aligned}$$

and then applying Theorem 4.3.1 to D^* and F^*.

Proof. Let

$$\begin{bmatrix} z \\ y \end{bmatrix} = \begin{bmatrix} D_{11} & D_{12} \\ D_{21} & D_{22} \end{bmatrix} \begin{bmatrix} w \\ u \end{bmatrix}, \qquad u = Fy. \tag{4.3.4}$$

Note that $D^*D \leq I$ is equivalent to $\|z\|^2 + \|y\|^2 \leq \|w\|^2 + \|u\|^2$ for all w and u, and that $F^*F \leq I$ is equivalent to $\|u\|^2 \leq \|y\|^2$ for all y. Also, $\|\mathcal{F}_\ell(D,F)\| \leq 1$ is equivalent to $\|z\|^2 - \|w\|^2 \leq 0$ for all w.

(a) If $\|D\| \leq 1$ and $\|F\| \leq 1$, then $\|z\|^2 - \|w\|^2 \leq \|u\|^2 - \|y\|^2 \leq 0$ for all w. Hence $\|\mathcal{F}_\ell(D,F)\| \leq 1$.

(b) Since $D^*D = I$, we may use the partitions of

$$\begin{bmatrix} D_{11}^* & D_{21}^* \\ D_{12}^* & D_{22}^* \end{bmatrix} \begin{bmatrix} D_{11} & D_{12} \\ D_{21} & D_{22} \end{bmatrix} = I$$

to prove that

$$\begin{aligned} & I - \mathcal{F}_\ell^*(D,F)\mathcal{F}_\ell(D,F) \\ &= D_{21}^*(I - F^*D_{22}^*)^{-1}(I - F^*F)(I - D_{22}F)^{-1}D_{21}. \end{aligned} \tag{4.3.5}$$

The result is now immediate.

(c) Immediate from (4.3.5).

(d) We note that $D^*D = I$ yields $\|z\|^2 + \|y\|^2 = \|w\|^2 + \|u\|^2$. Also, since $y = (I - D_{22}F)^{-1}D_{21}w$ and D_{21} has full row rank, it follows that y ranges over the domain of F as w ranges over the input space.

(i) ($\Leftarrow$) is just (a). If $\|\mathcal{F}_\ell(D,F)\| \leq 1$, then $\|u\|^2 - \|y\|^2 = \|z\|^2 - \|w\|^2 \leq 0$ for all w and hence also for all y, since D_{21} is full row rank. That is, $\|F\| \leq 1$. Alternatively, consider (4.3.5).

(ii) Since $\|z\| < \|w\|$ for all $w \neq 0$, it follows that $\|u\| < \|y\|$ for all $y \neq 0$ and therefore that $\|F\| < 1$. D_{21} must be nonsingular by (c). Conversely, if D_{21} is nonsingular, $\|F\| < 1$ implies $\|u\| < \|y\|$ for all $y \neq 0$, giving $\|z\| < \|w\|$ for all $w \neq 0$, which is equivalent to $\|\mathcal{F}_\ell(D,F)\| < 1$.

(iii)($\Rightarrow$) This is just (b). ($\Leftarrow$) This follows from (4.3.5) and the fact that$(I - D_{22}F)^{-1}D_{21}$ has full row rank.

(iv) ($\Rightarrow$) Since $u = Fy$ and since $\|F\| > 1$ there exists a $\widehat{u} = F\widehat{y}$ such that $\|\widehat{u}\| > \|\widehat{y}\|$. Next, we observe that $\widehat{y}$ may be generated by setting $\widehat{w} = D_{21}^R(I - D_{22}F)\widehat{y}$, in which $(\cdot)^R$ denotes a right inverse. Since $\|\widehat{z}\|^2 - \|\widehat{w}\|^2 = \|\widehat{u}\|^2 - \|\widehat{y}\|^2 > 0$ we conclude that $\|\mathcal{F}_\ell(D,F)\| > 1$.

($\Leftarrow$) Since there exists a $\widehat{w}$ such that $\|\widehat{z}\| > \|\widehat{w}\|$, we conclude that there exists a $\widehat{y}$ such that $\|\widehat{u}\| > \|\widehat{y}\|$. The result now follows because $u = Fy$. ■

4.3.2 Dynamic matrix case

The aim of this section is to generalize the results of Theorem 4.3.1 to the case of LFTs that involve transfer function matrices. The dynamic case is complicated by the possibility of cancellation phenomena, stability questions and minimality issues. Our first result is a generalization of Theorem 4.3.1.

Theorem 4.3.2 *Suppose* $\det\big(I - \boldsymbol{P}_{22}(\infty)\boldsymbol{K}(\infty)\big) \neq 0$.

(a) If $\|\boldsymbol{P}\|_\infty \leq 1$, *then* $\|\boldsymbol{K}\|_\infty \leq 1$ *implies that* $\|\mathcal{F}_\ell(\boldsymbol{P},\boldsymbol{K})\|_\infty \leq 1$.

(b) If $\boldsymbol{P}^\sim\boldsymbol{P} = I$, *then* $\boldsymbol{K}^\sim\boldsymbol{K} = I$ *implies that* $\mathcal{F}_\ell^\sim(\boldsymbol{P},\boldsymbol{K})\mathcal{F}_\ell(\boldsymbol{P},\boldsymbol{K}) = I$.

(c) If $\boldsymbol{P}^\sim\boldsymbol{P} = I$ *and* $\|\mathcal{F}_\ell(\boldsymbol{P},\boldsymbol{K})\|_\infty < 1$, *then* $\boldsymbol{P}_{21}(j\omega)$ *has full column rank for all real values of* ω.

(d) Suppose $\boldsymbol{P}^\sim\boldsymbol{P} = I$ *with* $\boldsymbol{P}_{21}(j\omega)$ *full row rank for all real values of* ω.

(i) $\|\mathcal{F}_\ell(\boldsymbol{P},\boldsymbol{K})\|_\infty \leq 1$ *if and only if* $\|\boldsymbol{K}\|_\infty \leq 1$.

(ii) If $\|\mathcal{F}_\ell(\boldsymbol{P},\boldsymbol{K})\|_\infty < 1$ *then* $\|\boldsymbol{K}\|_\infty < 1$ *and* $\boldsymbol{P}_{21}(j\omega)$ *is nonsingular for all real values of* ω. *If* $\boldsymbol{P}_{21}(j\omega)$ *is nonsingular for all real values of* ω *and* $\|\boldsymbol{K}\|_\infty < 1$ *then* $\|\mathcal{F}_\ell(\boldsymbol{P},\boldsymbol{K})\|_\infty < 1$.

(iii) $\boldsymbol{K}^\sim\boldsymbol{K} = I$ *if and only if* $\mathcal{F}_\ell^\sim(\boldsymbol{P},\boldsymbol{K})\mathcal{F}_\ell(\boldsymbol{P},\boldsymbol{K}) = I$.

(iv) $\|\boldsymbol{K}\|_\infty > 1$ *if and only if* $\|\mathcal{F}_\ell(\boldsymbol{P},\boldsymbol{K})\|_\infty > 1$.

Proof.

(a) The condition $\det\left(I - \boldsymbol{P}_{22}\boldsymbol{K}(\infty)\right) \neq 0$ is required to ensure well-posedness. If

$$\begin{bmatrix} z \\ y \end{bmatrix} = \begin{bmatrix} \boldsymbol{P}_{11} & \boldsymbol{P}_{12} \\ \boldsymbol{P}_{21} & \boldsymbol{P}_{22} \end{bmatrix} \begin{bmatrix} w \\ u \end{bmatrix},$$

then $\|\boldsymbol{P}\|_\infty \leq 1$ implies that $\|z\|_2^2 - \|w\|_2^2 \leq \|u\|_2^2 - \|y\|_2^2$. Since $u = \boldsymbol{K}y$ and $\|\boldsymbol{K}\|_\infty \leq 1$, we have $\|u\|_2^2 \leq \|y\|_2^2$, which implies $\|z\|_2^2 \leq \|w\|_2^2$.

(b) Since $\boldsymbol{P}^\sim \boldsymbol{P} = I$, we may use essentially the same calculations as those used in the constant case to establish that

$$\begin{aligned} & I - \mathcal{F}_\ell^\sim(\boldsymbol{P}, \boldsymbol{K})\mathcal{F}_\ell(\boldsymbol{P}, \boldsymbol{K}) \\ &= \boldsymbol{P}_{21}^\sim (I - \boldsymbol{K}^\sim \boldsymbol{P}_{22}^\sim)^{-1}(I - \boldsymbol{K}^\sim \boldsymbol{K})(I - \boldsymbol{P}_{22}\boldsymbol{K})^{-1}\boldsymbol{P}_{21}, \end{aligned}$$

which completes the proof.

(c) Immediate from the above identity.

(d) Since $\boldsymbol{P}^\sim \boldsymbol{P} = I$, it follows that $\|z\|_2^2 - \|w\|_2^2 = \|u\|_2^2 - \|y\|_2^2$. Parts (i), (ii) and (iii) follow in the same way as their constant counterparts.

(iv) ($\Rightarrow$) Since $\|\boldsymbol{K}\|_\infty > 1$, there exists a frequency $\widehat{\omega}$ such that $\|\boldsymbol{K}(j\widehat{\omega})\|_2 > 1$ and a $\widehat{y}$ such that $\|\widehat{u}\|_2 > \|\widehat{y}\|_2$. Setting $\widehat{w} = \boldsymbol{P}_{21}^R\left(I - \boldsymbol{P}_{22}\boldsymbol{K}(j\widehat{\omega})\right)\widehat{y}$ gives $\|\widehat{u}\|_2 > \|\widehat{y}\|_2$ and $\|\widehat{z}\|_2 > \|\widehat{w}\|_2$ and so $\|\mathcal{F}_\ell(\boldsymbol{P}, \boldsymbol{K})\|_\infty > 1$. (iv) ($\Leftarrow$) Since there exists a $\widehat{w}$ such that $\|\widehat{z}\|_2 > \|\widehat{w}\|_2$, we conclude that there exists a $\widehat{y}$ such that $\|\widehat{u}\|_2 > \|\widehat{y}\|_2$ and therefore that $\|\boldsymbol{K}\|_\infty > 1$. ■

If $\boldsymbol{P}^\sim \boldsymbol{P} = I$ with $\boldsymbol{P}_{21}(j\omega)$ nonsingular for all real values of ω, it follows from Theorem 4.3.2 Part d(ii) that $\|\boldsymbol{K}\|_\infty < 1$ if and only if $\|\mathcal{F}_\ell(\boldsymbol{P}, \boldsymbol{K})\|_\infty < 1$. If we suppose in addition that $\boldsymbol{P}$ is stable, then we would like to show that the stability of $\boldsymbol{K}$ is equivalent to the internal stability of $\mathcal{F}_\ell(\boldsymbol{P}, \boldsymbol{K})$.

Theorem 4.3.3 *Suppose* $\boldsymbol{P} \in \mathcal{RH}_\infty$, $\boldsymbol{P}^\sim \boldsymbol{P} = I$ *and that* $\boldsymbol{P}_{21}^{-1} \in \mathcal{RH}_\infty$. *The following are equivalent:*

1. *There exists a* $\boldsymbol{K}$ *such that* $\mathcal{F}_\ell(\boldsymbol{P}, \boldsymbol{K})$ *is well-posed, internally stable and* $\|\mathcal{F}_\ell(\boldsymbol{P}, \boldsymbol{K})\|_\infty < 1$.

2. $\boldsymbol{K} \in \mathcal{RH}_\infty$ *and* $\|\boldsymbol{K}\|_\infty < 1$.

Proof.

($2 \Rightarrow 1$): Since $\|\boldsymbol{K}\|_\infty < 1$ and $\|\boldsymbol{P}_{22}\|_\infty \leq 1$ it is clear that $\|\boldsymbol{P}_{22}\boldsymbol{K}\|_\infty < 1$ and that the closed loop is well-posed. It follows from $\boldsymbol{K} \in \mathcal{RH}_\infty$ and the small gain theorem that the closed loop is internally stable. The fact that $\|\mathcal{F}_\ell(\boldsymbol{P}, \boldsymbol{K})\|_\infty < 1$ follows from Theorem 4.3.2 part (d)(ii).

(1 $\Rightarrow$ 2): $\|\mathcal{F}_\ell(\boldsymbol{P},\boldsymbol{K})\|_\infty < 1 \Rightarrow \|\boldsymbol{K}\|_\infty < 1$ by Theorem 4.3.2 part (d)(ii).

We now prove that $\boldsymbol{K}$ is stable using a Nyquist argument. Let $\boldsymbol{K}$ have n_K poles in the closed-right-half plane (CRHP) and note that none are on the imaginary axis, since $\|\boldsymbol{K}\|_\infty < 1$. We also note that $\|\boldsymbol{P}_{22}\|_\infty \leq 1$ and $\|\boldsymbol{K}\|_\infty < 1$ implies that $\det(I - \epsilon \boldsymbol{P}_{22}\boldsymbol{K}) \neq 0$ on the imaginary axis, for all $\epsilon \in [0,1]$. The Nyquist contour D_R will consist of the imaginary axis from $-jR$ to jR and a semicircular arc of radius R in the right-half plane. The radius R is large enough to enclose all the CRHP poles of $\boldsymbol{K}$ and all the CRHP zeros of $\det(I - \epsilon\boldsymbol{P}_{22}\boldsymbol{K})$, $\epsilon \in [0,1]$.

Because $\boldsymbol{P} \in \mathcal{RH}_\infty$ and $\boldsymbol{P}_{21}^{-1} \in \mathcal{RH}_\infty$, internal stability of the LFT is equivalent to internal stability of the loop defined by

$$y = \boldsymbol{P}_{22}u + v_1, \qquad u = \boldsymbol{K}y + v_2.$$

By the Nyquist theorem (Theorem 2.4.2) and the assumed internal stability of the LFT, $\det\big(I - \boldsymbol{P}_{22}\boldsymbol{K}(s)\big)$ makes n_K encirclements of the origin as s traverses D_R. To conclude that $n_K = 0$, we argue that the number of encirclements of the origin made by $\det\big(I - \boldsymbol{P}_{22}\boldsymbol{K}(s)\big)$ must be zero.

Let $\boldsymbol{K} = \boldsymbol{N}\boldsymbol{D}^{-1}$ be a coprime factorization over $\mathcal{RH}_\infty$. That is, $\boldsymbol{N}$ and $\boldsymbol{D}$ are in $\mathcal{RH}_\infty$ and $\begin{bmatrix} \boldsymbol{N}' & \boldsymbol{D}' \end{bmatrix}$ has full rank in the closed-right-half plane (see Appendix A for more details). The CRHP poles of $\boldsymbol{K}$ are the CRHP zeros of $\det(\boldsymbol{D})$. Since

$$\det\big(I - \epsilon\boldsymbol{P}_{22}\boldsymbol{K}(s)\big) = \frac{\det\big(\boldsymbol{D}(s) - \epsilon\boldsymbol{P}_{22}\boldsymbol{N}(s)\big)}{\det\big(\boldsymbol{D}(s)\big)} \tag{4.3.6}$$

and $\det\big(I - \epsilon\boldsymbol{P}_{22}\boldsymbol{K}(s)\big)$ is nonzero $s \in D_R$ and $\epsilon \in [0,1]$, it follows that $\Gamma_\epsilon(s) = \det\big(\boldsymbol{D}(s) - \epsilon\boldsymbol{P}_{22}\boldsymbol{N}(s)\big)$ is never zero for $s \in D_R$ and $\epsilon \in [0,1]$. Because Γ_ϵ deforms continuously from $\det\big(\boldsymbol{D}(s)\big)$ to $\det\big(\boldsymbol{D}(s) - \boldsymbol{P}_{22}\boldsymbol{N}(s)\big)$ as ϵ moves from 0 to 1, the number of encirclements of the origin made by $\det D(s)$ is the same as the number of encirclements of the origin made by $\det\big(\boldsymbol{D}(s) - \boldsymbol{P}_{22}\boldsymbol{N}(s)\big)$. Since $\det(\boldsymbol{D}) \in \mathcal{RH}_\infty$ has n_K zeros within D_R, it follows that $\det \boldsymbol{D}(s)$ and hence also $\det\big(\boldsymbol{D}(s) - \boldsymbol{P}_{22}\boldsymbol{N}(s)\big)$ makes n_K encirclements of the origin. By (4.3.6), $\det\big(I - \boldsymbol{P}_{22}\boldsymbol{K}(s)\big)$ makes no encirclements of the origin as s traverses D_R. That is, $n_K = 0$ and we conclude that $\boldsymbol{K}$ is stable. ■

It is possible to generalize this result to the case that $\boldsymbol{P}$ and $\boldsymbol{K}$ have a specific number of left half-plane poles.

Lemma 4.3.4 *Suppose $\boldsymbol{P}$ has state-space realization*

$$\boldsymbol{P} \stackrel{s}{=} \left[\begin{array}{c|cc} A & B_1 & B_2 \\ \hline C_1 & 0 & D_{12} \\ C_2 & D_{21} & 0 \end{array}\right].$$

Suppose also that:

1. *The matrix A has exactly r eigenvalues in the open-left-half plane.*

2. The matrix $A - B_2 D_{12}^{-1} C_1$ *has no eigenvalues in the closed-left-half plane and*

3. The matrix $A - B_1 D_{21}^{-1} C_2$ *has no eigenvalues in the closed-left-half plane.*

If $\boldsymbol{K}$ *has minimal state-space realization*

$$\boldsymbol{K} \stackrel{s}{=} \left[\begin{array}{c|c} \tilde{A} & \tilde{B} \\ \hline \tilde{C} & \tilde{D} \end{array}\right],$$

and $\|\boldsymbol{P}_{22}\boldsymbol{K}\|_\infty < 1$, *then* $\mathcal{F}_\ell(\boldsymbol{P}, \boldsymbol{K})$ *has exactly* $r+l$ *poles in the open-left-half plane if and only if* $\boldsymbol{K}$ *has exactly* l *poles there.*

Proof. Since the zeros of $\boldsymbol{P}_{12}$ and $\boldsymbol{P}_{21}$ are all in the open-right-half plane, we conclude from Lemma 4.1.2 that the open-left-half plane (OLHP) poles of $\mathcal{F}_\ell(\boldsymbol{P}, \epsilon\boldsymbol{K})$ are the OLHP zeros of $\det(A_{cl}(\epsilon) - sI)$, in which

$$A_{cl}(\epsilon) = \begin{bmatrix} A + \epsilon B_2 \tilde{D} C_2 & \epsilon B_2 \tilde{C} \\ \tilde{B} C_2 & \tilde{A} \end{bmatrix}.$$

After a "Schur complement" calculation, we get:

$$\begin{aligned} &\det(A_{cl}(\epsilon) - sI) \\ &\quad = \det(\tilde{A} - sI)\det(A - sI + \epsilon B_2 \boldsymbol{K}(s) C_2) \\ &\quad = \det(\tilde{A} - sI)\det(A - sI)\det(I - \epsilon(sI - A)^{-1} B_2 \boldsymbol{K}(s) C_2) \\ &\quad = \det(\tilde{A} - sI)\det(A - sI)\det\big(I - \epsilon C_2 (sI - A)^{-1} B_2 \boldsymbol{K}(s)\big) \\ &\quad = \det(\tilde{A} - sI)\det(A - sI)\det(I - \epsilon \boldsymbol{P}_{22}\boldsymbol{K}). \end{aligned} \tag{4.3.7}$$

Let D_R be a contour consisting of the imaginary axis from $-j\omega R$ to $j\omega R$ and a semicircular arc of radius R in the *left-half* plane, with R large enough for the contour to enclose all the left-half-plane eigenvalues of A and $\tilde{A}$ and all the left-half-plane poles and zeros of $\det(I - \epsilon\boldsymbol{P}_{22}\boldsymbol{K})$, $\epsilon \in [0, 1]$. Furthermore, since $\|\boldsymbol{P}_{22}\boldsymbol{K}\|_\infty < 1$ and $\boldsymbol{P}$ and $\boldsymbol{K}$ have only a finite number of poles in the left-half plane, we can choose R such that $\overline{\sigma}\big(\boldsymbol{P}_{22}\boldsymbol{K}(s)\big) < 1$ for all $s \in D_R$.

With D_R as indicated above, we argue as follows. Since $\overline{\sigma}\big(\boldsymbol{P}_{22}\boldsymbol{K}(s)\big) < 1$ for all $s \in D_R$, $\det(I - \epsilon\boldsymbol{P}_{22}\boldsymbol{K})$ is never zero for $s \in D_R$ and $\epsilon \in [0, 1]$. From (4.3.7) we see that $\det(A_{cl}(\epsilon) - sI)$ deforms continuously as ϵ moves from zero to one without touching the origin. This means that $\det(A_{cl}(0) - sI)$ and $\det(A_{cl}(1) - sI)$ make the same number of encirclements of the origin as s traverses D_R. Since $\det(A_{cl}(0) - sI)$ makes $r+l$ encirclements of the origin, $\det(A_{cl}(1) - sI)$ also makes $r+l$ encirclements. We conclude that $\mathcal{F}_\ell(\boldsymbol{P}, \boldsymbol{K})$ has $r+l$ poles in the open-left-half plane if and only if $\boldsymbol{K}$ has l poles there. ∎

Main points of the section

1. If $\boldsymbol{P}^{\sim}\boldsymbol{P} \leq I$, then $\|\mathcal{F}_\ell(\boldsymbol{P},\boldsymbol{K})\|_\infty \leq 1$ whenever $\|\boldsymbol{K}\|_\infty \leq 1$.
2. If $\boldsymbol{P} \in \mathcal{RH}_\infty$, $\boldsymbol{P}_{21}^{-1} \in \mathcal{RH}_\infty$ and $\boldsymbol{P}^{\sim}\boldsymbol{P} = I$, then $\mathcal{F}_\ell(\boldsymbol{P},\boldsymbol{K})$ is internally stable and satisfies $\|\mathcal{F}_\ell(\boldsymbol{P},\boldsymbol{K})\|_\infty < 1$ if and only if $\boldsymbol{K} \in \mathcal{RH}_\infty$ and $\|\boldsymbol{K}\|_\infty < 1$. This is sometimes known as "Redheffer's theorem".
3. If $\|\boldsymbol{P}_{22}\boldsymbol{K}\|_\infty < 1$ and there are no left-half-plane pole-zero cancellations when $\mathcal{F}_\ell(\boldsymbol{P},\boldsymbol{K})$ is formed, then the number of open-left-half-plane poles in $\mathcal{F}_\ell(\boldsymbol{P},\boldsymbol{K})$ is the sum of the number of open-left-half-plane poles of $\boldsymbol{P}$ and $\boldsymbol{K}$.

4.4 Minimizing the norm of constant LFTs

The task of our controller synthesis theory is to find necessary and sufficient conditions for the existence of stabilizing controllers that satisfy a norm objective on a linear fractional transformation. This section considers the constant matrix version of the synthesis problem, which is the first step towards a general synthesis theory. It is also of some pedagogical value, since the basic structure of the solution approach carries over to the dynamic case. The need to address stability phenomena makes the dynamic case more complex.

Consider the constant matrix LFT

$$\mathcal{F}_\ell\left(\begin{bmatrix} D_{11} & D_{12} \\ D_{21} & D_{22} \end{bmatrix}, F\right) = D_{11} + D_{12}F(I - D_{22}F)^{-1}D_{21},$$

in which F and the D_{ij}'s are complex constant matrices as in (4.3.3). Unless stated otherwise, assume that $(I - D_{22}F)^{-1}$ exists.

We pose the following problem:

> Given the matrix $D = \begin{bmatrix} D_{11} & D_{12} \\ D_{21} & D_{22} \end{bmatrix}$, what is the minimum achievable value of $\|\mathcal{F}_\ell(D,F)\|$ and how do we select a constant matrix F such that $\|\mathcal{F}_\ell(D,F)\|$ is minimized?

The norm is the norm induced by the Euclidean vector norm, *i.e.*, $\|X\| = \overline{\sigma}(X)$.

If D_{12} and D_{21} are nonsingular, the problem is easily solved by finding an $\widehat{F}$ such that $\mathcal{F}_\ell(D,\widehat{F}) = 0$. Carrying out the necessary rearrangement gives

$$\widehat{F} = -(D_{12} - D_{11}D_{21}^{-1}D_{22})^{-1}D_{11}D_{21}^{-1}.$$

If D_{21} is nonsingular and D_{12} has full column rank, the problem is harder and the lowest achievable norm may be greater than zero. We may set $Q = F(I - D_{22}F)^{-1}D_{21}$ and consider the problem of minimizing $\|D_{11} + D_{12}Q\|$, because there is an invertible transformation between Q and F. Once we have a solution $\widehat{Q}$, say, $\widehat{F}$ may be found by back substitution via

$$\widehat{F} = \mathcal{F}_\ell\left(\begin{bmatrix} 0 & I \\ D_{21}^{-1} & -D_{21}^{-1}D_{22} \end{bmatrix}, \widehat{Q}\right).$$

Lemma 4.4.1 *Suppose D_{12} has full column rank and let $R = D_{12}^*D_{12}$.*

1. *The following are equivalent:*

   (a) *There exists a $\widehat{Q}$ such that*

   $$\|D_{11} + D_{12}\widehat{Q}\| \le \gamma; \tag{4.4.1}$$

   (b)

   $$D_{11}^*(I - D_{12}R^{-1}D_{12}^*)D_{11} \le \gamma^2 I; \tag{4.4.2}$$

   (c)

   $$\|\widehat{D}_{12}^*D_{11}\| \le \gamma, \tag{4.4.3}$$

   in which $\widehat{D}_{12}$ is any matrix such that $\begin{bmatrix} \widehat{D}_{12} & D_{12} \end{bmatrix}$ is nonsingular and

   $$\widehat{D}_{12}^*\begin{bmatrix} \widehat{D}_{12} & D_{12} \end{bmatrix} = \begin{bmatrix} I & 0 \end{bmatrix}.$$

2. *If the conditions in Item 1 hold, then $\widehat{Q}$ satisfies (4.4.1) if and only if*

   $$\widehat{Q} = \Theta_{11} + \Theta_{12}U\Theta_{21}, \quad \|U\| \le \gamma, \tag{4.4.4}$$

   in which

   $$\Theta_{11} = -R^{-1}D_{12}^*D_{11}$$

   and Θ_{12} and Θ_{21} are matrices which satisfy

   $$\begin{aligned} \Theta_{12}\Theta_{12}^* &= R^{-1} \\ \Theta_{21}^*\Theta_{21} &= I - \gamma^{-2}D_{11}^*(I - D_{12}R^{-1}D_{12}^*)D_{11} \\ &= I - \gamma^{-2}D_{11}^*\widehat{D}_{12}\widehat{D}_{12}^*D_{11}. \end{aligned}$$

Proof. By completing the square we have

$$\begin{aligned} &(D_{11} + D_{12}\widehat{Q})^*(D_{11} + D_{12}\widehat{Q}) \\ &= D_{11}^*(I - D_{12}R^{-1}D_{12}^*)D_{11} + (\widehat{Q} - \Theta_{11})^*R(\widehat{Q} - \Theta_{11}) \\ &\ge D_{11}^*(I - D_{12}R^{-1}D_{12}^*)D_{11}. \end{aligned}$$

Hence (4.4.2) is necessary and is seen to be sufficient by setting $\widehat{Q} = \Theta_{11}$. To show that (4.4.2) and (4.4.3) are equivalent, we observe that $\begin{bmatrix} \widehat{D}_{12} & D_{12}\Theta_{12} \end{bmatrix}$ is a unitary matrix, which gives

$$\begin{aligned} I &= \begin{bmatrix} \widehat{D}_{12} & D_{12}\Theta_{12} \end{bmatrix} \begin{bmatrix} \widehat{D}_{12}^* \\ \Theta_{12}^* D_{12}^* \end{bmatrix} \\ &= \widehat{D}_{12}\widehat{D}_{12}^* + D_{12}R^{-1}D_{12}^*. \end{aligned}$$

To show that (4.4.4) generates all solutions, note that the completion of squares identity results in

$$\gamma^2\Theta_{21}^*\Theta_{21} - (\widehat{Q} - \Theta_{11})^*(\Theta_{12}^{-1})^*\Theta_{12}^{-1}(\widehat{Q} - \Theta_{11}) \geq 0$$

for any $\widehat{Q}$ that satisfies (4.4.1). Consequently, there exists a matrix U with the property $U^*U \leq I$ which satisfies $\Theta_{12}^{-1}(\widehat{Q} - \Theta_{11}) = \gamma U \Theta_{21}$ (note that if $A^*A = B^*B$ there exists a matrix U with the property $U^*U = I$ such that $UA = B$; see also Problem 9.1). Hence $\gamma^{-1}(D_{11} + D_{12}\widehat{Q}) = \mathcal{F}_\ell(X, \gamma^{-1}U)$, in which

$$X = \begin{bmatrix} \gamma^{-1}(D_{11} + D_{12}\Theta_{11}) & D_{12}\Theta_{12} \\ \Theta_{21} & 0 \end{bmatrix}.$$

Since $X^*X = I$ it follows from Theorem 4.3.1 that $\|D_{11} + D_{12}\widehat{Q}\| \leq \gamma$ for any $\|U\| \leq \gamma$, which is equivalent to (4.4.4). ■

If D_{12} is nonsingular and D_{21} has full row rank, we set $Q = D_{12}F(I - D_{22}F)^{-1}$ and apply Lemma 4.4.1 to the problem of minimizing $\|D_{11}^* + D_{21}^*Q^*\|$. The lowest achievable value of $\|\mathcal{F}_\ell(D, F)\|$ is given by $\|D_{11}\widehat{D}_{21}^*\|$ where $\widehat{D}_{21}$ is any matrix such that $\begin{bmatrix} \widehat{D}_{21}' & D_{21}' \end{bmatrix}$ is nonsingular and

$$\begin{bmatrix} \widehat{D}_{21} \\ D_{21} \end{bmatrix} \widehat{D}_{21}^* = \begin{bmatrix} I \\ 0 \end{bmatrix}.$$

In the case that D_{12} has full column rank and D_{21} has full row rank, we are faced with the problem of finding Q such that

$$\|D_{11} + D_{12}QD_{21}\| \leq \gamma, \tag{4.4.5}$$

in which

$$Q = F(I - D_{22}F)^{-1}.$$

By considering $\|D_{11} + (D_{12}Q)D_{21}\|$ and $\|D_{11} + D_{12}(QD_{21})\|$ separately, it is clear that there exists a Q such that (4.4.5) holds only if

$$\gamma \geq \max\{\|D_{11}\widehat{D}_{21}^*\|, \|\widehat{D}_{12}^*D_{11}\|\}. \tag{4.4.6}$$

Surprisingly, it may be proved that

$$\inf_Q \|D_{11} + D_{12}QD_{21}\| = \max\{\|D_{11}\widehat{D}_{21}^*\|, \|\widehat{D}_{12}^*D_{11}\|\},$$

which is a special case of a more general result known as Parrott's theorem. We supply a proof of this and a formula for all solutions in Chapter 11.[5] For the purposes of our work here, it is enough for us to know that there exists an F such that (4.4.5) is satisfied for any $\gamma \geq \max\{\|D_{11}\widehat{D}_{21}^*\|, \|\widehat{D}_{12}^*D_{11}\|\}$.

Main point of the section

We can solve the constant matrix optimization problem $\min_F \|\mathcal{F}_\ell(D,F)\|$ and we can find all F's that satisfy $\|\mathcal{F}_\ell(D,F)\| \leq \gamma$. This solves the synthesis problem for LFTs defined by constant matrices.

4.5 Simplifying constant LFTs

Consider the LFT

$$\mathcal{F}_\ell\left(\begin{bmatrix} D_{11} & D_{12} \\ D_{21} & D_{22} \end{bmatrix}, F\right) = D_{11} + D_{12}F(I - D_{22}F)^{-1}D_{21}, \tag{4.5.1}$$

in which F and the D_{ij}'s are complex constant matrices as in (4.3.3). Unless stated otherwise, we will assume that $(I - D_{22}F)^{-1}$ exists.

The aim of this section is to show that the LFT may be reduced to a simpler LFT. Firstly, we will show that D_{12} and D_{21} can be orthogonalized using a simple scaling on F. Secondly, we establish that D_{22} can be absorbed into F using a simple change of variable. This means that we will be able to assume $D_{22} = 0$ without loss of generality. Finally, we will show that when considering the minimization of $\|\mathcal{F}_\ell(D,F)\|$, we may without loss of generality assume that $D_{11} = 0$.

Taken together, these steps may be used to show that

$$\|\mathcal{F}_\ell(D,F)\| \leq \gamma \Leftrightarrow \|\mathcal{F}_\ell(\widehat{D},\widehat{F})\| \leq \gamma,$$

in which

$$\widehat{D} = \begin{bmatrix} 0 & \widehat{D}_{12} \\ \widehat{D}_{21} & 0 \end{bmatrix}, \quad \widehat{D}_{12}^*\widehat{D}_{12} = I \quad \text{and} \quad \widehat{D}_{21}\widehat{D}_{21}^* = I.$$

[5] The reader may like to pursue the following argument. From (4.4.4), it follows that

$$\|D_{11} + D_{12}QD_{21}\| \leq \gamma \Leftrightarrow \|\Theta_{12}^{-1}(QD_{21} - \Theta_{11})\Theta_{21}^{-1}\| \leq \gamma,$$

in which Θ_{ij} are as defined in Lemma 4.4.1. Applying Lemma 4.4.1 to $\|\widehat{D}_{11} + \widehat{D}_{12}(\Theta_{12}^{-1}Q)^*\|$, in which $\widehat{D}_{11} = -(\Theta_{12}^{-1}\Theta_{11}\Theta_{21}^{-1})^*$ and $\widehat{D}_{12} = (D_{21}\Theta_{21}^{-1})^*$, we may obtain necessary and sufficient conditions for the existence of Q satisfying $\|D_{11} + D_{12}QD_{21}\| \leq \gamma$ and a characterization of all such Q. It requires some considerable effort, however, to deduce that the condition obtained by this route is just (4.4.6).

The value of this observation lies in the fact that $\mathcal{F}_\ell(\widehat{D}, \widehat{F}) = \widehat{D}_{12}\widehat{F}\widehat{D}_{21}$ and $\|\mathcal{F}_\ell(\widehat{D}, \widehat{F})\| \le \gamma$ if and only if $\|\widehat{F}\| \le \gamma$.

Scaling D_{12} and D_{21}

If D_{12} and D_{21} have full column and row rank respectively, then there exist invertible scaling matrices S_1 and S_2 such that

$$\widehat{D}_{12} = D_{12}S_1 \quad \text{and} \quad \widehat{D}_{21} = S_2 D_{21}$$

satisfy $\widehat{D}_{12}^*\widehat{D}_{12} = I_m$ and $\widehat{D}_{21}\widehat{D}_{21}^* = I_q$. These scaling matrices may be found from singular value decompositions of D_{12} and D_{21}. The scale factors may be absorbed into the LFT by defining

$$\widehat{D}_{22} = S_2 D_{22} S_1 \quad \text{and} \quad \widehat{F} = S_1^{-1} F S_2^{-1},$$

since this results in

$$\begin{aligned}
&\mathcal{F}_\ell\left(\begin{bmatrix} D_{11} & D_{12} \\ D_{21} & D_{22} \end{bmatrix}, F\right) \\
&= D_{11} + D_{12}F(I - D_{22}F)^{-1}D_{21} \\
&= D_{11} + \widehat{D}_{12}S_1^{-1}FS_2^{-1}(I - S_2D_{22}S_1S_1^{-1}FS_2^{-1})^{-1}\widehat{D}_{21} \\
&= D_{11} + \widehat{D}_{12}\widehat{F}(I - \widehat{D}_{22}\widehat{F})^{-1}\widehat{D}_{21} \\
&= \mathcal{F}_\ell\left(\begin{bmatrix} D_{11} & \widehat{D}_{12} \\ \widehat{D}_{21} & \widehat{D}_{22} \end{bmatrix}, \widehat{F}\right).
\end{aligned}$$

This shows that given the LFT $\mathcal{F}_\ell\left(\begin{bmatrix} D_{11} & D_{12} \\ D_{21} & D_{22} \end{bmatrix}, F\right)$, there is an equivalent LFT $\mathcal{F}_\ell\left(\begin{bmatrix} D_{11} & \widehat{D}_{12} \\ \widehat{D}_{21} & \widehat{D}_{22} \end{bmatrix}, \widehat{F}\right)$ such that $\widehat{D}_{12}^*\widehat{D}_{12} = I_m$ and $\widehat{D}_{21}\widehat{D}_{21}^* = I_q$.

Setting $D_{22} = 0$

We will now show that the D_{22} term may always be set to zero by a change of controller variable. Returning to (4.5.1), we observe that by setting

$$\tilde{F} = F(I - D_{22}F)^{-1},$$

we have

$$\mathcal{F}_\ell\left(\begin{bmatrix} D_{11} & D_{12} \\ D_{21} & D_{22} \end{bmatrix}, F\right) = \mathcal{F}_\ell\left(\begin{bmatrix} D_{11} & D_{12} \\ D_{21} & 0 \end{bmatrix}, \tilde{F}\right).$$

Since there is a one-to-one correspondence between F and $\tilde{F}$ if $(I - D_{22}F)$ is non-singular, any study of $\mathcal{F}_\ell\left(\begin{bmatrix} D_{11} & D_{12} \\ D_{21} & D_{22} \end{bmatrix}, F\right)$ may be replaced by an equivalent study of $\mathcal{F}_\ell\left(\begin{bmatrix} D_{11} & D_{12} \\ D_{21} & 0 \end{bmatrix}, \tilde{F}\right)$.

Removing the D_{11} term

The aim of this section is to show how a LFT with $D_{11} \neq 0$ may be replaced with an equivalent LFT with a zero D_{11} term. The equivalence is in terms of the two LFTs satisfying certain norm requirements.

The procedure requires two steps. In the first, we introduce a loop shifting transformation that minimizes the size of the D_{11} entry. The second step replaces the LFT with the nonzero D_{11} entry with an equivalent LFT in which this term is zero.

Consider Figure 4.9, in which F is a loop-shifting transformation and $\boldsymbol{K}$ is some (possibly dynamic) controller. It follows by calculation that

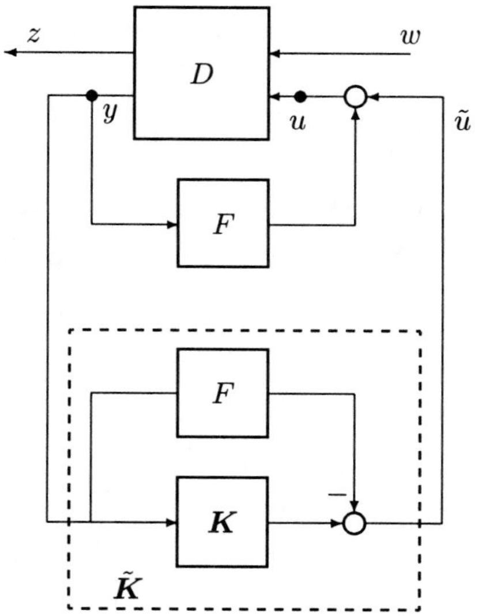

Figure 4.9: Minimizing the norm of D_{11}.

$$\begin{aligned}
&\mathcal{F}_\ell(D, \boldsymbol{K}) \\
&= D_{11} + D_{12}\boldsymbol{K}(I - D_{22}\boldsymbol{K})^{-1}D_{21} \\
&= D_{11} + D_{12}(\tilde{\boldsymbol{K}} + F)\big(I - D_{22}(\tilde{\boldsymbol{K}} + F)\big)^{-1}D_{21}, \\
&\qquad \text{in which} \quad \tilde{\boldsymbol{K}} = \boldsymbol{K} - F \\
&= D_{11} + D_{12}[\tilde{\boldsymbol{K}} + F](I - (I - D_{22}F)^{-1}D_{22}\tilde{\boldsymbol{K}})^{-1}(I - D_{22}F)^{-1}D_{21} \\
&= (D_{11} + D_{12}F(I - D_{22}F)^{-1}D_{21}) \\
&\quad + D_{12}(I - FD_{22})^{-1}\tilde{\boldsymbol{K}}(I - (I - D_{22}F)^{-1}D_{22}\tilde{\boldsymbol{K}})^{-1} \\
&\qquad \times(I - D_{22}F)^{-1}D_{21}
\end{aligned}$$

$$
\begin{aligned}
&= \mathcal{F}_\ell\left(\left[\begin{array}{cc} \mathcal{F}_\ell(D,F) & D_{12}(I-FD_{22})^{-1} \\ (I-D_{22}F)^{-1}D_{21} & (I-D_{22}F)^{-1}D_{22} \end{array}\right], \tilde{\boldsymbol{K}}\right) \\
&= \mathcal{F}_\ell\left(\left[\begin{array}{cc} \bar{D}_{11} & \bar{D}_{12} \\ \bar{D}_{21} & \bar{D}_{22} \end{array}\right], \tilde{\boldsymbol{K}}\right).
\end{aligned}
$$

This shows that $\mathcal{F}_\ell(D, \boldsymbol{K})$ can be replaced by $\mathcal{F}_\ell(\bar{D}, \tilde{\boldsymbol{K}})$ because $\boldsymbol{K}$ and $\tilde{\boldsymbol{K}}$ are interchangeable via $\tilde{\boldsymbol{K}} = \boldsymbol{K} - F$.

Suppose that F has been selected to minimize $\|\bar{D}_{11}\|$; as we have already shown, $\min_F \|\bar{D}_{11}\| = \max(\|D_{11}\widehat{D}_{21}^*\|, \|\widehat{D}_{12}^* D_{11}\|)$. The removal of $\bar{D}_{11}$ may now be accomplished by introducing the matrix

$$
\begin{aligned}
\Theta &= \left[\begin{array}{cc} \Theta_{11} & \Theta_{12} \\ \Theta_{21} & \Theta_{22} \end{array}\right] \\
&= \gamma^{-1}\left[\begin{array}{cc} \gamma^{-1}\bar{D}_{11} & (I-\gamma^{-2}\bar{D}_{11}\bar{D}_{11}^*)^{1/2} \\ -(I-\gamma^{-2}\bar{D}_{11}^*\bar{D}_{11})^{1/2} & \gamma^{-1}\bar{D}_{11}^* \end{array}\right] \qquad (4.5.2)
\end{aligned}
$$

in Figure 4.10, which has the property $\Theta\Theta^* = \gamma^{-2}I$ for any $\gamma \geq \|\bar{D}_{11}\|$.[6]

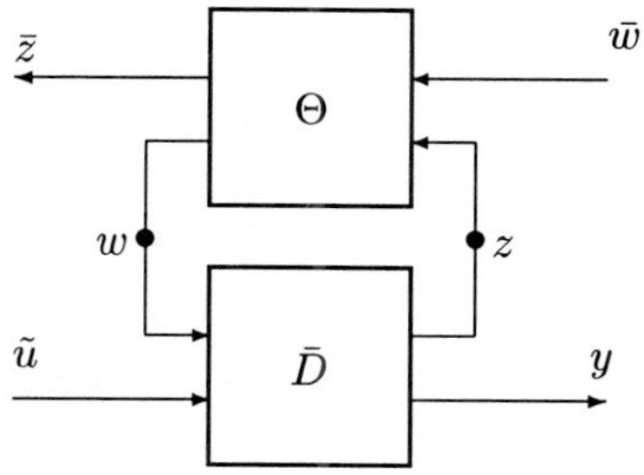

Figure 4.10: The removal of D_{11}.

It follows from the composition formula (4.1.9) that the matrix mapping $\left[\begin{array}{c} \bar{w} \\ \tilde{u} \end{array}\right]$ to $\left[\begin{array}{c} \bar{z} \\ y \end{array}\right]$ is given by

$$
\widehat{D} = \left[\begin{array}{cc} 0 = \mathcal{F}_\ell(\Theta, \bar{D}_{11}) & \Theta_{12}(I-\bar{D}_{11}\Theta_{22})^{-1}\bar{D}_{12} \\ \bar{D}_{21}(I-\Theta_{22}\bar{D}_{11})^{-1}\Theta_{21} & \bar{D}_{22}+\bar{D}_{21}\Theta_{22}(I-\bar{D}_{11}\Theta_{22})^{-1}\bar{D}_{12} \end{array}\right],
$$

which has the required property that $\widehat{D}_{11} = 0$.

[6]In order to establish this property, the square root of A must satisfy $(A^{1/2})^* A^{1/2} = I$ rather than $A^{1/2}A^{1/2} = I$. By invoking the singular value decomposition (of A) it may be proved that $(I - AA^*)^{1/2}A = A(I - A^*A)^{1/2}$.

Since $\Theta\Theta^* = \gamma^{-2}I$, it follows from Theorem 4.3.1 that $\|\mathcal{F}_\ell(\bar{D}, \tilde{\boldsymbol{K}})\| \leq \gamma$ if and only if $\|\mathcal{F}_\ell(\widehat{D}, \tilde{\boldsymbol{K}})\| \leq \gamma^{-1}$, for any $\gamma \geq \|\bar{D}_{11}\|$. Thus the two LFTs $\mathcal{F}_\ell(\bar{D}, \tilde{\boldsymbol{K}})$ and $\mathcal{F}_\ell(\widehat{D}, \tilde{\boldsymbol{K}})$ are equivalent in terms of satisfying an upper bound on their respective norms.

Main points of the section

We have discovered several properties of the constant LFT

$$\mathcal{F}_\ell\left(\left[\begin{array}{cc} D_{11} & D_{12} \\ D_{21} & D_{22} \end{array}\right], F\right).$$

1. There is no loss of generality in assuming that $D_{12}^*D_{12} = I_m$ and $D_{21}D_{21}^* = I_q$ in the case that D_{12} has full column rank and D_{21} has full row rank. This is proved by a simple scaling argument.
2. There is no loss of generality in assuming that $D_{22} = 0$. This property may be established by a simple loop shifting procedure.
3. When analyzing the problem $\|\mathcal{F}_\ell(D, F)\| < \gamma$, we may consider an equivalent problem in which the D_{11}-term is zero, provided γ satisfies the necessary condition given in (4.4.6). The equivalence is in terms of the satisfaction of a norm constraint. *We warn the reader that the transformations used to remove D_{11} do not preserve* trace$\mathcal{F}_\ell(D, F)\mathcal{F}_\ell(D, F)'$ *and therefore cannot be used in the case of 2-norm optimization problems.*

4.6 Simplifying the generalized plant

The aim of this section is to combine the results of Sections 4.5 into a loop shifting and scaling procedure for generalized plant descriptions in controller synthesis problems. As we have already mentioned, our future theoretical development is simplified by the assumption that $D_{11} = 0$ and $D_{22} = 0$. This assumption also leads to a major reduction in the complexity of all the central formulas for $\mathcal{H}_\infty$ and LQG control. A further simplification is achieved by scaling the problem so that D_{12} and D_{21} are parts of orthogonal matrices.

Suppose we are given a generalized plant described by

$$\boldsymbol{P} \stackrel{s}{=} \left[\begin{array}{c|cc} A & B_1 & B_2 \\ \hline C_1 & D_{11} & D_{12} \\ C_2 & D_{21} & D_{22} \end{array}\right] \qquad (4.6.1)$$

and that the state-space data satisfies the following assumptions:

1. (A, B_2, C_2) is stabilizable and detectable.
2. $\text{rank}(D_{12}) = m$ and $\text{rank}(D_{21}) = q$.

3. rank $\begin{bmatrix} j\omega I - A & -B_2 \\ C_1 & D_{12} \end{bmatrix} = m + n$ for all real ω.

4. rank $\begin{bmatrix} j\omega I - A & -B_1 \\ C_2 & D_{21} \end{bmatrix} = q + n$ for all real ω.

The aim of the general scaling and loop shifting procedure is to replace (4.6.1) with an *equivalent* problem of the form

$$\widehat{\boldsymbol{P}} \stackrel{s}{=} \left[\begin{array}{c|cc} \widehat{A} & \widehat{B}_1 & \widehat{B}_2 \\ \hline \widehat{C}_1 & 0 & \widehat{D}_{12} \\ \widehat{C}_2 & \widehat{D}_{21} & 0 \end{array}\right], \tag{4.6.2}$$

in which the data satisfies the following similar assumptions:

$\hat{1}$. $(\widehat{A}, \widehat{B}_2, \widehat{C}_2)$ is stabilizable and detectable.

$\hat{2}$. $\widehat{D}_{12}^*\widehat{D}_{12} = I_m$ and $\widehat{D}_{21}\widehat{D}_{21}^* = I_q$.

$\hat{3}$. rank $\begin{bmatrix} j\omega I - \widehat{A} & -\widehat{B}_2 \\ \widehat{C}_1 & \widehat{D}_{12} \end{bmatrix} = m + n$ for all real ω.

$\hat{4}$. rank $\begin{bmatrix} j\omega I - \widehat{A} & -\widehat{B}_1 \\ \widehat{C}_2 & \widehat{D}_{21} \end{bmatrix} = q + n$ for all real ω.

The scaling and loop shifting procedure may be broken down into four steps. In the fifth step a controller is designed for the derived plant. The controller for the original problem is then found by back substitution in the final step.

Step 1

The purpose of this step is to minimize $\|\bar{D}_{11}\|$. Suppose F is a constant gain matrix to be found and that $\boldsymbol{P}$ is given by (4.6.1). Now consider Figure 4.9 and suppose that the constant D matrix is replaced by the transfer function matrix $\boldsymbol{P}$. The resulting setup appears in Figure 4.11. If

$$\begin{bmatrix} u_2 \\ y \end{bmatrix} = \begin{bmatrix} \boldsymbol{P}_{11} & \boldsymbol{P}_{12} \\ \boldsymbol{P}_{21} & \boldsymbol{P}_{22} \end{bmatrix} \begin{bmatrix} y_2 \\ u \end{bmatrix}$$

with

$$u = Fy + \tilde{u}, \tag{4.6.3}$$

then

$$\begin{aligned} \begin{bmatrix} u_2 \\ y \end{bmatrix} &= \mathcal{F}_\ell\left(\left[\begin{array}{cc|c} \boldsymbol{P}_{11} & \boldsymbol{P}_{12} & \boldsymbol{P}_{12} \\ \boldsymbol{P}_{21} & \boldsymbol{P}_{22} & \boldsymbol{P}_{22} \\ \hline \boldsymbol{P}_{21} & \boldsymbol{P}_{22} & \boldsymbol{P}_{22} \end{array}\right], F \right) \begin{bmatrix} y_2 \\ \tilde{u} \end{bmatrix} \\ &= \begin{bmatrix} \bar{\boldsymbol{P}}_{11} & \bar{\boldsymbol{P}}_{12} \\ \bar{\boldsymbol{P}}_{21} & \bar{\boldsymbol{P}}_{22} \end{bmatrix} \begin{bmatrix} y_2 \\ \tilde{u} \end{bmatrix}. \end{aligned}$$

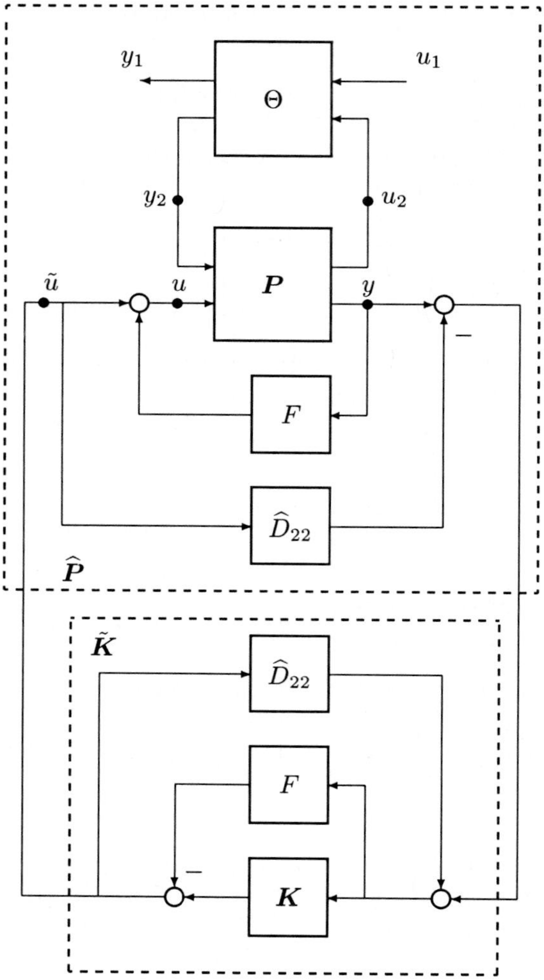

Figure 4.11: The loop transformation procedure.

Eliminating u from

$$\begin{aligned} \dot{x} &= Ax + B_1 y_2 + B_2 u \\ u_2 &= C_1 x + D_{11} y_2 + D_{12} u \\ y &= C_2 x + D_{21} y_2 + D_{22} u \end{aligned}$$

using (4.6.3) yields a realization of $\bar{\boldsymbol{P}} = \begin{bmatrix} \bar{\boldsymbol{P}}_{11} & \bar{\boldsymbol{P}}_{12} \\ \bar{\boldsymbol{P}}_{21} & \bar{\boldsymbol{P}}_{22} \end{bmatrix}$:

$$\bar{\boldsymbol{P}} = \left[\begin{array}{c|cc} A+B_2F(I-D_{22}F)^{-1}C_2 & B_1+B_2F(I-D_{22}F)^{-1}D_{21} & B_2(I-FD_{22})^{-1} \\ \hline C_1+D_{12}F(I-D_{22}F)^{-1}C_2 & D_{11}+D_{12}F(I-D_{22}F)^{-1}D_{21} & D_{12}(I-FD_{22})^{-1} \\ (I-D_{22}F)^{-1}C_2 & (I-D_{22}F)^{-1}D_{21} & (I-D_{22}F)^{-1}D_{22} \end{array}\right] \tag{4.6.4}$$

$$\stackrel{s}{=} \left[\begin{array}{c|cc} \bar{A} & \bar{B}_1 & \bar{B}_2 \\ \hline \bar{C}_1 & \bar{D}_{11} & \bar{D}_{12} \\ \bar{C}_2 & \bar{D}_{21} & \bar{D}_{22} \end{array}\right].$$

Observing that $\bar{D}_{11} = \mathcal{F}_\ell(D, F)$, we select an F such that $\|\bar{D}_{11}\| = \gamma_0$ where

$$\gamma_0 = \max\{\|\widehat{D}_{12}^* D_{11}\|, \|D_{11}\widehat{D}_{21}^*\|\}.$$

(The construction of such an F is considered in detail in Chapter 11—such an F can also be constructed using Lemma 4.4.1). From now on, we suppose that such an F has been found and implemented.

By considering the point $s = \infty$, we see that $\gamma > \gamma_0$ is necessary for the existence of $\boldsymbol{K}$ such that $\|\mathcal{F}_\ell(\boldsymbol{P}, \boldsymbol{K})\|_\infty < \gamma$. Also notice that $\|\bar{\boldsymbol{P}}_{11}\|_2$ is infinite unless $\gamma_0 = 0$. It follows that

$$\max\{\|\widehat{D}_{12}^* D_{11}\|, \|D_{11}\widehat{D}_{21}^*\|\} = 0$$

is necessary for the existence of a time-invariant state-space system $\boldsymbol{K}$ such that $\|\mathcal{F}_\ell(\boldsymbol{P}, \boldsymbol{K})\|_2 < \infty$. Consequently, $\bar{D}_{11} = 0$ whenever a finite 2-norm solution exists. Since the transformation of Step 2 does not preserve the 2-norm, it must be omitted in the case of 2-norm optimization.

Step 2

(Infinity norm optimization only) In this step, we select the orthogonal Θ-matrix in Figures 4.10 and 4.11 that enforces $\mathcal{F}_\ell(\Theta, \bar{D}_{11}) = 0$. To do this, we define

$$\begin{bmatrix} \Theta_{11} & \Theta_{12} \\ \Theta_{21} & \Theta_{22} \end{bmatrix} = \gamma^{-1} \begin{bmatrix} \gamma^{-1}\bar{D}_{11} & (I - \gamma^{-2}\bar{D}_{11}\bar{D}_{11}^*)^{1/2} \\ -(I - \gamma^{-2}\bar{D}_{11}^*\bar{D}_{11})^{1/2} & \gamma^{-1}\bar{D}_{11}^* \end{bmatrix}, \tag{4.6.5}$$

which satisfies $\Theta\Theta^* = \gamma^{-2}I$ and $\|\Theta_{22}\|_2 < \gamma^{-1}$ for all $\gamma > \gamma_0$. Since $\|y_1\|_2^2 - \gamma^{-2}\|u_1\|_2^2 = \gamma^{-2}\|u_2\|_2^2 - \|y_2\|_2^2$ (see Figure 4.11 for a definition of the signals), we conclude that $\|\mathcal{F}_\ell(\widehat{\boldsymbol{P}}, \boldsymbol{K})\|_\infty \leq \gamma^{-1}$ if and only if $\|\mathcal{F}_\ell(\bar{\boldsymbol{P}}, \boldsymbol{K})\|_\infty \leq \gamma$. Since Θ is a constant matrix with $\|\Theta_{22}\|_2 < \gamma^{-1}$, the small gain theorem may be used to show that $\mathcal{F}_\ell(\widehat{\boldsymbol{P}}, \boldsymbol{K})$ is internally stable if and only if $\mathcal{F}_\ell(\bar{\boldsymbol{P}}, \boldsymbol{K})$ is. From this we conclude that $\widehat{\boldsymbol{P}}$ and $\bar{\boldsymbol{P}}$ describe equivalent problems from an internal stability point of view and from the perspective of satisfying an infinite norm condition. By direct computation, $\widehat{\boldsymbol{P}} = \mathcal{C}_\ell(\Theta, \bar{\boldsymbol{P}})$ is given by the realization:

$$\left[\begin{array}{c|cc} \bar A+\bar B_1\Theta_{22}(I-\bar D_{11}\Theta_{22})^{-1}\bar C_1 & \bar B_1(I-\Theta_{22}\bar D_{11})^{-1}\Theta_{21} & \bar B_2+\bar B_1\Theta_{22}(I-\bar D_{11}\Theta_{22})^{-1}\bar D_{12} \\ \hline \Theta_{12}(I-\bar D_{11}\Theta_{22})^{-1}\bar C_1 & 0 & \Theta_{12}(I-\bar D_{11}\Theta_{22})^{-1}\bar D_{12} \\ \bar C_2+\bar D_{21}\Theta_{22}(I-\bar D_{11}\Theta_{22})^{-1}\bar C_1 & \bar D_{21}(I-\Theta_{22}\bar D_{11})^{-1}\Theta_{21} & \bar D_{22}+\bar D_{21}\Theta_{22}(I-\bar D_{11}\Theta_{22})^{-1}\bar D_{12} \end{array}\right]$$

$$= \left[\begin{array}{c|cc} \widehat A & \widehat B_1 & \tilde B_2 \\ \hline \widehat C_1 & 0 & \tilde D_{12} \\ \tilde C_2 & \tilde D_{21} & \widehat D_{22} \end{array}\right], \tag{4.6.6}$$

which has the desired property $\widehat D_{11} = 0$.

Step 3

In this step, we eliminate $\widehat D_{22}$ by connecting $-\widehat D_{22}$ in parallel with $\widehat{\boldsymbol{P}}_{22}$ as illustrated in Figure 4.11.

Step 4

Select scaling matrices S_1 and S_2 so that $\widehat D_{12} = \tilde D_{12} S_1$ satisfies $\widehat D_{12}^* \widehat D_{12} = I_m$, and $\widehat D_{21} = S_2 \tilde D_{21}$ satisfies $\widehat D_{21} \widehat D_{21}^* = I_q$. The scaled generalized regulator problem data becomes

$$\widehat{\boldsymbol{P}} \overset{s}{=} \left[\begin{array}{c|cc} \widehat A & \widehat B_1 & \widehat B_2 \\ \hline \widehat C_1 & 0 & \widehat D_{12} \\ \widehat C_2 & \widehat D_{21} & 0 \end{array}\right], \tag{4.6.7}$$

in which $\widehat B_2 = \tilde B_2 S_1$ and $\widehat C_2 = S_2 \tilde C_2$. This completes the replacement of (4.6.1) with (4.6.2).

Step 5

Compute $\tilde{\boldsymbol{K}}$ for the scaled generalized regulator problem described by (4.6.7). Chapters 5 to 8 will supply all the details about the construction of $\tilde{\boldsymbol{K}}$.

Step 6

Reverse the loop shifting and scaling to obtain the controller $\boldsymbol{K}$ to be used with the original problem characterized by $\boldsymbol{P}$ in (4.6.1). It follows from Figure 4.11 that

$$\boldsymbol{K} = \mathcal{F}_\ell\left(\left[\begin{array}{cc} F & I \\ I & -\widehat D_{22} \end{array}\right], S_2 \tilde{\boldsymbol{K}} S_1 \right).$$

This is the end of the generalized regulator problem replacement and solution procedure.

Before leaving this section, we have to ensure that we do not destroy the properties of the original data given in (4.6.1) while passing to the derived problem given in

(4.6.2) and (4.6.7). We have to show that provided γ is big enough, the realization for $\boldsymbol{P}$ in (4.6.1) satisfies assumptions in Items 1 to 4 if and only if the realization for $\widehat{P}$ given in (4.6.2) satisfies the assumptions in Items $\widehat{1}$ to $\widehat{4}$. In our analysis we treat the transformation between $\boldsymbol{P}$ and $\bar{\boldsymbol{P}}$ first, and the transformation between $\bar{\boldsymbol{P}}$ and $\widehat{\boldsymbol{P}}$ second.

Lemma 4.6.1 *The generalized regulator assumptions in Items 1 to 4 apply to realization (4.6.1) if and only if they apply to realization (4.6.4).*

Proof. The assumption in Item 1 follows from the fact that stabilizability and detectability are invariant under output feedback. The assumption in Item 2 is immediate from (4.6.4) since $(I - FD_{22})^{-1}$ exists. The assumptions in Items 3 and 4 are preserved because

$$\begin{bmatrix} sI - \bar{A} & -\bar{B}_2 \\ \bar{C}_1 & \bar{D}_{12} \end{bmatrix} = \begin{bmatrix} sI - A & -B_2 \\ C_1 & D_{12} \end{bmatrix} \begin{bmatrix} I & 0 \\ F(I - D_{22}F)^{-1}C_2 & (I - FD_{22})^{-1} \end{bmatrix}$$

and

$$\begin{bmatrix} sI - \bar{A} & -\bar{B}_1 \\ \bar{C}_2 & \bar{D}_{21} \end{bmatrix} = \begin{bmatrix} I & -B_2F(I - D_{22}F)^{-1} \\ 0 & (I - D_{22}F)^{-1} \end{bmatrix} \begin{bmatrix} sI - A & -B_1 \\ C_2 & D_{21} \end{bmatrix}. \qquad \blacksquare$$

Lemma 4.6.2 *Suppose there exists an internally-stabilizing controller such that* $\|\mathcal{F}_\ell(\boldsymbol{P}, \boldsymbol{K})\|_\infty < \gamma$*. Then:*

1. $(\widehat{A}, \widehat{B}_2, \widehat{C}_2)$ *is stabilizable and detectable.*

2. $\operatorname{rank}(D_{12}) = m \Leftrightarrow \operatorname{rank}(\widehat{D}_{12}) = m$, *and* $\operatorname{rank}(D_{21}) = q \Leftrightarrow \operatorname{rank}(\widehat{D}_{21}) = q$.

3. $$\operatorname{rank} \begin{bmatrix} j\omega I - A & -B_2 \\ C_1 & D_{12} \end{bmatrix} = \operatorname{rank} \begin{bmatrix} j\omega I - \widehat{A} & -\widehat{B}_2 \\ \widehat{C}_1 & \widehat{D}_{12} \end{bmatrix}.$$

4. $$\operatorname{rank} \begin{bmatrix} j\omega I - A & -B_1 \\ C_2 & D_{21} \end{bmatrix} = \operatorname{rank} \begin{bmatrix} j\omega I - \widehat{A} & -\widehat{B}_1 \\ \widehat{C}_2 & \widehat{D}_{21} \end{bmatrix}.$$

Proof.

Item 1: Since $\|\Theta_{22}\|_2 < \gamma^{-1}$, it follows from the small gain theorem that $\mathcal{F}_\ell(\widehat{\boldsymbol{P}}, \boldsymbol{K})$ is internally stable. Since $\boldsymbol{K}$ is an internally-stabilizing controller for $\widehat{\boldsymbol{P}}$, it follows that $(\widehat{A}, \widehat{B}_2, \widehat{C}_2)$ is stabilizable and detectable.

Item 2: This follows from the invertibility of Θ_{12} and Θ_{21}, equation (4.6.4) and equation (4.6.6).

Items 3 and 4: These follow from Lemma 4.6.1 and the identities:

$$\begin{bmatrix} sI - \widehat{A} & -\widehat{B}_2 \\ \widehat{C}_1 & \widehat{D}_{12} \end{bmatrix} = \begin{bmatrix} I & -\bar{B}_1\Theta_{22}(I - \bar{D}_{11}\Theta_{22})^{-1} \\ 0 & \Theta_{12}(I - \bar{D}_{11}\Theta_{22})^{-1} \end{bmatrix} \begin{bmatrix} sI - \bar{A} & -\bar{B}_2S_1 \\ \bar{C}_1 & \bar{D}_{12}S_1 \end{bmatrix}$$

and

$$\begin{bmatrix} sI-\widehat{A} & -\widehat{B}_1 \\ \widehat{C}_2 & \widehat{D}_{21} \end{bmatrix}$$
$$= \begin{bmatrix} sI-\bar{A} & -\bar{B}_1 \\ S_2\bar{C}_2 & S_2\bar{D}_{21} \end{bmatrix} \begin{bmatrix} I & 0 \\ \Theta_{22}(I-\bar{D}_{11}\Theta_{22})^{-1}\bar{C}_1 & (I-\Theta_{22}\bar{D}_{11})^{-1}\Theta_{21} \end{bmatrix}. \quad \blacksquare$$

Finally, we remark that the loop shifting and scaling transformations described in this section may be extended to the case of time-varying systems. For details, see [130].

Main points of the section

1. The theory and equations associated with controller synthesis are greatly simplified when $D_{11}=0$ and $D_{22}=0$.
2. The condition $\gamma > \max(\|\widehat{D}_{12}^*D_{11}\|, \|D_{11}\widehat{D}_{21}^*\|)$ is necessary for the existence of $\boldsymbol{K}$ such that $\|\mathcal{F}_\ell(\boldsymbol{P},\boldsymbol{K})\|_\infty < \gamma$. In this case, the problem of finding $\boldsymbol{K}$ such that $\|\mathcal{F}_\ell(\boldsymbol{P},\boldsymbol{K})\|_\infty < \gamma$ may be replaced by an equivalent problem of the form (4.6.2).
3. The condition $\max\{\|\widehat{D}_{12}^*D_{11}\|, \|D_{11}\widehat{D}_{21}^*\|\} = 0$ is necessary for the existence of $\boldsymbol{K}$ such that $\|\mathcal{F}_\ell(\boldsymbol{P},\boldsymbol{K})\|_2 < \infty$. In this case, the problem of finding $\boldsymbol{K}$ such that $\|\mathcal{F}_\ell(\boldsymbol{P},\boldsymbol{K})\|_2 < \gamma$ may be replaced by an equivalent problem of the form (4.6.2).
4. The problem replacement procedure involves several changes of variable, but is otherwise straightforward.
5. If a solution to the problem described by (4.6.1) and assumptions in Items 1 to 4 exists, then a solution to the problem described by (4.6.2) exists also. Under these conditions, assumptions in Items $\widehat{1}$ to $\widehat{4}$ are satisfied.

4.7 Notes and References

Linear fractional or bilinear transformations have a long history in complex analysis. Reviews of this material can be found in many books that deal with conformal mapping theory. A particularly good treatment of the classical properties of simple bilinear transformations of the form

$$\xi = \frac{as+b}{cs+d},$$

in which (a,b,c,d) are numbers, can be found in Nevanlinna and Paatero [157].

Our main references for operator valued linear fractional transformations are the papers of Redheffer [171, 170]. Reference [171] contains a number of interesting results pertaining to the transformation

$$f(\boldsymbol{z}) = \boldsymbol{u} + \boldsymbol{r}\boldsymbol{z}(1 - \boldsymbol{w}\boldsymbol{z})^{-1}\boldsymbol{s},$$

in which $(\boldsymbol{u}, \boldsymbol{r}, \boldsymbol{s}, \boldsymbol{w}, \boldsymbol{z})$ are operators defined on a Hilbert space and such that

$$\left\| \begin{bmatrix} \boldsymbol{r} & \boldsymbol{u} \\ \boldsymbol{w} & \boldsymbol{s} \end{bmatrix} \right\| \leq 1.$$

This paper also deals with the properties of the so called "star product", which is of great importance to us here. (It is, in essence, identical to the composition operator $\mathcal{C}_\ell(\cdot,\cdot)$.) In his earlier paper [170], Redheffer studies linear fractional transformations of the form

$$\Xi = U + SK(I - WK)^{-1}R$$

in the context of Riccati equations. The objects (U, R, S, W, Z) are all $n \times n$ complex matrices that are functions of the variables (x, y) with y real. Redheffer's Theorem IV is of some interest:

> "Let U, R, S, W be complex $n \times n$ matrices such that S or R is non-singular and such that the matrix
>
> $$\begin{bmatrix} S & U \\ W & R \end{bmatrix}$$
>
> is dissipative (*i.e.*, has norm ≤ 1). Then the matrix
>
> $$U + SK(I - WK)^{-1}R$$
>
> is dissipative whenever K is dissipative. If the first matrix is not only dissipative but unitary, then the second is unitary for all unitary K."

There is a nice treatment of this type of result (in the unitary case) in Young's book [222].

Linear fractional transformations have been used in circuits and systems theory for many decades. Examples that are of direct relevance to us can be found in Safonov [177] and Zames [225, 226] in the context of conic sector stability theory and Doyle [52] who popularized their use in the $\mathcal{H}_\infty$ control. Another source for the use of linear fractional transformations in $\mathcal{H}_\infty$ is Safonov *et at* [181]. This paper also discusses the use of bilinear transformations in the design of controllers that ensure that a certain closed-loop operator lies in a sector $[a, b]$. Zames [225, 226] shows that the transformation

$$\boldsymbol{S} = \left(\frac{2/b}{1 - a/b}\right)\boldsymbol{T} + \left(\frac{a/b + 1}{a/b - 1}\right) I$$

is a bijective map between $\boldsymbol{T}$ in sector $[a, b]$ and $\|\boldsymbol{S}\|_\infty \leq 1$. If it is possible to find a controller $\boldsymbol{K}$ in the figure below

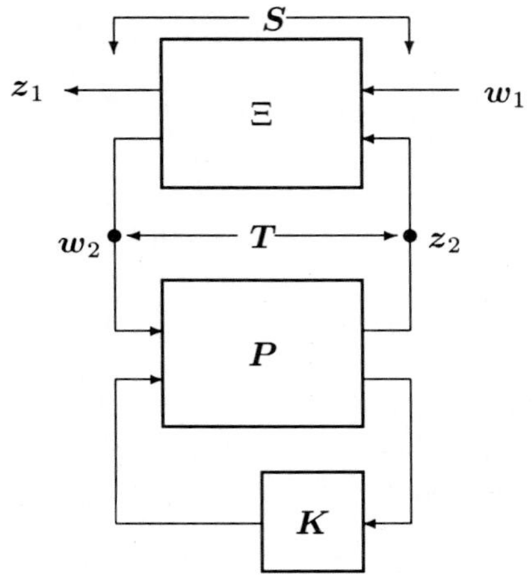

such that $\|\boldsymbol{S}\|_\infty \leq 1$, then $\boldsymbol{T} \in$ sector $[a, b]$. The linear fractional transformation Ξ is given by

$$\Xi = \begin{bmatrix} \left(\frac{a/b+1}{a/b-1}\right) I & \left(\frac{2/b}{1-a/b}\right) I \\ I & 0 \end{bmatrix}.$$

A summary of some of the results in this chapter can be found in Glover [74], who used linear fractional transformations in his work on model reduction. The loop shifting trick used to remove D_{11} first appeared in Safonov, Limebeer and Chiang [183, 184], although the most comprehensive treatment of this material is contained in Glover *et al* [78]. Parrott's theorem [160], which plays a key role in the loop shifting argument, can be used to solve the generalized regulator problem (see Chapter 11). The books of Power [168] and Young [222] contain a clear and highly readable treatment of Parrott's theorem. Lemma 4.1.2, which pins down the cancellation locations in linear fractional transformations, first appeared in Limebeer and Hung[134].

4.8 Problems

Unless stated otherwise, the following assumptions may be made in connection with each of the problems:

1. Every transfer function matrix is an element of $\mathcal{RL}_\infty$.

2. Every indicated inverse exists.

3. Every indicated LFT is well-posed.

Problem 4.1.

1. Determine linear fractional transformations $w = \frac{as+b}{cs+d}$ that: (a) map the imaginary axis in the s-plane to the circle $|1/(1-w)| = \gamma$ in the w-plane; (b) map the imaginary axis in the s-plane to the circle $|w/(1-w)| = \gamma$ in the w-plane.
2. With $\boldsymbol{g} = \frac{1}{s-1}$, determine a stabilizing controller $\boldsymbol{k}$ such that $\boldsymbol{q} = \boldsymbol{gk}$ satisfies: (a) $|1/(1-\boldsymbol{q}(j\omega))| = \gamma$ for all ω; (b) $|\boldsymbol{q}(j\omega)/(1-\boldsymbol{q}(j\omega))| = \gamma$ for all ω. In each case, determine the greatest lower bound on the values of γ for which a solution exists.
3. Repeat Exercise 2(a) for the plant $\boldsymbol{g} = \frac{1}{(s-1)^2}$. Note that in this case two encirclements of the $+1$ point are required for closed-loop stability.

Problem 4.2. Consider the LFT $\mathcal{F}_\ell\left(\begin{bmatrix} \boldsymbol{P}_{11} & \boldsymbol{P}_{12} \\ \boldsymbol{P}_{21} & \boldsymbol{P}_{22} \end{bmatrix}, \boldsymbol{K}\right)$. If $\boldsymbol{P}_{12}$ has full column rank for almost all s and $\boldsymbol{P}_{21}$ has full row rank for almost all s, show that $\mathcal{F}_\ell(\boldsymbol{P}, \boldsymbol{K}_1) = \mathcal{F}_\ell(\boldsymbol{P}, \boldsymbol{K}_2)$ implies that $\boldsymbol{K}_1 = \boldsymbol{K}_2$.

Problem 4.3. If $\boldsymbol{R} = \mathcal{F}_\ell(\boldsymbol{P}, \boldsymbol{K})$, show that $\boldsymbol{K} = \mathcal{F}_u(\boldsymbol{P}^{-1}, \boldsymbol{R})$. The "upper" LFT $\mathcal{F}_u(\boldsymbol{P}, \boldsymbol{K})$ is defined by

$$\mathcal{F}_u(\boldsymbol{P}, \boldsymbol{K}) = \boldsymbol{P}_{22} + \boldsymbol{P}_{21}\boldsymbol{K}(I - \boldsymbol{P}_{11}\boldsymbol{K})^{-1}\boldsymbol{P}_{12},$$

in which

$$\boldsymbol{P} = \begin{bmatrix} \boldsymbol{P}_{11} & \boldsymbol{P}_{12} \\ \boldsymbol{P}_{21} & \boldsymbol{P}_{22} \end{bmatrix}.$$

Problem 4.4. Suppose $\boldsymbol{Z} = (I+\boldsymbol{S})(I-\boldsymbol{S})^{-1}$, in which $(I-\boldsymbol{S})^{-1}$ is assumed to exist for all $\mathrm{R}_e(s) > 0$. Show that

$$\boldsymbol{Z} = \mathcal{F}_\ell\left(\begin{bmatrix} I & I \\ 2I & I \end{bmatrix}, \boldsymbol{S}\right).$$

Problem 4.5. Suppose $\boldsymbol{P}$ and $\boldsymbol{\Theta}$ are related by

$$\begin{aligned}
\begin{bmatrix} \boldsymbol{\Theta}_{11} & \boldsymbol{\Theta}_{12} \\ \boldsymbol{\Theta}_{21} & \boldsymbol{\Theta}_{22} \end{bmatrix} &= \begin{bmatrix} \boldsymbol{P}_{12} - \boldsymbol{P}_{11}\boldsymbol{P}_{21}^{-1}\boldsymbol{P}_{22} & \boldsymbol{P}_{11}\boldsymbol{P}_{21}^{-1} \\ -\boldsymbol{P}_{21}^{-1}\boldsymbol{P}_{22} & \boldsymbol{P}_{21}^{-1} \end{bmatrix} \\
&= \begin{bmatrix} \boldsymbol{P}_{11} & \boldsymbol{P}_{12} \\ I & 0 \end{bmatrix}\begin{bmatrix} 0 & I \\ \boldsymbol{P}_{21} & \boldsymbol{P}_{22} \end{bmatrix}^{-1}.
\end{aligned}$$

1. Verify that

$$\mathcal{F}_\ell(\boldsymbol{P}, \boldsymbol{K}) = (\boldsymbol{\Theta}_{11}\boldsymbol{K} + \boldsymbol{\Theta}_{12})(\boldsymbol{\Theta}_{21}\boldsymbol{K} + \boldsymbol{\Theta}_{22})^{-1}.$$

2. Show that $\boldsymbol{P}^\sim\boldsymbol{P} = I$ if and only if $\boldsymbol{\Theta}^\sim J\boldsymbol{\Theta} = J$, where $J = \begin{bmatrix} I & 0 \\ 0 & -I \end{bmatrix}$.

3. If $\boldsymbol{P}$ has realization

$$\boldsymbol{P} \stackrel{s}{=} \left[\begin{array}{c|cc} A & B_1 & B_2 \\ \hline C_1 & D_{11} & D_{12} \\ C_2 & D_{21} & D_{22} \end{array}\right],$$

show that $\boldsymbol{\Theta}$ has realization

$$\boldsymbol{\Theta} \stackrel{s}{=} \left[\begin{array}{c|cc} A - B_1 D_{21}^{-1} C_2 & B_2 - B_1 D_{21}^{-1} D_{22} & B_1 D_{21}^{-1} \\ \hline C_1 - D_{11} D_{21}^{-1} C_2 & D_{12} - D_{11} D_{21}^{-1} D_{22} & D_{11} D_{21}^{-1} \\ -D_{21}^{-1} C_2 & -D_{21}^{-1} D_{22} & D_{21}^{-1} \end{array}\right].$$

Problem 4.6. Show that X satisfies the fixed point property

$$X = (-DX - C)(BX + A)^{-1}$$

if and only if it satisfies the Riccati equation

$$0 = DX + XA + XBX + C.$$

Problem 4.7. Consider the interconnection

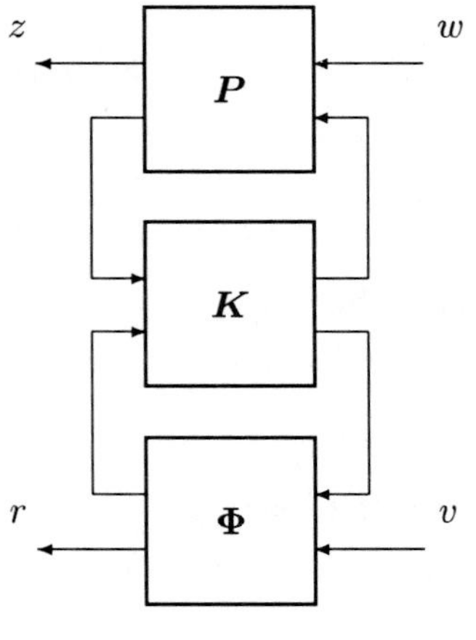

in which

$$\boldsymbol{P} = \begin{bmatrix} \boldsymbol{P}_{11} & \boldsymbol{P}_{12} \\ \boldsymbol{P}_{21} & \boldsymbol{P}_{22} \end{bmatrix}, \quad \boldsymbol{K} = \begin{bmatrix} \boldsymbol{K}_{11} & \boldsymbol{K}_{12} \\ \boldsymbol{K}_{21} & \boldsymbol{K}_{22} \end{bmatrix}, \quad \boldsymbol{\Phi} = \begin{bmatrix} \boldsymbol{\Phi}_{11} & * \\ * & * \end{bmatrix}.$$

Show that

$$\begin{bmatrix} z \\ r \end{bmatrix} = \begin{bmatrix} \mathcal{F}_\ell(\boldsymbol{P}, \mathcal{F}_\ell(\boldsymbol{K}, \boldsymbol{\Phi}_{11})) & * \\ * & * \end{bmatrix} \begin{bmatrix} w \\ v \end{bmatrix}$$

where "*" denotes an irrelevant entry.

Problem 4.8. This problem is intended to illustrate various properties of the inverses of LFTs of the type illustrated below:

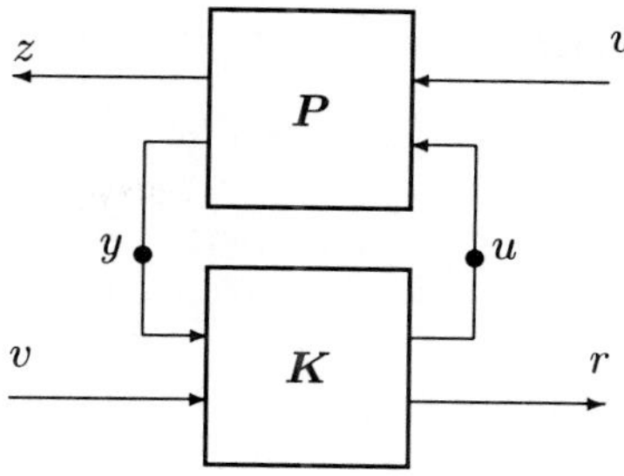

1. Find general formula for the mapping $\begin{bmatrix} w \\ v \end{bmatrix} \mapsto \begin{bmatrix} z \\ r \end{bmatrix}$ (*i.e.*, verify the composition formula in equation (4.1.8)).
2. If $\boldsymbol{P}_{12}$ and $\boldsymbol{P}_{21}$ are invertible, show that $\boldsymbol{P}^{\#}$ given by

$$\begin{bmatrix} -(\boldsymbol{P}_{12} - \boldsymbol{P}_{11}\boldsymbol{P}_{21}^{-1}\boldsymbol{P}_{22})^{-1}\boldsymbol{P}_{11}\boldsymbol{P}_{21}^{-1} & (\boldsymbol{P}_{12} - \boldsymbol{P}_{11}\boldsymbol{P}_{21}^{-1}\boldsymbol{P}_{22})^{-1} \\ (\boldsymbol{P}_{21} - \boldsymbol{P}_{22}\boldsymbol{P}_{12}^{-1}\boldsymbol{P}_{11})^{-1} & -\boldsymbol{P}_{21}^{-1}\boldsymbol{P}_{22}(\boldsymbol{P}_{12} - \boldsymbol{P}_{11}\boldsymbol{P}_{21}^{-1}\boldsymbol{P}_{22})^{-1} \end{bmatrix}$$

inverts $\boldsymbol{P}$ in the sense that $\mathcal{C}_\ell(\boldsymbol{P}, \boldsymbol{P}^{\#}) = \begin{bmatrix} 0 & I \\ I & 0 \end{bmatrix}$. Compare $\boldsymbol{P}^{\#}$ with a partitioned formula for $\boldsymbol{P}^{-1}$.
3. If $\boldsymbol{P}\boldsymbol{P}^{\sim} = I$ with $\boldsymbol{P}_{12}$ and $\boldsymbol{P}_{21}$ invertible, show that

$$\boldsymbol{P}^{\#} = \begin{bmatrix} \boldsymbol{P}_{22}^{\sim} & \boldsymbol{P}_{12}^{\sim} \\ \boldsymbol{P}_{21}^{\sim} & \boldsymbol{P}_{11}^{\sim} \end{bmatrix}.$$

Problem 4.9. Consider the set $\mathcal{P}$ of nonsingular 2×2 block transfer function matrices $\begin{bmatrix} \boldsymbol{P}_{11} & \boldsymbol{P}_{12} \\ \boldsymbol{P}_{21} & \boldsymbol{P}_{22} \end{bmatrix}$, in which $\boldsymbol{P}_{12}$ and $\boldsymbol{P}_{21}$ are also nonsingular for almost all values of s. The composition operator $\mathcal{C}_\ell(\cdot,\cdot)$ is a binary operation on $\mathcal{P}$ defined as the 2×2 block matrix mapping $\begin{bmatrix} w' & v' \end{bmatrix}' \mapsto \begin{bmatrix} z' & r' \end{bmatrix}'$ in the figure below:

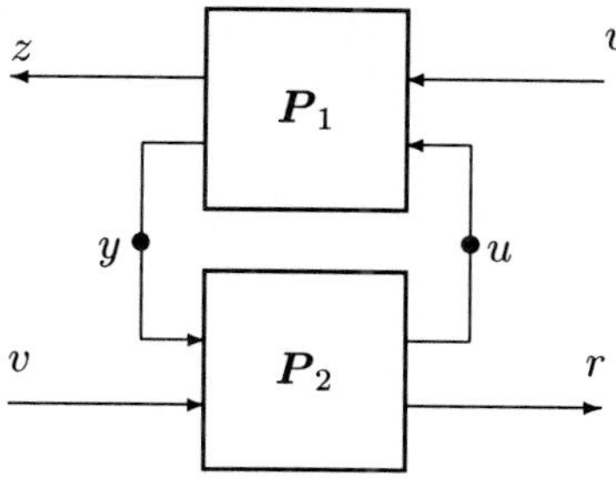

1. If $\boldsymbol{P}_1$ and $\boldsymbol{P}_2$ are elements of $\mathcal{P}$, show that $\mathcal{C}_\ell(\boldsymbol{P}_1, \boldsymbol{P}_2)$ is also an element of $\mathcal{P}$; this is the closure property of $\mathcal{P}$ with respect to $\mathcal{C}_\ell(\cdot,\cdot)$.

2. If $\boldsymbol{P}_1$, $\boldsymbol{P}_2$ and $\boldsymbol{P}_3$ are elements of $\mathcal{P}$, show that

$$\mathcal{C}_\ell(\mathcal{C}_\ell(\boldsymbol{P}_1,\boldsymbol{P}_2),\boldsymbol{P}_3) = \mathcal{C}_\ell\big(\boldsymbol{P}_1,\mathcal{C}_\ell(\boldsymbol{P}_2,\boldsymbol{P}_3)\big),$$

which is the associativity property.
3. Show there exists an identity element $\boldsymbol{P}_I \in \mathcal{P}$ such that $\boldsymbol{P} = \mathcal{C}_\ell(\boldsymbol{P},\boldsymbol{P}_I)$ and $\boldsymbol{P} = \mathcal{C}_\ell(\boldsymbol{P}_I,\boldsymbol{P})$.
4. Show that for every element in $\mathcal{P}$ there exists an inverse $\boldsymbol{P}^{\#} \in \mathcal{P}$ such that $\boldsymbol{P}_I = \mathcal{C}_\ell(\boldsymbol{P}^{\#},\boldsymbol{P})$ and $\boldsymbol{P}_I = \mathcal{C}_\ell(\boldsymbol{P},\boldsymbol{P}^{\#})$.
5. Conclude that $\mathcal{P}$ is a group with respect to $\mathcal{C}_\ell(\cdot,\cdot)$.

In the above calculations, assume that all the LFTs are well-posed. By including an additional condition like $\left\| \begin{bmatrix} \boldsymbol{P}_{11} & \boldsymbol{P}_{12} \\ \boldsymbol{P}_{21} & \boldsymbol{P}_{22} \end{bmatrix} \right\|_\infty \leq 1$, well-posedness would be assured.

Problem 4.10. Suppose $\boldsymbol{G} = D + C(sI - A)^{-1}B$ and $w = \frac{as+b}{cs+d}$, in which $ad - bc \neq 0$ and $cA + dI$ is nonsingular.

1. Show that $\boldsymbol{G}(s) = \widehat{\boldsymbol{G}}(w)$, in which $\widehat{\boldsymbol{G}}$ has realization $(\widehat{A},\widehat{B},\widehat{C},\widehat{D})$ given by

$$\begin{aligned} \widehat{A} &= (aA + bI)(cA + dI)^{-1} \\ \widehat{B} &= (cA + dI)^{-1}B \\ \widehat{C} &= (ad - bc)C(cA + dI)^{-1} \\ \widehat{D} &= D - cC(cA + dI)^{-1}B. \end{aligned}$$

(Hint: write $\boldsymbol{G} = \mathcal{F}_\ell(P, 1/s)$ in which $P = \begin{bmatrix} D & C \\ B & A \end{bmatrix}$ and $1/s = \mathcal{F}_\ell(R, 1/w)$ for some matrix R and use the composition formula for LFTs)
2. Show that $(\widehat{A},\widehat{C})$ is observable if and only if (A,C) is observable and that $(\widehat{A},\widehat{B})$ is controllable if and only if (A,B) is controllable.

Problem 4.11. Suppose we seek a stabilizing controller that satisfies

$$\left\| \begin{bmatrix} \boldsymbol{W}_1(I - \boldsymbol{G}\boldsymbol{K})^{-1} \\ \boldsymbol{W}_2\boldsymbol{K}(I - \boldsymbol{G}\boldsymbol{K})^{-1} \end{bmatrix} \right\|_\infty < 1.$$

1. Show that the generalized plant for this problem is

$$\boldsymbol{P} = \left[\begin{array}{c|c} \boldsymbol{W}_1 & \boldsymbol{W}_1\boldsymbol{G} \\ 0 & \boldsymbol{W}_2 \\ \hline I & \boldsymbol{G} \end{array}\right]$$

2. If

$$\boldsymbol{G} \stackrel{s}{=} \begin{bmatrix} A & B \\ C & D \end{bmatrix}, \quad \boldsymbol{W}_1 \stackrel{s}{=} \begin{bmatrix} A_1 & B_1 \\ C_1 & D_1 \end{bmatrix}, \quad \boldsymbol{W}_2 \stackrel{s}{=} \begin{bmatrix} A_2 & B_2 \\ C_2 & D_2 \end{bmatrix},$$

show that

$$P \stackrel{s}{=} \left[\begin{array}{ccc|cc} A_1 & 0 & B_1C & B_1 & B_1D \\ 0 & A_2 & 0 & 0 & B_2 \\ 0 & 0 & A & 0 & B \\ \hline C_1 & 0 & D_1C & D_1 & D_1D \\ 0 & C_2 & 0 & 0 & D_2 \\ 0 & 0 & C & I & D \end{array}\right].$$

Problem 4.12. Consider the block diagram given below:

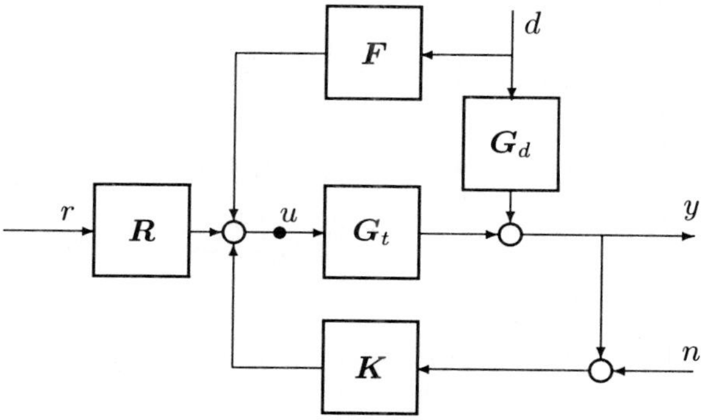

Show that

$$\begin{bmatrix} y \\ r-y \\ u \end{bmatrix} = \mathcal{F}_\ell(\left[\begin{array}{ccc|c} \boldsymbol{G}_d & 0 & 0 & \boldsymbol{G}_t \\ -\boldsymbol{G}_d & I & 0 & -\boldsymbol{G}_t \\ 0 & 0 & 0 & I \\ \hline I & 0 & 0 & 0 \\ 0 & I & 0 & 0 \\ \boldsymbol{G}_d & 0 & I & \boldsymbol{G}_t \end{array}\right], [\ \boldsymbol{F} \quad \boldsymbol{R} \quad \boldsymbol{K}\ ]) \begin{bmatrix} d \\ r \\ n \end{bmatrix}.$$

Problem 4.13. If $\boldsymbol{P} \in \mathcal{RH}_\infty$ and $\boldsymbol{K} \in \mathcal{RH}_\infty$ such that $\|\boldsymbol{P}_{22}\boldsymbol{K}\|_\infty < 1$, show that $\mathcal{F}_\ell(\boldsymbol{P}, \boldsymbol{K}) \in \mathcal{RH}_\infty$.

Problem 4.14. Consider the LFT described by $\mathcal{F}_\ell(D, f)$, in which

$$D = \left[\begin{array}{cc|c} 1 & 0 & 0 \\ 0 & 0 & 1 \\ \hline 0 & 1 & 0 \end{array}\right].$$

1. Show that $D'D = I$.
2. Show that $|f| < 1$ does not imply that $\|\mathcal{F}_\ell(D, f)\| < 1$.
3. Show that $|f| > 1$ does imply that $\|\mathcal{F}_\ell(D, f)\| > 1$.

Problem 4.15. Suppose

$$D = \left[\begin{array}{c|c} I & X \\ 0 & I \\ \hline I & X \end{array}\right].$$

Show that there exists an F such that $\|\mathcal{F}_\ell(D,F)\| \le \gamma$ if and only if $\gamma \ge 1/\sqrt{\underline{\sigma}(I+XX^*)}$. Determine an $\widehat{F}$ such that $\|\mathcal{F}_\ell(D,\widehat{F})\| = 1/\sqrt{\underline{\sigma}(I+XX^*)}$.

Problem 4.16. Suppose $\boldsymbol{G} = D + C(sI-A)^{-1}B$ and $\gamma > \|D\|$.

1. Show that $\|\boldsymbol{G}\|_\infty < \gamma$ if and only if $\|\widehat{\boldsymbol{G}}\|_\infty < \gamma$, in which $\widehat{\boldsymbol{G}} = \gamma\mathcal{F}_\ell(\Theta, \gamma^{-1}\boldsymbol{G})$ and
$$\Theta = \left[\begin{array}{cc} \gamma^{-1}D & (I-\gamma^{-2}DD')^{1/2} \\ -(I-\gamma^{-2}D'D)^{1/2} & \gamma^{-1}D' \end{array}\right].$$
2. Find a realization of $\widehat{\boldsymbol{G}}$ and show that it has the form
$$\widehat{\boldsymbol{G}} \stackrel{s}{=} \left[\begin{array}{c|c} \widehat{A} & \widehat{B} \\ \hline \widehat{C} & 0 \end{array}\right].$$
3. Show that A is asymptotically stable and $\|\boldsymbol{G}\|_\infty < \gamma$ if and only if $\widehat{A}$ asymptotically stable and $\|\widehat{\boldsymbol{G}}\|_\infty < \gamma$.

Problem 4.17. Suppose $\boldsymbol{G} \stackrel{s}{=} \left[\begin{array}{c|c} A & B \\ \hline C & D \end{array}\right]$ has all its poles in the open unit disc. If $\left\|\left[\begin{array}{cc} D & C \\ B & A \end{array}\right]\right\| \le 1$, show that $\|\boldsymbol{G}\|_\infty \le 1$; in this case $\|\cdot\|_\infty = \sup_{\theta, r\ge 1}\|\boldsymbol{G}(re^{i\theta})\|$.

Problem 4.18. Use the bilinear transformation $z = (1+s)/(1-s)$ to derive the discrete bounded real equations.

(Hint: show that if $\boldsymbol{G}(z) = D + C(zI-A)^{-1}B$, then $\widehat{\boldsymbol{G}}(s) = \widehat{D} + \widehat{C}(sI-\widehat{A})^{-1}\widehat{B}$ where

$$\begin{aligned}
\widehat{A} &= (I+A)^{-1}(A-I) \\
\widehat{B} &= \sqrt{2}(I+A)^{-1}B \\
\widehat{C} &= \sqrt{2}C(I+A)^{-1} \\
\widehat{D} &= D - C(I+A)^{-1}B.
\end{aligned}$$

Then substitute into the continuous bounded real equations.)

Problem 4.19. Suppose $\boldsymbol{G}(z)$ has all its poles in the open unit disc. If $\|\boldsymbol{G}\|_\infty = \sup_{\theta, r\ge 1}\|\boldsymbol{G}(re^{i\theta})\| < 1$, show that it has a realization such that $\left\|\left[\begin{array}{cc} D & C \\ B & A \end{array}\right]\right\| \le 1$.

(Hint: use the discrete bounded real equations derived in the previous question.)

5

LQG Control

5.1 Introduction

The aim of this chapter is to clarify the connections between $\mathcal{H}_\infty$ optimal control and its Linear Quadratic Gaussian (LQG) counterpart. Although there are many excellent texts on LQG theory, we will re-examine this topic to emphasize points of contact between the two theories and to make comparisons between the structure of the two types of controller. It also allows us to develop some ideas, such as the parametrization of all controllers achieving prescribed performance objectives, in a familiar environment. Our solution of the LQG control problem follows standard lines of argument, exploiting the famous separation principle.

In order to establish the structural aspects of the solution before tackling any internal stability questions, we consider the finite-horizon optimization problem first. The infinite-horizon case can then be considered as a limiting case of the finite-horizon solution.

The finite-horizon problem

We consider the plant described by the time-varying state-space system

$$\begin{aligned}
\dot{x}(t) &= A(t)x(t) + B_1(t)w(t) + B_2(t)u(t), \qquad x(0) = 0, &(5.1.1)\\
z(t) &= C_1(t)x(t) + D_{12}(t)u(t) &(5.1.2)\\
y(t) &= C_2(t)x(t) + D_{21}(t)w(t). &(5.1.3)
\end{aligned}$$

The time dependence of the matrices and signals will not always be shown explicitly in what follows. We assume that u is an m-vector of control inputs, w is an l-vector of external disturbance inputs, z is a p-vector of objectives, y is a q-vector of controller inputs (measurements) and x is the n-dimensional state vector. It is assumed that $p \geq m$, that $l \geq q$ and also that D_{12} and D_{21} satisfy

$$D_{12}'D_{12} = I_m \quad \text{and} \quad D_{21}D_{21}' = I_q \tag{5.1.4}$$

for all times of interest. This simplified plant may be considered instead of (4.2.1) by assuming that the loop shifting and scaling transformations described in Section 4.6 have been carried out.

We seek a causal, linear controller $u = \boldsymbol{K}y$ such that the finite-horizon 2-norm of the closed-loop system $\boldsymbol{R}_{zw}$ mapping w to z is minimized. Since

$$\|\boldsymbol{R}_{zw}\|_{2,[0,T]} = \mathcal{E}\left\{\frac{1}{T}\int_0^T z'z\,dt\right\}^{\frac{1}{2}},$$

we are seeking a controller that minimizes the average RMS power in z when the input w is a unit intensity white noise.

We will also describe all controllers that satisfy $\|\boldsymbol{R}_{zw}\|_{2,[0,T]} \leq \gamma$, when they exist—*i.e.*, when γ is not less than the minimum.

The infinite-horizon problem

In the infinite-horizon problem, we assume that the plant description (5.1.1) to (5.1.3) is time-invariant and we seek an internally-stabilizing, causal, linear and time-invariant controller $u = \boldsymbol{K}y$ that minimizes

$$\|\boldsymbol{R}_{zw}\|_2 = \lim_{T\to\infty} \mathcal{E}\left\{\frac{1}{T}\int_0^T z'z\,dt\right\}^{\frac{1}{2}}.$$

In order that an internally-stabilizing controller exists, it is necessary to assume that (A, B_2) is stabilizable and that (A, C_2) is detectable (see Appendix A). We also assume that (5.1.4) holds and that

$$\text{rank}\begin{bmatrix} A - j\omega I & B_2 \\ C_1 & D_{12} \end{bmatrix} = n + m \quad \text{for all real } \omega \tag{5.1.5}$$

$$\text{rank}\begin{bmatrix} A - j\omega I & B_1 \\ C_2 & D_{21} \end{bmatrix} = n + q \quad \text{for all real } \omega. \tag{5.1.6}$$

The reasons for these assumptions will become apparent during the solution process.

We will also describe all internally-stabilizing, causal, linear and time-invariant controllers that satisfy $\|\boldsymbol{R}_{zw}\|_2 \leq \gamma$.

Measurement feedback and full information

The LQG control problem may be tackled in several separate steps, because any measurement feedback controller is also a full-information controller:

$$u = \boldsymbol{K}y$$

$$= \begin{bmatrix} KC_2 & KD_{21} \end{bmatrix} \begin{bmatrix} x \\ w \end{bmatrix}.$$

Therefore, as a stepping stone to the solution of the measurement feedback problem, we look for a control law based on full information that minimizes $\|R_{zw}\|_{2,[0,T]}$ or $\|R_{zw}\|_2$.

The Kalman filter allows us to reconstruct usable state and disturbance estimates from the measurements (5.1.3), enabling us to solve the measurement feedback synthesis problem, which is our main interest.

5.2 Full information

Consider the plant described by (5.1.1) and (5.1.2). In the finite-horizon case, we seek a causal, linear, full-information controller

$$u = \begin{bmatrix} K_1 & K_2 \end{bmatrix} \begin{bmatrix} x \\ w \end{bmatrix} \tag{5.2.1}$$

that minimizes $\|R_{zw}\|_{2,[0,T]}$. The system R_{zw} mapping w to z is shown in block diagram form in Figure 5.1.

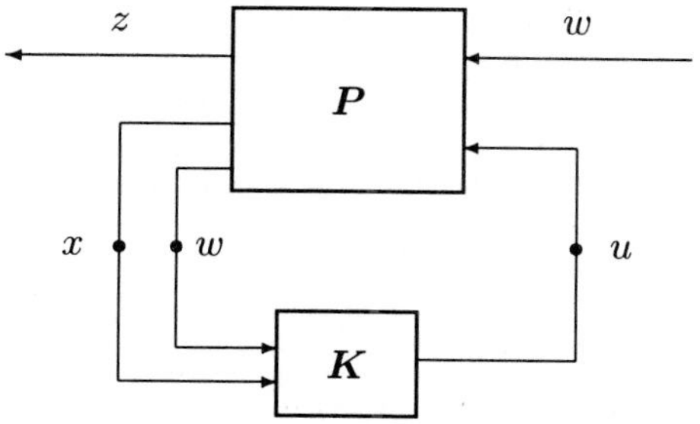

Figure 5.1: The full-information configuration.

In the infinite-horizon case, we seek an internally-stabilizing, causal, linear, time-invariant controller of the form (5.2.1) that minimizes $\|R_{zw}\|_2$.

If z is given by (5.1.2), then $z'z$ contains cross terms between u and x that complicate the formulas. To avoid this, we consider the simplified system

$$\dot{x} = Ax + B_1 w + B_2 u, \qquad x(0) = 0 \tag{5.2.2}$$

$$z = \begin{bmatrix} Cx \\ Du \end{bmatrix}, \tag{5.2.3}$$

in which $D'D \equiv I$. This gives $z'z = x'C'Cx + u'u$. Considering the simplified objective (5.2.3) does not result in a loss of generality, because (5.1.2) can be reduced to the form of (5.2.3) by a standard change of control variable (which is given by $\tilde{u} = u + D_{12}'C_1x$). This extension is considered in Section 5.2.3.

5.2.1 The finite-horizon case

Consider the time-varying linear system described by (5.2.2) and (5.2.3). We seek to minimize

$$\begin{aligned} \|\boldsymbol{R}_{zw}\|_{2,[0,T]}^2 &= \mathcal{E}\left\{\frac{1}{T}\int_0^T z'z\,dt\right\} \\ &= \mathcal{E}\left\{\frac{1}{T}\int_0^T x'C'Cx + u'u\,dt\right\} \end{aligned}$$

over the class of causal, linear, full-information controllers.

From standard texts on LQG theory, the solution to this problem is the memoryless, linear, state-feedback controller

$$u = -B_2'Px, \tag{5.2.4}$$

in which P is the solution to the Riccati equation

$$-\dot{P} = PA + A'P - PB_2B_2'P + C'C, \qquad P(T) = 0. \tag{5.2.5}$$

Before proving that this is indeed the solution, we consider a closely related deterministic problem.

LQ optimal control

Consider the problem of minimizing the cost function

$$J_t(\boldsymbol{K}, x_t, T, \Delta) = \int_t^T z'z\,d\tau + x'(T)\Delta x(T), \tag{5.2.6}$$

in which $\Delta \geq 0$ and z is given by

$$\begin{aligned} \dot{x} &= Ax + B_2u, \qquad x(t) = x_t, \\ z &= \begin{bmatrix} Cx \\ Du \end{bmatrix} \end{aligned}$$

with $D'D = I$ for all times of interest. The minimization is over the class of causal, linear, full-information controllers. If the Riccati equation

$$-\dot{P} = PA + A'P - PB_2B_2'P + C'C, \qquad P(T) = \Delta, \tag{5.2.7}$$

has a solution on $[t, T]$, we obtain

$$\begin{aligned}
&J_t(\boldsymbol{K}, x_t, T, \Delta) - x_t' P(t) x_t \\
&= \int_t^T z'z + \frac{d}{dt}(x'Px)\, d\tau, \qquad \text{since } P(T) = \Delta, \\
&= \int_t^T x'C'Cx + u'u + (Ax + B_2u)'Px + x'P(Ax + B_2u) + x'\dot{P}x\, d\tau \\
&= \int_t^T u'u + u'B_2'Px + x'PB_2u + x'PB_2B_2'Px\, d\tau, \qquad \text{by (5.2.7)}, \\
&= \int_t^T (u + B_2'Px)'(u + B_2'Px)\, d\tau.
\end{aligned}$$

This calculation is known as "completing the square" and it shows that

$$J_t(\boldsymbol{K}, x_t, T, \Delta) = x_t' P(t) x_t + \int_t^T (u + B_2'Px)'(u + B_2'Px)\, d\tau \tag{5.2.8}$$

for any $\boldsymbol{K}$. It is now immediate that the optimal controller $\boldsymbol{K}^*$ is

$$\begin{aligned}
u^* &= \begin{bmatrix} -B_2'P & 0 \end{bmatrix} \begin{bmatrix} x \\ w \end{bmatrix} \\
&= -B_2'Px,
\end{aligned}$$

and the optimal cost is

$$J_t(\boldsymbol{K}^*, x_t, T, \Delta) = x_t' P(t) x_t. \tag{5.2.9}$$

Non-negativity of P: Since $J_t(\boldsymbol{K}, x_t, T, \Delta) \geq 0$ for any $\boldsymbol{K}$ and any x_t, we must have $x_t' P(t) x_t \geq 0$ for any x_t. Hence $P(t) \geq 0$ for all $t \leq T$ for which a solution exists.

Existence of P: We now show that a solution to the Riccati equation (5.2.7) always exists by showing that $P(t)$ is bounded above for any finite $t \leq T$. This shows that the Riccati equation has no finite escape time.[1]

Since $\boldsymbol{K}^*$ is minimizing, its associated cost must not exceed that of the zero controller. That is,

$$\begin{aligned}
x_t' P(t) x_t &= J_t(\boldsymbol{K}^*, x_t, T, \Delta) \\
&\leq J_t(0, x_t, T, \Delta) \\
&= \|\tilde{z}\|_{2,[t,T]}^2 + \tilde{x}'(T)\Delta\tilde{x}(T),
\end{aligned} \tag{5.2.10}$$

[1]A differential equation is said to have a finite escape time if the solution is unbounded on a finite time interval.

in which

$$\begin{aligned}\dot{\tilde{x}} &= A\tilde{x}, \qquad \tilde{x}(t) = x_t,\\ \tilde{z} &= C\tilde{x}.\end{aligned}$$

By Theorem 3.1.1, the right-hand side of (5.2.10) is finite for any $t \leq T$ and any x_t. Indeed, it is equal to $x_t'\big(Q(t) + \Phi'(T,t)\Delta\Phi(T,t)\big)x_t$, in which Q is the observability gramian satisfying the linear differential equation

$$-\dot{Q} = QA + A'Q + C'C \qquad Q(T) = 0,$$

and $\Phi(\cdot,\cdot)$ is the transition matrix associated with A. The Riccati equation (5.2.7) therefore has no finite escape time and we conclude that a solution exists for all finite $t \leq T$.

Solution of the full-information problem

We now verify that $u^* = -B_2'Px$, with P satisfying (5.2.5), is indeed the optimal, full-information controller.

Consider *any* full-information controller described by a time-varying state-space system:

$$\dot{\xi} = F\xi + G_1x + G_2w, \qquad \xi(0) = 0, \tag{5.2.11}$$

$$u = H\xi + J_1x + J_2w. \tag{5.2.12}$$

If this controller is combined with the system described by (5.2.2) and (5.2.3), we see that the closed-loop system $\boldsymbol{R}_{zw}$ is given by

$$\begin{aligned}\dot{\tilde{x}} &= \tilde{A}\tilde{x} + \tilde{B}w \\ z &= \tilde{C}\tilde{x} + \tilde{D}w,\end{aligned} \tag{5.2.13}$$

in which $\tilde{x} = \left[\begin{array}{cc} x' & \xi' \end{array}\right]'$ and

$$\tilde{A} = \left[\begin{array}{cc} A + B_2J_1 & B_2H \\ G_1 & F \end{array}\right], \qquad \tilde{B} = \left[\begin{array}{c} B_1 + B_2J_2 \\ G_2 \end{array}\right], \tag{5.2.14}$$

and

$$\tilde{C} = \left[\begin{array}{cc} C & 0 \\ DJ_1 & DH \end{array}\right], \qquad \tilde{D} = \left[\begin{array}{c} 0 \\ DJ_2 \end{array}\right]. \tag{5.2.15}$$

By Theorem 3.3.1, $\|\boldsymbol{R}_{zw}\|_{2,[0,T]} < \infty$ if and only if $DJ_2 \equiv 0$. Thus $J_2 \equiv 0$ in any controller that achieves a finite cost, since $D'D \equiv I$. Theorem 3.3.1 then gives

$$\|\boldsymbol{R}_{zw}\|_{2,[0,T]}^2 = \frac{1}{T}\int_0^T \operatorname{trace}(\tilde{B}'\tilde{Q}\tilde{B})\,dt, \tag{5.2.16}$$

in which

$$-\dot{\tilde{Q}} = \tilde{A}'\tilde{Q} + \tilde{Q}\tilde{A} + \tilde{C}'\tilde{C}, \qquad \tilde{Q}(T) = 0.$$

Now consider the matrix

$$\tilde{P} = \begin{bmatrix} P & 0 \\ 0 & 0 \end{bmatrix},$$

in which P is the solution to (5.2.5) and $\tilde{P}$ has the same dimensions as $\tilde{Q}$. A straightforward calculation shows that

$$\begin{aligned} -\frac{d}{dt}(\tilde{Q} - \tilde{P}) &= (\tilde{Q} - \tilde{P})\tilde{A} + \tilde{A}'(\tilde{Q} - \tilde{P}) \\ &\quad + \begin{bmatrix} (J_1 + B_2'P)' \\ H' \end{bmatrix} \begin{bmatrix} J_1 + B_2'P & H \end{bmatrix}. \end{aligned} \tag{5.2.17}$$

Since $(\tilde{Q} - \tilde{P})(T) = 0$, $\tilde{Q} - \tilde{P}$ is the observability gramian of $(\tilde{A}, \begin{bmatrix} J_1 + B_2'P & H \end{bmatrix})$ and we conclude that $\tilde{Q}(t) - \tilde{P}(t) \geq 0$ for all $t \leq T$. As equality can be achieved by setting $J_1 \equiv -B_2'P$ and $H \equiv 0$, the minimum cost is

$$\min_{\boldsymbol{K}} \|\boldsymbol{R}_{zw}\|_{2,[0,T]} = \left\{ \frac{1}{T} \int_0^T \operatorname{trace}(B_1'PB_1)\, dt \right\}^{\frac{1}{2}} \tag{5.2.18}$$

and the *unique* optimal controller $\boldsymbol{K}^*$ is

$$u^* = \begin{bmatrix} -B_2'P & 0 \end{bmatrix} \begin{bmatrix} x \\ w \end{bmatrix}. \tag{5.2.19}$$

(If $H \equiv 0$, the values of F, G_1 and G_2 are irrelevant.)

Remark 5.2.1. We have only shown that (5.2.18) is the minimal cost for controllers that can be described by state-space systems. That is, causal, linear systems that are finite dimensional. Since the minimizing controller (over this class) has state dimension zero, it is unlikely that a lower cost could be achieved by an infinite-dimensional controller.

All controllers with prescribed performance

We now obtain a parametrization of all controllers leading to

$$\|\boldsymbol{R}_{zw}\|_{2,[0,T]} \leq \gamma \tag{5.2.20}$$

for any γ that is not less than the right-hand side of (5.2.18).

Our interest in this problem is motivated by the fact that when we re-impose the restriction that the controller must be a measurement feedback controller, the minimum cost that can be obtained may be larger than the right-hand side of (5.2.18).

Consider any controller described by (5.2.11) and (5.2.12), with $J_2 \equiv 0$. By Theorem 3.3.1 and (5.2.17),

$$\frac{1}{T}\int_0^T \operatorname{trace}\bigl(\tilde{B}'(\tilde{Q}-\tilde{P})\tilde{B}\bigr)\,dt = \|\boldsymbol{U}\|^2_{2,[0,T]},$$

in which $\boldsymbol{U}$ is the system with realization $(\tilde{A},\tilde{B},\left[\begin{array}{cc} J_1+B_2'P & H\end{array}\right])$, which is the system that maps w to $u-u^*$. From (5.2.16) and the identity

$$\tilde{B}'\tilde{Q}\tilde{B} = \tilde{B}'(\tilde{Q}-\tilde{P})\tilde{B} + B_1'PB_1,$$

we see that

$$\|\boldsymbol{R}_{zw}\|^2_{2,[0,T]} = \|\boldsymbol{U}\|^2_{2,[0,T]} + \frac{1}{T}\int_0^T \operatorname{trace}(B_1'PB_1)\,dt. \tag{5.2.21}$$

Because of (5.2.21), it is convenient to parametrize an arbitrary full-information controller in terms of system $\boldsymbol{U}$ that maps w to $u-u^*$. To do this, we write the controller equations (5.2.11) and (5.2.12), with $J_2 \equiv 0$, as

$$\begin{aligned}
\frac{d}{dt}\begin{bmatrix}\widehat{x}\\ \xi\end{bmatrix} &= \tilde{A}\begin{bmatrix}\widehat{x}\\ \xi\end{bmatrix} + \tilde{B}w + \begin{bmatrix}0\\ G_1\end{bmatrix}(x-\widehat{x}), \qquad \begin{bmatrix}\widehat{x}(0)\\ \xi(0)\end{bmatrix} = \begin{bmatrix}0\\ 0\end{bmatrix},\\
u &= -B_2'Px + \left[\begin{array}{cc} J_1+B_2'P & H\end{array}\right]\begin{bmatrix}\widehat{x}\\ \xi\end{bmatrix} + (J_1+B_2'P)(x-\widehat{x}),
\end{aligned}$$

This representation has the form

$$\begin{aligned}
u &= -B_2'Px + r & (5.2.22)\\
r &= \boldsymbol{U}w + \boldsymbol{V}(x-\widehat{x}). & (5.2.23)
\end{aligned}$$

Since $\widehat{x} \equiv x$ (see (5.2.13)), $\widehat{x}$ is a copy of the system state. Therefore, as $\boldsymbol{V}$ is driven by the zero signal, it has no effect on the control signal or the closed-loop system $\boldsymbol{R}_{zw}$.

Since the controller was arbitrary, the systems $\boldsymbol{U}$ and $\boldsymbol{V}$ in the above may be *any* causal, linear systems. Notice too, that for u written in the form (5.2.22), the state x satisfies

$$\dot{x} = (A - B_2B_2'P)x + B_1w + B_2r.$$

We therefore generate all controllers from the LFT defined by the equations

$$\begin{bmatrix}\dot{\widehat{x}}\\ u\\ \begin{bmatrix} w\\ x-\widehat{x}\end{bmatrix}\end{bmatrix} = \begin{bmatrix} A-B_2B_2'P & \left[\begin{array}{cc}0 & B_1\end{array}\right] & B_2\\ 0 & \left[\begin{array}{cc}-B_2'P & 0\end{array}\right] & I\\ \begin{bmatrix}0\\ -I\end{bmatrix} & \begin{bmatrix}0 & I\\ I & 0\end{bmatrix} & \begin{bmatrix}0\\ 0\end{bmatrix}\end{bmatrix}\begin{bmatrix}\widehat{x}\\ \begin{bmatrix}x\\ w\end{bmatrix}\\ r\end{bmatrix} \tag{5.2.24}$$

$$r = \left[\begin{array}{cc}\boldsymbol{U} & \boldsymbol{V}\end{array}\right]\begin{bmatrix}w\\ x-\widehat{x}\end{bmatrix}, \tag{5.2.25}$$

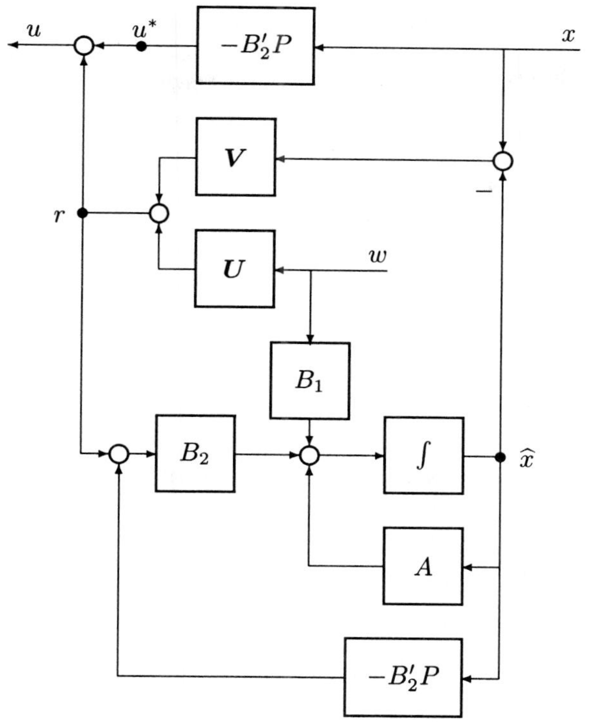

Figure 5.2: All full-information controllers.

which are shown in block diagram form in Figure 5.2. The fact that this LFT has invertible (1, 2)- and (2, 1)-blocks confirms that it captures all the full-information controllers.

From (5.2.21), the controller has the prescribed performance (5.2.20) if and only if

$$\|\boldsymbol{U}\|_{2,[0,T]}^2 + \frac{1}{T}\int_0^T \operatorname{trace}(B_1'PB_1)\,dt \leq \gamma^2. \tag{5.2.26}$$

Remark 5.2.2. We conclude from (5.2.21) that the cost of *any* full-information controller $\boldsymbol{K}$ is given by

$$\|\boldsymbol{R}_{zw}\|_{2,[0,T]}^2 = \|\boldsymbol{U}\|_{2,[0,T]}^2 + \frac{1}{T}\int_0^T \operatorname{trace}(B_1'PB_1)\,dt,$$

in which $\boldsymbol{U}$ is the system that maps w to the difference between the control signal generated by $\boldsymbol{K}$ and the optimal control signal u^*. This fact is crucial in the solution of the measurement feedback problem.

Remark 5.2.3. In our later work on the Kalman filter, which is a dual problem to the optimal control problem, it is of interest to know which full-information controllers do not use the state. Examining (5.2.22) and (5.2.23), we see that u does not depend on x if and only if $\boldsymbol{V} = B_2'P$. All full-information controllers that do not make use of the state are therefore generated by

$$\begin{bmatrix} \widehat{x} \\ u \\ w \end{bmatrix} = \begin{bmatrix} A - B_2B_2'P & B_1 & B_2 \\ -B_2'P & 0 & I \\ 0 & I & 0 \end{bmatrix} \begin{bmatrix} \widehat{x} \\ w \\ r \end{bmatrix} \tag{5.2.27}$$

$$r = \boldsymbol{U}w \tag{5.2.28}$$

and the performance (5.2.20) is achieved if and only if $\boldsymbol{U}$ satisfies (5.2.26).

Main points of the section

1. The 2-norm of the closed-loop system $\|\boldsymbol{R}_{zw}\|_{2,[0,T]}$ is minimized by the state-feedback control law $u^* = -B_2'Px$, in which P is the solution of the Riccati equation (5.2.5); the solution to this equation always exists.
2. The 2-norm of the optimal closed loop is given by

$$\|\boldsymbol{R}_{zw}\|_{2,[0,T]} = \left\{ \frac{1}{T} \int_0^T \operatorname{trace}(B_1'PB_1)\, dt \right\}^{\frac{1}{2}}.$$

3. All controllers that satisfy $\|\boldsymbol{R}_{zw}\|_{2,[0,T]} \le \gamma$ are generated by the formulas (5.2.24) and (5.2.25), in which

$$\|\boldsymbol{U}\|_{2,[0,T]}^2 + \frac{1}{T} \int_0^T \operatorname{trace}(B_1'PB_1)\, dt \le \gamma^2.$$

   The system $\boldsymbol{U}$ maps w to $u - u^*$ and generates all closed loop systems. The system $\boldsymbol{V}$, on the other hand, has no effect on the control signal or the closed loop, but is required in order to parametrize all controllers.

5.2.2 The infinite-horizon case

Most problems of practical interest require a closed-loop system that is internally stable as well as optimal. In order to determine the optimal, stabilizing controller, we consider the limit $T \to \infty$ in the finite-horizon problem. In this work, we assume that the plant is described by the time-invariant state-space system (5.2.2) and (5.2.3).

In order that a stabilizing controller exists, it is necessary that (A, B_2) is stabilizable (see Appendix A). We will therefore assume this from now on.

We expect that the optimal controller will be the controller $u^* = -B_2'Px$, in which P is a solution to the algebraic Riccati equation

$$PA + A'P - PB_2B_2'P + C'C = 0. \qquad (5.2.29)$$

This controller results in the closed-loop dynamics $\dot{x} = (A - B_2B_2'P)x + B_1w$, so we must choose a solution such that $A - B_2B_2'P$ is asymptotically stable. In order that such a solution exists, it is also necessary to assume that (A, C) has no unobservable modes on the imaginary axis. To see this, suppose that

$$Ax = j\omega x, \qquad Cx = 0.$$

Multiplying (5.2.29) on the left by x^* and on the right by x results in $B_2'Px = 0$, giving $(A - B_2B_2'P)x = j\omega x$.

The standard assumptions:

> The pair (A, B_2) is stabilizable and the pair (A, C) has no unobservable mode on the imaginary axis.

The standard assumptions are necessary for the existence of a stabilizing controller of the form $u = -B_2'Px$, with P a solution to (5.2.29). We show that they are sufficient by considering the LQ optimization problem on the finite horizon $[0, T]$ and letting $T \to \infty$.

LQ optimal control

Consider the problem of minimizing the cost function

$$J(\boldsymbol{K}, x_0) = \lim_{T \to \infty} \left\{ \int_0^T z'z \, d\tau + x'(T)\Delta x(T) \right\} \qquad (5.2.30)$$

subject to

$$\begin{aligned} \dot{x} &= Ax + B_2u, \qquad x(0) = x_0, \\ z &= \begin{bmatrix} Cx \\ Du \end{bmatrix}, \end{aligned}$$

in which $D'D = I$ and (A, B_2, C) satisfy the standard assumptions. The minimization is over all stabilizing, casual, linear, time-invariant full-information controllers $\boldsymbol{K}$. We will see that the standard assumptions are necessary and sufficient for a minimum to exist.

Let $P(t, T, \Delta)$ denote the solution to Riccati differential equation

$$-\dot{P} = PA + A'P - PB_2B_2'P + C'C, \qquad P(T) = \Delta. \qquad (5.2.31)$$

(The notation $P(t, T, \Delta)$ is used to flag the fact that $P(t)$ satisfies the terminal constraint $P(T) = \Delta$.)

In order that $P(t, T, \Delta)$ converges to the stabilizing solution to the algebraic Riccati equation, it is important to choose the terminal condition correctly. To see this, we simply note that if $C = 0$ and $\Delta = 0$, then the solution to the Riccati equation is identically zero, which is a stabilizing solution if and only if A is asymptotically stable.

Choice of Δ: Suppose we select any $\Delta \geq 0$ such that

$$\Delta A + A'\Delta - \Delta B_2 B_2' \Delta + C'C \leq 0 \tag{5.2.32}$$

and

$$\left(A, \begin{bmatrix} C \\ \Delta \end{bmatrix} \right) \quad \text{is detectable.} \tag{5.2.33}$$

To see that such a choice is possible, let F be any matrix such that $A - B_2F$ is asymptotically stable and let $\Delta \geq 0$ be the unique solution to

$$\Delta(A - B_2F) + (A - B_2F)'\Delta + C'C + F'F = 0. \tag{5.2.34}$$

We may rewrite this equation as

$$\Delta A + A'\Delta - \Delta B_2 B_2' \Delta + C'C = -(F - B_2'\Delta)'(F - B_2'\Delta),$$

which shows that Δ satisfies (5.2.32). Now suppose that $Ax = \lambda x$, $Cx = 0$ and $\Delta x = 0$. Multiplying (5.2.34) on the left by x^* and on the right by x results in $Fx = 0$. This means that $\lambda x = (A - B_2F)x$ and we conclude that $\mathrm{R}_e(\lambda) < 0$ or $x = 0$, since $(A - B_2F)$ is assumed to be asymptotically stable. That is, Δ satisfies (5.2.33).

Monotonicity of $P(t, T, \Delta)$: The inequality (5.2.32) results in $P(t, T, \Delta)$ being a monotonically nonincreasing function of T. To see this, differentiate (5.2.31) to obtain

$$-\ddot{P} = \dot{P}(A - B_2B_2'P) + (A - B_2B_2'P)'\dot{P}.$$

Hence

$$\dot{P}(t) = \Phi(t, T)\dot{P}(T)\Phi'(t, T),$$

in which Φ is the transition matrix associated with $-(A - B_2B_2'P)'$. Since

$$-\dot{P}(t, T, \Delta)|_{t=T} = \Delta A + A'\Delta - \Delta B_2 B_2' \Delta + C'C,$$

we conclude that $\dot{P}(t, T, \Delta) \geq 0$ whenever the terminal condition Δ satisfies (5.2.32). This establishes that $P(t, T, \Delta)$ is monotonically nondecreasing as a function of t. But, by time-invariance, $P(t, T+\tau, \Delta) = P(t-\tau, T, \Delta)$ and it follows that $P(t, T, \Delta)$ is monotonically nonincreasing as a function of T.

Boundedness of $P(t,T,\Delta)$: From the discussion of the finite-horizon LQ problem, $P(t,T,\Delta) \geq 0$ for all $t \leq T$, since $\Delta \geq 0$. Furthermore, by the monotonicity property, $P(t,T,\Delta) \leq \Delta$ for all $t \leq T$. That is, $P(t,T,\Delta)$ is uniformly bounded.

Existence of a steady-state solution: $P(t,T,\Delta)$ is a monotonic and uniformly bounded function of T. Therefore, $\Pi(t) = \lim_{T\to\infty} P(t,T,\Delta)$ exists.

To see that $\Pi(t)$ is constant, we observe that

$$\begin{aligned}
\Pi(t_1) &= \lim_{T\to\infty} P(t_1,T,\Delta) \\
&= \lim_{T\to\infty} P(t_2, T+t_2-t_1, \Delta), \quad \text{by time-invariance,} \\
&= \Pi(t_2).
\end{aligned}$$

To see that Π satisfies (5.2.29), we make use of the fact that a solution the differential equation (5.2.31) depends continuously on the terminal condition Δ. Therefore

$$\begin{aligned}
\Pi &= \lim_{T\to\infty} P(t,T,\Delta) \\
&= \lim_{T\to\infty} P\big(t,T_1,P(T_1,T,\Delta)\big) \\
&= P\big(t,T_1,\lim_{T\to\infty} P(T_1,T,\Delta)\big) \quad \text{by continuity} \\
&= P(t,T_1,\Pi).
\end{aligned}$$

That is, Π is a solution to the Riccati equation (5.2.31) with terminal condition Π. Noting that $\dot{\Pi} = 0$, we see that Π satisfies

$$\Pi A + A'\Pi - \Pi B_2 B_2' \Pi + C'C = 0. \tag{5.2.35}$$

Stability of $A - B_2B_2'P(0,T,\Delta)$: Because of the choice of Δ, the control law $u(t) = -F_T x(t)$, in which

$$F_T = B_2' P(0,T,\Delta), \tag{5.2.36}$$

is stabilizing, for any finite T. This is seen by employing the "fake algebraic Riccati technique" introduced by Poubelle *et al* [167].

Write the Riccati equation (5.2.31) as

$$P_T(A - B_2F_T) + (A - B_2F_T)'P_T + F_T'F_T + C'C + \dot{P}_T = 0, \tag{5.2.37}$$

in which $P_T = P(0,T,\Delta)$ and $\dot{P}_T = \frac{d}{dt}P(t,T,\Delta)|_{t=0}$. Since $P_T \geq 0$ and $\dot{P}_T \geq 0$, we conclude from Theorem 3.1.1 that any unstable mode of $A - B_2F_T$ is unobservable through $\begin{bmatrix} F_T' & C' & \dot{P}_T \end{bmatrix}'$. To conclude that $A - B_2F_T$ is asymptotically stable, we must show that there can in fact be no such unstable, unobservable mode.

Suppose that λ and x satisfy

$$(A - B_2 F_T)x = \lambda x, \quad \mathrm{R}_e(\lambda) \geq 0, \qquad \begin{bmatrix} F_T \\ C \\ \dot{P}_T \end{bmatrix} x = 0.$$

Multiplying (5.2.37) on the left by x^* and on the right by x gives $(\lambda + \bar{\lambda})x^* P_T x = 0$, and we see that either $\lambda + \bar{\lambda} = 0$ or $P_T x = 0$. In the case that $\lambda = j\omega$, we note that $F_T x = 0$ is equivalent to $B_2' P_T x = 0$ and multiplying (5.2.37) on the right by x results in

$$A' P_T x = -j\omega P_T x.$$

Since (A, B_2) is stabilizable, $P_T x = 0$. Hence $P(t, T, \Delta)x$ is a solution to $\dot{\alpha} = 0$, $\alpha(0) = 0$, giving $P(t, T, \Delta)x = 0$ for all $t \leq T$. Setting $t = T$, we see that $\Delta x = 0$, and combining this with $Ax = \lambda x$ and $Cx = 0$ we obtain

$$\begin{bmatrix} A - \lambda I \\ C \\ \Delta \end{bmatrix} x = 0.$$

From (5.2.33), we have that $x = 0$, which shows that $A - B_2 F_T$ has no unstable mode that is unobservable through $\begin{bmatrix} F_T' & C' & \dot{P}_T \end{bmatrix}'$.

We conclude that $A - B_2 F_T$ is asymptotically stable.

Π is stabilizing: Now $\lim_{T\to\infty}(A - B_2 F_T) = A - B_2 B_2' \Pi$. Since F_T is continuous in T and the eigenvalues of a matrix are continuous functions of the entries, we conclude that $\mathrm{R}_e\big(\lambda_i(A - B_2 B_2' \Pi)\big) \leq 0$ for all i. To see that equality cannot hold, suppose $(A - B_2 B_2' \Pi)x = j\omega x$. Multiplying (5.2.35) on the left by x^* and on the right by x results in $\|B_2 \Pi x\|^2 + \|Cx\|^2 = 0$. Hence $Cx = 0$ and $B_2' \Pi x = 0$, giving $Ax = j\omega x$. We conclude that $x = 0$ by invoking the assumption that (A, C) has no unobservable modes on the imaginary axis.

Remark 5.2.4. In the above, the assumption that (A, C) has no unobservable modes on the imaginary axis was not invoked until the very last sentence. In particular, the controller $u = -F_T x$, with F_T given by (5.2.36), is stabilizing for any finite $T \geq 0$, irrespective of whether (A, C) has unobservable modes on the imaginary axis or not. From Theorem 3.1.1, this controller has the cost

$$\|z\|_2^2 = x_0' P(0, T, \Delta) x_0. \tag{5.2.38}$$

It follows from "completing the square" with $\Pi = \lim_{T\to\infty} P(0, T, \Delta)$ that

$$\|z\|_2^2 = \|u + B_2' \Pi x\|_2^2 + x_0' \Pi x_0, \tag{5.2.39}$$

for any controller that stabilizes the system. Hence $\|z\|_2^2 \geq x_0'\Pi x_0$ for any stabilizing controller. Since $P(0,T,\Delta) \to \Pi$, (5.2.38) implies that

$$\inf_{\boldsymbol{K} \text{ stabilizing}} \|z\|_2 = \sqrt{x_0'\Pi x_0}. \tag{5.2.40}$$

By (5.2.39), the only control that could achieve the infimal cost is $u = -B_2'\Pi x$, which is a stabilizing controller if and only if (A, C) has no unobservable mode on the imaginary axis. We therefore conclude that the standard assumptions are necessary and sufficient for the existence of a stabilizing controller that minimizes $\|z\|_2$.

Solution of the full-information problem

The preceding discussion of the LQ optimal control problem shows that, under the standard assumptions, a stabilizing solution P to the algebraic Riccati equation (5.2.29) exists. It also shows that the controller $u^* = -B_2'Px$ is optimal with respect to the performance index $\|z\|_2$. In this section, we show that the controller $u^* = -B_2'Px$ is also the optimal stabilizing, full-information controller for the performance index $\|\boldsymbol{R}_{zw}\|_2$.

Consider any full-information controller described by a time-invariant, state-space system:

$$\dot{\xi} = F\xi + G_1x + G_2w, \qquad \xi(0) = 0, \tag{5.2.41}$$

$$u = H\xi + J_1x + J_2w. \tag{5.2.42}$$

Assume that $(F, \begin{bmatrix} G_1 & G_2 \end{bmatrix})$ is stabilizable and that (F, H) is detectable, which does not restrict the class of controllers in any way.

As before, the closed loop is described by

$$\begin{aligned} \dot{\tilde{x}} &= \tilde{A}\tilde{x} + \tilde{B}w \\ z &= \tilde{C}\tilde{x} + \tilde{D}w, \end{aligned}$$

in which $\tilde{x} = \begin{bmatrix} x' & \xi' \end{bmatrix}'$ and $\tilde{A}$, $\tilde{B}$, $\tilde{C}$ and $\tilde{D}$ are given in (5.2.14) and (5.2.15).

The controller is internally stabilizing if and only if $\tilde{A}$ is asymptotically stable (see Lemma A.4.1), and $\|\boldsymbol{R}_{zw}\|_2 < \infty$ if and only if, in addition, $J_2 = 0$. Theorem 3.3.1 then gives

$$\|\boldsymbol{R}_{zw}\|_2^2 = \operatorname{trace}(\tilde{B}'\tilde{Q}\tilde{B}),$$

in which

$$\tilde{A}'\tilde{Q} + \tilde{Q}\tilde{A} + \tilde{C}'\tilde{C} = 0.$$

Now consider the matrix

$$\tilde{P} = \begin{bmatrix} P & 0 \\ 0 & 0 \end{bmatrix},$$

in which P is the stabilizing solution to (5.2.29) and $\tilde{P}$ has the same dimensions as $\tilde{Q}$. As before,

$$(\tilde{Q}-\tilde{P})\tilde{A}+\tilde{A}'(\tilde{Q}-\tilde{P})+\begin{bmatrix}(J_1+B_2'P)'\\ H'\end{bmatrix}\begin{bmatrix}J_1+B_2'P & H\end{bmatrix}=0.$$

Thus $\tilde{Q}-\tilde{P}$ is the observability gramian of $(\tilde{A}, \begin{bmatrix}J_1+B_2'P & H\end{bmatrix})$ and hence $\tilde{Q}-\tilde{P}\geq 0$, since $\tilde{A}$ is asymptotically stable. As equality can be achieved by setting $J_1=-B_2'P$ and $H=0$, we conclude that the minimum cost is

$$\min_{\boldsymbol{K}}\|\boldsymbol{R}_{zw}\|_2=\sqrt{\operatorname{trace}(B_1'PB_1)} \tag{5.2.43}$$

and the unique controller that achieves this minimum cost is

$$u^*=\begin{bmatrix}-B_2'P & 0\end{bmatrix}\begin{bmatrix}x\\ w\end{bmatrix}. \tag{5.2.44}$$

Remark 5.2.5. As before, we have only shown that (5.2.43) is the minimal cost for controllers that can be described by time-invariant state-space systems.

All full-information controllers with prescribed performance

By reviewing the arguments presented in the finite-horizon case, noting that $\tilde{A}$ is asymptotically stable for any internally-stabilizing controller, we conclude that all full-information controllers are generated by the LFT

$$\boldsymbol{K}=\mathcal{F}_\ell(\boldsymbol{K}_a,\begin{bmatrix}\boldsymbol{U} & \boldsymbol{V}\end{bmatrix}), \tag{5.2.45}$$

in which

$$\boldsymbol{K}_a \stackrel{s}{=} \left[\begin{array}{c|cc} A-B_2B_2'P & \begin{bmatrix}0 & B_1\end{bmatrix} & B_2\\ \hline 0 & \begin{bmatrix}-B_2'P & 0\end{bmatrix} & I\\ \begin{bmatrix}0\\ -I\end{bmatrix} & \begin{bmatrix}0 & I\\ I & 0\end{bmatrix} & \begin{bmatrix}0\\ 0\end{bmatrix}\end{array}\right]. \tag{5.2.46}$$

This LFT captures all the stabilizing full-information controllers as $\boldsymbol{U}$ and $\boldsymbol{V}$ range over $\mathcal{H}_\infty$ because its $(1,2)$- and $(2,1)$-blocks and their inverses are in $\mathcal{H}_\infty$, since they all have $A-B_2B_2'P$ as their A-matrix. Moreover, the LFT (5.2.45) generates controllers that satisfy $\|\boldsymbol{R}_{zw}\|_2\leq\gamma$ if and only if

$$\|\boldsymbol{U}\|_2^2+\operatorname{trace}(B_1'PB_1)\leq\gamma^2.$$

5.2.3 Inclusion of cross terms

In the introduction to the full information problem, we mentioned that the objective

$$z=C_1x+D_{12}u$$

could be replaced by one of the form (5.2.3) by the change of control variable $\tilde{u} = u + D_{12}'C_1x$. This follows from the identity

$$\begin{aligned} z'z &= (C_1x + D_{12}u)'(C_1x + D_{12}u) \\ &= x'C_1'(I - D_{12}D_{12}')C_1x + (u + D_{12}'C_1x)'(u + D_{12}'C_1x). \end{aligned}$$

Since $\|D_{12}\| = 1$, we have that $C_1'(I - D_{12}D_{12}')C_1 \geq 0$. Setting

$$\begin{aligned} \tilde{u} &= u + D_{12}'C_1x \\ \tilde{A} &= A - B_2D_{12}'C_1 \\ \tilde{C}'\tilde{C} &= C_1'(I - D_{12}D_{12}')C_1 \end{aligned}$$

results in

$$\begin{aligned} \dot{x} &= \tilde{A}x + B_1w + B_2\tilde{u} \\ \tilde{z} &= \begin{bmatrix} \tilde{C}x \\ \tilde{u} \end{bmatrix}, \end{aligned}$$

and we have $\tilde{z}'\tilde{z} = z'z$.

It follows that the solution to a problem containing cross terms may be obtained by considering this simplified structure. In particular, the optimal controller for the finite horizon $[0, T]$ is

$$u^* = -Fx, \qquad F = D_{12}'C_1 + B_2'X,$$

in which X is the solution to the Riccati differential equation

$$-\dot{X} = X\tilde{A} + \tilde{A}'X - XB_2B_2'X + \tilde{C}'\tilde{C}, \qquad X(T) = 0.$$

In the infinite-horizon case, the optimal controller is

$$u^* = -Fx, \qquad F = D_{12}'C_1 + B_2'X,$$

in which X is the stabilizing solution to the algebraic Riccati equation

$$X\tilde{A} + \tilde{A}'X - XB_2B_2'X + \tilde{C}'\tilde{C} = 0.$$

Such a solution exists if and only if the standard assumptions hold; that is $(\tilde{A}, B_2)$ must be stabilizable and $(\tilde{A}, \tilde{C})$ must have no unobservable modes on the imaginary axis. Since stabilizability is invariant under state feedback, $(\tilde{A}, B_2)$ is stabilizable if and only if (A, B_2) is stabilizable. The condition that $(\tilde{A}, \tilde{C})$ has no unobservable mode on the imaginary axis is equivalent to the condition that

$$\operatorname{rank}\begin{bmatrix} A - j\omega I & B_2 \\ C_1 & D_{12} \end{bmatrix} = n + m \qquad (5.2.47)$$

(*i.e.*, full column rank) for all real ω.

To see this equivalence, note that

$$\begin{bmatrix} A - j\omega I & B_2 \\ C_1 & D_{12} \end{bmatrix} \begin{bmatrix} x \\ u \end{bmatrix} = 0 \tag{5.2.48}$$

only if $u = -D_{12}'C_1x$, since $D_{12}'D_{12} = I$. Now

$$\begin{bmatrix} A - j\omega I & B_2 \\ C_1 & D_{12} \end{bmatrix} \begin{bmatrix} I & 0 \\ -D_{12}'C_1 & I \end{bmatrix} = \begin{bmatrix} \tilde{A} - j\omega I & B_2 \\ (I - D_{12}D_{12}')C_1 & D_{12} \end{bmatrix}.$$

Hence $\tilde{A}x = j\omega x$ and $\tilde{C}x = 0$ if and only if

$$\begin{bmatrix} x \\ u \end{bmatrix} = \begin{bmatrix} I \\ -D_{12}'C_1 \end{bmatrix} x$$

satisfies (5.2.48).

The formulas for all the controllers that achieve prescribed objectives may be obtained by replacing $B_2'P$ with F, giving

$$\begin{aligned} \begin{bmatrix} \dot{\widehat{x}} \\ u \\ \begin{bmatrix} w \\ x - \widehat{x} \end{bmatrix} \end{bmatrix} &= \begin{bmatrix} A - B_2F & \begin{bmatrix} 0 & B_1 \end{bmatrix} & B_2 \\ 0 & \begin{bmatrix} -F & 0 \end{bmatrix} & I \\ \begin{bmatrix} 0 \\ -I \end{bmatrix} & \begin{bmatrix} 0 & I \\ I & 0 \end{bmatrix} & \begin{bmatrix} 0 \\ 0 \end{bmatrix} \end{bmatrix} \begin{bmatrix} \widehat{x} \\ \begin{bmatrix} x \\ w \end{bmatrix} \\ r \end{bmatrix} \\ r &= \begin{bmatrix} \boldsymbol{U} & \boldsymbol{V} \end{bmatrix} \begin{bmatrix} w \\ x - \widehat{x} \end{bmatrix}. \end{aligned}$$

Main points of the section

1. A stabilizing solution to the algebraic Riccati equation (5.2.29) exists if and only if (A, B_2) is stabilizable and (C, A) has no unobservable mode on the imaginary axis. This solution may be obtained as the limit of a solution to a Riccati differential equation, provided the terminal condition is chosen with care.[2]
2. The 2-norm of the closed-loop system $\|\boldsymbol{R}_{zw}\|_2$ is minimized, over the class of controllers that are internally stabilizing, by the state-feedback control law $u^* = -B_2'Px$. The matrix P is the stabilizing solution of the algebraic Riccati equation (5.2.29).
3. The 2-norm of the optimal closed loop is given by

$$\|\boldsymbol{R}_{zw}\|_2 = \sqrt{\operatorname{trace}(B_1'PB_1)}.$$

[2] An exercise at the end of the chapter shows that any nonnegative definite terminal condition will do if (A, C) is detectable.

4. All stabilizing, full-information controllers satisfying $\|\boldsymbol{R}_{zw}\|_2 \leq \gamma$ are generated by the LFT (5.2.45), in which $\boldsymbol{U}$ and $\boldsymbol{V} \in \mathcal{H}_\infty$ with

$$\|\boldsymbol{U}\|_2^2 + \operatorname{trace}(B_1' P B_1) \leq \gamma^2.$$

The system $\boldsymbol{U}$ maps w to $u - u^*$. The system $\boldsymbol{V}$ has no effect on the control signal or the closed loop; its only role is to parametrize all stabilizing controllers.

5. The effect of cross terms is easily accounted for by a change of control variable.

5.3 The Kalman filter

All the work we presented in Section 5.2 relies on the controller having perfect knowledge of the disturbance input and the state. Since the problem we want to solve has (5.1.3) as the only measurement, we need to find some way of estimating the states and the disturbances from the measurements y. As is well known, the Kalman filter is the optimal solution to this problem.

5.3.1 The finite-horizon case

Consider the time-varying signal generator

$$\dot{x}(t) = A(t)x(t) + B(t)w(t), \qquad x(0) = 0, \tag{5.3.1}$$

$$y(t) = C(t)x(t) + D(t)v(t), \tag{5.3.2}$$

in which $DD' = I$ for all times of interest.

We seek a causal, linear filter $\boldsymbol{F}$ such that $\widehat{z} = \boldsymbol{F}y$ is an optimal estimate of $z = Lx$, with L a continuous matrix valued function (which may be the identity). We take optimality to mean that the 2-norm $\|\boldsymbol{R}\|_{2,[0,T]}$ is minimized, with $\boldsymbol{R} : \begin{bmatrix} w' & v' \end{bmatrix}' \mapsto \widehat{z} - z$. By the definition of the 2-norm of a system, this means that we are minimizing

$$\|\boldsymbol{R}\|_{2,[0,T]} = \mathcal{E}\left\{\frac{1}{T}\int_0^T (\widehat{z} - Lx)'(\widehat{z} - Lx)\, dt\right\}^{\frac{1}{2}} \tag{5.3.3}$$

when $\begin{bmatrix} w' & v' \end{bmatrix}'$ is a unit intensity white noise. Note that (5.3.3) is just the average RMS power of the estimation error.

It is well known that the estimate of Lx that is optimal in the above sense is $L\widehat{x}$, in which $\widehat{x}$ is the optimal estimate of x; this fact will be proved, not assumed.

The filtering problem in question may be considered as the LFT problem

$$\begin{bmatrix} \dot{x} \\ \widehat{z} - z \\ y \end{bmatrix} = \begin{bmatrix} A & \begin{bmatrix} B & 0 \end{bmatrix} & 0 \\ -L & \begin{bmatrix} 0 & 0 \end{bmatrix} & I \\ C & \begin{bmatrix} 0 & D \end{bmatrix} & 0 \end{bmatrix} \begin{bmatrix} x \\ \begin{bmatrix} w \\ v \end{bmatrix} \\ \widehat{z} \end{bmatrix}, \quad x(0) = 0, \tag{5.3.4}$$

$$\widehat{z} = \boldsymbol{F} y. \tag{5.3.5}$$

The optimal filter and optimal cost

Recall that the 2-norm of a system and the 2-norm of its adjoint are equal. Recall also that the adjoint of $\mathcal{F}_\ell(\boldsymbol{P}, \boldsymbol{K})$ is $\mathcal{F}_\ell(\boldsymbol{P}^\sim, \boldsymbol{K}^\sim)$, in which $(\cdot)^\sim$ denotes the adjoint. Therefore, minimizing $\|\boldsymbol{R}\|_{2,[0,T]}$ is equivalent to minimizing $\|\boldsymbol{R}^\sim\|_{2,[0,T]}$, in which $\boldsymbol{R}^\sim$ is generated by the LFT

$$\begin{bmatrix} \frac{d}{d\tau} p(\tau) \\ \tilde{z}(\tau) \\ \tilde{w}(\tau) \end{bmatrix} = \begin{bmatrix} A'(\tau) & -L'(\tau) & C'(\tau) \\ \begin{bmatrix} B'(\tau) \\ 0 \end{bmatrix} & \begin{bmatrix} 0 \\ 0 \end{bmatrix} & \begin{bmatrix} 0 \\ D'(\tau) \end{bmatrix} \\ 0 & I & 0 \end{bmatrix} \begin{bmatrix} p(\tau) \\ \tilde{w}(\tau) \\ \tilde{u}(\tau) \end{bmatrix} \tag{5.3.6}$$

$$\tilde{u} = \boldsymbol{F}^\sim \tilde{w}, \tag{5.3.7}$$

in which τ is the time-to-go variable $\tau = T - t$ associated with the adjoint system and $p(\tau)|_{\tau=0} = 0$. We note also that $\boldsymbol{F}$ is causal if and only if $\boldsymbol{F}^\sim$ is causal in τ.

This is a control problem in which the controller $\boldsymbol{F}^\sim$ only has access to the exogenous signal $\tilde{w}$, rather than to p and $\tilde{w}$. From our discussion of the full-information problem in Section 4.2.2, we know that for the purpose of achieving particular closed loops or control signals, knowledge of $\tilde{w}$ is equivalent to knowledge of p and $\tilde{w}$, since we can always replace p in any full-information controller for the adjoint system with a copy generated from $\tilde{w}$ by

$$\frac{d}{d\tau}\widehat{p}(\tau) = A'(\tau)\widehat{p}(\tau) - L'(\tau)\tilde{w}(\tau) + C'\tilde{u}(\tau), \qquad \widehat{p}(\tau)|_{\tau=0} = 0.$$

With this comment in mind, it is immediate that the optimal controller for the adjoint problem is $\tilde{u}^*(\tau) = -C(\tau)Q(\tau)\widehat{p}(\tau)$, in which

$$-\frac{d}{d\tau}Q(\tau) = Q(\tau)A'(\tau) + A(\tau)Q(\tau) - Q(\tau)C'(\tau)C(\tau)Q(\tau) + B(\tau)B'(\tau),$$

with the terminal condition $Q(\tau)|_{\tau=T} = 0$. The optimal cost is

$$\|\boldsymbol{R}^\sim\|_{2,[0,T]} = \left\{ \frac{1}{T}\int_0^T \operatorname{trace}\big(L(\tau)Q(\tau)L'(\tau)\big)\, d\tau \right\}^{\frac{1}{2}}.$$

Substituting $\tilde{u}^*$ into the equation defining the duplicate adjoint state, we see that the adjoint of the optimal filter is given by

$$\begin{aligned} \frac{d}{d\tau}\widehat{p}(\tau) &= (A' - C'CQ)(\tau)\widehat{p}(\tau) - L'(\tau)\tilde{w}(\tau), \qquad \widehat{p}(\tau)|_{\tau=0} = 0, \\ \tilde{u}^*(\tau) &= -C(\tau)Q(\tau)\widehat{p}(\tau). \end{aligned}$$

Hence, the optimal filter is given by

$$\begin{aligned} \dot{\widehat{x}}(t) &= (A - QC'C)(t)\widehat{x}(t) + Q(t)C'(t)y(t), \qquad \widehat{x}(0) = 0, && (5.3.8) \\ &= A(t)\widehat{x}(t) + Q(t)C'(t)\big(y(t) - C(t)\widehat{x}(t)\big) && (5.3.9) \\ \widehat{z}(t) &= L(t)\widehat{x}(t), && (5.3.10) \end{aligned}$$

in which

$$\dot{Q}(t) = Q(t)A'(t) + A(t)Q(t) - Q(t)C'(t)C(t)Q(t) + B(t)B'(t), \quad Q(0) = 0. \quad (5.3.11)$$

Since the Riccati equation (5.3.11) does not depend on L, the optimal estimate of Lx is indeed $L\widehat{x}$, with $\widehat{x}$ being the optimal estimate of x. The matrix QC' is known as the Kalman filter gain and $y - C\widehat{x}$, which drives the filter, is the innovations process. The optimal cost is given by

$$\begin{aligned} \|\boldsymbol{R}\|_{2,[0,T]} &= \mathcal{E}\left\{\frac{1}{T}\int_0^T (\widehat{z} - Lx)'(\widehat{z} - Lx)\, dt\right\}^{\frac{1}{2}} \\ &= \left\{\frac{1}{T}\int_0^T \operatorname{trace}(LQL')\, dt\right\}^{\frac{1}{2}}. && (5.3.12) \end{aligned}$$

Optimal terminal state estimation

The Kalman filter is most widely known for its role as a terminal-state estimator. That is, it is the filter that minimizes

$$\mathcal{E}\left\{\big(\widehat{x}(T) - x(T)\big)\big(\widehat{x}(T) - x(T)\big)'\right\},$$

rather than (5.3.3), given the observations $y(\tau)$, $\tau \leq T$. A proof of this optimality property is requested in Problem 5.13.

All filters with prescribed performance

The filtering problem does not have a degenerate information structure and its adjoint is a full-information problem in which the controller (the adjoint of the filter) does not have access to the state. All such controllers achieving a given performance level were parametrized in Remark 5.2.3.

Applying this parametrization to the adjoint problem associated with the Kalman filter, we obtain

$$\begin{bmatrix} \dot{\widehat{x}} \\ \widehat{z} \\ \eta \end{bmatrix} = \begin{bmatrix} A - QC'C & QC' & 0 \\ L & 0 & I \\ -C & I & 0 \end{bmatrix} \begin{bmatrix} \widehat{x} \\ y \\ r \end{bmatrix}$$
$$r = \boldsymbol{U}\eta.$$

Again, the fact that the $(1,2)$- and $(2,1)$-blocks of this LFT are invertible confirms that this LFT captures all filters.

It is interesting to note that $\boldsymbol{U}$ has no effect on $\widehat{x}$, which therefore remains the optimal state estimate; it just degrades our estimate of Lx from $L\widehat{x}$ to $L\widehat{x} + \boldsymbol{U}\eta$, in which $\eta = y - C\widehat{x}$ is the innovations process. That is, we obtain all filters that satisfy

$$\mathcal{E}\left\{\frac{1}{T}\int_0^T (\widehat{z} - Lx)'(\widehat{z} - Lx)\,dt\right\}^{\frac{1}{2}} \leq \gamma$$

by letting

$$\widehat{z} = L\widehat{x} + \boldsymbol{U}\eta,$$

in which $\widehat{x}$ is the optimal state estimate estimate, η is the innovations process and

$$\|\boldsymbol{U}\|_{2,[0,T]}^2 + \frac{1}{T}\int_0^T \operatorname{trace}(LQL')\,dt \leq \gamma^2. \tag{5.3.13}$$

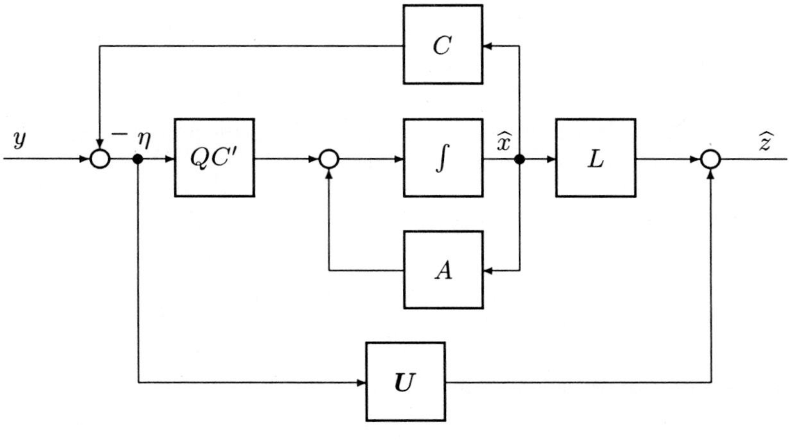

Figure 5.3: All filters.

Filter with control signal

Suppose we have the signal generator

$$\begin{aligned} \dot{x} &= Ax + Bw + B_2u \\ y &= Cx + v, \end{aligned}$$

in which u is a known signal—we have in mind the situation in which u is a control signal. Consider the filter

$$\dot{\widehat{x}} = A\widehat{x} + QC'(y - C\widehat{x}) + B_2u, \tag{5.3.14}$$

in which Q is the solution to (5.3.11). Then $\widehat{x} - x$ satisfies

$$\frac{d}{dt}(\widehat{x} - x) = A(\widehat{x} - x) + QC'(y - C\widehat{x}) - Bw,$$

which is independent of u, and we conclude that $\widehat{x}$ generated by (5.3.14) is the optimal estimate of x.

5.3.2 The infinite-horizon case

We are now in a position to extend the optimal state estimation results to the infinite horizon case. As always, we limit our attention to the case when the signal generator given by (5.3.1) and (5.3.2) is time-invariant. We seek to minimize

$$\|\boldsymbol{R}\|_2 = \lim_{T\to\infty} \mathcal{E}\left\{\frac{1}{T}\int_0^T (\widehat{z} - Lx)'(\widehat{z} - Lx)\,dt\right\}^{\frac{1}{2}}.$$

Naturally, we expect that the optimal filter will be

$$\begin{aligned} \dot{\widehat{x}} &= A\widehat{x} + QC'(y - C\widehat{x}) && (5.3.15) \\ \widehat{z} &= L\widehat{x}, && (5.3.16) \end{aligned}$$

in which Q is the stabilizing solution to the Riccati equation

$$AQ + QA' - QC'CQ + BB' = 0; \tag{5.3.17}$$

the solution Q is stabilizing if $\lambda_i(A - QC'C) < 0$. We note that such a Q exists if and only if (A, C) is detectable and (A, B) has no uncontrollable modes on the imaginary axis, which we now assume.

Because filtering is an open-loop problem, the LFT defining the filtering problem in (5.3.4) and (5.3.5) is not stabilizable in the sense of the internal stability of LFT's defined in Section 4.2.1, except when A is asymptotically stable. However, this definition is inappropriate to the filtering applications we are now considering. We do not care what happens to the state, only that our estimate of it is good.

Therefore, the notion of stability that is appropriate is that the filter should be stable and that the system $\boldsymbol{R}$ that maps the driving noise(s) to the estimation error should also be stable. This will ensure that the estimation error tends to zero for any $\mathcal{L}_2[0,\infty)$ driving noise(s). Since $A-QC'C$ is asymptotically stable, the Kalman filter is stable. Subtracting (5.3.1) from (5.3.15) gives

$$\frac{d}{dt}(\widehat{x}-x) = (A-QC'C)(\widehat{x}-x) - Bw + QC'Dv$$

and it follows that the system $\boldsymbol{R} : \begin{bmatrix} w' & v' \end{bmatrix}' \mapsto (\widehat{x}-x)$ is also stable. Therefore, the Kalman filter possesses the desired stability properties.

Since the adjoint problem defined by (5.3.6) and (5.3.7) satisfies the assumptions of the infinite-horizon, full-information control problem, we conclude that the Kalman filter is indeed the optimal filter, and that the optimal cost is

$$\|\boldsymbol{R}\|_2 = \sqrt{\operatorname{trace}(LQL')}. \tag{5.3.18}$$

All stable filters with prescribed performance

$$\|\boldsymbol{R}\|_2 \leq \gamma$$

are generated by

$$\widehat{z} = L\widehat{x} + \boldsymbol{U}(y - C\widehat{x}),$$

in which $\widehat{x}$ is the optimal state estimate, and $\boldsymbol{U} \in \mathcal{H}_\infty$ with

$$\|\boldsymbol{U}\|_2^2 + \operatorname{trace}(LQL') \leq \gamma^2. \tag{5.3.19}$$

Main points of the section

1. The adjoint of the filtering problem is a full-information control problem in which the controller does not have access to the state.
2. The optimal estimate of Lx is $L\widehat{x}$, in which $\widehat{x}$ is the optimal estimate of x generated by the Kalman filter.
3. The Kalman filter is

   $$\dot{\widehat{x}} = A\widehat{x} + QC'(y - Cx), \qquad \widehat{x}(0) = 0,$$

   in which Q is the solution to the Riccati equation (5.3.11). In the case of an infinite horizon, Q is the stabilizing solution to the algebraic Riccati equation (5.3.17).
4. All filters with prescribed performance γ are obtained by setting $\widehat{z} = L\widehat{x} + \boldsymbol{U}\eta$, in which $\eta = y - C\widehat{x}$ is the innovations process, and $\boldsymbol{U}$ satisfies (5.3.13) in the case of a finite horizon or (5.3.19) in the case of an infinite horizon.

5.4 Measurement feedback

We now consider the problem of real interest, in which the controller must generate the control signal according to $u = \boldsymbol{K}y$. Again, we begin with the finite-horizon problem.

5.4.1 The finite-horizon case

We consider the time-varying plant

$$\begin{aligned} \dot{x} &= Ax + B_1 w + B_2 u, \qquad x(0) = 0, && (5.4.1)\\ z &= C_1 x + D_{12} u && (5.4.2)\\ y &= C_2 x + D_{21} w, && (5.4.3) \end{aligned}$$

in which $D_{12}'D_{12} = I$ and $D_{21}D_{21}' = I$ for all times of interest.

Our aim is to find a controller $u = \boldsymbol{K}y$ that minimizes $\|\boldsymbol{R}_{zw}\|_{2,[0,T]}$. As usual, $\boldsymbol{R}_{zw}$ is the closed-loop system mapping w to z.

The solution is based on the fact that any measurement feedback controller is also a full-information controller, since

$$\boldsymbol{K}y = \begin{bmatrix} \boldsymbol{K}C_2 & \boldsymbol{K}D_{21} \end{bmatrix} \begin{bmatrix} x \\ w \end{bmatrix}.$$

It follows that the cost of any measurement feedback controller is

$$\|\boldsymbol{R}_{zw}\|_{2,[0,T]}^2 = \|\boldsymbol{U}\|_{2,[0,T]}^2 + \frac{1}{T}\int_0^T \operatorname{trace}(B_1'PB_1)\,dt, \qquad (5.4.4)$$

with $\boldsymbol{U}$ being the system that maps w to $u - u^*$ and $u^* = -Fx$ being the optimal, full-information controller. (Equation (5.4.4) is a copy of equation (5.2.21).) Therefore, the measurement feedback controller that minimizes $\|\boldsymbol{R}_{zw}\|_{2,[0,T]}$ is the optimal estimator of $u^* = -Fx$ given the measurements y. This is known as the separation principle. It is now immediate that the optimal controller is

$$\begin{aligned} \dot{\widehat{x}} &= A\widehat{x} + H(y - C_2\widehat{x}) + B_2 u\\ u &= -F\widehat{x}, \end{aligned}$$

in which $F = D_{12}'C_1 + B_2'X$ and $H = B_1D_{21}' + YC_2'$. The matrices X and Y are the solutions to the Riccati differential equations

$$\begin{aligned} -\dot{X} &= X\tilde{A} + \tilde{A}'X - XB_2B_2'X + \tilde{C}'\tilde{C}, \qquad X(T) = 0,\\ \dot{Y} &= \bar{A}Y + Y\bar{A}' - YC_2'C_2Y + \bar{B}\bar{B}', \qquad Y(0) = 0, \end{aligned}$$

in which

$$\begin{aligned} \tilde{A} &= A - B_2D_{12}'C_1, \qquad \tilde{C}'\tilde{C} = C_1'(I - D_{12}D_{12}')C_1, && (5.4.5)\\ \bar{A} &= A - B_1D_{21}'C_2, \qquad \bar{B}\bar{B}' = B_1(I - D_{21}'D_{21})B_1'. && (5.4.6) \end{aligned}$$

(These formulas result from including cross terms in $z'z$ and correlated process and measurement noise—see Section 5.2.3.)

The optimal cost is

$$\|\boldsymbol{R}_{zw}\|_{2,[0,T]} = \left\{ \frac{1}{T} \int_0^T \big(\text{trace}(B_1' X B_1) + \text{trace}(FYF')\big)\, dt \right\}^{\frac{1}{2}},$$

which is just the square root of the sum of the square of the optimal, full-information cost and the square of the cost of optimally estimating the optimal, full-information controller $-Fx$.

All full-information controllers that achieve the performance level

$$\|\boldsymbol{R}_{zw}\|_{2,[0,T]} \leq \gamma \tag{5.4.7}$$

are generated by using a suboptimal estimator of $-Fx$. From the parametrization of all filters achieving specified performance and (5.4.4), it is evident that the control is

$$u = -F\widehat{x} + \boldsymbol{Q}(y - C_2\widehat{x}),$$

in which

$$\|\boldsymbol{Q}\|_{2,[0,T]}^2 + \frac{1}{T}\int_0^T \big(\text{trace}(B_1' X B_1) + \text{trace}(FYF')\big)\, dt \leq \gamma^2. \tag{5.4.8}$$

In LFT form, all measurement feedback controllers with performance level (5.4.7) are generated by

$$\begin{bmatrix} \dot{\widehat{x}} \\ u \\ \eta \end{bmatrix} = \begin{bmatrix} A - B_2F - HC_2 & H & B_2 \\ -F & 0 & I \\ -C_2 & I & 0 \end{bmatrix} \begin{bmatrix} \widehat{x} \\ y \\ r \end{bmatrix} \tag{5.4.9}$$

$$r = \boldsymbol{Q}\eta, \tag{5.4.10}$$

in which $\boldsymbol{Q}$ satisfies (5.4.8). The nonsingularity of the $(1,2)$- and $(2,1)$-blocks of this LFT confirms that we capture all measurement feedback controllers as $\boldsymbol{Q}$ varies (without restriction on its norm). This parametrization of all controllers is shown in block diagram form in Figure 5.4.

Remark 5.4.1. Notice that the cost of estimating $u^* = -Fx$ is zero if $Y \equiv 0$. This happens when $\bar{B}\bar{B}' \equiv 0$. Since $\bar{B}\bar{B}' = B_1(I - D_{21}'D_{21})B_1'$, we see that this occurs when D_{21} is an orthogonal matrix—the identity, for example. We conclude that when $y = C_2x + w$, the additional cost of measurement feedback over full information is zero. This is essentially because the filter

$$\begin{aligned} \dot{\widehat{x}} &= Ax + B_1\widehat{w} + B_2u, \qquad \widehat{x}(0) = 0, \\ \widehat{w} &= y - C_2\widehat{x} \end{aligned}$$

reconstructs w and x perfectly from the measurements y.

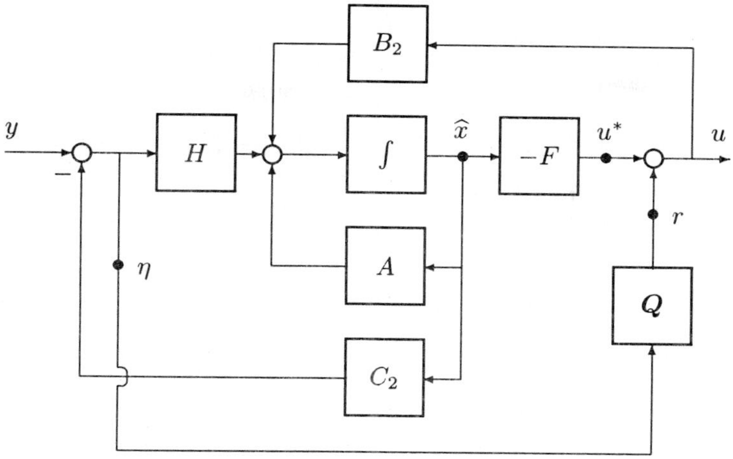

Figure 5.4: All measurement feedback controllers.

5.4.2 The infinite-horizon case

In the infinite-horizon case, we assume that the plant is described by (5.4.1) to (5.4.3) with all the matrices of the realization constant. We also assume that (A, B_2) is stabilizable and that (A, C_2) is detectable. These are necessary conditions for the existence of a stabilizing controller (see Appendix A). Our last assumption is that the full-rank-on-the-axis conditions (5.1.5) and (5.1.6) hold. These assumptions are equivalent to $(\tilde{A}, \tilde{C})$ having no unobservable mode on the imaginary axis and $(\bar{A}, \bar{B})$ having no uncontrollable mode on the imaginary axis (see Section 5.2.3). The matrices $\tilde{A}$, $\tilde{C}$, $\bar{A}$ and $\bar{B}$ are defined by (5.4.5) and (5.4.6) as before. Under these assumptions, the algebraic Riccati equations

$$X\tilde{A} + \tilde{A}'X - XB_2B_2'X + \tilde{C}'\tilde{C} = 0 \qquad (5.4.11)$$

$$\bar{A}Y + \bar{A}'Y - YC_2'C_2Y + \bar{B}\bar{B}' = 0 \qquad (5.4.12)$$

have stabilizing solutions.

As in the finite-horizon case, the identity

$$\boldsymbol{K}y = \begin{bmatrix} \boldsymbol{K}C_2 & \boldsymbol{K}D_{21} \end{bmatrix} \begin{bmatrix} x \\ w \end{bmatrix}$$

means that any stabilizing measurement feedback controller is also a stabilizing full-information controller. Hence

$$\|\boldsymbol{R}_{zw}\|_2^2 = \|\boldsymbol{U}\|_2^2 + \text{trace}(B_1'XB_1)$$

for some $\boldsymbol{U} \in \mathcal{H}_\infty$. As before, $\boldsymbol{U}$ is the system mapping w to $u - u^*$. The signal $u^* = -Fx$, with $F = D_{12}'C_1 + B_2'X$, is the optimal, full-information controller.

The optimal, measurement feedback controller is therefore the best stable estimator of $u = -Fx$. It is given by

$$\begin{aligned} \dot{\widehat{x}} &= A\widehat{x} + H(y - C_2\widehat{x}) + B_2 u \\ u &= -F\widehat{x}, \end{aligned}$$

in which $H = B_1 D_{21}' + YC_2$. The optimal cost is

$$\|\boldsymbol{R}_{zw}\|_{2,[0,T]} = \sqrt{\operatorname{trace}(B_1'XB_1) + \operatorname{trace}(FYF')}.$$

All measurement feedback controllers that achieve the performance level

$$\|\boldsymbol{R}_{zw}\|_2 \le \gamma \tag{5.4.13}$$

are generated by

$$\begin{aligned} \begin{bmatrix} \dot{\widehat{x}} \\ u \\ \eta \end{bmatrix} &= \begin{bmatrix} A - B_2F - HC_2 & H & B_2 \\ -F & 0 & I \\ -C_2 & I & 0 \end{bmatrix} \begin{bmatrix} \widehat{x} \\ y \\ r \end{bmatrix} \\ r &= \boldsymbol{Q}\eta, \end{aligned}$$

in which $\boldsymbol{Q} \in \mathcal{H}_\infty$ satisfies

$$\|\boldsymbol{Q}\|_2^2 + \operatorname{trace}(B_1'XB_1) + \operatorname{trace}(FYF') \le \gamma^2.$$

Notice that the inverses of the $(1,2)$- and $(2,1)$-blocks of this LFT are in $\mathcal{H}_\infty$, since their A-matrices are $A - B_2F$ and $A - HC_2$ respectively, confirming that we capture all internally-stabilizing controllers as $\boldsymbol{Q} \in \mathcal{H}_\infty$ is varied (without restriction on its norm). See Appendix A for more details.

Main points of the section

1. Any measurement feedback controller is also a full-information controller.
2. The optimal, measurement feedback controller is an optimal estimator of the optimal, ful-information control.
3. The optimal 2-norm with measurement feedback is given by

   $$\|\boldsymbol{R}_{zw}\|_{2,[0,T]} = \left\{ \frac{1}{T} \int_0^T \left(\operatorname{trace}(B_1'XB_1) + \operatorname{trace}(FYF')\right) dt \right\}^{\frac{1}{2}}$$

   in the case of a finite horizon, or by

   $$\|\boldsymbol{R}_{zw}\|_2 = \sqrt{\operatorname{trace}(B_1'XB_1) + \operatorname{trace}(FYF')}$$

in the case of an infinite horizon. In these expressions, F is the optimal state-feedback gain and X and Y are the stabilizing solutions to the Riccati equations defining the optimal, full-information controller and the Kalman filter respectively.

4. In the infinite-horizon case, it is assumed that the plant is time-invariant and satisfies:

   (i) (A, B_2) stabilizable.

   (ii) $\operatorname{rank}\begin{bmatrix} A - j\omega I & B_2 \\ C_1 & D_{12} \end{bmatrix} = n + m$ for all real ω.

   (iii) (A, C_2) is detectable.

   (iv) $\operatorname{rank}\begin{bmatrix} A - j\omega I & B_1 \\ C_2 & D_{21} \end{bmatrix} = n + q$ for all real ω.

5. All measurement feedback controllers that achieve a given performance level $\|\boldsymbol{R}_{zw}\|_{2,[0,T]} \leq \gamma$ or $\|\boldsymbol{R}_{zw}\|_2 \leq \gamma$ are obtained by adding $\boldsymbol{Q}\eta$ to the optimal control. The signal η is the innovations process and $\boldsymbol{Q}$ is a causal linear system that satisfies

$$\|\boldsymbol{Q}\|_{2,[0,T]}^2 + \frac{1}{T}\int_0^T \big(\operatorname{trace}(B_1'XB_1) + \operatorname{trace}(FYF')\big)\, dt \leq \gamma^2$$

   in the case of a finite horizon, or $\boldsymbol{Q} \in \mathcal{H}_\infty$ such that

$$\|\boldsymbol{Q}\|_2^2 + \operatorname{trace}(B_1'XB_1) + \operatorname{trace}(FYF') \leq \gamma^2$$

   in the case of an infinite horizon.

6. If $\boldsymbol{Q} \in \mathcal{H}_\infty$ is allowed to vary without restriction on its norm, we capture all internally-stabilizing controllers.

5.5 Notes and References

This chapter considers only a fraction of what is known about LQ optimal control, Kalman filtering and LQG control. Indeed, the volume of work on these subjects is so vast that it would be a considerable task to provide a comprehensive guide to the literature. A bibliography of LQG control compiled by Mendel and Gieseking [149] in 1971 lists 73 books, 452 journal papers and numerous conference papers, reports and theses.

Most of our knowledge of the subject originates from the texts by Anderson and Moore [11, 12], Kwakernaak and Sivan [125], Brockett [33] and Davis [40]. These texts contain extensive bibliographies.

The seminal papers on optimal estimation are Kalman [106] and Kalman and Bucy [110]. Wonham [213] is regarded as having proved the LQG separation theorem.

The parametrization of all control signals and filters that achieve a prescribed performance level is a relatively recent addition to LQG theory introduced by Doyle, Glover, Khargonekar and Francis [54].

A special issue of the *IEEE Transactions on Automatic Control* was devoted to LQG control in 1971 [17]. It contains expository articles by Athans [16] and Luenberger [141]; the paper by Willems [211] on the connections between Riccati equations, optimal control and factorization theory; and the paper by Rosenbrock and Moran [173], which takes a critical view of optimal control.

We conclude with a quotation from Athans' editorial in the special issue [15]:

> "It appears that the most pressing issue is related to the modelling issue; namely, how accurate should the plant model be? how accurate should the model of uncertainties be? and how should the performance index be defined to consolidate design specifications and model inaccuracy. Furthermore, how can one guarantee the relative insensitivity of the final control system right from the start?"

5.6 Problems

Problem 5.1. Suppose

$$\dot{x}(t) = Ax + Bu, \qquad x(0) = x_0,$$

and

$$J(x_0, u) = \int_0^T x'C'Cx + u'u\,dt.$$

Show that $J(x_0, u)$ is convex in u.

Problem 5.2. Consider the system

$$\begin{aligned} \dot{x} &= Ax + Bu, \qquad x(0) = x_0, \\ z &= \begin{bmatrix} Cx \\ Du \end{bmatrix} \end{aligned}$$

with $D'D = I$ and the cost functional

$$J(u, x_0) = \int_0^T z'z\,dt.$$

1. Suppose an optimal control u^* exists that minimizes $J(u, x_0)$ and let x^* be the corresponding optimal state trajectory. If the optimal control is perturbed to $u = u^* + \epsilon\tilde{u}$, where $\tilde{u}$ is an arbitrary function of time and ϵ is an arbitrary number, show that the state trajectory is perturbed to $x = x^* + \epsilon\tilde{x}$, in which

$$\tilde{x}(t) = \int_0^t \Phi(t, \tau)B\tilde{u}\,d\tau,$$

with $\Phi(\cdot,\cdot)$ the transition matrix associated with A.

2. Show that

$$\begin{aligned} J(u,x_0) &= \int_0^T (x^{*'}C'Cx^* + (u^*)'u^*)dt \\ &+2\epsilon \int_0^T (\tilde{x}'C'Cx^* + \tilde{u}'u^*)dt \\ &+\epsilon^2 \int_0^T (\tilde{x}'C'C\tilde{x} + \tilde{u}'\tilde{u})dt. \end{aligned}$$

3. Use the fact that u^* minimizes $J(u,x_0)$, to show that

$$\int_0^T (\tilde{x}'C'Cx^* + \tilde{u}'u^*)dt = 0.$$

4. Using your answers to Parts (1), (2) and (3), show that

$$\int_0^T \tilde{u}'(B'\lambda + u^*)dt = 0, \qquad (5.6.1)$$

with

$$\lambda(t) = \int_t^T \Phi'(\tau,t)C'Cx^*d\tau.$$

Conclude that $u^* = -B_2'\lambda$ (almost everywhere) from the fact that (5.6.1) must hold for any $\tilde{u} \in \mathcal{L}_2[0,T]$.[3]

5. Show that

$$\dot{\lambda} = -A'\lambda - C'Cx^* \qquad \lambda(T) = 0.$$

Hence show that x^* and λ satisfy the two-point-boundary-value problem (TPBVP)

$$\begin{bmatrix} \dot{x}^* \\ \dot{\lambda} \end{bmatrix} = \begin{bmatrix} A & -BB' \\ -C'C & -A' \end{bmatrix} \begin{bmatrix} x^* \\ \lambda \end{bmatrix}, \qquad \begin{bmatrix} x^*(0) \\ \lambda(T) \end{bmatrix} = \begin{bmatrix} x_0 \\ 0 \end{bmatrix}.$$

6. If $\Phi(t,T)$ is the transition matrix associated with the TPBVP, show that

$$\begin{aligned} \lambda(t) &= \Phi_{21}(t,T)\Phi_{11}^{-1}(t,T)x^*(t) \\ &= P(t)x^*(t). \end{aligned}$$

Show that the inverse always exists!

7. By differentiating P, show that

$$-\dot{P} = A'P + PA - PBB'P + C'C$$

with terminal condition $P(T) = 0$. Conclude that the optimal control is given by $u = -B'Px$.

---

[3] This deduction is known as the Fundamental Lemma of the calculus of variations.

Problem 5.3. Suppose that the standard assumptions on (A, B_2, C) are satisfied. Let P be the stabilizing solution to (5.2.29) and let $\bar{P}$ be *any* other solution. Show that

$$(P-\bar{P})(A-B_2B_2'P)+(A-B_2B_2'P)'(P-\bar{P})+(P-\bar{P})B_2B_2'(P-\bar{P})=0$$

and conclude that $P \geq \bar{P}$. Show that when (A, C) is detectable, $\bar{P} \geq 0$ implies $\bar{P} = P$.[4]

Problem 5.4. Consider the loop-gain transfer function $B_2'P(sI-A)^{-1}B_2$, in which P is the stabilizing solution to (5.2.29).

1. Show that

$$\begin{aligned}&\left(I+B_2'(-sI-A')^{-1}PB_2\right)\left(I+B_2'P(sI-A)^{-1}B_2\right)\\ &\quad = \quad I+B_2'(-sI-A')^{-1}C'C(sI-A)^{-1}B_2.\end{aligned}$$

   This equation is known as the "return-difference equality".
   Let $\boldsymbol{W} = I + B_2'P(sI-A)^{-1}B_2$. Draw a block diagram that contains three signal paths having transfer function matrix $\boldsymbol{S} = \boldsymbol{W}^{-1}$ or $-\boldsymbol{S}$. (Hint: Anderson and Moore [11], pages 66–71.) Give three reasons for calling $\boldsymbol{S}$ the sensitivity operator associated with the controller $u = -B_2'Px$. Show that $\|\boldsymbol{S}\|_\infty \leq 1$ follows from the return-difference equality.
2. The return-difference equality can also be written as $\boldsymbol{W}^\sim\boldsymbol{W} = \boldsymbol{G}^\sim\boldsymbol{G}$, in which

$$\boldsymbol{G} = \begin{bmatrix} C(sI-A)^{-1}B_2 \\ I \end{bmatrix}.$$

   Show that $\boldsymbol{G}\boldsymbol{W}^{-1} \in \mathcal{H}_\infty$ and that $\boldsymbol{G}\boldsymbol{W}^{-1}$ is allpass. Conclude that

$$\left(\boldsymbol{G}\boldsymbol{W}^{-1}(s)\right)^*\left(\boldsymbol{G}\boldsymbol{W}^{-1}(s)\right) \leq I, \text{ for all } \mathrm{R}_e(s) \geq 0.$$

3. Show that a state-feedback controller $u = -Kx$ is optimal with respect to some performance index of the form $\int_0^\infty (x'C'Cx + u'u)\,dt$ if and only if

$$\left(I+K(sI-A)^{-1}B_2\right)^\sim\left(I+K(sI-A)^{-1}B_2\right) \geq I$$

   and $A - B_2K$ is asymptotically stable. (Hint: Use the bounded real lemma.) This question, known as the inverse problem of optimal control, was considered in Kalman [109]. See also Anderson and Moore [11, 13].
4. Suppose that the input u is scalar, making $B_2 = b_2$ a vector. Show that

$$|1 + b_2'P(j\omega I - A)^{-1}b_2| \geq 1.$$

   Conclude that the closed-loop system, with $u = -b_2'Px$, has a guaranteed phase margin of $\pm 60°$, an arbitrarily large gain marin and a gain-reduction tolerance of up to 50%.

---

[4] The literature often speaks of the unique positive solution to the LQ Riccati equation; it is only unique when (A, C) is detectable, in which case it is the stabilizing solution.

Problem 5.5. Consider the exponentially weighted performance index

$$J = \int_0^\infty e^{2\alpha t}(x'C'Cx + u'u)\, dt,$$

in which $\dot{x} = Ax + B_2 u$.

1. Show that the optimal (minimizing) controller is $u = -B_2' P_\alpha x$, in which P_α is the stabilizing solution to the Riccati equation

$$P_\alpha(\alpha I + A) + (\alpha I + A)' P_\alpha - P_\alpha B_2' B_2' P_\alpha + C'C = 0.$$

   Under what assumptions does P_α exist?
2. Show that the closed-loop poles are all in the half-plane $\mathrm{R}_e(s) < -\alpha$. This is known as the regulator with prescribed degree of stability.

(Hint: Consider the change of variable $\tilde{x}(t) = e^{\alpha t} x(t)$.)

Problem 5.6. Suppose

$$\begin{aligned} \dot{x} &= Ax + B_1 w + B_2 u \\ z &= \begin{bmatrix} Cx \\ Du \end{bmatrix}, \end{aligned}$$

with $D'D = I$ and (A, B_2) stabilizable.

1. If $u = -Kx$ and $A - B_2 K$ is asymptotically stable, show that $\|\boldsymbol{R}_{zw}\|_2^2 = \mathrm{trace}(B_1' Q B_1)$, in which Q is the unique nonnegative definite solution to

$$(A - B_2 K)' Q + Q(A - B_2 K) + C'C + K'K = 0. \qquad (5.6.2)$$

2. Show that

$$(A - B_2 K)'(Q - P) + (Q - P)(A - B_2 K) + (K - B_2' P)'(K - B_2' P) = 0,$$

   in which P the stabilizing solution to (5.2.29) and conclude that $(Q - P) \geq 0$.
3. Prove that $\|\boldsymbol{R}_{zw}\|_2$ is minimized by setting $K = B_2' P$, and that the norm of the associated closed loop is $\|\boldsymbol{R}_{zw}\|_2^2 = \mathrm{trace}(B_1' P B_1)$.

Problem 5.7. If

$$A'P + PA + S = 0$$

and

$$AQ + QA' + R = 0,$$

verify that $\mathrm{trace}(QS) = \mathrm{trace}(PR)$.

Problem 5.8. Show that $\Delta_1 \geq \Delta_2 \geq 0$ implies $P(t, T, \Delta_1) \geq P(t, T, \Delta_2)$ for all $t \leq T$.

Problem 5.9. Consider the Riccati equation (5.2.31) with terminal condition $\Delta \geq 0$. If (A, B_2) is stabilizable and Δ is such that

$$\Delta A + A'\Delta - \Delta B_2 B_2' \Delta + C'C \tag{5.6.3}$$

is semidefinite, show that $P(t, T, \Delta)$ is monotonic, $\Pi = \lim_{T \to \infty} P(t, T, \Delta)$ exists, is constant and satisfies (5.2.29).

Problem 5.10. Suppose (A, B_2, C) is stabilizable and detectable.

1. Show that $P(t, T, 0)$ converges to the stabilizing solution to (5.2.29).
2. Show that for any $\Gamma \geq 0$, there exists a $\Delta \geq \Gamma$ such that (5.6.3) is nonpositive definite.
3. Conclude that $\Pi = \lim_{T \to \infty} P(t, T, \Gamma)$ is the stabilizing solution of the algebraic Riccati equation for any $\Gamma \geq 0$.

Problem 5.11. (Receding horizon control) Suppose

$$\begin{aligned} \dot{x} &= Ax + Bu \\ z &= \begin{bmatrix} Cx \\ Du \end{bmatrix} \end{aligned}$$

with $D'D = I$. The receding horizon performance index is

$$J(u, t, t+T, x_t) = \int_t^{t+T} z'z \, d\tau + x'(t+T)\Delta x(t+T)$$

and the optimal control is therefore $u_T^* = -F_T x$, in which $F_T(t) = B_2' P(t, t + T, \Delta)$. Observe that the optimal receding horizon feedback gain F_T is constant if the problem data are constant. We will now make this assumption and assume that the standard assumptions hold. Consider the decomposition

$$\int_t^\infty z'z \, d\tau = \int_t^{t+T} z'z \, d\tau + \int_{t+T}^\infty z'z \, d\tau.$$

If a controller is stabilizing, we must have

$$\int_{t+T}^\infty z'z \, d\tau \geq x'(t+T)Px(t+T),$$

in which P is the stabilizing solution to (5.2.29). Therefore, in order that the controller that minimizes $J(u, t, t+T, \Delta)$ is stabilizing, Δ must represent a conservative estimate of $\int_{t+T}^\infty z'z \, d\tau$. That is, $\Delta \geq P$.

Fallacious conjecture: F_T is stabilizing if and only if $\Delta \geq P$, in which P is the stabilizing solution to (5.2.29).

Give a counter-example that shows this conjecture is indeed fallacious. This fallacy provides a warning against simply choosing a very large Δ.

(The arguments in the text show that F_T is stabilizing if and only if $\Delta \geq P$ *and* $\frac{d}{dt}P(t,T,\Delta)|_{t=0} \geq 0$ by exploiting the "fake algebraic Riccati technique" introduced by Poubelle *et al* [167] , which is simply the identity

$$P_T(A - B_2B_2'F_T) + (A - B_2B_2'F_T)'P_T + P_TB_2B_2'P_T + C'C + R_T = 0,$$

in which $P_T = P(0,T,\Delta)$ and $R_T = \dot{P}(t,T,\Delta)|_{t=0}$.)

For more details on receding horizon LQ control and related matters see Bitmead, Gevers and Wertz [29].

Problem 5.12. Consider the signal generator

$$\begin{aligned} \dot{x} &= Ax + Bw, \qquad x(0) = 0, \\ y &= Cx + Dv, \end{aligned}$$

in which $\begin{bmatrix} w' & v' \end{bmatrix}'$ is a unit intensity white noise. Show that the innovations process $\eta = y - C\widehat{x}$ in the Kalman filter is white and has unit intensity.

(Hint: Show that the system $\boldsymbol{A}$ mapping $\begin{bmatrix} w' & v' \end{bmatrix}'$ to η satisfies $\boldsymbol{A}\boldsymbol{A}^{\sim} = I$.)

Problem 5.13. Consider the signal generator

$$\begin{aligned} \dot{x} &= Ax + Bw, \qquad \mathcal{E}\{x(0)\} = 0, \quad \mathcal{E}\{x(0)x'(0)\} = P_0 \\ y &= Cx + Dv, \end{aligned}$$

in which $\begin{bmatrix} w' & v' \end{bmatrix}'$ is a unit intensity white noise that is independent of $x(0)$. Show that the Kalman filter

$$\dot{\widehat{x}} = A\widehat{x} + QC'(y - C\widehat{x}), \qquad \widehat{x}(0) = 0,$$

with

$$\dot{Q} = AQ + QA' - QC'CQ + C'C, \qquad Q(0) = P_0,$$

minimizes $\mathcal{E}\left\{(\widehat{x}(t) - x(t))(\widehat{x}(t) - x(t))'\right\}$ given $y(\sigma)$, $\sigma \in [0,t]$, over the class of causal, linear (finite-dimensional) filters. Show that $Q(t)$ is the optimal state error variance at time t.

(Hint: Write an arbitrary filter as

$$\begin{aligned} \frac{d}{dt}\begin{bmatrix} \tilde{x} \\ \xi \end{bmatrix} &= \begin{bmatrix} A - QC'C & 0 \\ 0 & F \end{bmatrix}\begin{bmatrix} \tilde{x} \\ \xi \end{bmatrix} + \begin{bmatrix} QC' \\ G \end{bmatrix} y \\ \widehat{x} &= \begin{bmatrix} H_1 & H_2 \end{bmatrix}\begin{bmatrix} \tilde{x} \\ \xi \end{bmatrix} + Jy. \end{aligned}$$

Work out $\mathcal{E}\left\{(\widehat{x}(t) - x(t))(\widehat{x}(t) - x(t))'\right\}$ in terms of a matrix $\tilde{P}$ that is the solution to a controllability type Lyapunov equation.)

Problem 5.14. Consider the LQG problem defined by

$$\begin{aligned}
\begin{bmatrix} \dot{x}_1 \\ \dot{x}_2 \end{bmatrix} &= \begin{bmatrix} 1 & 1 \\ 0 & 1 \end{bmatrix} \begin{bmatrix} x_1 \\ x_2 \end{bmatrix} + \sqrt{\sigma} \begin{bmatrix} 1 & 0 \\ 1 & 0 \end{bmatrix} w + \begin{bmatrix} 0 \\ 1 \end{bmatrix} u \\
z &= \begin{bmatrix} \sqrt{\rho}(x_1 + x_2) \\ u \end{bmatrix} \\
y &= \begin{bmatrix} 1 & 0 \end{bmatrix} \begin{bmatrix} x_1 \\ x_2 \end{bmatrix} + \begin{bmatrix} 0 & 1 \end{bmatrix} w.
\end{aligned}$$

1. Show that the optimal controller is given by

$$\boldsymbol{k} = \frac{\alpha\beta(1 - 2s)}{s^2 + (\alpha + \beta - 2)s + 1 + \alpha\beta}$$

   with

$$\alpha = 2 + \sqrt{4 + \rho} \quad ; \quad \beta = 2 + \sqrt{4 + \sigma}.$$

   (This solution was quoted in Example 2.1.2.)
2. What is the optimal cost? How does it vary with σ and ρ?

6

Full-Information $\mathcal{H}_\infty$ Controller Synthesis

6.1 Introduction

We begin our attack on the problem of finding controllers that meet $\mathcal{H}_\infty$ norm objectives by analyzing the full-information problem described in Section 4.2.2. In the full-information problem, the controller has access to both the state x and the exogenous input w as shown in Figure 6.1.

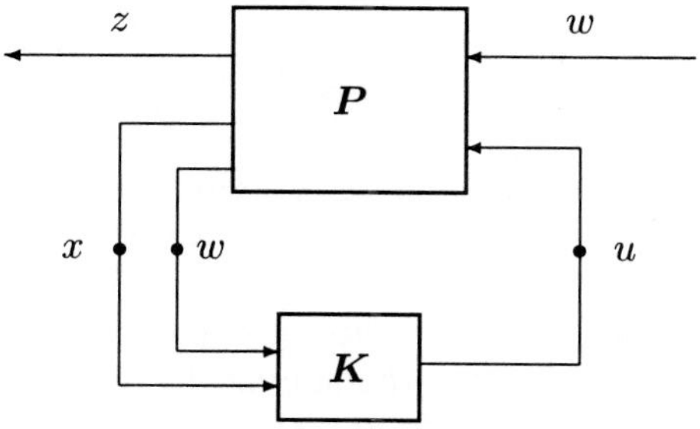

Figure 6.1: The full-information configuration.

The controller $\boldsymbol{K}$ is required to be causal and linear[1], and generates the control signal u according to

$$u = \boldsymbol{K}\begin{bmatrix} x \\ w \end{bmatrix}. \tag{6.1.1}$$

The state x is the solution to the linear differential equation

$$\dot{x} = Ax + B_1 w + B_2 u, \qquad x(0) = 0. \tag{6.1.2}$$

We consider the objective signal

$$z = C_1 x + D_{12} u, \tag{6.1.3}$$

in which $D_{12}' D_{12} = I$ for all times of interest. Recall that we may consider the objective (6.1.3) instead of $z = C_1x + D_{11}w + D_{12}u$ by assuming that loop-shifting and scaling transformations that remove D_{11} and scale D_{12} have already been carried out. These transformations are described in Section 4.6. As noted in Chapter 5, a standard change of control variable ($\tilde{u} = u + D_{12}'C_1x$) reduces (6.1.3) to an objective of the form

$$z = \begin{bmatrix} Cx \\ Du \end{bmatrix}, \tag{6.1.4}$$

in which $D'D = I$. We develop our results for the objective (6.1.4) in preference to (6.1.3) because the elimination of cross terms between u and x in $z'z$ simplifies the resulting formulas. The manipulations required to extend the results to the objective (6.1.3) are described in Section 5.2.3—Problem 6.1 requests the reader to fill in the details.

In the first instance, we confine our attention to the finite time horizon problem, which allows us to establish the key structural features of the solution while postponing the need to address internal stability issues. We show that the full-information $\mathcal{H}_\infty$ controller synthesis problem has a solution if and only if a certain Riccati differential equation has a solution. Unlike the situation in LQ control, the $\mathcal{H}_\infty$ Riccati equation does not have a solution if the performance level γ is selected too low.

By considering the limit as the horizon length passes to infinity, we show that the infinite-horizon, full-information $\mathcal{H}_\infty$ controller synthesis problem has a solution if and only if the corresponding algebraic Riccati equation has a stabilizing solution that is nonnegative definite. This is markedly different from the situation in LQ control, where, provided the the standard assumptions hold, the Riccati equation always has a nonnegative definite, stabilizing solution.

The finite-horizon problem

In the case of a finite time horizon, the plant (6.1.2) and (6.1.4) may be time-varying and we seek a causal, linear, full-information controller such that the closed-loop

[1] We will see that nonlinear controllers offer no advantage over linear ones when controlling linear plants.

system $\boldsymbol{R}_{zw}$ in Figure 6.1 satisfies

$$\int_0^T (z'z - \gamma^2 w'w)\, dt + x'(T)\Delta x(T) \leq -\epsilon \|w\|_{2,[0,T]}^2 \tag{6.1.5}$$

for all $w \in \mathcal{L}_2[0,T]$ and some $\epsilon > 0$. The matrix Δ is assumed to be nonnegative definite and (6.1.5) ensures that

$$\|\boldsymbol{R}_{zw}\|_{[0,T]} < \gamma, \tag{6.1.6}$$

in which $\|\cdot\|_{[0,T]}$ is the $\mathcal{L}_2[0,T]$ induced norm. Conversely, (6.1.6) implies that (6.1.5) holds for some $\epsilon > 0$ and some $\Delta \geq 0$.

When controllers satisfying the objective (6.1.5) exist, we would like a parametrization of them all.

The terminal state penalty term will be used to ensure that a stabilizing control law is obtained when we consider the limit $T \to \infty$.

The infinite-horizon problem

In the infinite-horizon case, the plant described by (6.1.2) and (6.1.4) is assumed to be time-invariant. In this case, we seek a causal, linear and stabilizing full-information controller such that the closed-loop system $\boldsymbol{R}_{zw}$ satisfies

$$\|\boldsymbol{R}_{zw}\|_\infty < \gamma. \tag{6.1.7}$$

The objective (6.1.7) can be written in the equivalent form

$$\|z\|_2^2 - \gamma^2\|w\|_2^2 \leq -\epsilon\|w\|_2^2 \tag{6.1.8}$$

for all $w \in \mathcal{L}_2[0,\infty)$ and some $\epsilon > 0$. Again, we would like a parametrization of all controllers that satisfy (6.1.7), when they exist.

In order that a stabilizing controller exists, it is necessary to assume that the pair (A, B_2) is stabilizable (see Appendix A). We will also make the assumption that the pair (A, C) has no unobservable mode on the imaginary axis. These are the assumptions we made in the infinite-horizon, LQG full-information problem. As we will see in Section 6.3.4, the assumption that (A, C) has no unobservable mode on the imaginary axis involves *no loss of generality.*

6.2 The finite-horizon case

In this section, we consider the time-varying system (6.1.2) and (6.1.4), with $D'D = I$ for all times of interest. The control signal is generated by a full-information controller (6.1.1), in which $\boldsymbol{K}$ is causal and linear. We denote this set of control laws by $\mathcal{K}$. Our objective is to determine when there is a $\boldsymbol{K} \in \mathcal{K}$ such that (6.1.5) is satisfied for all $w \in \mathcal{L}_2[0,T]$ and to parametrize all such controllers when they exist. We assume that $\Delta \geq 0$ and that $\gamma > 0$.

6.2.1 Connection to differential games

The problem we are faced with is closely related to a linear quadratic differential game. We may think of the designer and nature as playing a game in which the designer's goal is to choose a $\boldsymbol{K} \in \mathcal{K}$ such that (6.1.5) is satisfied, while nature's aim is to foil the designer's strategy by choosing a maximally malevolent w.

Specifically, define the performance index

$$J(\boldsymbol{K}, w, T, \Delta) = \int_0^T (z'z - \gamma^2 w'w)\, dt + x(T)'\Delta x(T), \tag{6.2.1}$$

in which $\boldsymbol{K}$ is a controller, w is a disturbance and Δ is an arbitrary nonnegative definite matrix. If the designer chooses $\boldsymbol{K} \in \mathcal{K}$ and nature chooses $w \in \mathcal{L}_2[0,T]$, the cost to the designer is $J(\boldsymbol{K}, w, T, \Delta)$ while the payoff to nature is also $J(\boldsymbol{K}, w, T, \Delta)$. Thus the designer wishes to minimize $J(\boldsymbol{K}, w, T, \Delta)$ and nature wishes to maximize it.

The game has a *saddle point* if there exists a pair $(\boldsymbol{K}^*, w^*)$ such that for all $w \in \mathcal{L}_2[0,T]$ and all $\boldsymbol{K} \in \mathcal{K}$ the inequalities

$$J(\boldsymbol{K}^*, w, T, \Delta) \le J(\boldsymbol{K}^*, w^*, T, \Delta) \le J(\boldsymbol{K}, w^*, T, \Delta) \tag{6.2.2}$$

hold. We may think of $\boldsymbol{K}^*$ as the "best" controller in $\mathcal{K}$, while w^* is the "worst" exogenous input in $\mathcal{L}_2[0,T]$.

The existence of a saddle point is a necessary condition for the existence of a controller that satisfies (6.1.5). To see this, suppose $\widehat{\boldsymbol{K}} \in \mathcal{K}$ satisfies (6.1.5). Then $J(\widehat{\boldsymbol{K}}, w, T, \Delta) \le 0$ for all $w \in \mathcal{L}_2[0,T]$. Also, $J(\boldsymbol{K}, 0, T, \Delta) = 0$ for any $\boldsymbol{K} \in \mathcal{K}$, since $x(0) = 0$ and $\boldsymbol{K}\begin{bmatrix} 0 \\ 0 \end{bmatrix} = 0$. Thus

$$J(\widehat{\boldsymbol{K}}, w, T, \Delta) \le J(\widehat{\boldsymbol{K}}, 0, T, \Delta) \le J(\boldsymbol{K}, 0, T, \Delta)$$

for all $w \in \mathcal{L}_2[0,T]$ and all $\boldsymbol{K} \in \mathcal{K}$. It is clear from the second inequality that $w^* = 0$ is the worst disturbance. We therefore conclude that the pair $(\widehat{\boldsymbol{K}}, 0)$ is a saddle point whenever $\widehat{\boldsymbol{K}}$ satisfies (6.1.5).

We may therefore determine a candidate controller by examining the first-order necessary conditions for the existence of a saddle point. Since this analysis is only provided for motivational purposes, we will only consider the case of open-loop controls. Nevertheless, a feedback controller with the correct properties will be given once the central Riccati equation of $\mathcal{H}_\infty$ control has been found.

6.2.2 First-order necessary conditions

Suppose there exists a control signal u^* and a disturbance w^* satisfying the saddle point inequalities in (6.2.2). Let x^* denote the state trajectory associated with u^* and w^*, which satisfies

$$\dot{x}^* = Ax^* + B_1 w^* + B_2 u^*, \qquad x^*(0) = 0. \tag{6.2.3}$$

We consider the optimization problems associated with the two inequalities in (6.2.2) in turn by invoking standard procedures from the calculus of variations.

The minimization problem

Suppose that $w \equiv w^*$ is fixed and that u^* is perturbed to $u = u^* + \eta\tilde{u}$, in which η is some number. This produces a corresponding perturbation in the state described by

$$\dot{x} = Ax + B_1 w^* + B_2 u, \qquad x(0) = 0.$$

Subtracting (6.2.3), we see that

$$x = x^* + \eta\tilde{x}, \qquad 0 \le t \le T,$$

in which $\tilde{x}$ satisfies

$$\dot{\tilde{x}} = A\tilde{x} + B_2\tilde{u}, \qquad \tilde{x}(0) = 0.$$

Thus

$$\tilde{x}(t) = \int_0^t \Phi(t,\tau) B_2 \tilde{u}\, d\tau, \tag{6.2.4}$$

in which $\Phi(\cdot,\cdot)$ is the transition matrix corresponding to A. Direct substitution into the value function J in (6.2.1) gives

$$\begin{aligned} J(u, w^*, T, \Delta) \\ = & \int_0^T (x^{*\prime}C'Cx^* + u^{*\prime}u^* - \gamma^2 w^{*\prime}w^*)\, dt + x^{*\prime}(T)\Delta x^*(T) \\ & +2\eta\left\{\int_0^T (\tilde{x}'C'Cx^* + \tilde{u}'u^*)\, dt + \tilde{x}'(T)\Delta x^*(T)\right\} \\ & +\eta^2\left\{\int_0^T (\tilde{x}'C'C\tilde{x} + \tilde{u}'\tilde{u})\, dt + \tilde{x}'(T)\Delta\tilde{x}(T)\right\}. \end{aligned}$$

Since u^* is minimizing, changing the control cannot decrease the value function $J(u, w^*, T, \Delta)$. Therefore, as a function of η, $J(u, w^*, T, \Delta)$ must take on its minimum value at $\eta = 0$. Since the cost function is quadratic in η, with a minimum at $\eta = 0$, the coefficient of the linear term must be zero. That is,

$$\int_0^T (\tilde{x}'C'Cx^* + \tilde{u}'u^*)\, dt + \tilde{x}'(T)\Delta x^*(T) = 0. \tag{6.2.5}$$

Substituting (6.2.4) into (6.2.5) and interchanging the order of integration gives

$$\int_0^T \tilde{u}'(B_2'\lambda + u^*)\, dt = 0, \tag{6.2.6}$$

in which λ is the adjoint variable defined by

$$\lambda(t) = \int_t^T \Phi'(\tau,t)C'Cx^* d\tau + \Phi'(T,t)\Delta x^*(T). \tag{6.2.7}$$

Since $\tilde{u}$ is arbitrary, we conclude that

$$u^* = -B_2'\lambda, \qquad 0 \le t \le T, \tag{6.2.8}$$

by invoking the Fundamental Lemma of the calculus of variations.

The maximization problem

Suppose now that $u = u^*$ is fixed and that w^* is perturbed to

$$w = w^* + \eta\tilde{w} \qquad 0 \le t \le T. \tag{6.2.9}$$

The signal $\tilde{w}$ is an arbitrary $\mathcal{L}_2[0,T]$ function and η is an arbitrary constant. The perturbation in w produces a perturbation in x:

$$x = x^* + \eta\tilde{x} \qquad 0 \le t \le T.$$

Here, $\tilde{x}$ is a function that is determined by $\tilde{w}$, u^* and the system dynamics. Subtracting (6.2.3) from (6.1.2), we obtain

$$\dot{\tilde{x}} = A\tilde{x} + B_1\tilde{w}, \qquad \tilde{x}(0) = 0,$$

giving

$$\tilde{x}(t) = \int_0^t \Phi(t,\tau)B_1\tilde{w}d\tau, \tag{6.2.10}$$

in which $\Phi(\cdot,\cdot)$ is the transition matrix corresponding to A. Substitution into (6.2.1) gives

$$\begin{aligned} & J(u^*,w,T,\Delta) \\ = & \int_0^T (x^{*\prime}C'Cx^* + u^{*\prime}u^* - \gamma^2 w^{*\prime}w^*)\,dt + x^{*\prime}(T)\Delta x^*(T) \\ & +2\eta\left\{\int_0^T (\tilde{x}'C'Cx^* - \gamma^2\tilde{w}'w^*)\,dt + \tilde{x}'(T)\Delta x^*(T)\right\} \\ & +\eta^2\left\{\int_0^T (\tilde{x}'C'C\tilde{x} - \gamma^2\tilde{w}'\tilde{w})\,dt + \tilde{x}'(T)\Delta\tilde{x}(T)\right\}. \end{aligned}$$

Since w^* is maximizing, changing the input to that given in (6.2.9) cannot increase $J(u^*,w,T,\Delta)$. Therefore, as before, the coefficient of the term linear in η must be zero. That is,

$$\int_0^T (\tilde{x}'C'Cx^* - \gamma^2\tilde{w}'w^*)\,dt + \tilde{x}'(T)\Delta x^*(T) = 0. \tag{6.2.11}$$

Substituting (6.2.10) into (6.2.11) and interchanging the order of integration gives

$$\int_0^T \tilde{w}'(B_1'\lambda - \gamma^2 w^*)\, dt = 0, \tag{6.2.12}$$

in which λ is the adjoint variable defined by (6.2.7). Since (6.2.12) must be true for all $\tilde{w}$, we conclude that

$$w^* = \gamma^{-2} B_1' \lambda. \tag{6.2.13}$$

The two-point-boundary-value problem

We may summarize our findings so far by assembling the dynamics of the saddle-point state trajectory and the dynamics associated with the adjoint variable into a two-point-boundary-value problem (TPBVP) that represents both optimal control problems.

Differentiating (6.2.7) with respect to t gives

$$\dot{\lambda}(t) = -A'\lambda - C'Cx^*, \qquad \lambda(T) = \Delta x^*(T), \tag{6.2.14}$$

and combining this with (6.2.3), (6.2.8) and (6.2.13) yields

$$\begin{bmatrix} \dot{x}^* \\ \dot{\lambda} \end{bmatrix} = \begin{bmatrix} A & -(B_2B_2' - \gamma^{-2}B_1B_1') \\ -C'C & -A' \end{bmatrix} \begin{bmatrix} x^* \\ \lambda \end{bmatrix}, \tag{6.2.15}$$

with boundary condition

$$\begin{bmatrix} x^*(0) \\ \lambda(T) \end{bmatrix} = \begin{bmatrix} 0 \\ \Delta x^*(T) \end{bmatrix}. \tag{6.2.16}$$

What has been shown is that control signal u^* and the exogenous input w^* associated with any saddle-point strategy must be given by

$$\begin{aligned} u^* &= -B_2'\lambda \\ w^* &= \gamma^{-2}B_1'\lambda, \end{aligned}$$

in which λ is a solution to the TPBVP. Note, however, that these are necessary conditions—we have not shown that a saddle-point strategy exists.

The TPBVP always has a solution, namely the trivial solution $x^* \equiv 0$ and $\lambda \equiv 0$. Whether or not there are also other solutions in addition to the trivial one turns out to be a crucial question to which we shall return.

6.2.3 The Riccati equation

Although we have obtained formulas for u^* and w^*, we have not exhibited a full-information control law $\boldsymbol{K}^*$. To do this, we show that x^* and λ may be related by the solution of a Riccati equation.

Let $\Phi(t,T)$ be the transition matrix corresponding to (6.2.15):

$$\frac{d}{dt}\Phi(t,T) = H\Phi(t,T), \qquad \Phi(T,T) = I, \tag{6.2.17}$$

in which

$$H = \begin{bmatrix} A & -(B_2B_2' - \gamma^{-2}B_1B_1') \\ -C'C & -A' \end{bmatrix}.$$

Then

$$\begin{bmatrix} x^*(t) \\ \lambda(t) \end{bmatrix} = \begin{bmatrix} \Phi_{11}(t,T) & \Phi_{12}(t,T) \\ \Phi_{21}(t,T) & \Phi_{22}(t,T) \end{bmatrix} \begin{bmatrix} x^*(T) \\ \lambda(T) \end{bmatrix}. \tag{6.2.18}$$

By eliminating $x^*(T)$ and $\lambda(T)$ in (6.2.18) using the boundary condition $\lambda(T) = \Delta x^*(T)$, one obtains

$$\lambda(t) = P(t)x^*(t),$$

with

$$P(t) = \big(\Phi_{21}(t,T) + \Phi_{22}(t,T)\Delta\big)\big(\Phi_{11}(t,T) + \Phi_{12}(t,T)\Delta\big)^{-1},$$

provided the indicated inverse exists for all times in $[t,T]$. We now have that

$$\begin{aligned} u^* &= -B_2'P(t)x^* \\ &= \begin{bmatrix} -B_2'P(t) & 0 \end{bmatrix} \begin{bmatrix} x^* \\ w^* \end{bmatrix} \end{aligned}$$

and therefore that

$$\boldsymbol{K}^* = \begin{bmatrix} -B_2'P(t) & 0 \end{bmatrix} \tag{6.2.19}$$

is a candidate control law.

Using the result of Problem 3.22, it is easily verified that P is the solution to the Riccati differential equation

$$-\dot{P} = A'P + PA - P(B_2B_2' - \gamma^{-2}B_1B_1')P + C'C, \quad P(T) = \Delta. \tag{6.2.20}$$

Notice that we can only write the control law as $u^* = -B_2'Px^*$ if the Riccati equation has a solution, which is equivalent to the nonsingularity of $\Phi_{11}(t,T) + \Phi_{12}(t,T)\Delta$ on the time interval $[0,T]$. If we set $\gamma^{-2} = 0$, (6.2.20) reduces to the LQ Riccati equation (5.2.31), which always has a solution. Hence we expect that the Riccati equation (6.2.20) will have a solution for γ sufficiently large. Indeed, if we reconsider the cost function given in (6.2.1) for a minute, we see that increasing γ has the effect of paralyzing nature—any activity by the w-player will reduce the payoff function. In the limit as $\gamma \to \infty$, the w-player is completely removed from the game and the optimization criterion reduces to one of minimizing

$$J = \int_0^T z'z\,dt + x'(T)\Delta x(T),$$

which is the cost function associated with LQ control.

Our aim in the remainder of this section is to show that the Riccati equation (6.2.20) has a solution on $[0,T]$ if and only if there exists a full-information control law satisfying the objective (6.1.5).

6.2.4 Sufficiency: completing the square

Assuming the Riccati equation (6.2.20) has a solution on the time interval $[0, T]$, we show that the full-information control law (6.2.19) satisfies the objective (6.1.5).

Theorem 6.2.1 *Suppose the Riccati differential equation (6.2.20) has a solution on $[0, T]$. Then*

$$\begin{aligned} u^* &= -B_2'Px & (6.2.21)\\ w^* &= \gamma^{-2}B_1'Px & (6.2.22)\end{aligned}$$

results in

$$J(\boldsymbol{K}, w, T, \Delta) = \|u - u^*\|_{2,[0,T]}^2 - \gamma^2\|w - w^*\|_{2,[0,T]}^2 \qquad (6.2.23)$$

for any controller $\boldsymbol{K}$ and any input w. If $u = u^*$, then the objective (6.1.5) is satisfied for some $\epsilon > 0$. We also have $\|\boldsymbol{R}_{zw}\|_{[0,T]} < \gamma$, which means that the full-information control law (6.2.21) is a solution to the full-information $\mathcal{H}_\infty$ controller synthesis problem on the time horizon $[0, T]$.

Proof. Since $P(T) = \Delta$ and $x(0) = 0$, we have for any u and w that

$$J(\boldsymbol{K}, w, T, \Delta) = \int_0^T \left(z'z - \gamma^2 w'w + \frac{d}{dt}(x'Px)\right) dt.$$

Since

$$\frac{d}{dt}(x'Px) = \dot{x}'Px + x'\dot{P}x + x'P\dot{x},$$

we may substitute for $\dot{x}$ and $\dot{P}$ from the state dynamics and the Riccati differential equation to obtain

$$\begin{aligned} &J(\boldsymbol{K}, w, T, \Delta)\\ &= \int_0^T \big(x'C'Cx + u'u - \gamma^2 w'w + (x'A' + w'B_1' + u'B_2')Px\\ &\qquad + x'\dot{P}x + x'P(Ax + B_1w + B_2u)\big)\, dt\\ &= \int_0^T \big(x'(C'C + A'P + PA + \dot{P})x + u'u - \gamma^2 w'w\\ &\qquad + (w'B_1' + u'B_2')Px + x'P(B_1w + B_2u)\big)\, dt\\ &= \int_0^T \big(x'P(B_2B_2' - \gamma^{-2}B_1B_1')Px + u'u - \gamma^2 w'w\\ &\qquad + (w'B_1' + u'B_2')Px + x'P(B_1w + B_2u)\big)\, dt\\ &= \int_0^T (u + B_2'Px)'(u + B_2'Px)\, dt\\ &\qquad - \gamma^2 \int_0^T (w - \gamma^{-2}B_1'Px)'(w - \gamma^{-2}B_1'Px)\, dt\\ &= \|u - u^*\|_{2,[0,T]}^2 - \gamma^2\|w - w^*\|_{2,[0,T]}^2,\end{aligned}$$

with u^* and w^* as in (6.2.21) and (6.2.22), which establishes (6.2.23).

To prove that this implies the objective (6.1.5) is satisfied, let $\boldsymbol{L}$ be the system that maps $w \mapsto (w - w^*)$ when $u = u^*$. Direct substitution shows that $\boldsymbol{L}$ has realization

$$\begin{aligned} \dot{x} &= (A - B_2B_2'P)x + B_1w & (6.2.24)\\ w - w^* &= -\gamma^{-2}B_1'Px + w. & (6.2.25)\end{aligned}$$

Setting $\boldsymbol{K} = \boldsymbol{K}^*$ (*i.e.*, $u = u^*$) in (6.2.23), we have

$$\begin{aligned} J(\boldsymbol{K}^*, w, T, \Delta) &= -\gamma^2\|w - w^*\|^2_{2,[0,T]}\\ &= -\gamma^2\|\boldsymbol{L}w\|^2_{2,[0,T]}\\ &\leq -\epsilon\|w\|^2_{2,[0,T]}\end{aligned}$$

for some positive constant ϵ ($\epsilon = \gamma^2/\|\boldsymbol{L}^{-1}\|^2_{[0,T]}$). The fact that $\epsilon > 0$ is a consequence of the fact that $\boldsymbol{L}^{-1}$ is given by a state-space system, so its induced norm is finite. We conclude also that $\|\boldsymbol{R}_{zw}\|_{[0,T]} < \gamma$, since $\Delta \geq 0$. ■

P is nonnegative definite

Suppose (6.2.20) has a solution on the interval $[0, T]$. Define

$$J_t(\boldsymbol{K}, w, T, \Delta) = \int_t^T (z'z - \gamma^2 w'w)\, d\tau + x'(T)\Delta x(T),$$

and complete the square to obtain

$$J_t(\boldsymbol{K}, w, T, \Delta) = x'(t)P(t)x(t) + \|u - u^*\|^2_{2,[t,T]} - \gamma^2\|w - w^*\|^2_{2,[t,T]}.$$

Consequently

$$x'(t)P(t)x(t) = J_t(\boldsymbol{K}^*, 0, \Delta, T) + \gamma^2\|w^*\|^2_{2,[t,T]}. \qquad (6.2.26)$$

Since $J_t(\boldsymbol{K}^*, 0, \Delta, T) \geq 0$ for all t, and since (6.2.26) is true for every $x(t)$, it follows that $P(t) \geq 0$ for all $t \in [0, T]$.[2]

6.2.5 Necessity

Our discussion of the connection between $\mathcal{H}_\infty$ control and differential games showed that any controller that satisfies the objective (6.1.5) must be a saddle point for a differential game. By analyzing the first-order necessary conditions for a saddle point, we obtained a two-point-boundary-value problem; any saddle-point strategy is given by $u^* = -B_2'\lambda$, $w^* = \gamma^{-2}B_1'\lambda$, in which the adjoint variable λ is a solution

[2]Just think of $x(t)$ as an arbitrary initial condition for the optimization interval $[t, T]$.

to the TPBVP. We then showed that λ could be related to x provided the Riccati differential equation (6.2.20) has a solution on $[0, T]$. By completing the square, we then showed that the existence of a solution to the Riccati differential equation did indeed provide a sufficient condition for the existence of the full-information $\mathcal{H}_\infty$ control problem. It remains for us to show that the existence of a solution to the Riccati differential equation (6.2.20) is also necessary for the the existence of the full-information $\mathcal{H}_\infty$ control problem.

To see that Riccati differential equations of this type do not always have a solution, consider the following example:

Example 6.2.1. Suppose

$$\begin{aligned} \dot{x} &= w + u \\ z &= \begin{bmatrix} x \\ u \end{bmatrix}. \end{aligned}$$

The associated Riccati equation is

$$-\dot{p} = 1 - p^2(1 - \gamma^{-2}), \qquad p(T) = \delta. \tag{6.2.27}$$

In the case that $\gamma > 1$, the solution to (6.2.27) is given by

$$\begin{aligned} p(\tau) &= \frac{\delta - \beta^{-1}\tanh(\beta\tau)}{1 - \delta\beta\tanh(\beta\tau)} \\ &= \beta^{-1}\tanh(\tanh^{-1}(\delta\beta) - \beta\tau), \end{aligned}$$

in which $\beta = \sqrt{1 - \gamma^{-2}}$ and $\tau = t - T$. Since $\tanh(\cdot)$ lies between -1 and 0 for all negative arguments, $p(\tau)$ is bounded for all $t \leq T$ and $\delta \geq 0$. When $\gamma = 1$, $p(\tau) = \delta - \tau$, which is finite for finite t and T.

In the case that $\gamma < 1$, the solution to (6.2.27) is

$$\begin{aligned} p(\tau) &= \frac{\delta - \phi^{-1}\tan(\phi\tau)}{1 + \delta\phi\tan(\phi\tau)} \\ &= \phi^{-1}\tan(\tan^{-1}(\delta\phi) - \phi\tau), \end{aligned}$$

in which $\phi = \sqrt{\gamma^{-2} - 1}$. In this case, there will be a finite escape time when

$$\frac{\pi}{2} = \tan^{-1}(\delta\phi) - \tau\phi$$

for the first time. That is, when

$$\tau^*(\gamma, \delta) = \begin{cases} \frac{2\tan^{-1}(\delta\phi) - \pi}{2\phi} & \text{if } \delta > 0 \\ \frac{-\pi}{2\phi} & \text{if } \delta = 0. \end{cases}$$

A small calculation shows that the escape time will occur in the interval $[0, T]$ (*i.e.*, $\tau \geq -T$) when $\gamma \leq \frac{1}{\sqrt{(\frac{\pi}{2T})^2+1}}$. This shows that a controller exists for any

$$\gamma > \gamma^*(T) = \frac{1}{\sqrt{(\frac{\pi}{2T})^2 + 1}}.$$

In the limit as $T \to \infty$, $\gamma^*(T) \to 1$. This is the least value of γ for which the infinite-horizon problem has a solution. ∇

We shall prove that the Riccati differential equation (6.2.20) has a solution whenever the full-information $\mathcal{H}_\infty$ control problem has a solution. Our proof requires us to return to the question of whether the two-point-boundary-value problem (6.2.15) has any nontrivial solutions. This question can be rephrased in terms of the existence conjugate points, which are used in the classical theory of the calculus of variations.

Conjugate points:

> Two times t_0, t_f with $t_0 \leq t_f$ are conjugate points of the TPBVP (6.2.15) if there is a *nontrivial* solution to (6.2.15) such that $x(t_0) = 0$ and $\lambda(t_f) = \Delta x(t_f)$ for a given fixed Δ.

This is slightly more general than the usual requirement that $\lambda(t_f) = 0$, which is only of interest when $\Delta = 0$. The next example illustrates the conjugate point properties of the TPBVP.

Example 6.2.2. The TPBVP associated with (6.2.27) is given by

$$\begin{bmatrix} \dot{x} \\ \dot{\lambda} \end{bmatrix} = \begin{bmatrix} 0 & \gamma^{-2} - 1 \\ -1 & 0 \end{bmatrix} \begin{bmatrix} x \\ \lambda \end{bmatrix}.$$

In the case that $\gamma < 1$ and $\delta = 0$, the TPBVP has a general solution of the form

$$\lambda(\tau) = \frac{-A\sin(\phi\tau)}{\phi}, \qquad x(\tau) = A\cos(\phi\tau)$$

in which $\tau = \tau - T$ and $\phi = \sqrt{\gamma^{-2} - 1}$. If $\tau^* = -\pi/2\phi$, we have

$$\begin{array}{ll} \lambda(\tau^*) = A\phi^{-1}, & x(\tau^*) = 0, \\ \lambda(0) = 0, & x(0) = A. \end{array}$$

This shows that $t_0 = T - \pi/2\phi$ and $t_f = T$ are conjugate points. ∇

Lemma 6.2.2 *Let $\Phi(t, \tau)$ be the transition matrix associated with the TPBVP (6.2.15). The matrix $\Phi_{11}(t_0, t_f) + \Phi_{12}(t_0, t_f)\Delta$ is singular if and only if t_0 and t_f are conjugate points.*

The Riccati equation (6.2.20) has a solution on $[0,T]$ provided $\Phi_{11}(t,T)+\Phi_{12}(t,T)\Delta$ is nonsingular for all $t \in [0,T]$, since

$$P(t) = (\Phi_{21}(t,T) + \Phi_{22}(t,T)\Delta)(\Phi_{11}(t,T) + \Phi_{12}(t,T)\Delta)^{-1}.$$

We conclude from this lemma that the Riccati equation (6.2.20) has a solution on $[0,T]$ if there is no $t \in [0,T]$ for which t and T conjugate points.

Proof. Suppose t_0 and t_f are conjugate points. Then there exists a nontrivial solution to (6.2.15) such that $x(t_0) = 0$ and $\lambda(t_f) = \Delta x(t_f)$. Hence

$$\begin{bmatrix} x(t) \\ \lambda(t) \end{bmatrix} = \begin{bmatrix} \Phi_{11}(t,t_f) & \Phi_{12}(t,t_f) \\ \Phi_{21}(t,t_f) & \Phi_{22}(t,t_f) \end{bmatrix} \begin{bmatrix} I \\ \Delta \end{bmatrix} x(t_f) \tag{6.2.28}$$

and we note that $x(t_f)$ must be nonzero, because x and λ are not identically zero and $\Phi(t,t_f)$ is nonsingular for all t, t_f. Since $x(t_0) = 0$, we have

$$0 = \big(\Phi_{11}(t_0,t_f) + \Phi_{12}(t_0,t_f)\Delta\big)x(t_f),$$

which means that $\Phi_{11}(t_0,t_f) + \Phi_{12}(t_0,t_f)\Delta$ is singular.

Now suppose that $\Phi_{11}(t_0,t_f) + \Phi_{12}(t_0,t_f)\Delta$ is singular. Then there exists a $g \neq 0$ such that

$$0 = \big(\Phi_{11}(t_0,t_f) + \Phi_{12}(t_0,t_f)\Delta\big)g.$$

By considering the solution to the final value problem (6.2.28) with $x(t_f) = g$, we see that $x(t_0) = 0$ and $\lambda(t_f) = \Delta x(t_f)$ and also that $x(t)$ is not identically zero. Hence t_0 and t_f are conjugate points. ∎

From time to time, we will need the fact that the TPBVP

$$\begin{bmatrix} \dot{x} \\ \dot{\lambda} \end{bmatrix} = \begin{bmatrix} A & -BB' \\ -C'C & -A' \end{bmatrix} \begin{bmatrix} x \\ \lambda \end{bmatrix}, \quad \begin{bmatrix} x(t_0) \\ \lambda(t_f) \end{bmatrix} = \begin{bmatrix} 0 \\ \Delta x(t_f) \end{bmatrix}, \tag{6.2.29}$$

which arises in standard LQ optimal control enjoys a "no conjugate point" property. By setting $\gamma^{-2} = 0$ in (6.2.15), we see from Lemma 6.2.2 that this is just a restatement of the fact that the Riccati equation (5.2.31) associated with the LQ optimal control problem always has a solution.

Lemma 6.2.3 *Let $t_0 \leq t_f$ be any two time points and let $\Delta \geq 0$. The unique solution to the TPBVP (6.2.29) is the trivial solution $x(t) \equiv 0$, $\lambda(t) \equiv 0$.*

Proof. Let x and λ be any solution to (6.2.29). Then

$$\begin{aligned} \frac{d}{dt}(\lambda' x) &= \dot{\lambda}' x + \lambda' \dot{x} \\ &= -\lambda' BB' \lambda - x'C'Cx. \end{aligned}$$

Integrating from t_0 to t_f gives

$$x'(t_f)\Delta x(t_f) = -\int_{t_0}^{t_f} (\lambda' BB'\lambda + x'C'Cx)d\tau.$$

Since $x'(t_f)\Delta x(t_f) \geq 0$, we must have

$$B'\lambda = 0, \qquad Cx = 0, \qquad \Delta x(t_f) = 0.$$

Consequently $\dot{x} = Ax$ with $x(t_0) = 0$ and $\dot{\lambda} = -A'\lambda$ with $\lambda(t_f) = 0$ and we conclude that the trivial solution is the only solution to (6.2.29). ■

We are now ready to prove the main result of this section.

Theorem 6.2.4 *Consider the linear system (6.1.2) with output (6.1.4) and cost (6.2.1) with $\Delta \geq 0$. If there exists a controller $\widehat{\boldsymbol{K}} \in \mathcal{K}$ such that*

$$J(\widehat{\boldsymbol{K}}, w, T, \Delta) \leq -\epsilon \|w\|^2_{2,[0,T]} \tag{6.2.30}$$

for all $w \in \mathcal{L}_2[0,T]$ and some $\epsilon > 0$, then $t \in [0,T]$ and T are not conjugate points.
Consequently, the matrix $\Phi_{11}(t,T) + \Phi_{12}(t,T)\Delta$ is nonsingular for all $t \in [0,T]$ and the Riccati differential equation (6.2.20) has a solution on $[0,T]$.

Proof. Choose an arbitrary $t^* \in [0,T]$. To show that t^* and T cannot be conjugate points, we must show that the trivial solution is the only solution to (6.2.15) that has the property

$$\begin{bmatrix} x(t^*) \\ \lambda(T) \end{bmatrix} = \begin{bmatrix} 0 \\ \Delta x(T) \end{bmatrix}. \tag{6.2.31}$$

Let x^*, λ be *any* solution to (6.2.15) satisfying (6.2.31). Define the truncated cost function

$$J_{t^*}(\boldsymbol{K}, w, T, \Delta) = \int_{t^*}^{T} (z'z - \gamma^2 w'w)\, dt + x'(T)\Delta x(T).$$

For any input w such that $w(t) = 0$ for $t < t^*$, we obtain $u(t) = 0$ and $x(t) = 0$ for $t < t^*$. This is because $x(0) = 0$ and $\boldsymbol{K}\begin{bmatrix} 0 \\ 0 \end{bmatrix} = 0$ for $\boldsymbol{K} \in \mathcal{K}$. Consequently, $w(t) = 0$ for $t \leq t^*$ implies that

$$J(\boldsymbol{K}, w, T, \Delta) = J_{t^*}(\boldsymbol{K}, w, T, \Delta).$$

We now show that $u^* = -B_2'\lambda$ solves the open-loop minimization problem

$$\min_u \int_{t^*}^{T} (\tilde{x}'C'C\tilde{x} + u'u - \gamma^2 w^{*\prime} w^*)\, dt + x'(T)\Delta x(T), \tag{6.2.32}$$

subject to

$$\dot{\tilde{x}} = A\tilde{x} + B_1 w^* + B_2 u, \qquad \tilde{x}(t^*) = 0, \tag{6.2.33}$$

in which $w^* = \gamma^{-2}B_1'\lambda$. The tilde is used to distinguish between the state trajectory in (6.2.15), the state trajectory resulting from $\widehat{\boldsymbol{K}}$ and the state trajectory associated with the minimization problem in (6.2.32), which may be analyzed in exactly the same manner as the analysis associated with minimizing the right-hand inequality in (6.2.2). The solution may be summarized as

$$u_{opt} = -B_2'p, \tag{6.2.34}$$

with

$$-\dot{p} = A'p + C'C\tilde{x}, \qquad p(T) = \Delta\tilde{x}(T). \tag{6.2.35}$$

The details are requested as an exercise. Combining this with (6.2.33) gives the following TPBVP

$$\begin{aligned}
\begin{bmatrix} \dot{\tilde{x}} \\ \dot{p} \end{bmatrix} &= \begin{bmatrix} A & -B_2B_2' \\ -C'C & -A' \end{bmatrix}\begin{bmatrix} \tilde{x} \\ p \end{bmatrix} + \begin{bmatrix} B_1 w^* \\ 0 \end{bmatrix}, \\
\begin{bmatrix} \tilde{x}(t^*) \\ p(T) \end{bmatrix} &= \begin{bmatrix} 0 \\ \Delta\tilde{x}(T) \end{bmatrix}.
\end{aligned}$$

Using $w^* = \gamma^{-2}B_1'\lambda$ and subtracting (6.2.15) gives

$$\begin{aligned}
\begin{bmatrix} \dot{\tilde{x}} - \dot{x} \\ \dot{p} - \dot{\lambda} \end{bmatrix} &= \begin{bmatrix} A & -B_2B_2' \\ -C'C & -A' \end{bmatrix}\begin{bmatrix} \tilde{x} - x \\ p - \lambda \end{bmatrix}, \\
\begin{bmatrix} (\tilde{x} - x)(t^*) \\ (p - \lambda)(T) \end{bmatrix} &= \begin{bmatrix} 0 \\ \Delta(\tilde{x} - x)(T) \end{bmatrix},
\end{aligned}$$

which has the unique solution $\tilde{x} - x \equiv 0$, $p - \lambda \equiv 0$ by Lemma 6.2.3. Thus $u_{opt} = u^* = -B_2'\lambda$ is the solution of the minimization problem (6.2.32).

The cost of the minimizing control $u^* = -B_2'\lambda$ is zero, since

$$\begin{aligned}
&\int_{t^*}^{T} (x^{*\prime}C'Cx^* + u^{*\prime}u^* - \gamma^2 w^{*\prime}w^*)\, dt + x^{*\prime}(T)\Delta x^*(T) \\
&= \int_{t^*}^{T} \left(x^{*\prime}C'Cx^* + \lambda' B_2B_2'\lambda - \gamma^{-2}\lambda' B_1B_1'\lambda + \frac{d}{dt}(x^{*\prime}\lambda)\right) dt \\
&= \int_{t^*}^{T} \left(-x^{*\prime}(\dot{\lambda} + A'\lambda) - \lambda'(\dot{x} - Ax) + \frac{d}{dt}(x^{*\prime}\lambda)\right) dt \\
&= 0.
\end{aligned}$$

Furthermore, since u^* is the solution to the minimization problem (6.2.32), we have

$$\begin{aligned}
J_{t^*}(\widehat{\boldsymbol{K}}, w^*, T, \Delta) &\geq \min_u \int_{t^*}^{T} (\tilde{x}'C'C\tilde{x} + u'u - \gamma^2 w^{*\prime}w^*)\, dt + x'(T)\Delta x(T) \\
&= \int_{t^*}^{T} (x^{*\prime}C'Cx^* + u^{*\prime}u^* - \gamma^2 w^{*\prime}w^*)\, dt + x^*(T)'\Delta x^*(T) \\
&= 0.
\end{aligned}$$

But

$$J_{t^*}(\widehat{\boldsymbol{K}}, w^*, T, \Delta) = J(\widehat{\boldsymbol{K}}, w, T, \Delta) \leq -\epsilon\|w\|^2_{2,[0,T]}$$

for all $w \in \mathcal{L}_2[0,T]$ that satisfy $w(t) = 0$ for $t < t^*$. Since this holds for the particular input

$$w = \begin{cases} w^*(t) & t \geq t^* \\ 0 & 0 \leq t < t^*, \end{cases}$$

we must have $w^*(t) = 0$ for all $t \in [t^*, T]$. This reduces the TPBVP (6.2.15) to the TPBVP

$$\begin{bmatrix} \dot{x}^* \\ \dot{\lambda} \end{bmatrix} = \begin{bmatrix} A & -B_2B_2' \\ -C'C & -A' \end{bmatrix} \begin{bmatrix} x^* \\ \lambda \end{bmatrix}, \qquad \begin{bmatrix} x^*(t^*) \\ \lambda(T) \end{bmatrix} = \begin{bmatrix} 0 \\ \Delta x^*(T) \end{bmatrix}.$$

We now conclude that λ and x^* are identically zero from Lemma 6.2.3.

Since we have shown that any solution to (6.2.15) that satisfies (6.2.31) must be trivial, we conclude that t^* and T are not conjugate points. Since t^* was chosen arbitrarily, we conclude that t^* and T cannot be conjugate points for any $t^* \in [0,T]$ when there exists a controller $\boldsymbol{K}$ satisfying (6.2.30). ■

Theorems 6.2.1 and 6.2.4 combined state that there exists a causal, linear, full-information controller satisfying the objective (6.1.5) if and only if the Riccati differential equation (6.2.20) has a solution on $[0,T]$. In this case, one controller that achieves the objective is the memoryless, state-feedback control law $u = -B_2'Px$, in which P is the solution to the Riccati differential equation (6.2.20). We also remark that the only facts concerning the controller that were used in the necessity proof were: (a) causality and (b) homogeneity, meaning that the

$$\boldsymbol{K}\begin{bmatrix} 0 \\ 0 \end{bmatrix} = 0.$$

Thus, existence of a solution to the Riccati equation (6.2.20) is also necessary for the existence of causal, homogeneous, but possibly nonlinear, controllers that satisfy (6.1.5).

6.2.6 All closed-loop systems

In the last section, we observed that the "central controller" is only a function of x although measurement access to w is allowed. We will now show how to construct all control signals resulting from full-information controllers $\boldsymbol{K}$ that satisfy

$$J(\boldsymbol{K}, w, T, \Delta) \leq -\epsilon\|w\|^2_{2,[0,T]} \tag{6.2.36}$$

for all $w \in \mathcal{L}_2[0,T]$ and some $\epsilon > 0$. Equivalently, we construct all closed-loop operators generated by full-information controllers that satisfy (6.2.36).

Because of the redundant information inherent in the full-information configuration (see Section 4.2.2), this does not generate all full-information controllers that lead to (6.2.36). The characterization of all controllers, rather than all control signals, is dealt with in the next section.

We know that there exists a full-information controller with the property (6.2.36) if and only if the Riccati equation (6.2.20) has a solution on $[0,T]$. In addition,

$$\begin{aligned} u^* &= -B_2'Px && (6.2.37)\\ w^* &= \gamma^{-2}B_1'Px && (6.2.38) \end{aligned}$$

results in

$$J(\boldsymbol{K}, w, T, \Delta) = \|u - u^*\|^2_{2,[0,T]} - \gamma^2\|w - w^*\|^2_{2,[0,T]}. \tag{6.2.39}$$

Consider the class of controllers obtained by setting

$$u - u^* = \boldsymbol{U}(w - w^*), \tag{6.2.40}$$

in which $\boldsymbol{U}$ is causal and linear. This is a full-information controller, since it is just

$$u = -(B_2'P + \gamma^{-2}\boldsymbol{U}B_1'P)x + \boldsymbol{U}w.$$

We claim that a controller generated by (6.2.40) satisfies (6.2.36) if and only if

$$\|\boldsymbol{U}\|_{[0,T]} < \gamma. \tag{6.2.41}$$

To see this, rewrite (6.2.39) as

$$J(\boldsymbol{K}, w, T, \Delta) = \|\boldsymbol{U}(w - w^*)\|^2_{2,[0,T]} - \gamma^2\|w - w^*\|^2_{2,[0,T]} \tag{6.2.42}$$

and let $\boldsymbol{L}$ be the system that maps w to $w - w^*$, which was given in equations (6.2.24) and (6.2.25). If $\|\boldsymbol{U}\|_{[0,T]} < \gamma$, we have

$$\begin{aligned} J(\boldsymbol{K}, w, T, \Delta) &\le (\|\boldsymbol{U}\|^2_{[0,T]} - \gamma^2)\|w - w^*\|^2_{2,[0,T]}\\ &= (\|\boldsymbol{U}\|^2_{[0,T]} - \gamma^2)\|\boldsymbol{L}w\|^2_{2,[0,T]}\\ &\le -\epsilon\|w\|^2_{2,[0,T]} \end{aligned}$$

for some $\epsilon > 0$ and we conclude that (6.2.36) holds. Conversely, if (6.2.36) is satisfied, then

$$\begin{aligned} \|\boldsymbol{U}(w - w^*)\|^2_{2,[0,T]} - \gamma^2\|w - w^*\|^2_{2,[0,T]} &\le -\epsilon\|w\|^2_{2,[0,T]}\\ &= -\epsilon\|\boldsymbol{L}^{-1}(w - w^*)\|^2_{2,[0,T]}\\ &\le -\frac{\epsilon}{\|\boldsymbol{L}\|^2_{[0,T]}}\|w - w^*\|^2_{2,[0,T]} \end{aligned}$$

for all w and hence also for all $w - w^*$, since the system $\boldsymbol{L} : w \mapsto w - w^*$ is invertible. Thus $\boldsymbol{U}$ satisfies (6.2.41).

To conclude that (6.2.40) generates all closed loops that satisfy (6.2.36), we need to show that any control signal (and hence any closed loop) that can be generated with a full-information control law can also be generated by a suitable $\boldsymbol{U}$ in (6.2.40). Substituting

$$u = \boldsymbol{L}_1 x + \boldsymbol{L}_2 w \tag{6.2.43}$$

and (6.2.38) into the dynamics (6.1.2) gives

$$\dot{x} = \left(A + \gamma^{-2} B_1 B_1' P + B_2(\boldsymbol{L}_1 + \gamma^{-2}\boldsymbol{L}_2 B_1' P)\right)x + (B_1 + B_2\boldsymbol{L}_2)(w - w^*).$$

Therefore

$$x = \boldsymbol{L}_3(w - w^*),$$

in which $\boldsymbol{L}_3$ is a causal, linear system. Substituting (6.2.37) and (6.2.38) into (6.2.43) gives

$$\begin{aligned} u - u^* &= (\boldsymbol{L}_1 + B_2'P + \gamma^{-2}\boldsymbol{L}_2 B_1' P)x + \boldsymbol{L}_2(w - w^*) \\ &= ((\boldsymbol{L}_1 + B_2'P + \gamma^{-2}\boldsymbol{L}_2 B_1' P)\boldsymbol{L}_3 + \boldsymbol{L}_2)(w - w^*) \\ &= \boldsymbol{U}(w - w^*) \end{aligned}$$

for some causal $\boldsymbol{U}$. This establishes the existence of the causal system in (6.2.40), which may also be written in the LFT form

$$u = \mathcal{F}_\ell\left(\left[\begin{array}{cc|c} -B_2'P & 0 & I \\ \hline -\gamma^{-2}B_1'P & I & 0 \end{array}\right], \boldsymbol{U}\right)\left[\begin{array}{c} x \\ w \end{array}\right]. \tag{6.2.44}$$

We therefore conclude that all control signals and closed loops that satisfy (6.2.36) are generated by letting $\boldsymbol{U}$ in (6.2.40), or equivalently (6.2.44), range over the space of causal linear systems that satisfy $\|\boldsymbol{U}\|_{[0,T]} < \gamma$.

Figure 6.2 shows the closed loops generated by (6.2.40) and hence all closed loops generated by full-information controllers. If $w = w^*$, there is no signal into the $\boldsymbol{U}$ parameter and the corresponding control is given by u^* (irrespective of $\boldsymbol{U}$). If $w \neq w^*$, we do not have to use the control u^* as a "downgraded" control may still be adequate—the controller only has to "play well enough" to ensure that $J(\boldsymbol{K}, w, T, \Delta) \leq -\epsilon\|w\|^2_{2,[0,T]}$. By choosing $\boldsymbol{U} = 0$, we may insist that the controller always "plays" $u = u^*$.

6.2.7 All controllers

Because of redundancy in the full-information configuration, equation (6.2.40) does not capture all the controllers, even though it does capture all the possible control signals. In order to capture all the controllers, we use the "duplicate state" technique described in Section 4.2.2 to augment the LFT in (6.2.44).

Equation (6.2.40), or (equivalently) (6.2.44), gives $u = u^* + r$, in which $r = \boldsymbol{U}(w - w^*)$. To obtain all controllers, we augment r with the signal $\boldsymbol{V}(x - \widehat{x})$, in which $\widehat{x}$ is a copy of the state and $\boldsymbol{V}$ is any causal, linear system. This gives

$$\begin{aligned} \dot{\widehat{x}} &= (A - B_2 B_2' P)\widehat{x} + B_1 w + B_2 r \\ u &= u^* + r \\ r &= \boldsymbol{U}(w - w^*) + \boldsymbol{V}(x - \widehat{x}). \end{aligned}$$

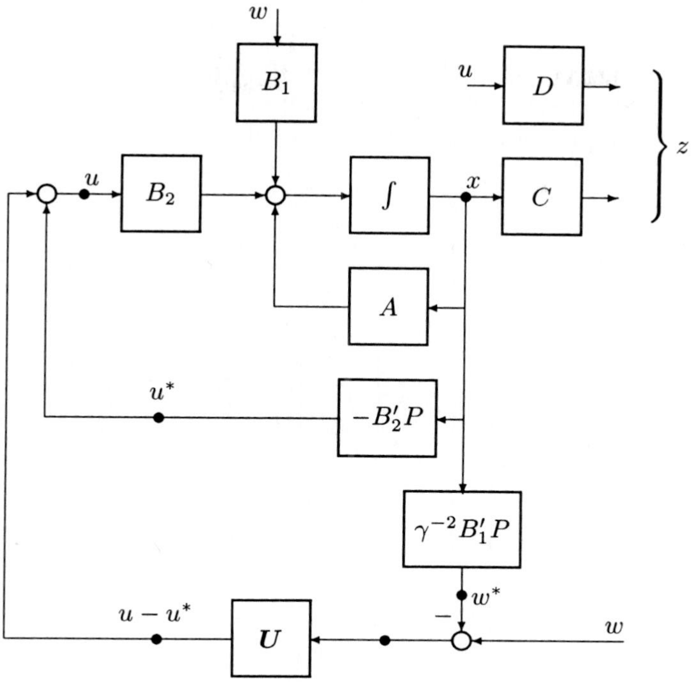

Figure 6.2: All closed-loops derived from full-information control laws.

These equations, together with the equations (6.2.37) and (6.2.38) describing w^* and u^*, give

$$\begin{bmatrix} \dot{\widehat{x}} \\ u \\ \begin{bmatrix} w - w^* \\ x - \widehat{x} \end{bmatrix} \end{bmatrix} = \begin{bmatrix} A - B_2B_2'P & \begin{bmatrix} 0 & B_1 \end{bmatrix} & B_2 \\ 0 & \begin{bmatrix} -B_2'P & 0 \end{bmatrix} & I \\ \begin{bmatrix} 0 \\ -I \end{bmatrix} & \begin{bmatrix} -\gamma^{-2}B_1'P & I \\ I & 0 \end{bmatrix} & \begin{bmatrix} 0 \\ 0 \end{bmatrix} \end{bmatrix} \begin{bmatrix} \widehat{x} \\ \begin{bmatrix} x \\ w \end{bmatrix} \\ r \end{bmatrix}$$

$$r = \begin{bmatrix} \boldsymbol{U} & \boldsymbol{V} \end{bmatrix} \begin{bmatrix} w - w^* \\ x - \widehat{x} \end{bmatrix}.$$

Setting

$$\boldsymbol{K}_a \stackrel{s}{=} \left[\begin{array}{c|cc} A - B_2B_2'P & \begin{bmatrix} 0 & B_1 \end{bmatrix} & B_2 \\ \hline 0 & \begin{bmatrix} -B_2'P & 0 \end{bmatrix} & I \\ \begin{bmatrix} 0 \\ -I \end{bmatrix} & \begin{bmatrix} -\gamma^{-2}B_1'P & I \\ I & 0 \end{bmatrix} & \begin{bmatrix} 0 \\ 0 \end{bmatrix} \end{array}\right] \qquad (6.2.45)$$

gives

$$\boldsymbol{K} = \mathcal{F}_\ell(\boldsymbol{K}_a, \begin{bmatrix} \boldsymbol{U} & \boldsymbol{V} \end{bmatrix}). \tag{6.2.46}$$

Since the $(1,2)$- and $(2,1)$-blocks of $\boldsymbol{K}_a$ have causal inverses, this LFT, which is illustrated in Figure 6.3, generates all full-information controllers. As before, the closed-loop satisfies (6.2.36) if and only if $\|\boldsymbol{U}\|_{[0,T]} < \gamma$.

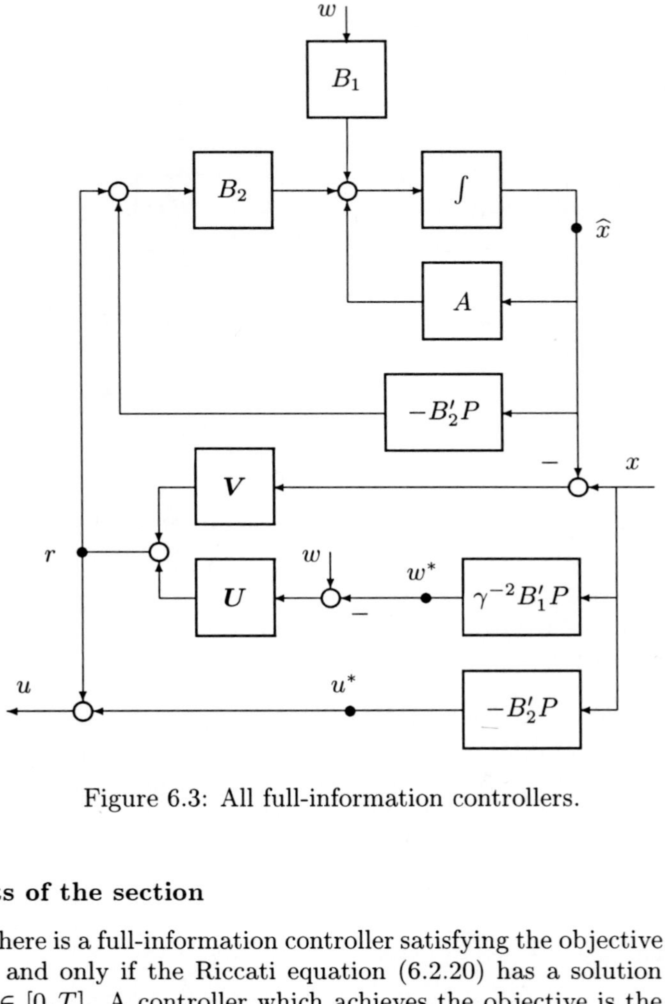

Figure 6.3: All full-information controllers.

Main points of the section

1. There is a full-information controller satisfying the objective (6.1.5) if and only if the Riccati equation (6.2.20) has a solution for all $t \in [0,T]$. A controller which achieves the objective is the linear, memoryless, state-feedback control $u = -B_2'Px$.
2. $P(t) \geq 0$ for all times $t \leq T$ for which a solution exists.

3. Reviewing the proof of the necessary conditions in Theorem 6.2.4, the only properties required of the controller were: (a) causality and (b) homogeneity (*i.e.*, $\boldsymbol{K}\begin{bmatrix} 0 \\ 0 \end{bmatrix} = 0$). It follows that (6.2.20) has a solution on $[0,T]$ if and only if there exists a causal, homogeneous controller satisfying (6.1.5). Therefore, if a causal, homogeneous but possibly nonlinear controller satisfying the objective (6.1.5) exists, there are also linear controllers satisfying this objective.
4. All full-information controllers that satisfy (6.1.5) are a generated by

$$\boldsymbol{K} = \mathcal{F}_\ell(\boldsymbol{K}_a, \begin{bmatrix} \boldsymbol{U} & \boldsymbol{V} \end{bmatrix}),$$

in which $\boldsymbol{U}$ and $\boldsymbol{V}$ are causal, linear systems with $\|\boldsymbol{U}\|_{[0,T]} < \gamma$. A state-space realization for $\boldsymbol{K}_a$ is given in (6.2.45). The parameter $\boldsymbol{V}$ has no effect on the control signal or the closed loop.

6.3 The infinite-horizon case

We now focus our attention on the problem of obtaining necessary and sufficient conditions for the existence of a stabilizing, full-information controller that satisfies

$$\|\boldsymbol{R}_{zw}\|_\infty < \gamma.$$

Our approach is to extend the finite-horizon results to the infinite-horizon case by taking limits as the horizon length T tends to infinity. The technical difficulties associated with this approach are concerned with establishing the existence of the limit $P = \lim_{T\to\infty} P(t,T,\Delta)$ and in guaranteeing that the control law $u^* = -B_2'Px$ has certain stabilization properties. The notation $P(t,T,\Delta)$ is used to flag the fact that $P(t)$ satisfies the terminal condition $P(T) = \Delta$.

In this section, we restrict our attention to the time-invariant plant

$$\dot{x} = Ax + B_1 w + B_2 u, \qquad x(0) = x_0, \tag{6.3.1}$$

$$z = \begin{bmatrix} Cx \\ Du \end{bmatrix}, \qquad D'D = I, \tag{6.3.2}$$

in which each of the five matrices is constant. We allow the possibility of nonzero initial conditions in order to address stability issues.

6.3.1 Preliminary observations

In an attempt to gain some insight into potential difficulties, we begin by deriving a closed formula for $P(t,T,\Delta)$. Since

$$H = \begin{bmatrix} A & -(B_2B_2' - \gamma^{-2}B_1B_1') \\ -C'C & -A' \end{bmatrix} \tag{6.3.3}$$

has the Hamiltonian property $SH = (SH)'$, where

$$S = \begin{bmatrix} 0 & -I_n \\ I_n & 0 \end{bmatrix},$$

there exists an eigenvector matrix Z satisfying

$$H \begin{bmatrix} Z_{11} & Z_{12} \\ Z_{21} & Z_{22} \end{bmatrix} = \begin{bmatrix} Z_{11} & Z_{12} \\ Z_{21} & Z_{22} \end{bmatrix} \begin{bmatrix} \Lambda & 0 \\ 0 & -\Lambda \end{bmatrix},$$

where Λ is $n \times n$ such that $\mathrm{R}_e\lambda_i(\Lambda) \le 0$. A routine calculation, which is left as an exercise (Problem 6.5), demonstrates that

$$P(t,T,\Delta) = \Psi_2(t,T,\Delta)\Psi_1^{-1}(t,T,\Delta), \tag{6.3.4}$$

in which

$$\begin{aligned} \Psi_1(t,T,\Delta) &= (Z_{11} + Z_{12}e^{\Lambda(T-t)}Xe^{\Lambda(T-t)}) \\ \Psi_2(t,T,\Delta) &= (Z_{21} + Z_{22}e^{\Lambda(T-t)}Xe^{\Lambda(T-t)}) \\ X &= -(Z_{22} - \Delta Z_{12})^{-1}(Z_{21} - \Delta Z_{11}). \end{aligned}$$

If Λ is asymptotically stable and nothing "goes wrong", $P(t,T,\Delta)$ will converge to the constant matrix $\Pi = Z_{21}Z_{11}^{-1}$ at an exponential rate equal to twice the largest real part of any eigenvalue of Λ. Since $P(t,T,\Delta) \ge 0$ for all $t \le T$, $\Pi \ge 0$. In addition, $P = \Pi$ is a solution of the algebraic Riccati equation

$$PA + A'P - P(B_2B_2' - \gamma^{-2}B_1B_1')P + C'C = 0 \tag{6.3.5}$$

such that $A - (B_2B_2' - \gamma^{-2}B_1B_1')P$ is asymptotically stable (since it has the same eigenvalues as Λ). This solution will be referred to as the stabilizing solution to the algebraic Riccati equation.

Notice that the matrix $A - (B_2B_2' - \gamma^{-2}B_1B_1')P$ is the closed-loop matrix corresponding to the implementation of the control laws

$$u^* = -B_2'Px \tag{6.3.6}$$
$$w^* = \gamma^{-2}B_1'Px \tag{6.3.7}$$

in (6.3.1). If we use the control law $u^* = -B_2'Px$ and any open loop w, one obtains

$$\dot{x} = (A - B_2B_2'P)x + B_1w,$$

which we will also require to be stable. It turns out that this stability property is assured by the nonnegative definiteness of P.

Unfortunately, there is a lot that can go wrong with the solution given in (6.3.4). In particular:

- The matrix X may not exist due to the singularity of $(Z_{22} - \Delta Z_{12})$. This focuses attention on the need to select a suitable terminal condition Δ.
- It is possible that Λ may have imaginary axis eigenvalues. In these cases, $P(t, T, \Delta)$ may not converge to a finite limit. This situation may occur in the optimal case, which we do not consider in this chapter.
- The matrix $\left(Z_{11} + Z_{12}e^{\Lambda(T-t)}Xe^{\Lambda(T-t)}\right)$ may be singular for some $t = t^*$; this gives rise to a finite escape time at t^*.
- The limit $\lim_{T\to\infty}\left(Z_{11} + Z_{12}e^{\Lambda(T-t)}Xe^{\Lambda(T-t)}\right)$ may be singular leading to an unbounded P. This situation is also associated with the optimal case.

Example 6.3.1. To illustrate these ideas, we re-examine Example 6.2.1, in which the system is described by

$$\begin{aligned} \dot{x} &= w + u, \qquad x(0) = 0,\\ z &= \begin{bmatrix} x \\ u \end{bmatrix}. \end{aligned}$$

This problem has $a = 0$, $b_1 = 1$, $b_2 = 1$ and $c = 1$, and the associated Riccati equation is

$$-\dot{p} = 1 - p^2(1 - \gamma^{-2}), \qquad p(T) = \delta.$$

When $\gamma > 1$,

$$p(t, T, \delta) = \beta^{-1}\tanh\left(\tanh^{-1}(\delta\beta) - \beta(t - T)\right),$$

in which $\beta = \sqrt{1 - \gamma^{-2}}$. The limit $\pi = \lim_{T\to\infty} p(t, T, \delta)$ exists and is given by $\pi = \beta^{-1}$. It is easy to see that this is the positive solution of the algebraic Riccati equation

$$0 = 1 - p^2(1 - \gamma^{-2}). \tag{6.3.8}$$

Notice also that $a - b_2^2\pi = -\beta^{-1}$ and $a - (b_2^2 - \gamma^{-2}b_1^2)\pi = -\beta$, which are both asymptotically stable. In this case, therefore, the solution of the Riccati differential equation approaches a solution of the corresponding algebraic equation with the correct stability properties.

When $\gamma \leq 1$, the solution to the Riccati equation is

$$p(t, T, \delta) = \phi^{-1}\tan\left(\tan^{-1}(\delta\phi) - \phi(t - T)\right),$$

with $\phi = \sqrt{\gamma^{-2} - 1}$. In this case, $p(t, T, \delta)$ does not converge as $T \to \infty$ and indeed there is no stabilizing solution to the algebraic Riccati equation (6.3.8). ∇

It is relatively straightforward to show that if (6.3.5) has a stabilizing solution which is nonnegative definite, the full-information controller (6.3.6) satisfies $\|\boldsymbol{R}_{zw}\|_\infty < \gamma$. We verify this in the next section. Subsequent sections establish that the existence of a stabilizing solution to (6.3.5) which is nonnegative is also necessary for the existence of a full-information controller such that $\|\boldsymbol{R}_{zw}\|_\infty < \gamma$, provided certain conditions on (A, B_2, C) are satisfied.

6.3.2 Sufficiency

Theorem 6.3.1 *Suppose the algebraic Riccati equation (6.3.5) has a solution $P \geq 0$ such that $A - (B_2B_2' - \gamma^{-2}B_1B_1')P$ is asymptotically stable. Then the control law $u = -B_2'Px$ is stabilizing and satisfies $\|\boldsymbol{R}_{zw}\|_\infty < \gamma$. ($\boldsymbol{R}_{zw}$ is the closed-loop mapping from w to z.)*

Proof. Applying the control law (6.3.6) leads to the closed-loop system $\boldsymbol{R}_{zw}$ with realization

$$\dot{x} = (A - B_2B_2'P)x + B_1w \tag{6.3.9}$$

$$z = \begin{bmatrix} C \\ -DB_2'P \end{bmatrix} x. \tag{6.3.10}$$

To see that this system is stable, re-write (6.3.5) as

$$P(A - B_2B_2'P) + (A - B_2B_2'P)'P + \gamma^{-2}PB_1B_1'P + PB_2B_2'P + C'C = 0.$$

Since $P \geq 0$, it follows from Theorem 3.1.1 that every unstable mode of $A - B_2B_2'P$ is unobservable through $\begin{bmatrix} -\gamma^{-1}PB_1 & PB_2 & C' \end{bmatrix}'$. However, since $A - (B_2B_2' - \gamma^{-2}B_1B_1')P$ is asymptotically stable, we conclude $A - B_2B_2'P$ can have no unstable mode that is unobservable through $\begin{bmatrix} -\gamma^{-1}PB_1 & PB_2 & C' \end{bmatrix}'$ from the Popov-Belevitch-Hautus test and the identity

$$A - (B_2B_2' - \gamma^{-2}B_1B_1')P = (A - B_2B_2'P) - \begin{bmatrix} \gamma^{-1}B_1 & 0 & 0 \end{bmatrix} \begin{bmatrix} -\gamma^{-1}B_1'P \\ B_2'P \\ C \end{bmatrix}.$$

Hence $A - B_2B_2'P$ is asymptotically stable.

Since $A - B_2B_2'P$ is asymptotically stable, the bounded real lemma implies that $\|\boldsymbol{R}_{zw}\|_\infty < \gamma$ if and only if there exists an X such that

$$X(A - B_2B_2'P) + (A - B_2B_2'P)'X + \gamma^{-2}XB_1B_1'X + PB_2B_2'P + C'C = 0,$$

with $(A - B_2B_2'P) + \gamma^{-2}B_1B_1'X$ asymptotically stable. Since $X = P$ is such a solution, we conclude that $\|\boldsymbol{R}_{zw}\|_\infty < \gamma$. ■

6.3.3 A monotonicity property

During the development of the necessary conditions for the existence of $\mathcal{H}_\infty$ controllers in the infinite-horizon case, we use the fact that $P(t, T, \Delta)$ is monotonic for certain Δ's when the plant is time-invariant.

Lemma 6.3.2 *For time-invariant plant matrices, $P(t, T, 0)$ and $P(t, T, P_2)$ are monotonically nonincreasing as functions of t. The matrix P_2 is any solution to the algebraic Riccati equation*

$$A'P_2 + P_2A - P_2B_2B_2'P_2 + C'C = 0,$$

associated with LQ optimal control.

Since the plant is time-invariant, $P(t,T,\Delta)$ is a function of $T-t$ only:

$$P(t,T,\Delta) = P(\tau, T-t+\tau, \Delta).$$

It follows that $P(t,T,0)$ and $P(t,T,P_2)$ are monotonically nondecreasing as a functions of T.

Proof. Differentiating (6.2.20) with respect to t gives

$$-\ddot{P} = \dot{P}\big(A - (B_2B_2' - \gamma^{-2}B_1B_1')P(t)\big) + \big(A - (B_2B_2' - \gamma^{-2}B_1B_1')P\big)'\dot{P}.$$

Hence $\dot{P}$ is given by

$$\dot{P}(t) = \Phi(t,T)\dot{P}(T)\Phi'(t,T),$$

in which $\Phi(\cdot,\cdot)$ is the transition matrix associated with $-\big(A-(B_2B_2'-\gamma^{-2}B_1B_1')P\big)'$. Now note that $\dot{P}(T)$ is obtained from $P(T)=\Delta$:

$$\begin{aligned} -\dot{P}(T) &= \Delta A + A'\Delta - \Delta(B_2B_2' - \gamma^{-2}B_1B_1')\Delta + C'C \\ &= \begin{cases} C'C & \text{if} \quad \Delta = 0 \\ \gamma^{-2}P_2B_1B_1'P_2 & \text{if} \quad \Delta = P_2. \end{cases} \end{aligned}$$

■

6.3.4 Assumptions

The aim of this section is to find a minimal set of hypotheses on which to base the necessity theory. If a stabilizing controller exists, it is necessarily the case that (A, B_2) is stabilizable (see Appendix A). The question of assumptions pertaining to the pair (A, C) is more subtle. We will attempt to uncover the essential issues by studying an example.

Example 6.3.2. Consider the system

$$\begin{aligned} \dot{x} &= ax + w + u, \qquad x(0) = 0, \\ z &= \begin{bmatrix} cx \\ u \end{bmatrix}, \end{aligned}$$

in which x, w and u are scalar. Since $b_1 = 1$ and $b_2 = 1$, the algebraic Riccati equation is

$$2ap - p^2(1-\gamma^{-2}) + c^2 = 0,$$

which has solutions

$$p = \frac{a \pm \sqrt{a^2 + c^2(1-\gamma^{-2})}}{1-\gamma^{-2}},$$

provided $\gamma \neq 1$. Note also that

$$\begin{aligned} a - (b_2^2 - \gamma^{-2}b_1^2)p &= a - (1-\gamma^{-2})p \\ &= \mp\sqrt{a^2 + c^2(1-\gamma^{-2})}. \end{aligned}$$

If $\gamma = 1$, the only solution is $p = -c^2/2a$. In this case, $a - (b_2^2 - \gamma^{-2}b_1^2)p = a$, which is stable if and only if $a \leq 0$, which is equivalent to $p \geq 0$. This corresponds to the optimal case, which will be considered in Chapter 11.

1. Suppose a and c are not both zero and $\gamma \neq 1$. Then there exists a real solution if and only if

$$\gamma^2 \geq \gamma_{min}^2 = \frac{c^2}{a^2 + c^2}.$$

If $\gamma = \gamma_{min}$, the conditions of Theorem 6.3.1 are never satisfied, because $a - (b_2^2 - \gamma^{-2}b_1^2)p = 0$ is not asymptotically stable. If $\gamma > \gamma_{min}$, the solution with the + sign is the stabilizing solution and it is nonnegative if and only if $\gamma > 1$. Therefore, by Theorem 6.3.1, there is a controller such that $\|\boldsymbol{R}_{zw}\|_\infty < \gamma$ for any $\gamma > 1$.

2. Suppose a and c are both zero and $\gamma \neq 1$. Then $p = 0$ is the only solution to the Riccati equation and this solution is never stabilizing, since $a-(b_2^2-\gamma^{-2}b_1^2)p = 0$. If $\gamma = 1$, any p will satisfy the Riccati equation but there is no stabilizing solution because $a - (b_2^2 - \gamma^{-2}b_1^2)p$ is still zero. That is, there is no solution to the Riccati equation that satisfies the conditions of Theorem 6.3.1 when a and c are both zero. This is a problem, because the controller $u = -kx$, $k > 0$, results in the stable closed-loop system

$$\boldsymbol{R}_{zw} = -\begin{bmatrix} 0 \\ \frac{k}{s+k} \end{bmatrix}$$

and $\|\boldsymbol{R}_{zw}\|_\infty = 1$. Thus there is a full-information controller ($u = -x$ for instance) that stabilizes the system and satisfies $\|\boldsymbol{R}_{zw}\|_\infty < \gamma$ for any $\gamma > 1$.

We conclude that Theorem 6.3.1 is *not* necessary for the existence of full-information controllers that satisfy $\|\boldsymbol{R}_{zw}\|_\infty < \gamma$ when a and c are both zero. ∇

The reader may begin to wonder why we bother with the Riccati equation at all, since it is does not provide a necessary condition for the existence of an $\mathcal{H}_\infty$ controller under all circumstances. The answer contains two parts:

1. The existence of a stabilizing nonnegative solution to the Riccati equation is necessary when (A, C) has no unobservable modes on the imaginary axis. This is what we will prove in the section dealing with necessity. We note that this condition corresponds to assuming a and c are not both zero in Example 6.3.2.

2. We may augment the objective by making the substitution

$$z = \begin{bmatrix} Cx \\ Du \end{bmatrix} \to z_a = \begin{bmatrix} C_a x \\ Du \end{bmatrix}$$

in such a way that $\boldsymbol{K}$ satisfies $\|\boldsymbol{R}_{zw}\|_\infty < \gamma$ if and only if $\boldsymbol{K}$ satisfies $\|\boldsymbol{R}_{z_a w}\|_\infty < \gamma$ for some C_a such that (A, C_a) has no unobservable modes on the imaginary axis.

We now verify that a C_a of the form

$$C_a = \begin{bmatrix} C \\ L \end{bmatrix}$$

with the desired properties can always be chosen.

(a) Suppose a controller $\boldsymbol{K}$ is internally stabilizing and satisfies $\|\boldsymbol{R}_{z_a w}\|_\infty < \gamma$, in which

$$z_a = \begin{bmatrix} Cx \\ Lx \\ Du \end{bmatrix}$$

and $(A, \begin{bmatrix} C' & L' \end{bmatrix}')$ has no unobservable mode on the imaginary axis. Then $\boldsymbol{K}$ also satisfies $\|\boldsymbol{R}_{zw}\|_\infty < \gamma$. This follows from the identity $\|z_a\|_2^2 = \|z\|_2^2 + \|Lx\|_2^2$.

(b) If $\boldsymbol{K}$ stabilizes the system, the closed-loop system $\boldsymbol{W} : w \mapsto x$ is stable and hence $\mu = \|\boldsymbol{W}\|_\infty < \infty$. If $\boldsymbol{K}$ also satisfies $\|\boldsymbol{R}_{zw}\|_\infty < \gamma$, we can choose $\epsilon > 0$ such that $\|\boldsymbol{R}_{zw}\|_\infty < \gamma - \epsilon$. Now choose L such that (i) $\|L\| \leq \epsilon/\mu$ and (ii) $(A, \begin{bmatrix} C' & L' \end{bmatrix}')$ has no unobservable modes on the imaginary axis. For example, choose $L = \epsilon/\mu I$. Then

$$\begin{aligned} \|\boldsymbol{R}_{z_a w}\|_\infty &\leq \|\boldsymbol{R}_{zw}\|_\infty + \|L\boldsymbol{W}\|_\infty \\ &< \gamma - \epsilon + \frac{\epsilon}{\mu}\mu \\ &= \gamma. \end{aligned}$$

We conclude that solving the the original problem is equivalent to solving an augmented problem for some L. Put another way, if (A, C) has unobservable modes on the axis, the designer should include some additional objective. We illustrate this procedure with another example.

Example 6.3.3. Consider the system in Example 6.3.2 with $a = 0$ and $c = 0$, and recall that $u = -kx$, $k > 0$, is stabilizing and satisfies $\|\boldsymbol{R}_{zw}\|_\infty = 1$. Hence $\|\boldsymbol{R}_{zw}\|_\infty < \gamma$ can be achieved for any $\gamma > 1$. We now show that all such controllers can be generated by considering the augmented objective

$$z_a = \begin{bmatrix} 0 \\ \ell x \\ u \end{bmatrix},$$

in which $\ell > 0$. The Riccati equation for the modified problem $\|\boldsymbol{R}_{z_a w}\|_\infty < \tilde{\gamma}$ is

$$-p^2(1 - \tilde{\gamma}^{-2}) + \ell^2 = 0,$$

which has a stabilizing nonnegative solution

$$p = \frac{\ell}{\sqrt{1-\tilde{\gamma}^{-2}}}$$

if $\tilde{\gamma} > 1$. The corresponding controller is $u = -px$. Thus, for *any* $\ell \neq 0$, the conditions of Theorem 6.3.1 can be satisfied if and only if $\tilde{\gamma} > 1$.

Since $\tilde{\gamma} > 1$ if and only if $\gamma = \tilde{\gamma} - \epsilon > 1$ for some $\epsilon > 0$, we conclude that the original problem (with $\ell = 0$) has a solution for any $\gamma > 1$. Furthermore, $u = -px$ generates all controllers of the form $u = -kx$ as ℓ is varied—selecting an ℓ in the augmented problem is equivalent to selecting a particular k that solves the original problem. ∇

The standard assumptions

1. The pair (A, B_2) is stabilizable.
2. The pair (C, A) has no unobservable modes on the imaginary axis.

Note that these assumptions are both necessary and sufficient for the existence of a stabilizing solution to the algebraic Riccati equation

$$A'P_2 + P_2A - P_2B_2B_2'P_2 + C'C = 0 \tag{6.3.11}$$

associated with LQ optimal control.

6.3.5 Necessity

We now want to show that the existence of a full-information $\mathcal{H}_\infty$ controller implies that the algebraic Riccati equation (6.3.5) has a nonnegative stabilizing solution. We assume from now on that the standard assumptions hold. Our proof takes the following form:

1. We show that if the infinite-horizon problem has a solution, then so does the finite-horizon problem for any horizon length. It then follows from our finite-horizon results that the Riccati differential equation (6.2.20) has a solution over any finite interval.

2. We show that the solution to the Riccati differential equation is bounded. Since it is also monotonic, the solution tends to a finite limit as the horizon length tends to infinity. Since this limiting solution must be constant, it satisfies the algebraic Riccati equation (6.3.5).

3. We show that the solution to the algebraic Riccati equation obtained by letting the horizon length tend to infinity has the required stability properties.

Before developing these ideas, we mention that the above statements are only true if the terminal condition $P(T) = \Delta$ is selected correctly. To illustrate this we consider another example.

Example 6.3.4. Consider the system

$$\begin{aligned} \dot{x} &= x + w + u \\ z &= \begin{bmatrix} cx \\ u \end{bmatrix}, \end{aligned}$$

its associated Riccati differential equation

$$-\dot{p} = 2p - p^2(1-\gamma^{-2}) + c^2, \qquad p(T) = \delta, \tag{6.3.12}$$

and its algebraic counterpart

$$0 = 2p - p^2(1-\gamma^{-2}) + c^2.$$

As noted in Example 6.3.2, there is no solution that satisfies the conditions of the Theorem 6.3.1 unless $\gamma > 1$. In this case, the required solution is

$$p = \frac{1+\phi}{1-\gamma^{-2}},$$

with $\phi = \sqrt{1 + c^2(1-\gamma^{-2})}$.

Now note that the solution to the differential equation is

$$p(t, T, \delta) = \frac{\phi\delta - (\delta + c^2)\tanh\big(\phi(t-T)\big)}{\phi + \big(1 - \delta(1-\gamma^{-2})\big)\tanh\big(\phi(t-T)\big)}.$$

If $\delta = 0$, then

$$\begin{aligned} \lim_{T\to\infty} p(t,T,0) &= \frac{c^2}{\phi - 1} \\ &= \frac{c^2(\phi+1)}{\phi^2 - 1} \\ &= \frac{c^2(\phi+1)}{c^2(1-\gamma^{-2})} \\ &= \frac{1+\phi}{1-\gamma^{-2}}, \qquad \text{provided } c \neq 0. \end{aligned}$$

Hence, provided $c \neq 0$, we obtain the correct solution to the algebraic Riccati equation. (We invite the reader to show that this holds for all $\delta \geq 0$.)

When $c = 0$, we have $\phi = 1$ and

$$\begin{aligned} \lim_{T\to\infty} p(t,T,\delta) &= \frac{2\delta}{1 - \big(1 - \delta(1-\gamma^{-2})\big)} \\ &= \frac{2}{1-\gamma^{-2}}, \qquad \text{provided } \delta \neq 0. \end{aligned}$$

Thus, by selecting $\delta \neq 0$, we can always get the differential equation to converge to the appropriate solution to the algebraic equation (when one exists). ▽

If (A, C) is detectable, the terminal condition $\Delta = 0$ will suffice. If (A, C) is not detectable, we can ensure that the correct solution to the algebraic Riccati equation (6.3.5) is obtained by selecting $\Delta \geq 0$. One cannot use any $\Delta \geq 0$, but as we will show, $\Delta = P_2$ always works—P_2 is the stabilizing solution to (6.3.11).

A solution to the algebraic Riccati equation exists

Lemma 6.3.3 *Suppose the standard assumptions hold and P_2 is the stabilizing solution to the LQ Riccati equation (6.3.11). Suppose also that there is a full-information controller $\widehat{\boldsymbol{K}}$ such that the closed-loop system $\boldsymbol{R}_{zw}$ defined by*

$$\begin{aligned} \dot{x} &= Ax + B_1 w + B_2 u, \qquad x(0) = 0, \\ z &= \begin{bmatrix} Cx \\ Du \end{bmatrix} \\ u &= \widehat{\boldsymbol{K}} \begin{bmatrix} x \\ w \end{bmatrix} \end{aligned}$$

is internally stable and satisfies $\|\boldsymbol{R}_{zw}\|_\infty < \gamma$. Then:

1. *The Riccati differential equation*
$$-\dot{P} = PA + A'P - P(B_2B_2' - \gamma^{-2}B_1B_1')P + C'C, \quad P(T) = P_2, \qquad (6.3.13)$$
has a solution $P(t, T, P_2)$ for all finite t, T with $t \leq T$.

2. *$P(t, T, P_2)$ is nonnegative definite and uniformly bounded above. That is, there is a real number β such that for all $t \leq T$*
$$0 \leq P(t, T, P_2) \leq \beta I.$$

3. *The limit $\Pi = \lim_{T\to\infty} P(t, T, P_2)$ exists, is independent of t, is nonnegative and satisfies the algebraic Riccati equation (6.3.5). We note, in addition, that $\Pi \geq P_2$.*

Proof. Because of the need to address stability issues, it is necessary to consider nonzero initial conditions:

$$\dot{x} = Ax + B_1 w + B_2 u, \qquad x(0) = x_0.$$

Note also that for any $0 \leq T < \infty$ and any $w \in \mathcal{L}_2[0, \infty)$ such that

$$w(t) = 0 \qquad \text{for all } t > T, \qquad (6.3.14)$$

we have

$$\begin{aligned} \|z\|_2^2 - \gamma^2\|w\|_2^2 &= \int_0^\infty (z'z - \gamma^2 w'w)\, dt \\ &= \int_0^T (z'z - \gamma^2 w'w)\, dt + \int_T^\infty z'z\, dt \\ &\geq \int_0^T (z'z - \gamma^2 w'w)\, dt + \min_{\boldsymbol{K}} \int_T^\infty \tilde{z}'\tilde{z}\, dt. \qquad (6.3.15) \end{aligned}$$

The notation $\tilde{z}$ is used to distinguish an arbitrary output trajectory from that obtained with the controller $\widehat{\boldsymbol{K}}$. As is well known from classical LQ theory, the cost function

$$\int_T^\infty \tilde{z}'\tilde{z}\,dt = \int_T^\infty (\tilde{x}'C'C\tilde{x} + \tilde{u}'\tilde{u})\,dt,$$

subject to

$$\begin{aligned}\dot{\tilde{x}} &= A\tilde{x} + B_2\tilde{u}, \qquad \tilde{x}(T) = x(T),\\ \tilde{u} &= \boldsymbol{K}\begin{bmatrix}\tilde{x}\\ \tilde{w}\end{bmatrix}\end{aligned}$$

is minimized by $\tilde{u} = -B_2'P_2\tilde{x}$ and

$$\min_{\boldsymbol{K}} \int_T^\infty \tilde{z}'\tilde{z}\,dt = x'(T)P_2x(T).$$

Hence, substituting into (6.3.15), we have

$$\|z\|_2^2 - \gamma^2\|w\|_2^2 \geq J(\boldsymbol{K}, w, T, P_2), \tag{6.3.16}$$

in which

$$J(\boldsymbol{K}, w, T, P_2) = \int_0^T (z'z - \gamma^2 w'w)\,dt + x'(T)P_2x(T),$$

for any $w \in \mathcal{L}_2[0,\infty)$ that satisfies (6.3.14). With this background, we now establish each of the claims of the lemma:

1. Let $x_0 = 0$. Then $\|\boldsymbol{R}_{zw}\|_\infty < \gamma$ is equivalent to $\|z\|_2^2 - \gamma^2\|w\|_2^2 \leq -\epsilon\|w\|_2^2$ for all $w \in \mathcal{L}_2[0,\infty)$ and some $\epsilon > 0$. Using (6.3.16), for any $w \in \mathcal{L}_2[0,\infty)$ that satisfies (6.3.14), we have have

$$J(\widehat{\boldsymbol{K}}, w, T, P_2) \leq -\epsilon\|w\|_2^2 = -\epsilon\|w\|_{2,[0,T]}^2. \tag{6.3.17}$$

We conclude that (6.3.17) holds for all $w \in \mathcal{L}_2[0,T]$ and hence that $P(t,T,P_2)$ exists on $[0,T]$ by Theorem 6.2.4. As T was arbitrary and $P(t,T,P_2) = P(\tau, T-t+\tau, P_2)$ for any τ, we conclude that $P(t,T,P_2)$ exists for all finite t, T with $t \leq T$.

2. Let w be an arbitrary signal in $\mathcal{L}_2[0,\infty)$ and x_0 an arbitrary initial condition. The response z of the closed-loop system depends on x_0 and w and by linearity may be decomposed as

$$z = z_{x_0} + z_w$$

with z_{x_0} and z_w denoting the contributions to the response due to x_0 and w respectively. Since $\|\boldsymbol{R}_{zw}\|_\infty < \gamma$, we have $\|z_w\|_2^2 - \gamma^2\|w\|_2^2 \leq -\epsilon\|w\|_2^2$ for some $\epsilon > 0$. Also, as the controller $\widehat{\boldsymbol{K}}$ stabilizes the system, $\|z_{x_0}\|_2$ and $\|z_w\|_2$ are finite,

$$\|z\|_2^2 \leq \|z_{x_0}\|_2^2 + \|z_w\|_2^2 + 2\|z_{x_0}\|_2\|z_w\|_2$$

and $\|z_{x_0}\|_2 \leq \alpha\|x_0\|$ for some number α. Using these properties we have

$$\begin{aligned}
\|z\|_2^2 - \gamma^2\|w\|_2^2 &\leq \|z_w\|_2^2 - \gamma^2\|w\|_2^2 + \|z_{x_0}\|_2^2 + 2\|z_{x_0}\|_2\|z_w\|_2 \\
&\leq -\epsilon\|w\|_2^2 + \alpha^2\|x_0\|^2 + 2\gamma\alpha\|x_0\|\ \|w\|_2 \\
&= \alpha^2\|x_0\|^2 - \epsilon(\|w\|_2^2 - \frac{2\gamma\alpha}{\epsilon}\|x_0\|\ \|w\|_2) \\
&= \left(\alpha^2 + \frac{\gamma^2\alpha^2}{\epsilon}\right)\|x_0\|^2 - \epsilon(\|w\|_2 - \frac{\gamma\alpha}{\epsilon}\|x_0\|)^2 \\
&\leq \left(\alpha^2 + \frac{\gamma^2\alpha^2}{\epsilon}\right)\|x_0\|^2 = \beta\|x_0\|^2 \qquad (6.3.18)
\end{aligned}$$

for all x_0 and all $w \in \mathcal{L}_2[0,\infty)$.

Now choose T finite and let w_T^* be the particular $\mathcal{L}_2[0,\infty)$ signal

$$w_T^*(t) = \begin{cases} \gamma^{-2}B_1'P(t,T,P_2)x(t) & \text{if} \quad t \leq T \\ 0 & \text{if} \quad t > T. \end{cases}$$

Since w_T^* satisfies (6.3.14), it satisfies (6.3.16). By completing the square using $P(t,T,P_2)$ we obtain

$$\begin{aligned}
J(\widehat{\boldsymbol{K}}, w_T^*, T, P_2) &= x_0'P(0,T,P_2)x_0 + \|u - u_T^*\|_{2,[0,T]}^2 \\
&\geq x_0'P(0,T,P_2)x_0,
\end{aligned}$$

in which $u_T^*(t) = -B_2'P(t,T,P_2)x(t)$. Hence

$$\begin{aligned}
x_0'P(0,T,P_2)x_0 &\leq J(\widehat{\boldsymbol{K}}, w_T^*, T, P_2) \\
&\leq \|z\|_2 - \gamma^2\|w_T^*\|_2^2 \qquad \text{by (6.3.16)} \\
&\leq \beta\|x_0\|^2 \qquad \text{by (6.3.18).}
\end{aligned}$$

Since x_0 was arbitrary, we conclude that $P(0,T,P_2) \leq \beta I$. The result follows for all $t \leq T$ because $P(t,T,P_2) = P(0,T-t,P_2)$.

As a final remark, we note that $P(t,T,P_2) \geq 0$ because the terminal condition is nonnegative definite.

3. Since $P(t,T,P_2)$ is monotonic (by Lemma 6.3.2) and uniformly bounded (when a controller exists such that $\|\boldsymbol{R}_{zw}\|_\infty < \gamma$), it converges to a finite limit Π as $T \to \infty$. The matrix Π is independent of t because $P(t,T,P_2) = P(0,T-t,P_2)$, so that $\Pi = \lim_{T\to\infty} P(0,T,P_2)$. We must have $\Pi \geq 0$ because $P(t,T,P_2) \geq 0$ for all $t \leq T$. The monotonicity property also ensures that $\Pi \geq P_2$.

   Since the solution to a Riccati equation depends continuously on the terminal condition, we have

$$\Pi = \lim_{T\to\infty} P(t,T,P_2)$$

$$\begin{aligned} &= \lim_{T\to\infty} P\big(t, T_1, P(T_1, T, P_2)\big) \\ &= P\big(t, T_1, \lim_{T\to\infty} P(T_1, T, P_2)\big) \\ &= P(t, T_1, \Pi). \end{aligned}$$

That is, Π satisfies the Riccati differential equation with the terminal condition $P(T_1) = \Pi$, for any T_1. Consequently, since Π is constant, it must be a solution to the algebraic Riccati equation

$$\Pi A + A'\Pi - \Pi(B_2B_2' - \gamma^{-2}B_1B_1')\Pi + C'C = 0, \tag{6.3.19}$$

and the lemma is proved. ■

Parametrization of the closed-loop system

In the finite-horizon case, we showed that all closed-loop systems that could be generated by full-information controllers could also be generated by controllers of the form $u = u^* + \boldsymbol{U}(w - w^*)$. We will use this parametrization to show that $\Pi = \lim_{T\to\infty} P(0, T, P_2)$ has the required stability properties whenever a stabilizing controller exists such that $\|\boldsymbol{R}_{zw}\|_\infty < \gamma$. Our first result shows that the asymptotic stability of $A - B_2B_2'\Pi$ follows from the fact that $\Pi \geq P_2$.

Lemma 6.3.4 *Suppose the standard assumptions hold and that P is any solution to the algebraic Riccati equation (6.3.5) such that $P \geq P_2$. Then $A - B_2B_2'P$ is asymptotically stable.*

Proof. Subtracting (6.3.11) from (6.3.5) gives

$$(P - P_2)A + A'(P - P_2) - P(B_2B_2' - \gamma^{-2}B_1B_1')P + P_2B_2B_2'P_2 = 0,$$

which we re-write as

$$\begin{aligned} (P - P_2)(A - B_2B_2'P) + (A - B_2B_2'P)'(P - P_2)& \\ +(P - P_2)B_2B_2'(P - P_2) + \gamma^{-2}PB_1B_1'P = 0.& \end{aligned} \tag{6.3.20}$$

Next, we observe that

$$(A - B_2B_2'P, \begin{bmatrix} B_2'(P - P_2) \\ B_1'P \end{bmatrix})$$

is detectable, since $A - B_2B_2'P_2$ is asymptotically stable and

$$(A - B_2B_2'P) + \begin{bmatrix} B_2 & 0 \end{bmatrix} \begin{bmatrix} B_2'(P - P_2) \\ B_1'P \end{bmatrix} = (A - B_2B_2'P_2).$$

From (6.3.20) and Theorem 3.1.1, we conclude that $A - B_2B_2'P$ is asymptotically stable. ■

The next result reminds us that closed-loop systems and control signals generated by full-information controllers may be parametrized in terms of a $\boldsymbol{U}$-parameter.

Lemma 6.3.5 *Suppose P is a solution to (6.3.5) such that $A - B_2B_2'P$ is asymptotically stable. Then the control signal generated by the full-information controller*

$$u = \begin{bmatrix} \widehat{\boldsymbol{K}}_1 & \widehat{\boldsymbol{K}}_2 \end{bmatrix} \begin{bmatrix} x \\ w \end{bmatrix} \tag{6.3.21}$$

is also generated by a full-information controller of the form

$$u = -B_2'Px + \boldsymbol{U}(w - \gamma^{-2}B_1'Px). \tag{6.3.22}$$

Furthermore, (6.3.21) is stabilizing if and only if (6.3.22) is stabilizing.

Proof. That (6.3.21) and (6.3.22) generate the same control signal and closed-loop system follows from calculations which mimic those given in Section 6.2.6. Furthermore, controller (6.3.22) is stabilizing if and only if (6.3.21) is, because $u = -B_2'P$ is a stabilizing controller. ■

A stabilizing nonnegative solution exists

We are now in a position to show that $\Pi = \lim_{T\to\infty} P(0, T, P_2)$ is the stabilizing solution to (6.3.5).

Theorem 6.3.6 *Suppose the standard assumptions hold and P_2 is the stabilizing solution to (6.3.11). If there is full-information controller $\widehat{\boldsymbol{K}}$ such that the closed-loop system $\boldsymbol{R}_{zw}$ defined by*

$$\begin{aligned} \dot{x} &= Ax + B_1w + B_2u, \qquad x(0) = 0, \\ z &= \begin{bmatrix} Cx \\ Du \end{bmatrix} \\ u &= \widehat{\boldsymbol{K}} \begin{bmatrix} x \\ w \end{bmatrix} \end{aligned}$$

is internally stable and satisfies $\|\boldsymbol{R}_{zw}\|_\infty < \gamma$, then $\Pi = \lim_{T\to\infty} P(0, T, P_2)$ is the stabilizing solution to (6.3.5) and $\Pi \geq P_2 \geq 0$.

In addition,

$$u = -B_2'\Pi x + \boldsymbol{U}(w - \gamma^{-2}B_1'\Pi x),$$

in which $\boldsymbol{U} \in \mathcal{H}_\infty$ and $\|\boldsymbol{U}\|_\infty < \gamma$, generates all the closed-loop systems satisfying $\|\boldsymbol{R}_{zw}\|_\infty < \gamma$ that can be generated by stabilizing, full-information controllers.

Proof. By Lemmas 6.3.3 and 6.3.4, $\Pi = \lim_{T\to\infty} P(0, T, P_2)$ exists, $\Pi \geq P_2 \geq 0$ and $A - B_2B_2'\Pi$ is asymptotically stable. By Lemma 6.3.5, there exist a stabilizing controller of the form

$$u = -B_2'\Pi x + \boldsymbol{U}(w - \gamma^{-2}B_1'\Pi x)$$

such that $\|\boldsymbol{R}_{zw}\|_\infty < \gamma$. For such a controller, $\boldsymbol{R}_{zw}$ is given by the LFT

$$\boldsymbol{R}_{zw} = \gamma \mathcal{F}_\ell(\widehat{\boldsymbol{R}}_a, \boldsymbol{U}/\gamma),$$

in which

$$\widehat{\boldsymbol{R}}_a \overset{s}{=} \left[\begin{array}{c|cc} A - B_2B_2'\Pi & \gamma^{-1}B_1 & B_2 \\ \hline \begin{bmatrix} C \\ -DB_2'\Pi \end{bmatrix} & \begin{bmatrix} 0 \\ 0 \end{bmatrix} & \begin{bmatrix} 0 \\ D \end{bmatrix} \\ -\gamma^{-1}B_1'\Pi & I & 0 \end{array}\right]. \tag{6.3.23}$$

Notice that $\widehat{\boldsymbol{R}}_a^\sim \widehat{\boldsymbol{R}}_a = I$. This fact comes from the "completion of squares" identity

$$\|z\|_2^2 - \gamma^2\|w\|_2^2 = \|u - u^*\|_2^2 - \gamma^2\|w - w^*\|_2^2.$$

It may also be verified using Theorem 3.2.1 by writing (6.3.19) as

$$\Pi(A - B_2B_2'\Pi) + (A - B_2B_2'\Pi)'\Pi + C'C + \Pi B_2B_2'\Pi + \gamma^{-2}\Pi B_2B_1'\Pi = 0.$$

Since $\|\mathcal{F}_\ell(\widehat{\boldsymbol{R}}_a, \widehat{\boldsymbol{U}})\|_\infty < 1$ where $\widehat{\boldsymbol{U}} = \boldsymbol{U}/\gamma$, the $(2,1)$-block of $\widehat{\boldsymbol{R}}_a$, which is

$$\widehat{\boldsymbol{R}}_{a21} \overset{s}{=} \left[\begin{array}{c|c} A - B_2B_2'\Pi & \gamma^{-1}B_1 \\ \hline -\gamma^{-1}B_1'\Pi & I \end{array}\right], \tag{6.3.24}$$

has no zeros on the imaginary axis. This follows since $I - \mathcal{F}_\ell^\sim(\widehat{\boldsymbol{R}}_a, \widehat{\boldsymbol{U}})\mathcal{F}_\ell(\widehat{\boldsymbol{R}}_a, \widehat{\boldsymbol{U}}) > 0$ and

$$\begin{aligned} & I - \mathcal{F}_\ell^\sim(\widehat{\boldsymbol{R}}_a, \widehat{U})\mathcal{F}_\ell(\widehat{\boldsymbol{R}}_a, \widehat{U}) \\ &= \widehat{\boldsymbol{R}}_{a21}^\sim(I - \widehat{U}^\sim\widehat{\boldsymbol{R}}_{a22}^\sim)^{-1}(I - \widehat{U}^\sim\widehat{U})(I - \widehat{\boldsymbol{R}}_{a22}\widehat{U})^{-1}\widehat{\boldsymbol{R}}_{a21}. \end{aligned}$$

(See Theorem 4.3.2.) Because $A - B_2B_2'\Pi$ is asymptotically stable, the realization (6.3.24) has no uncontrollable or unobservable modes on the imaginary axis, so that any eigenvalue of $A - (B_2B_2' - \gamma^{-2}B_1B_1')\Pi$ on the imaginary axis is a zero of $\widehat{\boldsymbol{R}}_{a21}$. We conclude that $A - (B_2B_2' - \gamma^{-2}B_1B_1')\Pi$ has no eigenvalue on the imaginary axis.

It remains to show that Π is actually the stabilizing solution. We do this using the technique employed for this purpose in the optimal control proof of the bounded real lemma.

Subtract (6.3.13) from (6.3.19) to obtain

$$-\dot{X} = X\widehat{A} + \widehat{A}'X + X(B_2B_2' - \gamma^{-2}B_1B_1')X,$$

in which $X(t) = \Pi - P(t)$ and $\widehat{A} = A - (B_2B_2' - \gamma^{-2}B_1B_1')\Pi$.

We now assume that $X(t)$ is nonsingular for all $t \le T$; the extension to the general case is requested as an exercise. Define $V(t) = \big(X(T-t)\big)^{-1}$. Then $\dot{V} = -V\big(\frac{d}{dt}X(T-t)\big)V$, giving

$$\dot{V} = -\widehat{A}V - V\widehat{A}' - (B_2B_2' - \gamma^{-2}B_1B_1'), \qquad V(0) = (\Pi - P_2)^{-1}.$$

Let $y \neq 0$ be such that $\widehat{A}'y = \lambda y$. Since $\overline{\sigma}\big(X(t)\big) \to 0$ as $t \to -\infty$, $\underline{\sigma}\big(V(t)\big) \to \infty$ as $t \to \infty$. Consequently, $y'V(t)y \to \infty$ as $t \to \infty$. Since

$$\frac{d}{dt}\big(y^*V(t)y\big) = -(\lambda + \bar{\lambda})\big(y^*V(t)y\big) - y^*(B_2B_2' - \gamma^{-2}B_1B_1')y,$$

we must have $-(\lambda+\bar{\lambda}) \geq 0$. Since $(\lambda+\bar{\lambda}) \neq 0$, we conclude that $\widehat{A}$ is asymptotically stable and that $\Pi = \lim_{T\to\infty} P(0,T,P_2)$ is the stabilizing solution to (6.3.5).

By Theorem 4.3.3, $\mathcal{F}_\ell(\widehat{\boldsymbol{R}}_a, \widehat{\boldsymbol{U}})$ is internally stable with $\|\mathcal{F}_\ell(\widehat{\boldsymbol{R}}_a, \widehat{\boldsymbol{U}})\|_\infty < 1$ if and only if $\widehat{\boldsymbol{U}} \in \mathcal{H}_\infty$ and $\|\widehat{\boldsymbol{U}}\|_\infty < 1$.

It follows from an elementary scaling by γ that $\boldsymbol{R}_{zw}$ is internally stable with $\|\boldsymbol{R}_{zw}\|_\infty < \gamma$ if and only if

$$\boldsymbol{R}_{zw} = \mathcal{F}_\ell(\boldsymbol{R}_a, \boldsymbol{U}), \qquad \boldsymbol{U} \in \mathcal{H}_\infty,\ \|\boldsymbol{U}\|_\infty < \gamma,$$

in which

$$\boldsymbol{R}_a \stackrel{s}{=} \left[\begin{array}{c|cc} A - B_2B_2'\Pi & B_1 & B_2 \\ \hline \begin{bmatrix} C \\ -DB_2'\Pi \end{bmatrix} & \begin{bmatrix} 0 \\ 0 \end{bmatrix} & \begin{bmatrix} 0 \\ D \end{bmatrix} \\ -\gamma^{-2}B_1'\Pi & I & 0 \end{array}\right].$$

■

6.3.6 All controllers

In Section 4.2.2, we showed that a representation formula for all controllers requires the introduction of a second free parameter, $\boldsymbol{V}$, driven by the error between the state x and a duplicate state $\widehat{x}$. This leads to a stabilizing control law if and only if $\boldsymbol{V}$ is stable.

This idea was used to generate all solution to the full-information problem on a finite horizon in Section 6.2.7. The LFT parametrization of all controllers is given in (6.2.46) and (6.2.45).

By replacing $P(t)$ in (6.2.45) with the stabilizing nonnegative solution to the algebraic Riccati equation (6.3.5), we see that all stabilizing, full-information controllers that satisfy $\|\boldsymbol{R}_{zw}\|_\infty < \gamma$ are given by

$$\boldsymbol{K} = \mathcal{F}_\ell(\boldsymbol{K}_a, [\ \boldsymbol{U}\ \ \boldsymbol{V}\ ]), \qquad [\ \boldsymbol{U}\ \ \boldsymbol{V}\ ] \in \mathcal{H}_\infty \text{ and } \|\boldsymbol{U}\|_\infty < \gamma. \tag{6.3.25}$$

The generator of all controllers, $\boldsymbol{K}_a$, is given by

$$\boldsymbol{K}_a \stackrel{s}{=} \left[\begin{array}{c|c|c} A - B_2B_2'P & \begin{bmatrix} 0 & B_1 \end{bmatrix} & B_2 \\ \hline 0 & \begin{bmatrix} -B_2'P & 0 \end{bmatrix} & I \\ \begin{bmatrix} 0 \\ -I \end{bmatrix} & \begin{bmatrix} -\gamma^{-2}B_1'P & I \\ I & 0 \end{bmatrix} & \begin{bmatrix} 0 \\ 0 \end{bmatrix} \end{array}\right], \tag{6.3.26}$$

and the controller $u^* = -B_2'Px$ corresponds to setting $\boldsymbol{U} = 0$ and $\boldsymbol{V} = 0$.

Main points of the section

1. Suppose (A, B_2) is stabilizable and that (A, C) has no unobservable modes on the imaginary axis. Then there exists a full-information control law such that the closed-loop system $\boldsymbol{R}_{zw}$ is internally stable and satisfies $\|\boldsymbol{R}_{zw}\|_\infty < \gamma$ if and only if the algebraic Riccati equation

$$PA + A'P - P(B_2B_2' - \gamma^{-2}B_1B_1')P + C'C = 0$$

has a solution $P \geq 0$ such that $A - (B_2B_2' - \gamma^{-2}B_1B_1')P$ is asymptotically stable.

2. The controller $u^* = -B_2'Px$ is stabilizing and leads to $\|\boldsymbol{R}_{zw}\|_\infty < \gamma$.

3. For any (A, C), a stabilizing, full-information controller $\boldsymbol{K}$ satisfies $\|\boldsymbol{R}_{zw}\|_\infty < \gamma$ if and only if it satisfies $\|\boldsymbol{R}_{z_a w}\|_\infty < \gamma$, in which

$$z_a = \begin{bmatrix} C_a x \\ Du \end{bmatrix},$$

for some C_a such that (A, C_a) has no unobservable modes on the imaginary axis.

4. Every full-information controller that satisfies $\|\boldsymbol{R}_{zw}\|_\infty < \gamma$ is given by $\mathcal{F}_\ell(\boldsymbol{K}_a, \begin{bmatrix} \boldsymbol{U} & \boldsymbol{V} \end{bmatrix})$ for some $\boldsymbol{U} \in \mathcal{H}_\infty$ with $\|\boldsymbol{U}\|_\infty < \gamma$ and some $\boldsymbol{V} \in \mathcal{H}_\infty$.

6.4 Notes and References

The theory of $\mathcal{H}_\infty$ controller synthesis has been developed using a variety of different techniques. In most approaches, however, the decomposition of the general output feedback problem into a full-information problem and an estimation problem is only implicit. In order to confine our bibliographical notes to a reasonable length, we will only review that literature that is directly related to the development and techniques used in this chapter. Even with this restriction, reviewing all the literature that could be regarded as relevant to this chapter is a formidable task.

The theory of zero-sum differential games goes back to the work of Isaacs [101, 102]. Another early reference is Berkovitz [27], who gives a rigorous treatment of two-player, zero-sum games. He obtains necessary conditions that must hold along an optimal path, and shows that the corresponding value function must satisfy a Hamilton-Jacobi type partial differential equation. The books by Bryson and Ho [34] and Başar and Olsder [22] are good sources for the early literature and standard results on zero-sum games. Başar and Olsder's text gives a treatment of zero-sum games which is more general than we require here, but the linear quadratic case is included in their book. The stability issues associated with linear quadratic differential games on an infinite horizon are considered in Mageirou [145], which contains results similar to those in Section 6.3—his assumptions are stronger, and he does not make the connection to $\mathcal{H}_\infty$ optimization. Başar and Bernhard [20] is a more recent book on games that deals explicitly with the connections between games and $\mathcal{H}_\infty$ control.

The paper by Mageirou and Ho [146] considers the design of decentralized controllers using game theoretic methods. The design of a controller $u_i = -F_i x_i$ for the ith subsystem is accomplished by assuming "the interactions between subsystems enter only as perturbation terms". Therefore, "so long as the total system is dissipative, stability will result". Frequency response conditions for dissipativeness are given and it is shown that appropriate controllers result from the solution of algebraic Riccati equations with indefinite quadratic terms.

$\mathcal{H}_\infty$ optimization for disturbance attenuation was investigated by Petersen [163], who proved that state-feedback controllers satisfying an $\mathcal{H}_\infty$ norm objective could be found using a Riccati equation with an indefinite quadratic term. The stabilization of an uncertain linear system by state-feedback controllers was also accomplished using a Riccati equation with an indefinite quadratic term in Petersen and Hollot [164]. The state-feedback $\mathcal{H}_\infty$ control problem was further developed by Khargonekar, Petersen and Rotea [116].

The full-information $\mathcal{H}_\infty$ control problem *per se* was first posed and solved by Doyle, Glover, Khargonekar and Francis [54] in the infinite-horizon case, and a parametrization of all the closed-loop transfer function matrices was given. Their approach, which uses mixed Hankel-plus-Toeplitz operators, is very different from the game theoretic methods used in this chapter. This paper also showed that the complete generalized regulator problem could be solved in a series of steps, with the full-information problem playing a key role.

Many papers have appeared since [54]. Some deal with extensions of the basic theory, such as the treatment of problems involving zeros on the imaginary axis by Scherer [192] and singular problems by Stoorvogel and Trentleman [202], and Scherer [193]. These extensions all follow easily from the discussion of the assumptions in Section 6.3.4 and the details are requested in Problems 6.17, 6.18 and 6.19.

The parametrization of all controllers, as opposed to all closed-loop systems, is relatively recent. Mita, Liu and Ohuchi [150], and Zhou [229], give treatments which are based on the Youla parametrization. Our "duplicate state" arguments are new and more direct.

The treatment of the finite-horizon theory is based on Limebeer, Anderson, Khargonekar and Green [130]. The limiting arguments that lead to the infinite-horizon results are essentially our own, although we do not claim to be the first authors to have pursued this approach—see Mageirou [145] and Ravi, Nagpal and Khargonekar [169]. Tadmor [204] also considered an approach to the infinite-horizon problem based on optimal control, although under very restrictive assumptions.

There are many topics related to the use of game theory in the solution of $\mathcal{H}_\infty$ control problems which are of peripheral interest. Banker [26] was probably the first to study the relationship between differential games and J-spectral factorization (see Problem 6.12), which has also been used in the context of $\mathcal{H}_\infty$ control for many years (see [65]). The connections between games, $\mathcal{H}_\infty$ control and indefinite factorization are more fully developed in the papers of Ball and Cohen [23]; Foias and Tannenbaum [63]; Glover and Doyle [76]; Green, Glover, Limebeer and Doyle [85] and Green [84].

There are interesting relationships between linear exponential Gaussian control, risk-sensitive optimal control, entropy minimization and game theory. These topics are investigated in Jacobson [103], Speyer, Deyst and Jacobson [196], Whittle [209], Limebeer and Hung [134], Glover and Mustafa [80] and Mustafa, Glover and Limebeer [154]. The titles of these papers will give an idea as to their exact contents.

There are obviously discrete-time counterparts to the results given in this chapter. These are considered in Appendix B and we postpone a review of the discrete-time literature until then.

6.5 Problems

Note: In the first four problems, the systems are not assumed to be time-invariant, except where this assumption is explicitly stated.

Problem 6.1. (Inclusion of cross terms). Suppose that a system is described by

$$\begin{aligned} \dot{x} &= Ax + B_1 w + B_2 u, \qquad x(0) = 0, \\ z &= C_1 x + D_{12} u \end{aligned}$$

with $D_{12}'D_{12} = I$. Suppose also that the cost function associated with the plant is

$$J(\boldsymbol{K}, w, T, \Delta) = \int_0^T (z'z - \gamma^2 w'w)\, dt + x'(T)\Delta x(T).$$

1. Show that if $\tilde{u} = u + D_{12}'C_1 x$, then

$$\begin{aligned} \dot{x} &= (A - B_2 D_{12}'C_1)x + B_1 w + B_2 \tilde{u} \\ z &= (I - D_{12}D_{12}')C_1 x + D_{12}\tilde{u}. \end{aligned}$$

Conclude that

$$J(\boldsymbol{K}, w, T, \Delta) = \tilde{J}(\tilde{\boldsymbol{K}}, w, T, \Delta),$$

in which $\tilde{\boldsymbol{K}} = \boldsymbol{K} + \begin{bmatrix} D_{12}'C_1 & 0 \end{bmatrix}$ and

$$\tilde{J}(\tilde{\boldsymbol{K}}, w, T, \Delta) = \int_0^T (\tilde{z}'\tilde{z} - \gamma^2 w'w)\, dt,$$

with

$$\begin{aligned}\tilde{z} &= \begin{bmatrix} \tilde{C}x \\ \tilde{u} \end{bmatrix}, \qquad \tilde{C}'\tilde{C} = C_1'(I - D_{12}D_{12}')C_1, \\ \tilde{u} &= \tilde{\boldsymbol{K}}\begin{bmatrix} x \\ w \end{bmatrix}.\end{aligned}$$

2. Show that there is a full-information controller such that $J(\boldsymbol{K}, w, T, \Delta) \leq -\epsilon\|w\|_{2,[0,T]}^2$ for all w and some $\epsilon > 0$ if and only if the Riccati equation

$$-\dot{P} = \tilde{A}'P + P\tilde{A} - P(B_2B_2' - \gamma^{-2}B_1B_1')P + \tilde{C}'\tilde{C}, \qquad P(T) = \Delta,$$

in which $\tilde{A} = A - B_2D_{12}'C_1$, has a solution on $[0, T]$.
3. Give a parametrization of all full-information controllers satisfying

$$J(\boldsymbol{K}, w, T, \Delta) \leq -\epsilon\|w\|_{2,[0,T]}^2 \text{ for all } w \text{ and some } \epsilon > 0.$$

4. Assume now that the system matrices are constant (*i.e.*, the system is time-invariant). Show that s_0 is a unobservable mode of $(\tilde{A}, \tilde{C})$ if and only if

$$\begin{bmatrix} A - s_0I & B_2 \\ C_1 & D_{12} \end{bmatrix} \tag{6.5.1}$$

does not have full column rank.
5. Assume that the system matrices are constant, that (A, B_2) is stabilizable and the matrix in (6.5.1) has full column rank on the imaginary axis. Determine necessary and sufficient conditions for the existence of a stabilizing, full-information controller that satisfies $\|\boldsymbol{R}_{zw}\|_\infty < \gamma$.

Problem 6.2. Show that the solution of the differential equation

$$-\dot{\lambda}(t) = A'(t)\lambda(t) + B(t)u(t), \qquad \lambda(T) = \lambda_T,$$

is

$$\lambda(t) = \int_t^T \Phi'(\sigma, t)B(\sigma)u(\sigma)\, d\sigma + \Phi'(T, t)\lambda_T,$$

in which $\frac{d}{dt}(\Phi(t, \sigma)) = A(t)\Phi(t, \sigma)$. Use this to show that (6.2.7) satisfies (6.2.14).

Problem 6.3. Suppose

$$\begin{aligned}\dot{x} &= Ax + B_1w + B_2u \qquad x(0) = 0, \\ z &= \begin{bmatrix} Cx \\ Du \end{bmatrix},\end{aligned}$$

in which $D'D = I$.
1. Show that $J(u, w) = \int_0^T (z'z - \gamma^2 w'w)\, dt$ is a convex function of u.

2. If Riccati equation (6.2.20) with $P(T) = 0$ has a solution for all $t \in [0, T]$, show that there exists a full-information controller that makes $J(\boldsymbol{K}, w) = \int_0^T (z'z - \gamma^2 w'w)\, dt$ concave in w.
3. If there exists a linear, full-information controller that makes $J(\boldsymbol{K}, w)$ strictly concave in w, show that (6.2.20) with $P(T) = 0$ has a solution for all $t \in [0, T]$.

Problem 6.4. Consider the system

$$\begin{aligned} \dot{x} &= Ax + B_1 w + B_2 u, \qquad x(0) = 0, \\ z &= \begin{bmatrix} Cx \\ Du \end{bmatrix} \end{aligned}$$

with $D'D = I$. Give a necessary and sufficient condition for the existence of a full-information controller $\boldsymbol{K} \in \mathcal{K}$ such that $\gamma(\boldsymbol{R}_{zw}) < \gamma$. Here, $\gamma(\cdot)$ denotes the incremental gain of the closed-loop system $\boldsymbol{R}_{zw}$.

Note: From now on all systems are assumed to be time invariant.

Problem 6.5.

1. Verify that $P(t, T, \Delta)$ given by (6.3.4) solves (6.2.20). (You may assume that Δ has been chosen so that $(Z_{22} - \Delta Z_{12})^{-1}$ exists!)
2. Show that Z_{22} is nonsingular if (A, C) is detectable. In fact, if (A, C) has no unobservable modes on the imaginary axis, the rank defect of Z_{22} is equal to the number of undetectable modes in (A, C)—try to show this.
3. Show that $\Pi = Z_{21} Z_{11}^{-1}$ results in

$$A - (B_2 B_2' - \gamma^{-2} B_1 B_1')\Pi = Z_{11} \Lambda Z_{11}^{-1}.$$

Problem 6.6. Suppose P solves the algebraic Riccati equation

$$PA + A'P - PSP + C'C = 0, \tag{6.5.2}$$

in which $S = S'$.

1. Show that (A, C) observable implies P is nonsingular.
2. Assume a stabilizing ($A - SP$ asymptotically stable) solution exists. Show that this solution is nonsingular if and only if every unobservable mode of (A, C) is unstable.
3. Suppose (A, C) is of the form

$$A = \begin{bmatrix} A_{11} & 0 \\ A_{21} & A_{22} \end{bmatrix}, \qquad C = \begin{bmatrix} C_1 & 0 \end{bmatrix},$$

with A_{22} stable. Show that the stabilizing solution P has the form

$$P = \begin{bmatrix} P_1 & 0 \\ 0 & 0 \end{bmatrix},$$

in which P_1 is the stabilizing solution to

$$P_1 A_{11} + A_{11}' P_1 - P_1 S_{11} P_1 + C_1' C_1 = 0.$$

Problem 6.7. Suppose that (A, C) is observable, that $X \geq 0$ and $Y \geq 0$ satisfy (6.5.2), with $A - SX$ asymptotically stable. Show that $Y \geq X$.

Problem 6.8. Consider the loop-gain transfer function $B_2'P(sI - A)^{-1}B_2$, in which $P \geq 0$ is the stabilizing solution to (6.3.5).

1. Show that

$$\begin{aligned} &(I + B_2'(-sI - A')^{-1}PB_2)(I + B_2'P(sI - A)^{-1}B_2) \\ &= \; I + B_2'(-sI - A')^{-1}(C'C + \gamma^{-2}PB_1B_1'P)(sI - A)^{-1}B_2. \end{aligned}$$

   This equation is known as the "return-difference equality".

2. If $B_2 = b_2$ is a vector, show that

$$|1 + b_2'P(j\omega I - A)^{-1}b_2| \geq 1.$$

3. Show that the closed-loop system has a guaranteed phase margin of $\pm 60°$, a gain reduction tolerance of up to 50% and an arbitrarily large gain increase tolerance. These are well known properties of LQ optimal regulators (see [11] for example).

Problem 6.9. Consider the system

$$\begin{aligned} \dot{x} &= x + w + u \\ z &= \begin{bmatrix} cx \\ u \end{bmatrix} \end{aligned}$$

introduced in Example 6.3.4. We showed that for $\gamma > 1$ the nonnegative stabilizing solution to $2p - p^2(1 - \gamma^{-2}) + c^2 = 0$ is given by

$$p = \frac{1 + \sqrt{1 + c^2(1 - \gamma^{-2})}}{1 - \gamma^{-2}}.$$

If we set $u = -px$, show that

$$\lim_{\gamma \to 1} z = \begin{bmatrix} 0 \\ -w \end{bmatrix}.$$

(Hint: Introduce the change of state variable $x = (1 - \gamma^{-2})q$ before taking limits.)

Problem 6.10. Suppose the Riccati equation (6.3.13) has a uniformly bounded solution $P(t, T, P_2)$ and let $\Pi = \lim_{T \to \infty} P(t, T, P_2)$. Show that Π is the stabilizing solution to the algebraic Riccati equation (6.3.5). The aim is to remove the nonsingularity assumption on $\Pi - P(t)$ that is made in the text.

(Hint: See Problem 3.24.)

Problem 6.11. Suppose P_2 is the stabilizing solution to (6.3.11) and that P_2 is nonsingular.

1. Show that $-(A + P_2^{-1}C'C)$ is asymptotically stable.
2. Show that there exists a stabilizing, nonnegative definite solution P to (6.3.5) if and only if there exists a stabilizing solution to the Riccati equation

$$-(A + P_2^{-1}C'C)Y - Y(A + P_2^{-1}C'C)' + \gamma^{-2}YC'CY + B_1B_1' = 0$$

such that $\gamma^2 > \rho(P_2Y)$. ($\rho(\cdot)$ denotes the spectral radius)
(Hint: $Y = \gamma^2(P_2^{-1} - P^{-1})$.)

3. Show that if $C = 0$ and $-A$ is stable, then there exists a control such that the closed loop $\boldsymbol{R}_{zw}$ is stable and satisfies $\|\boldsymbol{R}_{zw}\|_\infty < \gamma$ if and only if $\gamma^2 > \gamma_{opt}^2 = \rho(P_2Y)$, in which Y is the controllability gramian of $(-A, B_1)$.

Problem 6.12. (J-spectral factorization). Suppose P is the stabilizing solution to (6.3.5). Consider $\boldsymbol{G}$ given by

$$\boldsymbol{G} \stackrel{s}{=} \left[\begin{array}{c|cc} A & B_1 & B_2 \\ \hline C & 0 & 0 \\ 0 & 0 & D \\ 0 & I & 0 \end{array}\right],$$

in which $D'D = I$. Thus

$$\begin{bmatrix} z \\ w \end{bmatrix} = \boldsymbol{G} \begin{bmatrix} w \\ u \end{bmatrix}$$

is the solution to (6.1.2) and (6.1.4).

1. Show that

$$\|z\|_2^2 - \gamma^2\|w\|_2^2 = \frac{1}{2\pi}\int_{-\infty}^{\infty} \begin{bmatrix} w' & u' \end{bmatrix} \boldsymbol{G}^* J \boldsymbol{G} \begin{bmatrix} w \\ u \end{bmatrix} d\omega,$$

in which J is the signature matrix:

$$J = \begin{bmatrix} I & 0 & 0 \\ 0 & I & 0 \\ 0 & 0 & -\gamma^2 I \end{bmatrix}.$$

2. Let

$$\boldsymbol{W} \stackrel{s}{=} \left[\begin{array}{c|cc} A & B_1 & B_2 \\ \hline B_2'P & 0 & I \\ -\gamma^{-2}B_1'P & I & 0 \end{array}\right],$$

in which $\tilde{J}$ is another signature matrix and P is (any) solution to (6.3.5). Show that $\boldsymbol{G}^{\sim} J \boldsymbol{G} = \boldsymbol{W}^{\sim} \tilde{J} \boldsymbol{W}$.

3. Show that $\boldsymbol{W}^{-1}$ and $\boldsymbol{G}\boldsymbol{W}^{-1} \in \mathcal{H}_\infty$.

4. Show that $P \geq 0$ implies

$$(\boldsymbol{G}\boldsymbol{W}^{-1})^* J(\boldsymbol{G}\boldsymbol{W}^{-1}) \leq \tilde{J} \qquad \text{for all } s + \bar{s} \geq 0.$$

(That is, $\boldsymbol{G}\boldsymbol{W}^{-1}$ is J-lossless.) Show also that

$$\begin{bmatrix} u - u^* \\ w - w^* \end{bmatrix} = \boldsymbol{W} \begin{bmatrix} w \\ u \end{bmatrix}$$

and conclude that $u^* = -\boldsymbol{W}_{12}^{-1}\boldsymbol{W}_{11}w$.

Problem 6.13. Consider the system

$$\begin{aligned} \dot{x} &= Ax + B_1 w + B_2 u, \qquad x(0) = 0, \\ z &= \begin{bmatrix} Cx \\ Du \end{bmatrix}, \qquad D'D = I. \end{aligned}$$

1. Show that there exists a *measurement feedback* control law $u = \boldsymbol{K}y$, with the special measurement $y = C_2 x + w$, such that

$$J(\boldsymbol{K}, w, T, \Delta) \leq -\epsilon \|w\|_{2,[0,T]}^2$$

for all $w \in \mathcal{L}_2[0,T]$ and some $\epsilon > 0$ if and only if the Riccati differential equation (6.2.20) has a solution on $[0,T]$. Show that all controllers that achieve the objective are generated by the LFT $\boldsymbol{K} = \mathcal{F}_\ell(\boldsymbol{K}_a, \boldsymbol{U})$, in which $\boldsymbol{U}$ is causal, $\|\boldsymbol{U}\|_{[0,T]} < \gamma$ and

$$\boldsymbol{K}_a \stackrel{s}{=} \left[\begin{array}{c|cc} A - B_1 C_2 - B_2 B_2' P & B_1 & B_2 \\ \hline -B_2' P & 0 & I \\ -(C_2 + \gamma^{-2} B_1' P) & I & 0 \end{array}\right].$$

(Hint: Use u, $x(0)$ and y to generate a copy of x.)

2. Now consider the infinite-horizon case and suppose the algebraic Riccati equation (6.3.5) has a stabilizing, nonnegative definite solution. Show that all stabilizing controllers such that $\|\mathcal{F}_\ell(\boldsymbol{P}, \boldsymbol{K})\|_\infty < \gamma$ are generated by $\boldsymbol{K} = \mathcal{F}_\ell(\boldsymbol{K}_a, \boldsymbol{U})$ if and only if $A - B_1 C_2$ is asymptotically stable, $\boldsymbol{U} \in \mathcal{RH}_\infty$ and $\|\boldsymbol{U}\|_\infty < \gamma$.

Problem 6.14. (Nevanlinna-Pick interpolation). Suppose s_i, $i = 1 \ldots n$, are given distinct complex numbers with $\mathrm{R}_e(s_i) > 0$, and that g_i and h_i are given complex vectors. We seek a transfer function matrix $\boldsymbol{R} \in \mathcal{H}_\infty$ such that

$$g_i^* \boldsymbol{R}(s_i) = h_i^* \qquad (6.5.3)$$

$$\|\boldsymbol{R}\|_\infty < \gamma. \qquad (6.5.4)$$

1. Show that $\boldsymbol{R} \in \mathcal{H}_\infty$ satisfies (6.5.3) if and only if $\boldsymbol{R}$ is a closed-loop system that can be generated by a stabilizing, full-information controller for the system defined by

$$\begin{aligned} \dot{x} &= \begin{bmatrix} s_1 & 0 & 0 \\ 0 & \ddots & 0 \\ 0 & 0 & s_n \end{bmatrix} x - \begin{bmatrix} h_1^* \\ \vdots \\ h_n^* \end{bmatrix} w + \begin{bmatrix} g_1^* \\ \vdots \\ g_n^* \end{bmatrix} u \\ z &= u \\ u &= \boldsymbol{K} \begin{bmatrix} x \\ w \end{bmatrix}. \end{aligned}$$

2. Show that the interpolation problem described by (6.5.3) and (6.5.4) has a solution if and only if the Pick matrix defined by

$$M_{ij} = \frac{g_i^* g_j - \gamma^{-2} h_i^* h_j}{s_i + \bar{s}_j}$$

is positive definite.
(Hint: M^{-1} is the solution to a Riccati equation. You will need to convince yourself that complex systems make only a trivial difference—replace transposes with complex conjugate transposes.)
3. Find a parametrization of all solutions to (6.5.3) and (6.5.4).
4. Find a spectral radius formula for γ_{opt}, the greatest lower bound on the values of γ for which the interpolation problem in (6.5.3) and (6.5.4) has a solution.

Problem 6.15. (Decentralized control, Mageirou and Ho [146]) Consider the interconnected subsystems in Figure 6.4.

Suppose that $\boldsymbol{G}_1$ is given by

$$\begin{aligned} \dot{x}_1 &= A_1 x_1 + B_1 z_2 + B_2 u_1 \\ z_1 &= \begin{bmatrix} C_1 x_1 \\ D_1 u_1 \end{bmatrix} \end{aligned}$$

and that $\boldsymbol{G}_2$ is given by

$$\begin{aligned} \dot{x}_2 &= A_2 x_2 + E_1 z_1 + E_2 u_2 \\ z_2 &= \begin{bmatrix} C_2 x_2 \\ D_2 u_2 \end{bmatrix}, \end{aligned}$$

in which $D_i' D_i = I$.

1. If there exist decentralized, state-feedback controllers $u_i = -F_i x_i$ that stabilize their respective subsystems (with respect to loop-break points at z_1 and z_2) and satisfy $\|\mathcal{F}_\ell(\boldsymbol{G}_2, -F_2)\|_\infty < 1$ and $\|\mathcal{F}_u(\boldsymbol{G}_1, -F_1)\|_\infty < 1$, show that the overall closed-loop is stable.[3]

[3] $\mathcal{F}_u(\cdot,\cdot)$ denotes the upper LFT; $\mathcal{F}_\ell(\boldsymbol{G}_2, -F_2)$ and $\mathcal{F}_u(\boldsymbol{G}_1, -F_1)$ are the closed-loop transfer functions of the lower and upper subsystems defined by loop break-points z_1 and z_2.

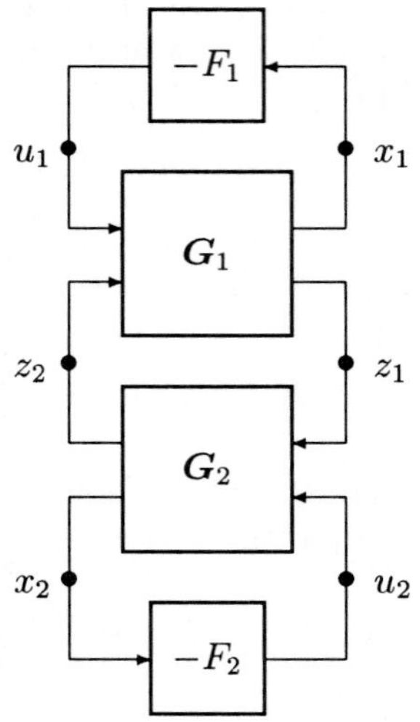

Figure 6.4: Decentralized control scheme.

2. Conclude that if the Riccati equations

$$\begin{aligned} P_1A_1 + A_1'P_1 - P_1(B_2B_2' - B_1B_1')P_1 + C_1'C_1 &= 0 \\ P_2A_2 + A_2'P_2 - P_1(E_2E_2' - E_1E_1')P_2 + C_2'C_2 &= 0 \end{aligned}$$

have stabilizing solutions $P_1 \geq 0$ and $P_2 \geq 0$, then $F_1 = B_2'P_1$ and $F_2 = E_2'P_2$ are suitable controllers.

Problem 6.16. Consider system

$$\begin{aligned} \dot{x} &= Ax + B_1w + B_2u, \qquad x(0) = x_0, \\ z &= \begin{bmatrix} Cx \\ Du \end{bmatrix}. \end{aligned}$$

Assume that a stabilizing, nonnegative definite solution P to the Riccati equation (6.3.5) exists and that the control law $u = -B_2'Px$ is implemented.

1. If $w \equiv 0$, show that

$$\int_0^\infty z'z\,dt \leq x_0'Px_0.$$

2. If $x_0 = 0$, show that

$$\|\boldsymbol{R}_{zw}\|_2^2 \leq \text{trace}(B_1'PB_1).$$

In the above, $\|\cdot\|_2$ denotes the 2-norm of a system, which is the average RMS power of z when w is a unit variance white noise process.

Problem 6.17. Suppose (A, B_2) is stabilizable and that

$$\begin{aligned} \dot{x} &= Ax + B_1 w + B_2 u \\ z &= \begin{bmatrix} Cx \\ Du \end{bmatrix}, \end{aligned}$$

with $D'D = I$. No assumptions are made on the pair (A, C). Show that there exists a stabilizing, full-information controller that satisfies $\|\boldsymbol{R}_{zw}\|_\infty < \gamma$ if and only if there exists a matrix P such that

$$PA + A'P - P(B_2B_2' - \gamma^{-2}B_1B_1')P + C'C \leq 0, \tag{6.5.5}$$

with $A - (B_2B_2' - \gamma^{-2}B_1B_1')P$ asymptotically stable and $P \geq 0$.
(Hint: See Section 6.3.4.)

Problem 6.18. (Singular problems) In Problem 6.17 we showed how to eliminate the assumption that (A, C) has no unobservable modes on the imaginary axis. The main idea behind the removal of this assumption is contained in the discussion in Section 6.3.4. We now show that a similar line of argument can be used to eliminate the assumption that D has full column rank.

Suppose

$$\begin{aligned} \dot{x} &= Ax + B_1 w + B_2 u \\ z &= \begin{bmatrix} Cx \\ Du \end{bmatrix}, \end{aligned}$$

in which D is arbitrary.

1. Show that a stabilizing, full-information controller satisfies $\|\boldsymbol{R}_{zw}\|_\infty < \gamma$ if and only if it also stabilizing for the objective

$$z_a = \begin{bmatrix} Cx \\ Du \\ \epsilon u \end{bmatrix}, \qquad \epsilon > 0$$

and satisfies $\|\boldsymbol{R}_{z_a w}\|_\infty < \gamma$ for some $\epsilon > 0$.
2. Suppose that (A, B_2) is stabilizable and that (A, C) has no unobservable modes on the imaginary axis. Show that there exists a stabilizing, full-information controller such that $\|\boldsymbol{R}_{zw}\|_\infty < \gamma$ if and only if there exists an $\epsilon \geq 0$ such that $R_\epsilon = D'D + \epsilon^2 I$ is nonsingular and a matrix P_ϵ such that

$$P_\epsilon A + A'P_\epsilon - P_\epsilon(B_2R_\epsilon^{-1}B_2' - \gamma^{-2}B_1B_1')P_\epsilon + C'C = 0$$

with $A - (B_2R_\epsilon^{-1}B_2' - \gamma^{-2}B_1B_1')P_\epsilon$ asymptotically stable and $P_\epsilon \geq 0$.

Problem 6.19. Suppose

$$\begin{aligned} \dot{x} &= Ax + B_1 w + B_2 u \\ z &= \begin{bmatrix} Cx \\ Du \end{bmatrix}, \end{aligned}$$

in which (A, B_2) is stabilizable—no other assumptions are imposed. Show that there exists a stabilizing, full-information controller such that the closed-loop system $\boldsymbol{R}_{zw}$ satisfies $\|\boldsymbol{R}_{zw}\|_\infty < \gamma$ if and only if there exists an $\epsilon \geq 0$ such that $R_\epsilon = D'D + \epsilon^2 I$ is nonsingular and a matrix P_ϵ such that

$$P_\epsilon A + A'P_\epsilon - P_\epsilon(B_2 R_\epsilon^{-1} B_2' - \gamma^{-2} B_1 B_1')P_\epsilon + C'C \leq 0$$

with $A - (B_2 R_\epsilon^{-1} B_2' - \gamma^{-2} B_1 B_1')P_\epsilon$ asymptotically stable and $P_\epsilon \geq 0$.

The technique of Section 6.3.4 and the results of Problems 6.17, 6.18 and 6.19 make use of the fact that a stabilizing controller must make the infinity norm of closed-loop transfer function matrices mapping w to x and u finite, even if there is no explicit norm objective on some components of x or u. By including an explicit, but arbitrary, norm constraint on these states and control signals, one obtains a problem that satisfies the standard assumptions.

7

The $\mathcal{H}_\infty$ Filter

7.1 Introduction

It is well known that the LQG control problem decomposes, or separates, into an optimal state-feedback control problem and an optimal state estimation problem. There is a well known duality between the optimal control and filtering problems and the optimal state estimator is the celebrated Kalman filter. These facts are touched on in Chapter 5. The aim of this chapter is to find an estimation dual to the full-information $\mathcal{H}_\infty$ control problem, thereby laying the foundations of a separation theory for $\mathcal{H}_\infty$ control with measurement feedback, which will be developed in Chapter 8.

In the Kalman filter problem description, the signal generating system is assumed to be a state-space system driven by a white-noise process with known statistical properties. The observed output is also corrupted by a white noise process with known statistical properties. The aim of the filter is to minimize either the average RMS power of the estimation error or the variance of the terminal state estimation error. Both these optimal estimation problems yield the Kalamn filter as the optimal filter.

The $\mathcal{H}_\infty$ filtering problem differs from the Kalman filtering problem in two respects:

- unknown deterministic disturbances of finite energy replace the white-noise processes that drive the signal generating system and corrupt the observations;
- the aim of the filter is to ensure that the energy gain from the disturbances to the estimation error is less than a prespecified level γ^2.

If this estimation problem is to be dual to the full-information $\mathcal{H}_\infty$ control problem, the Kalman filter should emerge from the $\mathcal{H}_\infty$ filter theory in the limit as $\gamma \to \infty$. In addition, the $\mathcal{H}_\infty$ filter should have predictable terminal state estimation properties as well as predictable performance in the face of unknown disturbance inputs. Since there are many solutions to the $\mathcal{H}_\infty$ control problem with full information, we expect the $\mathcal{H}_\infty$ estimation problem to have several solutions also. We will find a formula for all solutions; this allows one to solve secondary optimization problems such as entropy minimization.

The finite-horizon problem

Suppose the signal is generated by the time-varying state-space system

$$\dot{x} = Ax + Bw, \qquad x(0) = 0, \tag{7.1.1}$$

$$y = Cx + Dv, \tag{7.1.2}$$

in which $DD' = I$. The process disturbance w and the measurement disturbance v are $\mathcal{L}_2[0,T]$ signals. It is notationally convenient to define the combined process and measurement disturbance as

$$d = \begin{bmatrix} w \\ v \end{bmatrix}. \tag{7.1.3}$$

The aim is to find an estimate of $z = Lx$ of the form

$$\widehat{z} = \boldsymbol{F}y, \tag{7.1.4}$$

such that the ratio of the estimation error energy to the disturbance energy is less than γ^2, a prespecified performance level. This objective can be expressed as the requirement that

$$\|\widehat{z} - Lx\|_{2,[0,T]}^2 - \gamma^2\|d\|_{2,[0,T]}^2 \le -\epsilon\|d\|_{2,[0,T]}^2 \tag{7.1.5}$$

for all $d \in \mathcal{L}_2[0,T]$. The filter $\boldsymbol{F}$ is required to be causal and linear. If $\boldsymbol{R}$ denotes the system mapping d to $\widehat{z} - Lx$, the objective (7.1.5) can be written as

$$\|\boldsymbol{R}\|_{[0,T]} < \gamma, \tag{7.1.6}$$

in which $\|\cdot\|_{[0,T]}$ denotes the $\mathcal{L}_2[0,T]$ induced norm.

The infinite-horizon problem

In the infinite-horizon case, the signal generator (7.1.1) and (7.1.2) is time-invariant, and d given by (7.1.3) is an unknown $\mathcal{L}_2[0,\infty)$ driving input. We seek a causal, linear and time-invariant filter (7.1.4) such that

1. The system $\boldsymbol{F}$ is stable.
2. The system $\boldsymbol{R} : d \mapsto (\widehat{z} - Lx)$ is stable and satisfies

$$\|\boldsymbol{R}\|_\infty < \gamma. \tag{7.1.7}$$

We shall assume that (A, C) is detectable, and that (A, B) has no uncontrollable mode on the imaginary axis.

7.2 Finite-horizon results

We solve the $\mathcal{H}_\infty$ filtering problem by transforming it into an equivalent $\mathcal{H}_\infty$ control problem with full disturbance information. We are then able to invoke the full-information results of Chapter 6 to effect a solution.

7.2.1 Necessary and sufficient conditions

The filtering problem may be expressed as the LFT problem

$$\begin{bmatrix} \dot{x} \\ \widehat{z} - z \\ y \end{bmatrix} = \begin{bmatrix} A & \begin{bmatrix} B & 0 \end{bmatrix} & 0 \\ -L & \begin{bmatrix} 0 & 0 \end{bmatrix} & I \\ C & \begin{bmatrix} 0 & D \end{bmatrix} & 0 \end{bmatrix} \begin{bmatrix} x \\ \begin{bmatrix} w \\ v \end{bmatrix} \\ \widehat{z} \end{bmatrix}, \quad x(0) = 0, \qquad (7.2.1)$$

$$\widehat{z} = \boldsymbol{F} y. \qquad (7.2.2)$$

Recall that the induced norm of a system and its adjoint are equal, and that the adjoint of $\mathcal{F}_\ell(\boldsymbol{P}, \boldsymbol{F})$ is $\mathcal{F}_\ell(\boldsymbol{P}^\sim, \boldsymbol{F}^\sim)$. Therefore, the estimation objective $\|\boldsymbol{R}\|_{[0,T]} < \gamma$ on the map $\boldsymbol{R} : d \mapsto \widehat{z} - z$ is equivalent to the objective $\|\boldsymbol{R}^\sim\|_{[0,T]} < \gamma$, in which $\boldsymbol{R}^\sim$ is the adjoint system generated by the LFT

$$\begin{bmatrix} \frac{d}{d\tau} p(\tau) \\ \tilde{z}(\tau) \\ \tilde{w}(\tau) \end{bmatrix} = \begin{bmatrix} A'(\tau) & -L'(\tau) & C'(\tau) \\ \begin{bmatrix} B'(\tau) \\ 0 \end{bmatrix} & \begin{bmatrix} 0 \\ 0 \end{bmatrix} & \begin{bmatrix} 0 \\ D'(\tau) \end{bmatrix} \\ 0 & I & 0 \end{bmatrix} \begin{bmatrix} p(\tau) \\ \tilde{w}(\tau) \\ \tilde{u}(\tau) \end{bmatrix} \qquad (7.2.3)$$

$$\tilde{u} = \boldsymbol{F}^\sim \tilde{w}. \qquad (7.2.4)$$

The initial condition is $p(\tau)|_{\tau=0} = 0$, in which $\tau = T - t$ is the time-to-go variable associated with the adjoint system. We also note that $\boldsymbol{F}$ is causal in real time if and only if $\boldsymbol{F}^\sim$ is causal in τ.

The LFT (7.2.3) and (7.2.4) describes a control problem in which the controller $\boldsymbol{F}^\sim$ only has access to the exogenous signal $\tilde{w}$, rather than to p and $\tilde{w}$, which would be the full-information configuration of Section 4.2.2. From our discussion of the full-information problem in Section 4.2.2, we know that for the purpose of achieving particular closed loops or control signals, knowledge of $\tilde{w}$ is equivalent to knowledge of p and $\tilde{w}$. This is because we can always replace p in any full-information controller for the adjoint system with a copy generated from $\tilde{w}$ by

$$\frac{d}{d\tau}\widehat{p}(\tau) = A'(\tau)\widehat{p}(\tau) - L'(\tau)\tilde{w}(\tau) + C'\tilde{u}(\tau), \qquad \widehat{p}(\tau)|_{\tau=0} = 0. \qquad (7.2.5)$$

It is now immediate from our full-information control results that a suitable controller for the adjoint problem exists if and only if the Riccati differential equation

$$\begin{aligned} -\frac{d}{d\tau}Q(\tau) &= Q(\tau)A'(\tau) + A(\tau)Q(\tau) + B(\tau)B'(\tau) \\ &\quad -Q(\tau)\big(C'(\tau)C(\tau) - \gamma^{-2}L'(\tau)L(\tau)\big)Q(\tau), \qquad Q(\tau)|_{\tau=T} = 0, \end{aligned}$$

has a solution on $[0,T]$. In this case, the controller $\tilde{u}^*(\tau) = -C(\tau)Q(\tau)\widehat{p}(\tau)$ satisfies the objective for the adjoint system.

Substituting $\tilde{u}^*$ into equation (7.2.5) defining the duplicate adjoint state, we see that the adjoint of a suitable filter is given by

$$\begin{aligned}\frac{d}{d\tau}\widehat{p}(\tau) &= (A' - C'CQ)(\tau)\widehat{p}(\tau) - L'(\tau)\tilde{w}(\tau), \qquad \widehat{p}(\tau)|_{\tau=0} = 0,\\ \tilde{u}(\tau) &= -C(\tau)Q(\tau)\widehat{p}(\tau).\end{aligned}$$

Hence, taking adjoints to return to the original problem defined by (7.2.1) and (7.2.2), we see that a suitable filter exists if and only if the Riccati differential equation

$$\begin{aligned}\dot{Q}(t) &= A(t)Q(t) + Q(t)A'(t) + B(t)B'(t)\\ &\quad -Q(t)\big(C'(t)C(t) - \gamma^{-2}L'(t)L(t)\big)Q(t), \qquad Q(0) = 0, \qquad (7.2.6)\end{aligned}$$

has a solution on $[0,T]$, and that one filter that satisfies the objective (7.1.6) is given by

$$\begin{aligned}\dot{\widehat{x}}(t) &= (A - QC'C)(t)\widehat{x}(t) + Q(t)C'(t)y(t), \qquad \widehat{x}(0) = 0, \qquad (7.2.7)\\ &= A(t)\widehat{x}(t) + Q(t)C'(t)(y(t) - C(t)\widehat{x}(t)) \qquad (7.2.8)\\ \widehat{z}(t) &= L(t)\widehat{x}(t). \qquad (7.2.9)\end{aligned}$$

This filter has an observer structure like the Kalman filter and is illustrated in Figure 7.1. The estimate of Lx is $L\widehat{x}$, in which $\widehat{x}$ can be considered a state estimate.[1] Notice, however, that $\widehat{x}$ depends on L, since the Riccati equation defining the filter gain matrix QC' depends on L. The state estimate one uses in the $\mathcal{H}_\infty$ filter depends on the linear combination of the states that one is seeking to estimate, which is a significant difference between Kalman filtering and $\mathcal{H}_\infty$ filtering.

7.2.2 All solutions

All control signals that can be generated by full-information controllers for the adjoint problem introduced in the previous section are generated by

$$\tilde{u} = \tilde{u}^* + \boldsymbol{U}^{\sim}(\tilde{w} - \tilde{w}^*),$$

in which $\tilde{u}^* = -CQ\widehat{p}$, $\tilde{w}^* = -\gamma^{-2}LQ\widehat{p}$ and $\boldsymbol{U}^{\sim}$ is linear, causal in the adjoint time variable τ and such that $\|\boldsymbol{U}^{\sim}\|_{[0,T]} < \gamma$. Combining this with the dynamical equation (7.2.5) for $\widehat{p}$, we obtain the the LFT

$$\begin{aligned}\begin{bmatrix}\frac{d}{d\tau}\widehat{p}\\ \tilde{u}\\ \tilde{w} - \tilde{w}^*\end{bmatrix} &= \begin{bmatrix}(A' - C'CQ)(\tau) & -L'(\tau) & C'(\tau)\\ -CQ(\tau) & 0 & I\\ \gamma^{-2}LQ(\tau) & I & 0\end{bmatrix}\begin{bmatrix}\widehat{p}\\ \tilde{w}\\ \tilde{u} - \tilde{u}^*\end{bmatrix},\\ \tilde{u} - \tilde{u}^* &= \boldsymbol{U}^{\sim}(\tilde{w} - \tilde{w}^*).\end{aligned}$$

[1] A sense in which $\widehat{x}$ may be considered a state estimate is offered in Section 7.2.3.

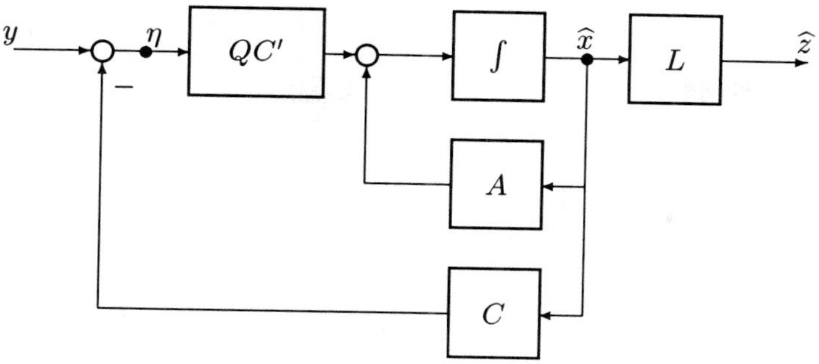

Figure 7.1: An $\mathcal{H}_\infty$ filter.

Taking adjoints, we see that all filters are generated by

$$\boldsymbol{F} = \mathcal{F}_\ell(\boldsymbol{F}_a, \boldsymbol{U}), \tag{7.2.10}$$

in which

$$\boldsymbol{F}_a \stackrel{s}{=} \left[\begin{array}{c|cc} A - QC'C & QC' & -\gamma^{-2}QL' \\ \hline L & 0 & I \\ -C & I & 0 \end{array}\right] \tag{7.2.11}$$

and $\boldsymbol{U}$ is a casual, linear system such that

$$\|\boldsymbol{U}\|_{[0,T]} < \gamma. \tag{7.2.12}$$

This parametrization is illustrated in Figure 7.2. It captures all causal, linear filters (as $\boldsymbol{U}$ varies without restriction on its norm), since the $(1,2)$- and $(2,1)$-blocks of $\boldsymbol{F}_a$ have causal inverses.

In parametrizing all suboptimal solutions to the Kalman filter problem, we observed that all solutions were obtained by simply adding $\boldsymbol{U}\eta$ to the optimal estimate. The signal $\eta = y - C\widehat{x}$ is the innovations process and $\widehat{x}$ is the optimal state estimate, which is independent of $\boldsymbol{U}$. The structure in the $\mathcal{H}_\infty$ filter case is more complex, since although we add $\boldsymbol{U}\eta$ to $\widehat{z}$, we also change the signal driving the integrator, which means that the choice of $\boldsymbol{U}$ affects the state estimate $\widehat{x}$.

We may summarize our results in a theorem:

Theorem 7.2.1 *Suppose the observation y is generated by (7.1.1) and (7.1.2) and d is defined by (7.1.3). Then there exists a causal, linear filter $\widehat{z} = \boldsymbol{F}y$ such that the system $\boldsymbol{R} : d \mapsto (\widehat{z} - Lx)$ satisfies the norm bound $\|\boldsymbol{R}\|_{[0,T]} < \gamma$ if and only if the Riccati differential equation*

$$\dot{Q} = AQ + QA' - Q(C'C - \gamma^{-2}L'L)Q + BB', \qquad Q(0) = 0. \tag{7.2.13}$$

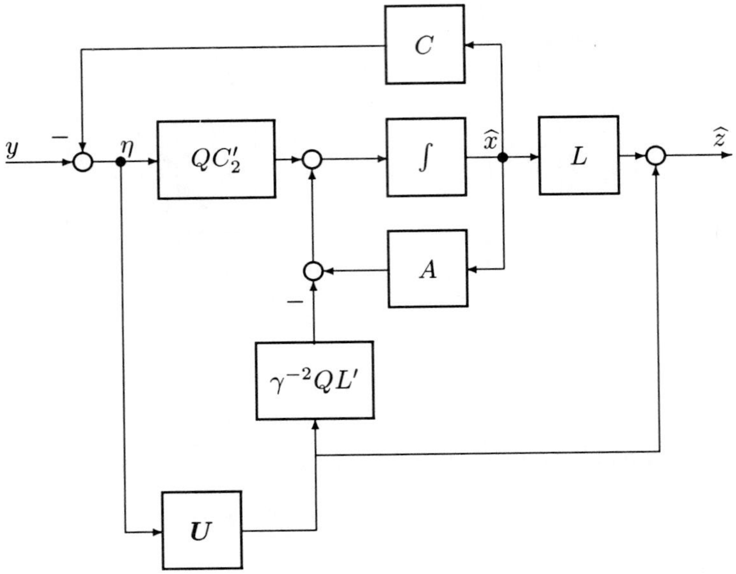

Figure 7.2: A parametrization of all filters.

has a solution on $[0,T]$. *In this case,* $\boldsymbol{F}$ *is a causal, linear filter that achieves the objective* $\|\boldsymbol{R}\|_{[0,T]} < \gamma$ *if and only if it is given by (7.2.10) for some causal, linear system* $\boldsymbol{U}$ *that satisfies (7.2.12).*

7.2.3 Terminal state estimation properties

To show that the central $\mathcal{H}_\infty$ filter shown in Figure 7.1 has terminal state estimation properties in the Kalman filtering sense, we assume that the driving signal d is a zero mean white noise process of unit intensity.[2] We also assume that $x(0)$ is a random variable with the properties

$$\mathcal{E}\{x(0)\} = m \tag{7.2.14}$$

$$\mathcal{E}\left\{\left(x(0)-m\right)\left(x(0)-m\right)'\right\} = Q_0, \tag{7.2.15}$$

with $x(0)$ independent of $d(t)$. If $x(0)$ is known, we set $Q_0 = 0$.

To ensure that our estimate is unbiased, we set $\widehat{x}(0) = m$ in (7.2.7) and use the terminal condition $Q(0) = Q_0$ in the Riccati differential equation (7.2.13). Assuming a solution to this equation exists on the time-interval of interest, we subtract (7.2.8)

[2]This is known as the central filter because it is obtain by setting $\boldsymbol{U} = 0$ in the parametrization of all filters; $\boldsymbol{U} = 0$ is the center of the "ball" $\|\boldsymbol{U}\|_{[0,T]} < \gamma$.

from (7.1.1) and use (7.1.2) to obtain the error system

$$\dot{x}_e = (A - QC'C)x_e + \begin{bmatrix} -B & QC'D \end{bmatrix} \begin{bmatrix} w \\ v \end{bmatrix},$$

in which $x_e = \widehat{x} - x$. Since $\mathcal{E}\{x_e\} = 0$, the state error variance matrix $\bar{Q}(t) = \mathcal{E}\{x_e(t)x_e'(t)\}$ propagates in time according to the linear equation

$$\dot{\bar{Q}} = (A - QC'C)\bar{Q} + \bar{Q}(A - QC'C)' + BB' + QC'CQ, \qquad (7.2.16)$$

with initial condition $\bar{Q}(0) = Q_0$. Subtracting (7.2.16) from (7.2.13) gives

$$(\dot{Q} - \dot{\bar{Q}}) = (A - QC'C)(Q - \bar{Q}) + (Q - \bar{Q})(A - QC'C)' + \gamma^{-2}QL'LQ,$$

and since $(Q - \bar{Q})(0) = 0$, this shows that $Q(t) - \bar{Q}(t) \geq 0$ for all $t \in [0, T]$. We conclude that the terminal state estimation error variance satisfies

$$\mathcal{E}\{x_e(t)x_e'(t)\} \leq Q(t).$$

The Riccati equation that defines the Kalman filter for the signal generator (7.1.1) and (7.1.2) is

$$\dot{\widehat{Q}} = A\widehat{Q} + \widehat{Q}A' - \widehat{Q}C'C\widehat{Q} + BB', \qquad \widehat{Q}(0) = Q_0. \qquad (7.2.17)$$

Since $\widehat{Q}(t)$ is the optimal terminal state error covariance, which is the error covariance obtained by the Kalman filter, we must have $\bar{Q}(t) \geq \widehat{Q}(t)$. This may also be verified by subtracting the Riccati equations (7.2.17) and (7.2.16).

Note also that the 2-norm of the system $\boldsymbol{R} : d \mapsto (\widehat{z} - Lx)$ satisfies

$$\begin{aligned} \|\boldsymbol{R}\|_{2,[0,T]} &= \left\{ \frac{1}{T} \int_0^T \operatorname{trace}(L\bar{Q}L')\, dt \right\}^{\frac{1}{2}} \\ &\leq \left\{ \frac{1}{T} \int_0^T \operatorname{trace}(LQL')\, dt \right\}^{\frac{1}{2}}. \end{aligned}$$

This may be seen by using (7.2.16) and Theorem 3.3.1.

These observations establish that the central $\mathcal{H}_\infty$ filter has predictable two-norm properties and terminal state estimation properties when driven by white noise, but that it is suboptimal with respect to these performance criteria.

Main points of the section

1. The $\mathcal{H}_\infty$ estimation problem is the dual of a control problem in which the controller has access to the exogenous input.

2. A solution to the $\mathcal{H}_\infty$ estimation problem exists if and only if the Riccati differential equation (7.2.13) has a solution.
3. The central $\mathcal{H}_\infty$ filter has an observer structure identical to that of the Kalman filter, and the estimate of Lx is $L\widehat{x}$ in which $\widehat{x}$ is a state estimate that depends on L. In contrast to the Kalman filter, the $\mathcal{H}_\infty$ filter gain is a function of L.
4. There is a LFT parametrizing all solutions to the $\mathcal{H}_\infty$ estimation problem.
5. The central $\mathcal{H}_\infty$ filter obtained by setting $\boldsymbol{U} = 0$ has predictable two-norm and terminal state estimation properties. In particular, $\mathcal{E}\{(\widehat{x} - x)(\widehat{x} - x)'\} \leq Q$, in which Q is the solution to the Riccati equation (7.2.13).

7.3 Infinite-horizon results

In the infinite-horizon case, the signal generator (7.1.1) and (7.1.2) is assumed to be time-invariant. We also assume that (A, C) is detectable and that (A, B) has no uncontrollable modes on the imaginary axis. Our aim is to determine conditions for the existence of a causal, linear, time-invariant and stable filter $\boldsymbol{F}$ such that the system $\boldsymbol{R} : d \mapsto (\widehat{z} - Lx)$ is stable and satisfies

$$\|\boldsymbol{R}\|_\infty < \gamma. \tag{7.3.1}$$

As before, we may express the relationship between the disturbance d and the estimation error $\widehat{z} - Lx$ as the LFT

$$\begin{aligned} \begin{bmatrix} \dot{x} \\ \widehat{z} - z \\ y \end{bmatrix} &= \begin{bmatrix} A & \begin{bmatrix} B & 0 \end{bmatrix} & 0 \\ -L & \begin{bmatrix} 0 & 0 \end{bmatrix} & I \\ C & \begin{bmatrix} 0 & D \end{bmatrix} & 0 \end{bmatrix} \begin{bmatrix} x \\ \begin{bmatrix} w \\ v \end{bmatrix} \\ \widehat{z} \end{bmatrix}, \\ \widehat{z} &= \boldsymbol{F} y. \end{aligned}$$

Notice that this LFT is not stablizable in the sense defined in Section 4.2.1, unless A is asymptotically stable, because the output of the filter does not affect the signal generator. We emphasize that *we do not demand that the filter* $\boldsymbol{F}$ *is internally stabilizing*. Rather, we demand that $\boldsymbol{F}$ and $\boldsymbol{R}$ are stable.[3]

Taking the adjoint, we obtain

$$\begin{aligned} \begin{bmatrix} \dot{p} \\ \tilde{z} \\ \tilde{w} \end{bmatrix} &= \begin{bmatrix} A' & -L' & C' \\ \begin{bmatrix} B' \\ 0 \end{bmatrix} & \begin{bmatrix} 0 \\ 0 \end{bmatrix} & \begin{bmatrix} 0 \\ D' \end{bmatrix} \\ 0 & I & 0 \end{bmatrix} \begin{bmatrix} p \\ \tilde{w} \\ \tilde{u} \end{bmatrix} \\ \tilde{u} &= \boldsymbol{F}^{\sim} \tilde{w}. \end{aligned}$$

[3] We do not care what happens to the state x, and indeed can do nothing about it. Our aim is to ensure that our estimate of Lx is a good one.

(All time arguments and derivatives are taken with respect to the adjoint time variable $\tau = -t$.) The adjoint filter $\boldsymbol{F}^{\sim}$ must be τ-stable (*i.e.*, stable in the adjoint time variable τ), and must lead to a τ-stable closed-loop system $\boldsymbol{R}^{\sim}$ that satisfies $\|\boldsymbol{R}^{\sim}\|_\infty < \gamma$.

Now consider the full-information controller

$$\tilde{u} = -H'p + \boldsymbol{G}^{\sim}\tilde{w}, \tag{7.3.2}$$

in which $\boldsymbol{G}^{\sim} : \tilde{w} \mapsto \widehat{\tilde{u}}$ is given by

$$\begin{aligned} \dot{\widehat{p}} &= A'\widehat{p} + (C'\boldsymbol{F}^{\sim} - L')\tilde{w} \\ \widehat{\tilde{u}} &= H'\widehat{p} + \boldsymbol{F}^{\sim}\tilde{w}. \end{aligned}$$

If $\boldsymbol{F}$ is a filter that satisfies our requirements and we choose H such that $A - HC$ is asymptotically stable, then the full-information controller (7.3.2) internally stabilizes the full-information configuration

$$\begin{bmatrix} \dot{p} \\ \tilde{z} \\ \begin{bmatrix} p \\ \tilde{w} \end{bmatrix} \end{bmatrix} = \begin{bmatrix} A' & -L' & C' \\ \begin{bmatrix} B' \\ 0 \end{bmatrix} & \begin{bmatrix} 0 \\ 0 \end{bmatrix} & \begin{bmatrix} 0 \\ D' \end{bmatrix} \\ \begin{bmatrix} I \\ 0 \end{bmatrix} & \begin{bmatrix} 0 \\ I \end{bmatrix} & \begin{bmatrix} 0 \\ 0 \end{bmatrix} \end{bmatrix} \begin{bmatrix} p \\ \tilde{w} \\ \tilde{u} \end{bmatrix},$$

and the infinity norm of the closed-loop system is less than γ. Consequently, there exists a stabilizing, nonnegative definite solution Q to the algebraic Riccati equation

$$AQ + QA' - Q(C'C - \gamma^{-2}L'L)Q + BB' = 0.$$

All the control signals that result from τ-internally-stabilizing controllers for the adjoint problem are generated by

$$\tilde{u} = \tilde{u}^* + \boldsymbol{U}^{\sim}(\tilde{w} - \tilde{w}^*),$$

in which $\boldsymbol{U}^{\sim}$ is τ-stable, $\|\boldsymbol{U}^{\sim}\|_\infty < \gamma$ and $\tilde{u}^* = -CQp$ with $\tilde{w}^* = -\gamma^{-2}LQp$. Hence $\boldsymbol{F}^{\sim}$ is generated by the LFT

$$\mathcal{F}_\ell(\boldsymbol{F}_a^{\sim}, \boldsymbol{U}^{\sim}),$$

in which

$$\boldsymbol{F}_a^{\sim} \overset{s}{=} \left[\begin{array}{c|cc} (A - QC'C)' & -L' & C' \\ \hline -CQ & 0 & I \\ \gamma^{-2}LQ & I & 0 \end{array}\right].$$

Taking the adjoint, we see that all stable filters such that $\boldsymbol{R} : d \mapsto (\widehat{z} - Lx)$ is stable and satisfies $\|\boldsymbol{R}\|_\infty < \gamma$ are generated by

$$\boldsymbol{F} = \mathcal{F}_\ell(\boldsymbol{F}_a, \boldsymbol{U}), \qquad \boldsymbol{U} \in \mathcal{H}_\infty, \|\boldsymbol{U}\|_\infty < \gamma, \tag{7.3.3}$$

in which

$$F_a \stackrel{s}{=} \left[\begin{array}{c|cc} A - QC'C & QC' & -\gamma^{-2}QL' \\ \hline L & 0 & I \\ -C & I & 0 \end{array}\right]. \tag{7.3.4}$$

Theorem 7.3.1 *Suppose the observation y is generated by (7.1.1) and (7.1.2) and that d is defined by (7.1.3). Suppose also that (A, C) is detectable and that (A, B) has no uncontrollable mode on the imaginary axis.*

There exists a stable filter $\boldsymbol{F}$ such that the system $\boldsymbol{R} : d \mapsto (\widehat{z} - Lx)$ is stable and satisfies the norm bound $\|\boldsymbol{R}\|_\infty < \gamma$ if and only if the algebraic Riccati equation

$$AQ + QA' - Q(C'C - \gamma^{-2}L'L)Q + BB' = 0 \tag{7.3.5}$$

has a solution such that $A - Q(C'C - \gamma^{-2}L'L)$ is asymptotically stable and $Q \geq 0$. In this case, $\boldsymbol{F}$ is a stable filter such that $\boldsymbol{R}$ is stable and $\|\boldsymbol{R}\|_\infty < \gamma$ if and only if it is given by (7.3.3).

7.3.1 The $\mathcal{H}_\infty$ Wiener filtering problem

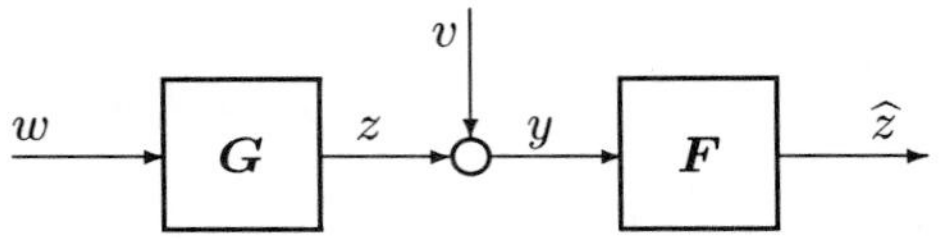

Figure 7.3: The Wiener problem.

As an illustration of the $\mathcal{H}_\infty$ filter, we consider the Wiener filter configuration given in Figure 7.3. The observation y is the sum of a signal z plus a noise v, and we wish to extract the signal z from y. In Wiener's formulation the system $\boldsymbol{G}$ is stable, strictly proper and driven by white noise. In the $\mathcal{H}_\infty$ formulation, the signals w and v are deterministic, but unknown.

It is immediate from Figure 7.3 that

$$\begin{aligned} z &= \boldsymbol{G}w \\ \widehat{z} &= \boldsymbol{F}(v + \boldsymbol{G}w) \\ \widehat{z} - z &= \left[\begin{array}{cc} (\boldsymbol{F} - I)\boldsymbol{G} & \boldsymbol{F} \end{array}\right] \left[\begin{array}{c} w \\ v \end{array}\right]. \end{aligned}$$

Ultimately we want a stable filter $\boldsymbol{F}$, but initially we ignore this restriction and consider a smoothing problem in which the aim is to choose $\boldsymbol{F}$ such that

$$\left\| \left[\begin{array}{cc} (\boldsymbol{F} - I)\boldsymbol{G} & \boldsymbol{F} \end{array}\right] \right\|_\infty \leq \gamma. \tag{7.3.6}$$

The objective (7.3.6) is equivalent to

$$(\boldsymbol{F}-I)\boldsymbol{G}\boldsymbol{G}^{\sim}(\boldsymbol{F}^{\sim}-I)+\boldsymbol{F}\boldsymbol{F}^{\sim}\leq\gamma^2 I. \tag{7.3.7}$$

Since

$$\begin{aligned}(\boldsymbol{F}-\boldsymbol{G}(I+\boldsymbol{G}^{\sim}\boldsymbol{G})^{-1}\boldsymbol{G}^{\sim})(I+\boldsymbol{G}\boldsymbol{G}^{\sim})(\boldsymbol{F}^{\sim}-\boldsymbol{G}(I+\boldsymbol{G}^{\sim}\boldsymbol{G})^{-1}\boldsymbol{G}^{\sim})\\ = \boldsymbol{F}\boldsymbol{F}^{\sim}+(\boldsymbol{F}-I)\boldsymbol{G}\boldsymbol{G}^{\sim}(\boldsymbol{F}^{\sim}-I)-\boldsymbol{G}(I+\boldsymbol{G}^{\sim}\boldsymbol{G})^{-1}\boldsymbol{G}^{\sim},\end{aligned}$$

the inequality (7.3.7) may be written as

$$\boldsymbol{G}(I+\boldsymbol{G}^{\sim}\boldsymbol{G})^{-1}\boldsymbol{G}^{\sim}+(\boldsymbol{F}-\boldsymbol{F}^*)(I+\boldsymbol{G}\boldsymbol{G}^{\sim})(\boldsymbol{F}-\boldsymbol{F}^*)^{\sim}\leq\gamma^2 I, \tag{7.3.8}$$

in which

$$\boldsymbol{F}^*=\boldsymbol{G}(I+\boldsymbol{G}^{\sim}\boldsymbol{G})^{-1}\boldsymbol{G}^{\sim}.$$

The inequality (7.3.8) can be satisfied if and only if

$$\boldsymbol{G}(I+\boldsymbol{G}^{\sim}\boldsymbol{G})^{-1}\boldsymbol{G}^{\sim}\leq\gamma^2 I, \tag{7.3.9}$$

in which case the filter $\boldsymbol{F}=\boldsymbol{F}^*$ satisfies (7.3.8) and hence achieves the objective (7.3.6). The condition (7.3.9) may be manipulated (Problem 7.5) to yield the equivalent condition

$$\gamma\geq\frac{1}{\sqrt{1+\delta^{-2}}}=\gamma_{opt}, \tag{7.3.10}$$

in which $\delta=\|\boldsymbol{G}\|_\infty$. Thus the minimum γ that can be achieved with any filter, stable or otherwise, is determined by $\|\boldsymbol{G}\|_\infty$. Surprisingly, if $\gamma>\gamma_{opt}$, we can also satisfy (7.3.6) with a stable filter. That is,

$$\gamma_{opt}=\inf_{\boldsymbol{F}\in\mathcal{H}_\infty}\|\left[\begin{array}{cc}(\boldsymbol{F}-I)\boldsymbol{G} & \boldsymbol{F}\end{array}\right]\|_\infty$$

where γ_{opt} is given in (7.3.10), although the infimum is not achievable with a stable filter due to the appearance of filter poles on the imaginary axis.

In order to prove this, suppose $\boldsymbol{G}$ has realization (A,B,C) with A asymptotically stable. Then

$$\begin{aligned}\dot{x} &= Ax+Bw\\ y &= Cx+v\end{aligned}$$

and we seek a stable estimator $\boldsymbol{F}$ such that the error system

$$\boldsymbol{R}=\left[\begin{array}{cc}(\boldsymbol{F}-I)\boldsymbol{G} & \boldsymbol{F}\end{array}\right]$$

is stable and satisfies $\|\boldsymbol{R}\|_\infty<\gamma$. Note that the stability of $\boldsymbol{R}$ follows from the stability of $\boldsymbol{F}$ and $\boldsymbol{G}$ in this case. Using Theorem 7.3.1, we see that such a filter $\boldsymbol{F}$ exists if and only if the Riccati equation

$$AQ+QA'-(1-\gamma^{-2})QC'CQ+BB'=0 \tag{7.3.11}$$

has a solution such that $A - (1-\gamma^{-2})QC'C$ is asymptotically stable and $Q \geq 0$.

If $\gamma > 1$, such a solution always exists, because we may write (7.3.11) as

$$AQ + QA' - Q\tilde{C}'\tilde{C}Q + BB' = 0,$$

in which $\tilde{C} = C\sqrt{1-\gamma^{-2}}$. This is the algebraic Riccati equation associated with the Kalman filter problem of estimating x given the measurement $\tilde{y} = \tilde{C}x + v$, which always has a stabilizing, nonnegative definite solution.[4]

If $\gamma < 1$, we conclude from the bounded real lemma (Theorem 3.7.1) that Q exists if and only if

$$\|\boldsymbol{G}\|_\infty < \frac{1}{\sqrt{\gamma^{-2}-1}},$$

which is equivalent to $\gamma > \gamma_{opt}$.

7.4 Example: Inertial navigation system

This example illustrates the properties of an $\mathcal{H}_\infty$ filter designed for a simple inertial navigation system (INS). The archetypal INS deduces velocity and position from acceleration measurements—velocity is found by integrating the acceleration once, while position is deduced via a double integration. Unfortunately, accelerometer biases, variations in the earth's gravitational field, noise and gyro platform misalignment cause the position estimate from the INS to drift away from the true position. One way to compensate for this effect is to use external position data such as a radio beacon or satellite. The INS and external device could then be combined as shown in Figure 7.4 to produce a compensated position estimate. The aim is to use the INS to track the high-frequency maneuvering of the vehicle, while the external position data should be favored in the long term.

For the purpose of illustration, we consider navigation in one dimension. The INS is modelled as a double integrator fed by a corrupted acceleration signal. The external radio navigation aid is represented by a true position together with an additive disturbance signal that represents radio transmission noise. This model is illustrated in Figure 7.5.

The state variables we have selected are the errors in the INS's position and speed:

$$\begin{aligned}\delta p &= p_i - p_t\\ \delta s &= s_i - s_t,\end{aligned}$$

in which p_t and s_t represent the true position and speed. The input to the filter is given by

$$\Delta p = p_i - p_r,$$

[4]The stability of A ensures $(A, \tilde{C})$ is stabilizable and that (A, B) has no uncontrollable mode on the imaginary axis.

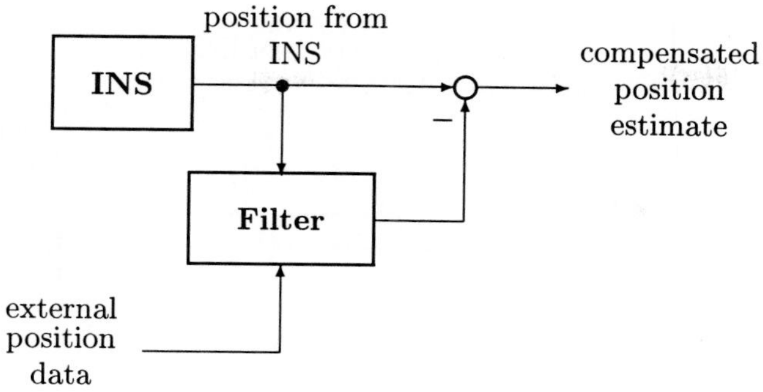

Figure 7.4: INS compensated by external position data.

which is the difference between the INS's position estimate and the radio navigation aid's estimate of the current position. From Figure 7.5 we obtain

$$\begin{aligned}\Delta p &= p_i - p_r \\ &= (p_t + \delta p) - (p_t - v) \\ &= \delta p + v.\end{aligned}$$

We also see from this diagram that the speed and position estimates produced by the inertial navigator are given by

$$\begin{bmatrix} \dot{p}_i \\ \dot{s}_i \end{bmatrix} = \begin{bmatrix} 0 & 1 \\ 0 & 0 \end{bmatrix} \begin{bmatrix} p_i \\ s_i \end{bmatrix} + \begin{bmatrix} 0 \\ 1 \end{bmatrix} (a_t + w).$$

The true speed and position are given by

$$\begin{bmatrix} \dot{p}_t \\ \dot{s}_t \end{bmatrix} = \begin{bmatrix} 0 & 1 \\ 0 & 0 \end{bmatrix} \begin{bmatrix} p_t \\ s_t \end{bmatrix} + \begin{bmatrix} 0 \\ 1 \end{bmatrix} a_t.$$

Consequently

$$\begin{aligned}\begin{bmatrix} \delta\dot{p} \\ \delta\dot{s} \end{bmatrix} &= \begin{bmatrix} 0 & 1 \\ 0 & 0 \end{bmatrix} \begin{bmatrix} \delta p \\ \delta s \end{bmatrix} + \begin{bmatrix} 0 \\ 1 \end{bmatrix} w \\ &= Ax + Bw\end{aligned}$$

and

$$\begin{aligned}\Delta p &= \begin{bmatrix} 1 & 0 \end{bmatrix} \begin{bmatrix} \delta p \\ \delta s \end{bmatrix} + v \\ &= Cx + v.\end{aligned}$$

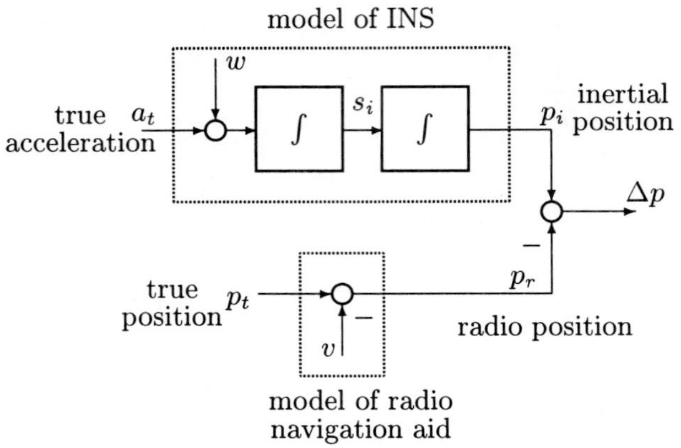

Figure 7.5: Model of INS with external position data.

Since we want the $\mathcal{H}_\infty$ filter to minimize the effects of w and v on the difference between δp and its estimate $\delta\widehat{p}$, we set

$$L = \begin{bmatrix} 1 & 0 \end{bmatrix}.$$

To complete the design data, we suppose that the energy in the acceleration error w and navigation aid error v are bounded:

$$\|w\|_2 < q \quad \text{and} \quad \|v\|_2 < r.$$

The filter gain is given by

$$\begin{bmatrix} k_1 \\ k_2 \end{bmatrix} = r^{-2}QC',$$

in which Q is the stabilizing solution of the algebraic Riccati equation

$$AQ + QA' - (1 - (r/\gamma)^2)r^{-2}QC'CQ + q^2BB' = 0.$$

If $\gamma > r$, this is the Riccati equation associated with the Kalman filter problem with measurement $\tilde{y} = r^{-1}\sqrt{1-(r/\gamma)^2}Cx + v$, so a stabilizing, nonnegative definite solution exists. We leave it as an exercise for the reader to show that no stabilizing, nonnegative definite solution exists for $\gamma \le r$. Figure 7.6 provides a block diagram representation of the central $\mathcal{H}_\infty$ filter for this problem.

We now obtain explicit formulas for the solution to the Riccati equation and hence the filter gain. Writing

$$Q = \begin{bmatrix} q_1 & q_2 \\ q_2 & q_3 \end{bmatrix}$$

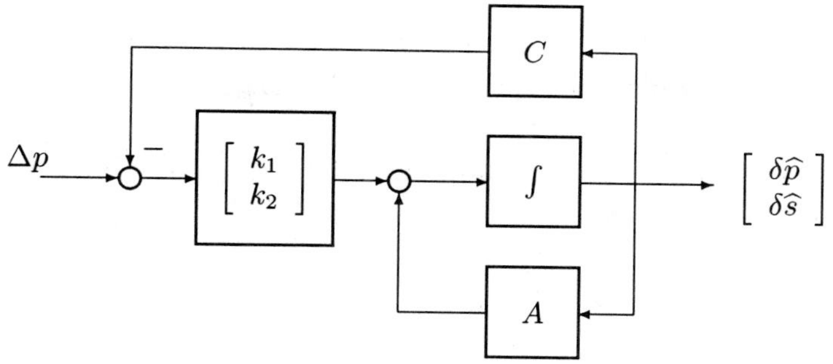

Figure 7.6: The INS $\mathcal{H}_\infty$ filter.

and substituting the data gives the Riccati equation

$$\begin{bmatrix} 2q_2 - \beta^{-2}q_1^2 & q_3 - \beta^{-2}q_1q_2 \\ q_3 - \beta^{-2}q_1q_2 & q^2 - \beta^{-2}q_2^2 \end{bmatrix} = 0,$$

in which

$$\beta^2 = \frac{r^2}{1-(r/\gamma)^2}.$$

Elementary algebra now reveals that

$$Q = \begin{bmatrix} \beta\sqrt{2q\beta} & q\beta \\ q\beta & q\sqrt{2q\beta} \end{bmatrix},$$

and the filter gain is therefore

$$\begin{bmatrix} k_1 \\ k_2 \end{bmatrix} = r^{-2}\begin{bmatrix} \beta\sqrt{2q\beta} \\ q\beta \end{bmatrix}.$$

If the exogenous input $\begin{bmatrix} w \\ v \end{bmatrix}$ is a white noise such that

$$\mathcal{E}\left\{\begin{bmatrix} w(t) \\ v(t) \end{bmatrix}\begin{bmatrix} w'(\tau) & v'(\tau) \end{bmatrix}\right\} = \begin{bmatrix} q^2 & 0 \\ 0 & r^2 \end{bmatrix}\delta(t-\tau),$$

the variance of the position estimate error satisfies

$$\mathcal{E}\{(\delta p - \delta\widehat{p})^2(t)\} \le q_1 = \beta\sqrt{2q\beta}.$$

The bound on the variance of the estimation error decreases as γ increases—in the case that $\gamma^{-2} = 0$, we get $\mathcal{E}\{(\delta p - \delta\widehat{p})^2(t)\} = r\sqrt{2qr}$, which is the error variance associated with the Kalman filter. Figure 7.7 gives a plot of the position error

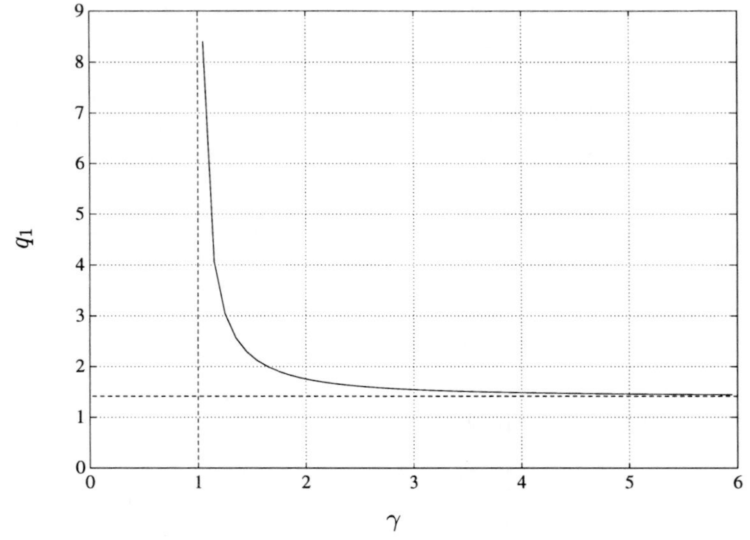

Figure 7.7: Upper bound on the error variance.

variance bound q_1 as a function of γ when $r = q = 1$. The interesting feature of this diagram is the fact that the upper bound on the error variance is almost as low as that obtained for the Kalman filter right down to γ values of the order of 2.

We conclude the example by examining the properties of the transfer functions linking w, v and the estimated position $\widehat{p}$. One implementation of the filter is given in Figure 7.8. It is immediate from this diagram that

$$\begin{aligned} \boldsymbol{g}_1 &= \frac{\widehat{p}}{w} = \frac{1}{s^2 + sk_1 + k_2} \\ \boldsymbol{g}_2 &= \frac{\widehat{p}}{v} = \frac{sk_1 + k_2}{s^2 + sk_1 + k_2}. \end{aligned}$$

The natural frequency of these transfer functions is

$$\omega_n = \sqrt{k_2} = r^{-1}\sqrt{q\beta},$$

while $2\zeta\omega_n = k_1$ gives

$$\zeta = \frac{\beta}{r\sqrt{2}}$$

as the damping ratio. These formulas show that both these quantities increase as γ decreases. Bode plots of $\boldsymbol{g}_1$ and $\boldsymbol{g}_2$ are shown in Figures 7.9 and 7.10 respectively

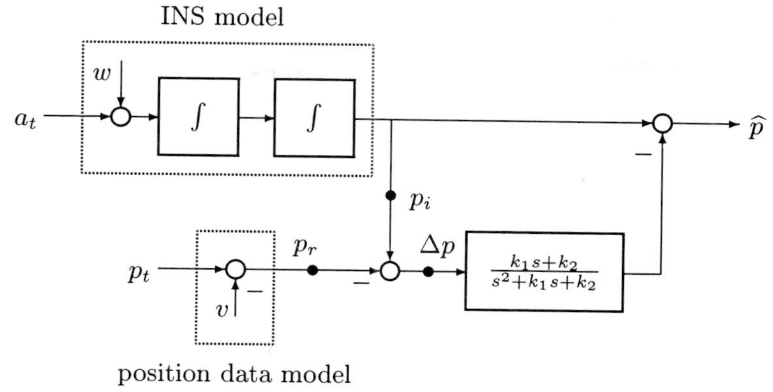

Figure 7.8: Open-loop implementation of compensated INS.

for $r = q = 1$ and various values of γ. These diagrams show that $\boldsymbol{g}_1$ and $\boldsymbol{g}_2$ act as low-pass filters of the INS disturbances and radio noise, and that the INS disturbance rejection improves as γ decreases, while $\widehat{p}$ becomes more susceptible to wide bandwidth radio beacon noise as γ decreases.

7.5 Notes and References

Minimax and game theoretic ideas have been employed in robust filtering for at least two decades. The general approach to these problems is to minimize the worst case error (in some sense) as one ranges over all admissible signal and noise models. Kassan and Poor [114] give a review of many of the established ideas in robust filtering. Başar and Mintz [21] and Hexner and Mintz [92] study an estimation problem that is motivated by tracking problems involving uncooperative targets under the control of intelligent adversaries.

Some of the early work on robust estimation in an $\mathcal{H}_\infty$ framework is due to Grimble, Ho and Elsayed [87, 88], who analyze the problem using polynomial methods. Bernstein and Haddad [28] study similar problems in a state-space setting using projection methods, which are particularly well suited to reduced order filter synthesis problems. They also study problems requiring the minimization of an upper bound on the $\mathcal{H}_2$ norm under and $\mathcal{H}_\infty$ norm constraint. Their problem turns out to be the same as entropy minimization.

For filtering work which emphasizes the connection with game theory, we refer the reader to Shaked and Yaesh [195, 215]; Khargonekar and Nagpal [115]; and Limebeer and Shaked [137]. Shaked and Yaesh also study frequency domain connections with J-spectral factorization. Başar [19] analyzes a wide variety of filtering, smoothing and prediction problems using game theoretic methods. Fer-

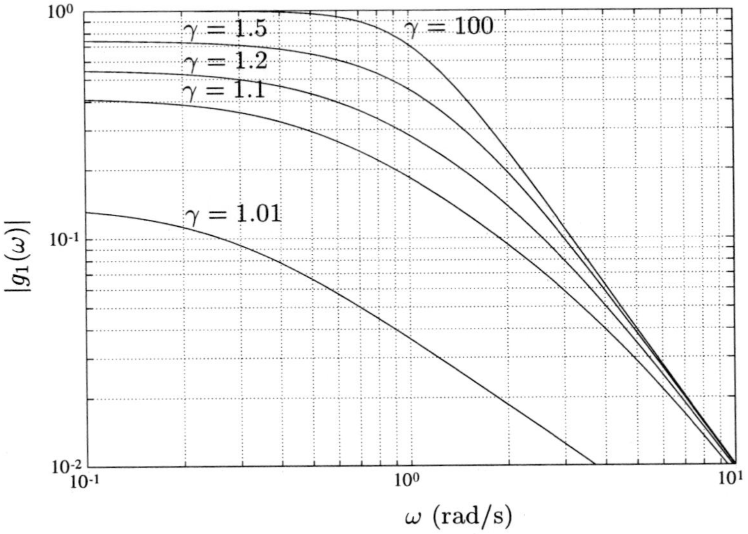

Figure 7.9: Bode magnitude plot of $\boldsymbol{g}_1$.

nandes, de Souza and Goodwin [61] study $\mathcal{L}_1$, $\mathcal{L}_2$ and $\mathcal{L}_\infty$ robust estimation via a parametrization of all estimators that is an affine function of an $\mathcal{H}_\infty$ transfer matrix function, which is the estimation dual of the well known $\boldsymbol{Q}$-parameterization of all stabilizing controllers.

The inertial navigation example comes from Maybeck [147].

7.6 Problems

Problem 7.1. Suppose $\bar{Q}(t)$ is the solution of (7.2.16) and that $\widehat{Q}(t)$ is the solution of (7.2.17). If the initial conditions for these equations are $\bar{Q}(0) = \widehat{Q}(0) = Q_0$, show that $\bar{Q}(t) \geq \widehat{Q}(t)$. If $Q(0) = Q_0$, conclude that $Q(t) \geq \bar{Q}(t) \geq \widehat{Q}(t)$ for all times for which a solution to (7.2.13) exists.

Problem 7.2. Suppose the noise descriptions in the problem statement satisfy

$$w = Q^{\frac{1}{2}}\tilde{w}, \quad \text{with } \|\tilde{w}\|_2 \leq 1$$

and

$$v = R^{\frac{1}{2}}\tilde{v}, \quad \text{with } \|\tilde{v}\|_2 \leq 1,$$

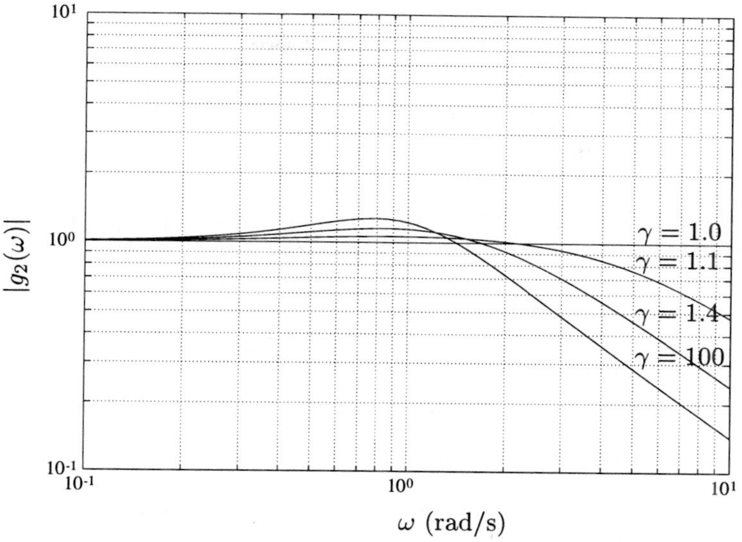

Figure 7.10: Bode magnitude plot of $\boldsymbol{g}_2$.

and that the observations are given by

$$y = Cx + v.$$

Show that there exists a causal filter $\boldsymbol{F}$ such that $\widehat{z} = \boldsymbol{F}y$ satisfies $\|\widehat{z} - Lx\|_2 \leq \gamma$ for all $\tilde{v}$ and $\tilde{w}$ if and only if the filtering Riccati differential equation

$$\dot{Q} = AQ + QA' - Q(C'R^{-1}C - \gamma^{-2}L'L)Q + BQB' \qquad Q(0) = 0$$

has a solution on $[0, T]$. Show that the filter gain is given by $H = QC'R^{-1}$.

Problem 7.3. Suppose A, B, L and C have been transformed to the form

$$A = \begin{bmatrix} A_{11} & A_{12} \\ 0 & A_{22} \end{bmatrix}, \; B = \begin{bmatrix} B_1 \\ 0 \end{bmatrix}, \; L = \begin{bmatrix} L_1 & L_2 \end{bmatrix}, \; C = \begin{bmatrix} C_1 & C_2 \end{bmatrix},$$

in which A_{22} is asymptotically stable. Suppose also that $\widehat{Q} \geq 0$ is the stabilizing solution to the algebraic Riccati equation

$$A_1\widehat{Q} + \widehat{Q}A_1' - \widehat{Q}(C_1'C_1 - \gamma^{-2}L_1'L_1)\widehat{Q} + B_1B_1' = 0.$$

Show that

$$Q = \begin{bmatrix} \widehat{Q} & 0 \\ 0 & 0 \end{bmatrix}$$

is the stabilizing solution to

$$AQ + QA' - Q(C'C - \gamma^{-2}L'L)Q + BB' = 0.$$

Problem 7.4. Suppose that the signal generator is

$$\begin{aligned} \dot{x} &= Ax + Bw, \qquad x(0) = 0, \\ y &= Cx + Dw, \end{aligned}$$

in which $DD' = I$. Show that the estimator gain for this problem is $H = QC' + BD'$, where Q satisfies the Riccati equation

$$\dot{Q} = \bar{A}Q + Q\bar{A}' - Q(C'C - \gamma^{-2}L'L)Q + \bar{B}\bar{B}'$$

with initial condition $Q(0) = 0$. The matrices $\bar{A}$ and $\bar{B}$ are given by

$$\bar{A} = A - BD'C \quad \text{and} \quad \bar{B}\bar{B}' = B(I - D'D)B'.$$

Write down the generator of all filters that satisfy $\|\boldsymbol{R}\|_{[0,T]} < \gamma$.

Problem 7.5. Verify that the inequality (7.3.9) is equivalent to the inequality (7.3.10).

Problem 7.6. Suppose the measurement noise $v(t)$ is frequency weighted by the causal and causally invertible system

$$\begin{aligned} \dot{\tilde{x}} &= \tilde{A}(t)\tilde{x}(t) + \tilde{B}(t)\tilde{v}(t) \\ v(t) &= \tilde{C}(t)\tilde{x}(t) + \tilde{D}(t)\tilde{v}(t). \end{aligned}$$

Show how one may reduce this frequency weighted estimation problem into a standard problem of the form given in Problem 7.4.

How would you deal with problems in which $w(t)$ is frequency weighted?

Problem 7.7.

In certain applications one may wish to frequency weight the estimation error as shown in Figure 7.11, with $\boldsymbol{W}$, $\boldsymbol{W}^{-1} \in \mathcal{RH}_\infty$.

If

$$\begin{bmatrix} \boldsymbol{G}_1 \\ \boldsymbol{G}_2 \end{bmatrix} \stackrel{s}{=} \left[\begin{array}{c|c} A & B \\ \hline C & 0 \\ L & 0 \end{array}\right],$$

carefully derive a formula for all filters with the property $\|\boldsymbol{R}\|_\infty < \gamma$ which is free of state inflation; $\boldsymbol{R}$ maps the disturbance to ϕ. Note that $\deg(\boldsymbol{F}) \leq \deg\left(\begin{bmatrix} \boldsymbol{G}_1 \\ \boldsymbol{G}_2 \end{bmatrix}\right) + \deg(\boldsymbol{W})$; $\deg(\cdot)$ denotes the McMillan degree.

(Hint: Redraw Figure 7.11 as Figure 7.12 and solve for $\tilde{\boldsymbol{F}}$ using the augmented function $\tilde{\boldsymbol{G}}_1$. The filter we seek may then be recovered by setting $\boldsymbol{F} = \boldsymbol{W}^{-1}\tilde{\boldsymbol{F}}$. Mind the extra states now!)

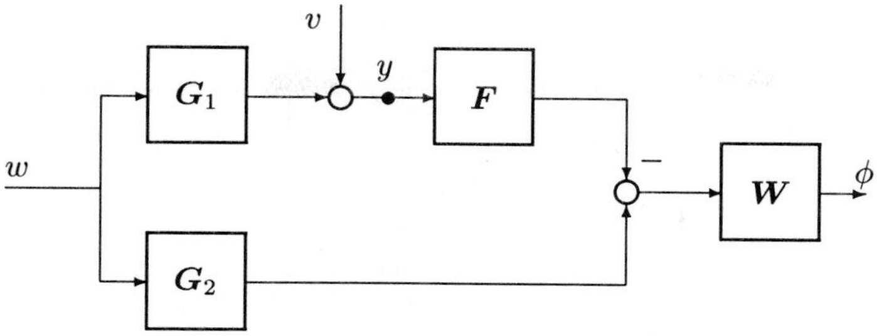

Figure 7.11: A configuration for frequency weighted estimation errors.

Problem 7.8. Consider the signal generator

$$\begin{aligned} \dot{x} &= Ax + Bw + B_2\widehat{z} \\ y &= Cx + v \\ \widehat{z} &= \boldsymbol{F}y. \end{aligned}$$

As usual, we seek to choose the filter $\boldsymbol{F}$ such that $\boldsymbol{R} : d \mapsto (\widehat{z} - Lx)$ has certain properties. Since the filter output affects the signal being estimated, this is a closed-loop estimation problem.

1. Show that a causal linear filter $\boldsymbol{F}$ satisfying $\|\boldsymbol{R}\|_{[0,T]} < \gamma$ exists if and only if the Riccati differential equation (7.2.13) has a solution on $[0, T]$. Show that all filters are generated by $\boldsymbol{F} = \mathcal{F}_\ell(\boldsymbol{F}_a, \boldsymbol{U})$, in which $\boldsymbol{U}$ is a causal, linear system such that $\|\boldsymbol{U}\|_{[0,T]} < \gamma$ and

$$\boldsymbol{F}_a \stackrel{s}{=} \left[\begin{array}{c|cc} A + B_2L - QC'C & QC' & B_2 - \gamma^{-2}QL' \\ \hline L & 0 & I \\ -C & I & 0 \end{array}\right].$$

2. If (A, C) is detectable, (A, B) has no uncontrollable modes on the imaginary axis and $A+B_2L$ is asymptotically stable, show that there exists an *internally-stabilizing* filter $\boldsymbol{F}$ for the generalized regulator problem defined by

$$\boldsymbol{P} \stackrel{s}{=} \left[\begin{array}{c|cc} A & \begin{bmatrix} B & 0 \end{bmatrix} & B_2 \\ \hline -L & \begin{bmatrix} 0 & 0 \end{bmatrix} & I \\ C & \begin{bmatrix} 0 & I \end{bmatrix} & 0 \end{array}\right]$$

if and only if the algebraic Riccati equation (7.3.5) has a stabilizing nonnegative definite solution. Give a parametrization of all such filters.

Problem 7.9. (Xie, de Souza and Fu [214]) Consider the signal generator

$$\begin{aligned} \dot{x} &= (A + H_1\boldsymbol{\Delta}E)x + Bw \\ y &= (C + H_2\boldsymbol{\Delta}E)x + v, \end{aligned}$$

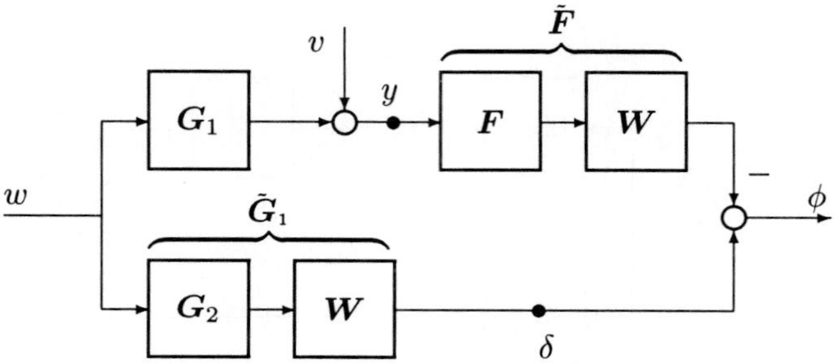

Figure 7.12: One solution to the frequency weighted estimation problem.

in which the matrices A, B, C, H_1, H_2 and E are known, but the stable perturbation $\boldsymbol{\Delta}$ is unknown with the property $\|\boldsymbol{\Delta}\|_\infty < 1$. We require an estimate $\widehat{z} = \boldsymbol{F}y$ of Lx such that $\|\boldsymbol{R}\|_\infty < 1$, where $\boldsymbol{R}$ maps the disturbance to the estimation error $\widehat{z} - Lx$.

Set up this configuration as a generalized regulator problem.

(Hint: Set up a generalized regulator problem that includes $\begin{bmatrix} H_1' & H_2' \end{bmatrix}' \tilde{w}$ as an additional input and Ex as an additional output.)

8

The $\mathcal{H}_\infty$ Generalized Regulator Problem

8.1 Introduction

We now turn to the problem of synthesizing controllers for the $\mathcal{H}_\infty$ generalized regulator problem posed in Section 4.2.1. In the case of the LQG generalized regulator problem, it is well known that the synthesis is achieved via a decomposition, or separation, into an optimal state-feedback control problem and an optimal state estimation problem. The optimal state-feedback controller is given in terms of the solution of a Riccati differential equation, which is solved backwards in time from a terminal condition. This state-feedback controller is also the optimal full-information controller. The optimal state estimator is the Kalman filter and the filter gain is given in terms of the solution of a second Riccati differential equation, which is solved forwards in time from an initial condition. In the infinite-horizon, time-invariant case, the solutions to the Riccati differential equations are replaced with the stabilizing solutions to the corresponding algebraic Riccati equations.

Although there are many similarities between the solution of the LQG problem and the $\mathcal{H}_\infty$ generalized regulator problem, the LQG problem and its $\mathcal{H}_\infty$ counterpart are also quite different in several respects. The following two facts are the source of these differences:

- Full-information $\mathcal{H}_\infty$ controllers depend on the way in which the exogenous signal enters the system dynamics—that is, on B_1. In full-information LQG control, B_1 does not affect the optimal controller, only the optimal cost.
- An $\mathcal{H}_\infty$ filter that estimates $-Fx$ is $-F\widehat{x}$, in which $\widehat{x}$ depends on F. In the Kalman filter situation, the optimal estimate of $-Fx$ is $-F\widehat{x}$, in which $\widehat{x}$, the

optimal state estimate, does not depend on F.

A further complication stems from the need to address existence questions, because the Riccati equations associated with $\mathcal{H}_\infty$ control and filtering problems do not always have solutions, unlike their LQG counterparts.

We will show that all solutions to the $\mathcal{H}_\infty$ generalized regulator problem have the form of an $\mathcal{H}_\infty$ filter that estimates the full-information $\mathcal{H}_\infty$ control law. This yields necessary and sufficient conditions for the existence of controllers in terms of two Riccati equations. The second Riccati equation depends on the solution to the first. Manipulations involving these Riccati equations enable us to show that the $\mathcal{H}_\infty$ generalized regulator problem has a solution if and only if:

1. the Riccati equation associated with the full-information control problem has a solution (on some appropriate time interval which may be infinite);
2. the Riccati equation associated with the $\mathcal{H}_\infty$ estimation of C_1x has a solution (on the same interval); and
3. a coupling condition is satisfied.

If solutions exist, there is a LFT parametrizing all controllers. The controller generator is given in terms of the problem data and the solutions of the two Riccati equations.

8.1.1 Problem statement

We consider the generalized plant $\boldsymbol{P}$ described by the state-space system

$$\dot{x} = Ax + B_1w + B_2u, \qquad x(0) = 0, \tag{8.1.1}$$

$$z = C_1x + D_{12}u \tag{8.1.2}$$

$$y = C_2x + D_{21}w, \tag{8.1.3}$$

in which w is an l-dimensional exogenous input, u is an m-dimensional control signal, y is a q-dimensional measurement and z is a p-dimensional objective signal. The state vector x has dimension n. We assume that for all times of interest

$$D_{12}'D_{12} = I_m \quad \text{and} \quad D_{21}D_{21}' = I_q. \tag{8.1.4}$$

By assuming that the loop shifting and scaling transformations described in Section 4.6 have already been carried out, the simplified objective (8.1.2) and measurement (8.1.3) may be considered instead of the more complicated expressions

$$\begin{aligned} z &= C_1x + D_{11}w + D_{12}u \\ y &= C_2x + D_{21}w + D_{22}u. \end{aligned}$$

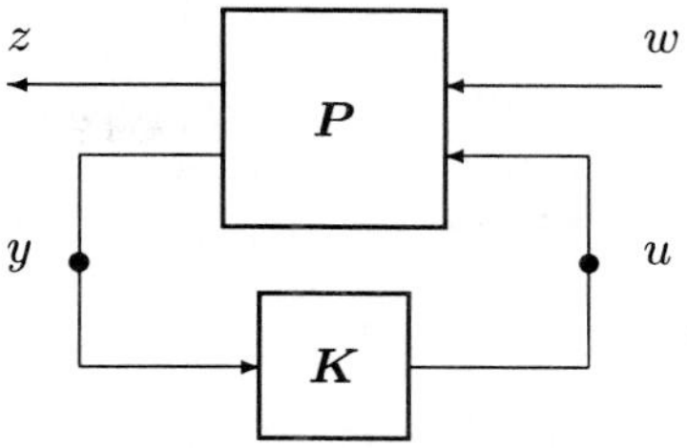

Figure 8.1: The generalized regulator configuration.

Finite-horizon problem

In the case of a finite horizon, the generalized plant $\boldsymbol{P}$ described by (8.1.1) to (8.1.3) may be time-varying and we seek a causal, linear controller

$$u = \boldsymbol{K}y \tag{8.1.5}$$

such that the closed-loop system $\boldsymbol{R}_{zw} = \mathcal{F}_\ell(\boldsymbol{P}, \boldsymbol{K})$ satisfies

$$\|\boldsymbol{R}_{zw}\|_{[0,T]} < \gamma. \tag{8.1.6}$$

Infinite-horizon problem

In the case of an infinite horizon, the generalized plant $\boldsymbol{P}$ described by (8.1.1) to (8.1.3) is assumed to be time-invariant. We consider the class of causal, linear, time-invariant and finite-dimensional controllers that internally stabilize $\boldsymbol{P}$. Any such controller will be called *admissible* for $\boldsymbol{P}$. Our aim is to find an admissible controller such that the closed-loop system $\boldsymbol{R}_{zw} = \mathcal{F}_\ell(\boldsymbol{P}, \boldsymbol{K})$ satisfies the infinity norm objective

$$\|\boldsymbol{R}_{zw}\|_\infty < \gamma. \tag{8.1.7}$$

The standard assumptions: We will assume that:

1. The pair (A, B_2) is stablizable and the pair (A, C_2) is detectable.

2. The matrices D_{12} and D_{21} satisfy (8.1.4).

3. $$\operatorname{rank}\begin{bmatrix} A - j\omega I & B_2 \\ C_1 & D_{12} \end{bmatrix} = n + m, \qquad \text{for all real } \omega, \tag{8.1.8}$$

4. $$\operatorname{rank}\begin{bmatrix} A - j\omega I & B_1 \\ C_2 & D_{21} \end{bmatrix} = n + q, \qquad \text{for all real } \omega. \tag{8.1.9}$$

The assumption that (A, B_2, C_2) is stabilizable and detectable is necessary and sufficient for the existence of admissible controllers. This is proved in Appendix A (see Lemma A.4.2). The "full rank on the imaginary axis" assumptions are necessary for the existence of stabilizing solutions to the Riccati equations that we use to characterize the solution to the $\mathcal{H}_\infty$ generalized regulator problem. Problem 8.14 explores a way in which these assumptions may be removed.

8.2 Finite-horizon results

As has been our practice throughout the synthesis theory chapters, we consider the finite-horizon case first. The plant (8.1.1) to (8.1.3) is time-varying and we seek a causal, linear controller $u = \boldsymbol{K}y$ such that the objective (8.1.6) is satisfied.

Before considering the general case, it is instructive to consider two special cases which can be solved using only one Riccati equation.

Simple measurement feedback problems

Consider the measurement feedback problem in which

$$y = C_2 x + w \tag{8.2.1}$$

is used instead of (8.1.3). In this case, the observer

$$\begin{aligned} \dot{\widehat{x}} &= A\widehat{x} + B_2 u + B_1(y - C_2\widehat{x}), \qquad \widehat{x}(0) = 0, &(8.2.2)\\ \widehat{w} &= y - C_2\widehat{x} &(8.2.3) \end{aligned}$$

perfectly reconstructs the state x and exogenous input w from the measurements y. Consequently, we may replace the state x in any full-information controller with $\widehat{x}$, generated from y by the observer (8.2.2) and (8.2.3). We conclude that a measurement feedback controller for this problem exists if and only if the Riccati equation

$$\begin{aligned} -\dot{X}_\infty &= X_\infty\tilde{A} + \tilde{A}'X_\infty + \tilde{C}'\tilde{C}\\ &\quad - X_\infty(B_2B_2' - \gamma^{-2}B_1B_1')X_\infty, \qquad X_\infty(T) = 0, &(8.2.4) \end{aligned}$$

has a solution on $[0, T]$. The matrices $\tilde{A}$ and $\tilde{C}$ are given by

$$\begin{aligned} \tilde{A} &= A - B_2D_{12}'C_1 &(8.2.5)\\ \tilde{C}'\tilde{C} &= C_1'(I - D_{12}D_{12}')C_1, &(8.2.6) \end{aligned}$$

which result from reducing (8.1.2) to the form

$$\tilde{z} = \begin{bmatrix} \tilde{C}x \\ \tilde{u} \end{bmatrix}$$

using the transformation $\tilde{u} = u + D_{12}'C_1x$. For more details, see Section 5.2.3 and Problem 6.1. One controller that achieves the objective is $u^* = -F_\infty\widehat{x}$, in which

$$F_\infty = D_{12}'C_1 + B_2'X_\infty.$$

We obtain all solutions to this special measurement feedback problem by combining the generator of all full-information controllers with the observer (8.2.2) and (8.2.3). This yields the LFT parametrization $\boldsymbol{K} = \mathcal{F}_\ell(\boldsymbol{K}_a, \boldsymbol{U})$, in which $\boldsymbol{U}$ is a causal linear system such that $\|\boldsymbol{U}\|_{[0,T]} < \gamma$ and $\boldsymbol{K}_a$ is given by

$$\boldsymbol{K}_a \stackrel{s}{=} \left[\begin{array}{c|cc} A - B_1C_2 - B_2F_\infty & B_1 & B_2 \\ \hline -F_\infty & 0 & I \\ -(C_2 + \gamma^{-2}B_1'X_\infty) & I & 0 \end{array}\right].$$

Since the observer has no effect on the achievable norm, a measurement of the form (8.2.1) is no worse than full information, in terms of achieving closed-loop norm objectives.

Another special situation is the case in which

$$z = C_1x + u \tag{8.2.7}$$

replaces (8.1.2). This problem is the adjoint of the problem just considered and is the closed-loop estimation problem discussed in Problem 7.8. A solution exists if and only if the Riccati equation

$$\begin{aligned} \dot{Y}_\infty &= \bar{A}Y_\infty + Y_\infty\bar{A}' + \bar{B}\bar{B}' \\ &\quad - Y_\infty(C_2'C_2 - \gamma^{-2}C_1'C_1)Y_\infty, \qquad Y_\infty(0) = 0, \end{aligned} \tag{8.2.8}$$

has a solution on $[0,T]$. The matrices $\bar{A}$ and $\bar{B}$ are given by

$$\bar{A} = A - B_1D_{21}'C_2 \tag{8.2.9}$$

$$\bar{B}\bar{B}' = B_1(I - D_{21}'D_{21})B_1'. \tag{8.2.10}$$

All solutions are generated by the LFT $\boldsymbol{K} = \mathcal{F}_\ell(\boldsymbol{K}_a, \boldsymbol{U})$ in which $\boldsymbol{U}$ is a causal linear system such that $\|\boldsymbol{U}\|_{[0,T]} < \gamma$ and $\boldsymbol{K}_a$ is given by

$$\boldsymbol{K}_a \stackrel{s}{=} \left[\begin{array}{c|cc} A - B_2C_1 - H_\infty C_2 & H_\infty & B_2 + \gamma^{-2}Y_\infty C_1' \\ \hline -C_1 & 0 & I \\ -C_2 & I & 0 \end{array}\right],$$

in which

$$H_\infty = B_1D_{21}' + Y_\infty C_2'.$$

8.2.1 Two necessary conditions

We now consider the general case in which $\boldsymbol{P}$ is described by (8.1.1) to (8.1.3).

Measurement feedback and full-information control

Any measurement feedback controller is also a full-information controller, since (8.1.3) and (8.1.5) imply that

$$u = \begin{bmatrix} \boldsymbol{K}C_2 & \boldsymbol{K}D_{21} \end{bmatrix} \begin{bmatrix} x \\ w \end{bmatrix}. \tag{8.2.11}$$

The existence of a measurement feedback controller that achieves the objective (8.1.6) therefore implies the existence of a full-information controller that achieves (8.1.6). Hence, by our full-information $\mathcal{H}_\infty$ control results, the existence of a solution to the Riccati differential equation (8.2.4) is necessary for the existence of a solution to the measurement feedback problem.

Measurement feedback and filtering

As a dual to the above observations, consider the signal generating system

$$\begin{aligned} \dot{x}_o &= Ax_o + B_1 w, \qquad x_o(0) = 0, && (8.2.12)\\ y_o &= C_2 x_o + D_{21} w && (8.2.13) \end{aligned}$$

and the filter $\boldsymbol{F}$ defined by

$$\begin{aligned} \dot{\tilde{x}} &= A\tilde{x} + B_2\boldsymbol{K}(y_o + C_2\tilde{x})\\ \tilde{z} &= C_1\tilde{x} + D_{12}\boldsymbol{K}(y_o + C_2\tilde{x}). \end{aligned}$$

Then the system mapping w to $C_1x_o + \tilde{z}$ is just $\mathcal{F}_\ell(\boldsymbol{P}, \boldsymbol{K})$ and we conclude that if $\boldsymbol{K}$ satisfies (8.1.6) for the signal generator (8.1.1) to (8.1.3), then $\boldsymbol{F}$ satisfies

$$\|C_1x_o + \tilde{z}\|_{2,[0,T]}^2 - \gamma^2\|w\|_{2,[0,T]}^2 \le -\epsilon\|w\|_{2,[0,T]}^2$$

for all $w \in \mathcal{L}_2[0,T]$ and some $\epsilon > 0$.[1] Hence, by invoking our $\mathcal{H}_\infty$ filtering results, the existence of a solution to the Riccati differential equation (8.2.8) is also necessary for the existence of a solution to the measurement feedback problem.

The separation principle

Let us now recall the solution to the LQG measurement feedback problem. The filtering problem there was to find an optimal estimate of the optimal full-information control law. Since this is of the form $u = -Fx$, this amounts to finding an optimal state estimate. The Kalman filter combined with the optimal, full-information control law therefore provides the solution. The control and estimation problems are completely decoupled. It is not necessary to decide on the noise covariances before designing the full-information controller, nor is it necessary to decide on the control objective before designing the Kalman filter.

[1] $x = x_o + \tilde{x}$, $y = y_0 + \tilde{y}$ and $z = C_1x_o + \tilde{z}$.

The decoupling of the control and estimation problems in LQG controller synthesis results from the fact that the optimal estimator of $-Fx$ is given by $-F\widehat{x}$, in which $\widehat{x}$ is the optimal state estimate, which is independent of F. As we know, this does not hold for $\mathcal{H}_\infty$ filtering, since the state estmate depends on F. For this reason, the filter cannot be designed independently of the control objective, as the filter required depends on the control law. This means that although the existence of solutions to the Riccati equations (8.2.4) and (8.2.8) are necessary conditions, they are not sufficient conditions for the existence of a solution to the $\mathcal{H}_\infty$ generalized regulator problem. Nevertheless, the solution to the $\mathcal{H}_\infty$ controller synthesis problem may be obtained by solving the full-information control problem and finding an $\mathcal{H}_\infty$ estimator for the full-information control. This is the separation principle of $\mathcal{H}_\infty$ control.

8.2.2 Necessary and sufficient conditions

Suppose the Riccati differential equations (8.2.4) and (8.2.8) have solutions on $[0, T]$.

We know from our full-information control results that the controller $u^* = -F_\infty x$, in which $F_\infty = D_{12}'C_1 + B_2'X_\infty$, achieves the objective (8.1.6). Moreover, any closed-loop system $\boldsymbol{R}_{zw} = \mathcal{F}_\ell(\boldsymbol{P}, \boldsymbol{K})$ satisfying the objective (8.1.6) is generated by

$$u - u^* = \tilde{\boldsymbol{U}}(w - w^*),$$

in which $w^* = \gamma^{-2}B_1'X_\infty x$, for some causal, linear system $\tilde{\boldsymbol{U}}$ satisfying

$$\|\tilde{\boldsymbol{U}}\|_{[0,T]} < \gamma. \tag{8.2.14}$$

Thus, in order to determine whether or not a measurement feedback controller $u = \boldsymbol{K}y$ satisfies the objective (8.1.6), we evaluate the system $\tilde{\boldsymbol{U}}$ that maps $w - w^*$ to $u - u^*$. Writing the state dynamics (8.1.1) and measurement equation (8.1.3) in terms of $w - w^*$ instead of w, we obtain

$$\begin{aligned} \dot{x} &= (A + \gamma^{-2}B_1B_1'X_\infty)x + B_1(w - w^*) + B_2u \\ y &= (C_2 + \gamma^{-2}D_{21}B_1'X_\infty)x + D_{21}(w - w^*). \end{aligned}$$

From this, we immediately see that the system $\tilde{\boldsymbol{U}}$ that maps $w - w^*$ to $u - u^*$ is generated by the LFT

$$\begin{aligned} \begin{bmatrix} \dot{x} \\ u - u^* \\ y \end{bmatrix} &= \begin{bmatrix} A + \gamma^{-2}B_1B_1'X_\infty & B_1 & B_2 \\ F_\infty & 0 & I \\ C_2 + \gamma^{-2}D_{21}B_1'X_\infty & D_{21} & 0 \end{bmatrix} \begin{bmatrix} x \\ w - w^* \\ u \end{bmatrix}, \\ u &= \boldsymbol{K}y. \end{aligned}$$

The parametrization of all solution to the full-information problem says that the controller $\boldsymbol{K}$ satisfies the objective (8.1.6) if and only if $\tilde{\boldsymbol{U}}$ satisfies (8.2.14). The advantage of considering this modified generalized regulator problem is that its objective signal $u - u^* = F_\infty x + u$ has precisely the form of the special objective (8.2.7) considered earlier. Applying these results, we conclude that $\boldsymbol{K}$ exists if and only the Riccati differential equation

$$\begin{aligned}\dot{Z}_\infty &= A_z Z_\infty + Z_\infty A_z' + \bar{B}\bar{B}' \\ &\quad - Z_\infty(C_{2z}'C_{2z} - \gamma^{-2}F_\infty' F_\infty)Z_\infty, \qquad Z_\infty(0) = 0, \end{aligned} \tag{8.2.15}$$

has a solution on $[0, T]$. In (8.2.15), C_{2z} and A_z are given by

$$C_{2z} = C_2 + \gamma^{-2} D_{21} B_1' X_\infty, \tag{8.2.16}$$

$$\begin{aligned} A_z &= A + \gamma^{-2} B_1 B_1' X_\infty - B_1 D_{21}' C_{2z} \\ &= A + \gamma^{-2} B_1 (I - D_{21}' D_{21}) B_1' X_\infty - B_1 D_{21}' C_2. \end{aligned} \tag{8.2.17}$$

Furthermore, all solutions are generated by the LFT

$$\boldsymbol{K} = \mathcal{F}_\ell(\boldsymbol{K}_a, \boldsymbol{U}), \tag{8.2.18}$$

in which $\boldsymbol{U}$ is a causal linear system such that

$$\|\boldsymbol{U}\|_{[0,T]} < \gamma. \tag{8.2.19}$$

The generator of all solutions $\boldsymbol{K}_a$ is given by the realization

$$\boldsymbol{K}_a \stackrel{s}{=} \left[\begin{array}{c|cc} A_k & B_{k1} & B_{k2} \\ \hline C_{k1} & 0 & I \\ C_{k2} & I & 0 \end{array}\right], \tag{8.2.20}$$

in which

$$\begin{aligned} A_k &= A + \gamma^{-2} B_1 B_1' X_\infty - B_2 F_\infty - B_{k1} C_{2z} \\ \begin{bmatrix} B_{k1} & B_{k2} \end{bmatrix} &= \begin{bmatrix} B_1 D_{21}' + Z_\infty C_{2z}' & B_2 + \gamma^{-2} Z_\infty F_\infty' \end{bmatrix} \\ \begin{bmatrix} C_{k1} \\ C_{k2} \end{bmatrix} &= \begin{bmatrix} -F_\infty \\ -C_{2z} \end{bmatrix}. \end{aligned}$$

The fact that the $(1,2)$- and $(2,1)$-blocks of $\boldsymbol{K}_a$ have causal inverses means that we capture all causal, linear, measurement feedback controllers if $\boldsymbol{U}$ is allowed to range over the class of causal, linear systems (without restriction on its norm).

The central controller: Notice that the central controller obtained by setting $\boldsymbol{U} = 0$ can be written as

$$\begin{aligned} \dot{\widehat{x}} &= A\widehat{x} + B_1 \widehat{w}^* + B_2 u + B_{k1}\big(y - (C_2 \widehat{x} + D_{21} \widehat{w}^*)\big) \\ u &= -F_\infty \widehat{x} \\ \widehat{w}^* &= \gamma^{-2} B_1' X_\infty \widehat{x}, \end{aligned}$$

which is shown in block diagram form in Figure 8.2. We see that u is generated by the feedback gain F_∞ acting on a state estimate resulting from an observer. The observer is driven by the difference between the measured y and the measurement estimate $\widehat{y}^* = C_2\widehat{x} + D_{21}\widehat{w}^*$ that would occur if the exogenous signal were w^*. Recall that w^* is the worst exogenous input in $\mathcal{L}_2[0,T]$ for the full-information control problem. It is therefore also the worst exogenous input in $\mathcal{L}_2[0,T]$ for the measurement feedback problem. The worst-case nature of $\mathcal{H}_\infty$ control is therefore evident in the structure of the controller.

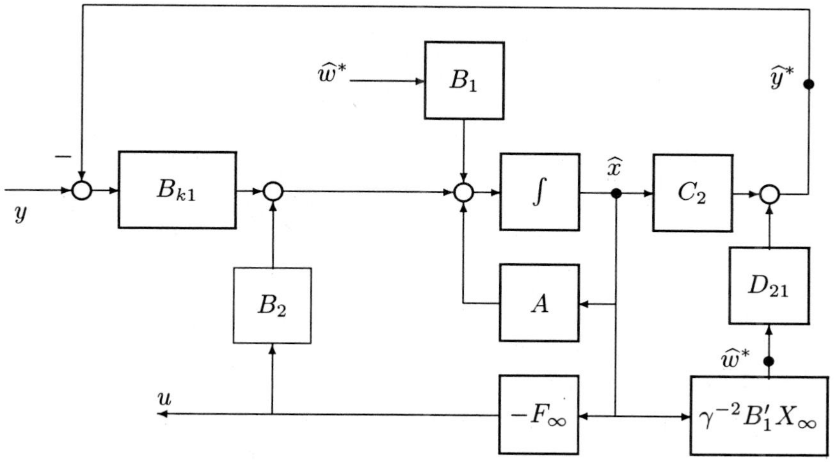

Figure 8.2: The central $\mathcal{H}_\infty$ controller.

Reformulation of the conditions

Although this analysis offers a complete solution to the finite-horizon, measurement feedback problem, we have not made use of Y_∞, the existence of which is necessary for the existence of a solution to the $\mathcal{H}_\infty$ measurement feedback problem. It must be that the existence of Y_∞ is necessary for the existence of Z_∞, and that the existence of Z_∞ is sufficient for the existence of Y_∞. In fact,

$$Z_\infty = Y_\infty(I - \gamma^{-2}X_\infty Y_\infty)^{-1} = (I - \gamma^{-2}Y_\infty X_\infty)^{-1}Y_\infty. \tag{8.2.21}$$

We summarize our results in the following theorem.

Theorem 8.2.1 *There exists a causal, linear measurement feedback controller for the time-varying plant defined by (8.1.1) to (8.1.3) that satisfies the objective (8.1.6) if and only if:*

1. *the Riccati differential equation (8.2.4) has a solution* X_∞ *on* $[0,T]$*;*

2. *the Riccati differential equation (8.2.8) has a solution* Y_∞ *on* $[0,T]$;

3. $\rho(X_\infty(t)Y_\infty(t)) < \gamma^2$ *for all* $t \in [0,T]$.[2]

If these conditions hold, $\boldsymbol{K}$ *is a causal, linear measurement feedback controller satisfying (8.1.6) if and only if* $\boldsymbol{K}$ *is given by the LFT (8.2.18) for some causal, linear* $\boldsymbol{U}$ *satisfying (8.2.19). The generator* $\boldsymbol{K}_a$ *is given by (8.2.20), with* Z_∞ *given by (8.2.21).*

Proof. We need to prove that Items 2 and 3 are equivalent to the existence of Z_∞.

Suppose Z_∞ exists. Since $X_\infty \geq 0$ and $Z_\infty \geq 0$, $I+\gamma^{-2}X_\infty Z_\infty$ is nonsingular for all $t \in [0,T]$. A calculation that is requested in Problem 8.4 shows that $Y_\infty = Z_\infty(I+\gamma^{-2}X_\infty Z_\infty)^{-1}$ is the solution to the Riccati equation (8.2.8). We also have

$$\begin{aligned} \rho(X_\infty Y_\infty) &= \rho\big(X_\infty Z_\infty(I+\gamma^{-2}X_\infty Z_\infty)^{-1}\big)) \\ &= \gamma^2 \frac{\rho(X_\infty Y_\infty)}{\gamma^2+\rho(X_\infty Y_\infty)} \\ &< \gamma^2. \end{aligned}$$

Conversely, if Items 2 and 3 are satisfied, then $I-\gamma^{-2}X_\infty Y_\infty$ is nonsingular and a calculation shows that $Z_\infty = Y_\infty(I-\gamma^{-2}X_\infty Y_\infty)^{-1}$ is the solution to (8.2.15). ∎

Main points of the section

1. If a solution to the $\mathcal{H}_\infty$ generalized regulator problem exists, then there exist solutions X_∞ and Y_∞ to the Riccati differential equations associated with the full-information $\mathcal{H}_\infty$ control problem and the $\mathcal{H}_\infty$ estimation of $C_1 x$ given y.
2. Any solution of the $\mathcal{H}_\infty$ generalized regulator problem is a $\mathcal{H}_\infty$ filter that estimates the full-information control law $u^* = -F_\infty x$ in such a way that

$$\sup_{w-w^* \in \mathcal{L}_2[0,T]} \frac{\|u-u^*\|_{2,[0,T]}}{\|w-w^*\|_{2,[0,T]}} < \gamma,$$

   with $w^* = \gamma^{-2}B_1'X_\infty x$.
3. A solution to the $\mathcal{H}_\infty$ generalized regulator problem exists if and only if X_∞ exists, Y_∞ exists and $\rho(X_\infty Y_\infty) < \gamma^2$.
4. The central controller is $u = -F_\infty \widehat{x}$, in which $\widehat{x}$ comes from an observer that assumes the exogenous signal is $\widehat{w}^* = \gamma^{-2}B_1'X_\infty \widehat{x}$, which is an estimate of the worst-case disturbance in $\mathcal{L}_2[0,T]$. The number of states in this controller is equal to the number of states in the generalized plant description.

---

[2] $\rho(\cdot)$ is the *spectral radius*: $\rho(Q) = \max_i |\lambda_i(Q)|$.

8.3 Infinite-horizon results

We now consider the time-invariant plant (8.1.1) to (8.1.3) and we assume that the standard assumptions hold. We seek an admissible controller (8.1.5) such that the closed-loop system $\boldsymbol{R}_{zw} = \mathcal{F}_\ell(\boldsymbol{P}, \boldsymbol{K})$ satisfies (8.1.7). In the infinite-horizon case, stability becomes an additional concern.

Internal stability

In this section, we note a fact concerning the internal stability of LFTs that can be found in Appendix A (see Lemma A.4.1).

Let (A_K, B_K, C_K, D_K) be a *minimal* realization of $\boldsymbol{K}$, and let the natural realization[3] of $\mathcal{F}_\ell(\boldsymbol{P}, \boldsymbol{K})$ be

$$\mathcal{F}_\ell(\boldsymbol{P}, \boldsymbol{K}) \stackrel{s}{=} \left[\begin{array}{c|c} A_{PK} & B_{PK} \\ \hline C_{PK} & D_{PK} \end{array}\right]. \tag{8.3.1}$$

(See Lemma 4.1.2 for more details.) Then $\boldsymbol{K}$ is admissible (*i.e.*, internally stabilizes $\boldsymbol{P}$) if and only if A_{PK} is asymptotically stable.

8.3.1 A necessary condition

If $\boldsymbol{K}$ is an admissible controller, A_{PK} is asymptotically stable, which implies that $x \in \mathcal{L}_2[0,\infty)$ for any $w \in \mathcal{L}_2[0,\infty)$ and any $x(0)$. Therefore, $\boldsymbol{K}\begin{bmatrix} C_2 & D_{21} \end{bmatrix}$ is a stabilizing, full-information controller. The existence of a stabilizing, full-information controller such that $\|\boldsymbol{R}_{zw}\|_\infty < \gamma$ implies that there is a solution to the algebraic Riccati equation

$$X_\infty \tilde{A} + \tilde{A}' X_\infty - X_\infty (B_2 B_2' - \gamma^{-2} B_1 B_1') X_\infty + \tilde{C}'\tilde{C} = 0 \tag{8.3.2}$$

such that $\tilde{A} - (B_2 B_2' - \gamma^{-2} B_1 B_1') X_\infty$ is asymptotically stable and $X_\infty \geq 0$. The matrices $\tilde{A}$ and $\tilde{C}$ are defined by (8.2.5) and (8.2.6) as before.

Furthermore, all internally-stable closed-loop systems that satisfy (8.1.7) are generated by

$$u - u^* = \tilde{\boldsymbol{U}}(w - w^*) \tag{8.3.3}$$

for some $\tilde{\boldsymbol{U}} \in \mathcal{H}_\infty$ such that $\|\tilde{\boldsymbol{U}}\|_\infty < \gamma$. In (8.3.3),

$$\begin{aligned} u^* &= -F_\infty x \\ F_\infty &= D_{12}' C_1 + B_2' X_\infty \\ w^* &= \gamma^{-2} B_1' X_\infty x. \end{aligned}$$

[3] The realization obtained by eliminating u and y

8.3.2 An equivalent problem

If u is generated by the measurement feedback $u = \boldsymbol{K}y$, then $\tilde{\boldsymbol{U}}$ in (8.3.3) is generated by the LFT

$$\tilde{\boldsymbol{U}} = \mathcal{F}_\ell(\boldsymbol{G}, \boldsymbol{K}), \tag{8.3.4}$$

in which the system $\boldsymbol{G}$ is given by

$$\boldsymbol{G} \stackrel{s}{=} \left[\begin{array}{c|cc} A + \gamma^{-2}B_1B_1'X_\infty & B_1 & B_2 \\ \hline F_\infty & 0 & I \\ C_2 + \gamma^{-2}D_{21}B_1'X_\infty & D_{21} & 0 \end{array}\right]. \tag{8.3.5}$$

We now establish that $\boldsymbol{K}$ stabilizes $\boldsymbol{P}$ and $\|\mathcal{F}_\ell(\boldsymbol{P}, \boldsymbol{K})\|_\infty < \gamma$ if and only if $\boldsymbol{K}$ stabilizes $\boldsymbol{G}$ and $\|\mathcal{F}_\ell(\boldsymbol{G}, \boldsymbol{K})\|_\infty < \gamma$.

Lemma 8.3.1 *Suppose $X_\infty \geq 0$ is the stabilizing solution to (8.3.2). The following are equivalent:*

1. *$\boldsymbol{K}$ is admissible for $\boldsymbol{P}$ and $\|\mathcal{F}_\ell(\boldsymbol{P}, \boldsymbol{K})\|_\infty < \gamma$;*
2. *$\boldsymbol{K}$ is admissible for $\boldsymbol{G}$ and $\|\mathcal{F}_\ell(\boldsymbol{G}, \boldsymbol{K})\|_\infty < \gamma$.*

Furthermore, for all λ,

$$\operatorname{rank}\begin{bmatrix} A + \gamma^{-2}B_1B_1'X_\infty - \lambda I & B_1 \\ C_2 + \gamma^{-2}D_{21}B_1'X_\infty & D_{21} \end{bmatrix} = \operatorname{rank}\begin{bmatrix} A - \lambda I & B_1 \\ C_2 & D_{21} \end{bmatrix}. \tag{8.3.6}$$

Proof. Let (A_K, B_K, C_K, D_K) be a minimal realization of $\boldsymbol{K}$, and let the natural realizations of $\mathcal{F}_\ell(\boldsymbol{P}, \boldsymbol{K})$ and $\mathcal{F}_\ell(\boldsymbol{G}, \boldsymbol{K})$ be (8.3.1) and

$$\mathcal{F}_\ell(\boldsymbol{G}, \boldsymbol{K}) \stackrel{s}{=} \left[\begin{array}{c|c} A_{GK} & B_{GK} \\ \hline C_{GK} & D_{GK} \end{array}\right]$$

respectively. An examination of these realizations shows that

$$\begin{aligned} &\begin{bmatrix} A_{GK} - \lambda I & B_{GK} \end{bmatrix} \\ &= \begin{bmatrix} A_{PK} - \lambda I & B_{PK} \end{bmatrix} \begin{bmatrix} I & 0 \\ \begin{bmatrix} \gamma^{-2}B_1'X_\infty & 0 \end{bmatrix} & I \end{bmatrix}, \end{aligned} \tag{8.3.7}$$

which is a restatement of the fact that $\boldsymbol{P}$ is driven by w and u, while $\boldsymbol{G}$ is driven by $w - w^*$ and u. (Problem 8.5 requests a verification of (8.3.7).)

Suppose Item 1 holds. Since $\boldsymbol{K}\begin{bmatrix} C_2 & D_{21} \end{bmatrix}$ is a stabilizing, full-information controller, we conclude from the parametrization of all full-information controllers that $\tilde{\boldsymbol{U}} = \mathcal{F}_\ell(\boldsymbol{G}, \boldsymbol{K}) \in \mathcal{RH}_\infty$ and $\|\mathcal{F}_\ell(\boldsymbol{G}, \boldsymbol{K})\|_\infty < \gamma$. We now show that the realization (A_{GK}, B_{GK}, C_{GK}) is stabilizable and detectable. By Lemma 4.1.2, any unobservable mode (A_{GK}, C_{GK}) is a zero of

$$\begin{bmatrix} A + \gamma^{-2}B_1B_1'X_\infty - \lambda I & B_2 \\ F_\infty & I \end{bmatrix}.$$

All such zeros are asymptotically stable, because they are the eigenvalues of $A - B_2F_\infty + \gamma^{-2}B_1B_1'X_\infty$, which are all in the closed-left-half plane, since X_∞ is the stabilizing solution to (8.3.2). By (8.3.7), any uncontrollable mode of (A_{GK}, B_{GK}) is an uncontrollable mode of (A_{PK}, B_{PK}); these modes are all stable since $\boldsymbol{K}$ stabilizes $\boldsymbol{P}$. Thus $(A_{GK}, B_{GK}, C_{GK}, D_{GK})$ is a stabilizable and detectable realization of the stable transfer function matrix $\mathcal{F}_\ell(\boldsymbol{G}, \boldsymbol{K})$. Hence A_{GK} is asymptotically stable, and we conclude that $\boldsymbol{K}$ is admissible for $\boldsymbol{G}$.

Suppose Item 2 holds. Then $\tilde{\boldsymbol{U}} = \mathcal{F}_\ell(\boldsymbol{G}, \boldsymbol{K}) \in \mathcal{RH}_\infty$ and $\|\tilde{\boldsymbol{U}}\|_\infty < \gamma$. By the parametrization of all stabilizing, full-information controllers, $u = -(F_\infty + \gamma^{-2}\tilde{\boldsymbol{U}}B_1'X_\infty)x + \tilde{\boldsymbol{U}}w$ is a stabilizing full-information controller, and we conclude that $\boldsymbol{K}$ stablizes $\boldsymbol{P}$.

Equation (8.3.6) follows from the identity

$$\begin{bmatrix} A + \gamma^{-2}B_1B_1'X_\infty - \lambda I & B_1 \\ C_2 + \gamma^{-2}D_{21}B_1'X_\infty & D_{21} \end{bmatrix} = \begin{bmatrix} A - \lambda I & B_1 \\ C_2 & D_{21} \end{bmatrix} \begin{bmatrix} I & 0 \\ \gamma^{-2}B_1'X_\infty & I \end{bmatrix}. \qquad \blacksquare$$

8.3.3 Necessary and sufficient conditions

Suppose that $X_\infty \geq 0$ is the stabilizing solution to (8.3.2). By Lemma 8.3.1, we may confine our attention to the problem of finding an admissible controller for $\boldsymbol{G}$ such that

$$\|\mathcal{F}_\ell(\boldsymbol{G}, \boldsymbol{K})\|_\infty < \gamma. \tag{8.3.8}$$

This is a closed-loop estimation problem—we seek an estimate of the control law $u = -F_\infty x$. By (8.1.9) and (8.3.6), $\boldsymbol{G}$ satisfies the assumptions required for the solution of this problem (see Problem 7.8). We conclude that an admissible $\boldsymbol{K}$ satisfying $\|\mathcal{F}_\ell(\boldsymbol{G}, \boldsymbol{K})\|_\infty < \gamma$ exists if and only if there is a solution to the algebraic Riccati equation

$$A_z Z_\infty + Z_\infty A_z' - Z_\infty(C_{2z}'C_{2z} - \gamma^{-2}F_\infty'F_\infty)Z_\infty + \bar{B}\bar{B}' = 0 \tag{8.3.9}$$

such that $A_z - Z_\infty(C_{2z}'C_{2z} - \gamma^{-2}F_\infty'F_\infty)$ is asymptotically stable and $Z_\infty \geq 0$. In this case, all admissible measurement feedback controllers satisfying (8.3.8), and hence also (8.1.7), are generated by

$$\boldsymbol{K} = \mathcal{F}_\ell(\boldsymbol{K}_a, \boldsymbol{U}), \qquad \boldsymbol{U} \in \mathcal{RH}_\infty, \ \|\boldsymbol{U}\|_\infty < \gamma. \tag{8.3.10}$$

The generator $\boldsymbol{K}_a$ is given by

$$\boldsymbol{K}_a \stackrel{s}{=} \left[\begin{array}{c|cc} A_k & B_{k1} & B_{k2} \\ \hline C_{k1} & 0 & I \\ C_{k2} & I & 0 \end{array}\right], \tag{8.3.11}$$

in which

$$\begin{aligned} A_k &= A + \gamma^{-2}B_1B_1'X_\infty - B_2F_\infty - B_{k1}C_{2z} \\ \begin{bmatrix} B_{k1} & B_{k2} \end{bmatrix} &= \begin{bmatrix} B_1D_{21}' + Z_\infty C_{2z}' & B_2 + \gamma^{-2}Z_\infty F_\infty' \end{bmatrix} \\ \begin{bmatrix} C_{k1} \\ C_{k2} \end{bmatrix} &= \begin{bmatrix} -F_\infty \\ -C_{2z} \end{bmatrix}. \end{aligned}$$

As in the finite-horizon case, we can rewrite everything in terms of a solution to the algebraic Riccati equation

$$\bar{A}Y_\infty + Y_\infty\bar{A}' - Y_\infty(C_2'C_2 - \gamma^{-2}C_1'C_1)Y_\infty + \bar{B}\bar{B}' = 0. \tag{8.3.12}$$

Theorem 8.3.2 *Suppose the standard assumptions hold. There exists an admissible* $\boldsymbol{K}$ *such that the closed-loop system* $\boldsymbol{R}_{zw} = \mathcal{F}_\ell(\boldsymbol{P}, \boldsymbol{K})$ *satisfies (8.1.7) if and only if:*

1. *there is a solution to the algebraic Riccati equation (8.3.2) such that* $\tilde{A} - (B_2B_2' - \gamma^{-2}B_1B_1')X_\infty$ *is asymptotically stable and* $X_\infty \geq 0$*;*
2. *there is a solution to the algebraic Riccati equation (8.3.12) such that* $\bar{A} - Y_\infty(C_2'C_2 - \gamma^{-2}C_1'C_1)$ *is asymptotically stable and* $Y_\infty \geq 0$*;*
3. $\rho(X_\infty Y_\infty) < \gamma^2$.

In case these conditions hold, $\boldsymbol{K}$ *is an admissible controller satisfying (8.1.7) if and only if* $\boldsymbol{K}$ *is given by the LFT (8.3.10). The generator* $\boldsymbol{K}_a$ *is given by (8.3.11) with* Z_∞ *given by*

$$Z_\infty = Y_\infty(I - \gamma^{-2}X_\infty Y_\infty)^{-1} = (I - \gamma^{-2}Y_\infty X_\infty)^{-1}Y_\infty.$$

Proof. We need to show that Items 2 and 3 are equivalent to the existence of a stabilizing, nonnegative definite Z_∞.

Suppose Z_∞ exists. Then $Y_\infty = Z_\infty(I + \gamma^{-2}X_\infty Z_\infty)^{-1}$ exists, is nonnegative definite (because X_∞ and Z_∞ are) and a calculation that is requested in Problem 8.2 shows that Y_∞ satisfies (8.3.12). The same argument as was used in the proof of the finite-horizon result shows that $\rho(X_\infty Y_\infty) < \gamma^2$. It remains to show that Y_∞ is the stabilizing solution. This follows from the identity

$$\begin{aligned} &\bar{A} - Y_\infty(C_2'C_2 - \gamma^{-2}C_1'C_1) \\ &= (I + \gamma^{-2}Z_\infty X_\infty)^{-1}(A_z - Z_\infty(C_{2z}'C_{2z} - \gamma^{-2}F_\infty'F_\infty)) \\ &\quad \times(I + \gamma^{-2}Z_\infty X_\infty), \end{aligned} \tag{8.3.13}$$

the verification of which is also requested in Problem 8.2.

Conversely, if Items 2 and 3 hold, then $Z_\infty = Y_\infty(I - \gamma^{-2}X_\infty Y_\infty)^{-1}$ exists, is nonnegative definite and satisfies (8.3.9). The identity (8.3.13) shows that it is the stabilizing solution to (8.3.9). ■

Main points of the section

1. A solution to the $\mathcal{H}_\infty$ generalized regulator problem exists if and only if there exist stabilizing, nonnegative definite solutions X_∞ and Y_∞ to the algebraic Riccati equations associated with the full-information $\mathcal{H}_\infty$ control problem and the $\mathcal{H}_\infty$ estimation of C_1x given y such that the coupling condition $\rho(X_\infty Y_\infty) < \gamma^2$ is satisfied.

2. Any solution of the $\mathcal{H}_\infty$ generalized regulator problem is a $\mathcal{H}_\infty$ filter that estimates the full-information control law $u^* = -F_\infty x$ in such a way that

$$\sup_{w-w^*\in\mathcal{L}_2[0,\infty)} \frac{\|u-u^*\|_2}{\|w-w^*\|_2} < \gamma,$$

with $w^* = \gamma^{-2}B_1'X_\infty x$.

3. The "central" controller has the same number of states as the generalized plant description.

8.4 Example

We conclude this chapter with a simple example, which illustrates the use of the generalized regulator. The system we will consider is the servomechanism illustrated in Figure 8.3, where the aim is to control the speed of the inertia J_2 by applying

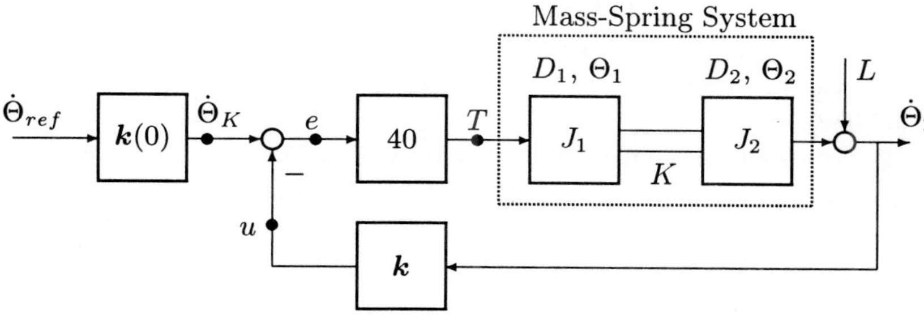

Figure 8.3: Mass-spring system, feedback controller and prefilter.

a controlled torque T to the inertia J_1. The control system is fed with a reference signal $\dot{\Theta}_{ref}$ and a speed measurement $\dot{\Theta}_2$. The drive motor is modelled by a simple gain of 40. The inertias J_1 and J_2 are coupled by a flexible shaft K. The damping coefficients associated with J_1 and J_2 are D_1 and D_2 respectively. Load variations are modelled as an additive disturbance L to $\dot{\Theta}_2$. Numerical values for the problem data are given Table 8.1 in mks units.

A torque balance on J_1 gives

$$\begin{aligned} T &= J_1\ddot{\Theta}_1 + D_1\dot{\Theta}_1 + K(\Theta_1 - \Theta_2) \\ \Rightarrow \quad \ddot{\Theta}_1 &= T/J_1 - \dot{\Theta}_1 D_1/J_1 - (\Theta_1 - \Theta_2)K/J_1, \end{aligned}$$

while a torque balance on J_2 yields

$$\begin{aligned} K(\Theta_1 - \Theta_2) &= J\ddot{\Theta}_2 + D_2\dot{\Theta}_2 \\ \Rightarrow \quad \ddot{\Theta}_2 &= (\Theta_1 - \Theta_2)K/J_2 - D_2\dot{\Theta}_2/J_2. \end{aligned}$$

J_1	1.0
J_2	2.0
D_1	0.01
D_2	0.02
K	30.0

Table 8.1: Problem data.

Combining these equations and defining $\Theta_e = \Theta_1 - \Theta_2$ gives

$$\begin{bmatrix} \ddot{\Theta}_1 \\ \ddot{\Theta}_2 \\ \dot{\Theta}_e \end{bmatrix} = \begin{bmatrix} -D_1/J_1 & 0 & -K/J_1 \\ 0 & -D_2/J_2 & K/J_2 \\ 1 & -1 & 0 \end{bmatrix} \begin{bmatrix} \dot{\Theta}_1 \\ \dot{\Theta}_2 \\ \Theta_e \end{bmatrix} + \begin{bmatrix} 40/J_1 \\ 0 \\ 0 \end{bmatrix} e$$

$$\dot{\Theta}_2 = \begin{bmatrix} 0 & 1 & 0 \end{bmatrix} \begin{bmatrix} \dot{\Theta}_1 \\ \dot{\Theta}_2 \\ \Theta_e \end{bmatrix},$$

which is the open-loop model $\boldsymbol{g}$ of the system. The open-loop frequency response is given in Figure 8.4, and the single shaft resonant frequency is clearly visible at 6.7082 rad/s.

One solution comes from evaluating a stabilizing controller that minimizes the transfer function matrix mapping $\begin{bmatrix} \dot{\Theta}_K \\ L \end{bmatrix}$ to $\begin{bmatrix} e \\ \dot{\Theta}_2 \end{bmatrix}$. This will ensure good tracking and load disturbance attenuation by keeping $\|e\|_2$ small. The mapping is given by the LFT

$$\begin{bmatrix} e \\ \dot{\Theta}_2 \\ \dot{\Theta}_2 \end{bmatrix} = \begin{bmatrix} 1 & 0 & -1 \\ \boldsymbol{g} & 1 & -\boldsymbol{g} \\ \boldsymbol{g} & 1 & -\boldsymbol{g} \end{bmatrix} \begin{bmatrix} \dot{\Theta}_K \\ L \\ u \end{bmatrix},$$

$$u = \boldsymbol{k}\dot{\Theta}_2.$$

Solving the two Riccati equations associated with this generalized regulator problem reveals that:

1. The optimum norm is $\gamma_{opt} = 3.8856$.

2. The optimal controller is

$$\boldsymbol{k}_{opt} \stackrel{s}{=} \left[\begin{array}{cc|c} 6.3057 & 33.3704 & 8.0177 \\ -16.2572 & -31.6275 & -11.3415 \\ \hline 4.2992 & 10.5358 & 3.6283 \end{array}\right]$$

$$= \frac{3.6283s^2 + 6.8628s + 88.0362}{s^2 + 25.3218s + 343.0775}.$$

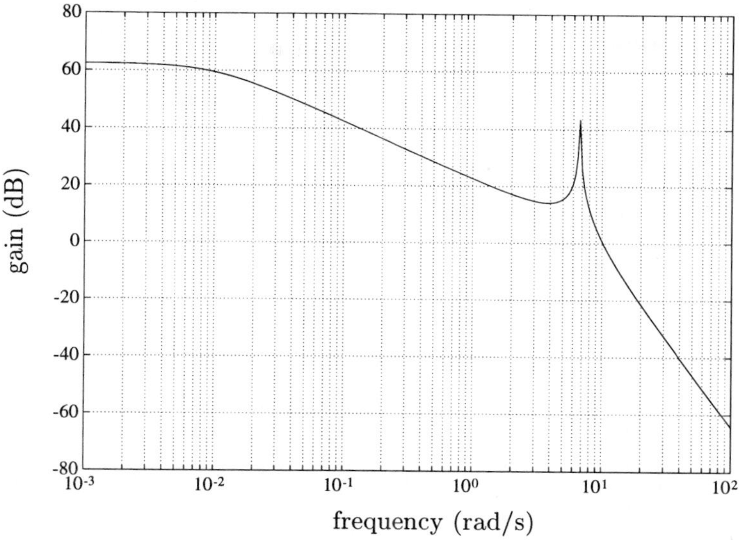

Figure 8.4: Open loop frequency response.

3. The closed-loop poles are -5.4056, $-2.6297 \pm j8.4329$ and $-7.3384 \pm j8.4702$.

Notice that the optimal controller has degree two, in contrast to central suboptimal controllers, which have degree three. We will have more to say about the solution and properties of optimal controllers in Chapter 11.

The design is completed by introducing the prefilter $\boldsymbol{k}(0) = 0.2566$. If the steady-state value of the speed is $\dot{\Theta}_{2ss}$, then $\boldsymbol{k}(0)\dot{\Theta}_{2ss} \approx \boldsymbol{k}(0)\dot{\Theta}_2$, implying that $\dot{\Theta}_{2ss} \approx \dot{\Theta}_2$. This follows from the fact that the steady-state torque required to overcome the inertial damping is low. In the case of no inertial damping, the system introduces its own integral action, thereby completely eliminating the steady-state error. This follows because, in this case, the steady-state torque is zero and $\dot{\Theta}_{2ss} = \dot{\Theta}_2$. Figure 8.5 shows the closed-loop step responses of the system—the solid curve is $\dot{\Theta}_2$ and the dashed curve is e. It is clear that the feedback system provides a fast and accurate closed-loop response.

It follows from Figure 8.3 that

$$\dot{\Theta}_2 - \dot{\Theta}_{ref} = \left((1 + \boldsymbol{gk})^{-1}\boldsymbol{gk}(0) - 1\right)\dot{\Theta}_{ref}.$$

Figure 8.6 shows a Bode magnitude plot of this transfer function, which indicates that the closed loop has good low-frequency tracking properties.

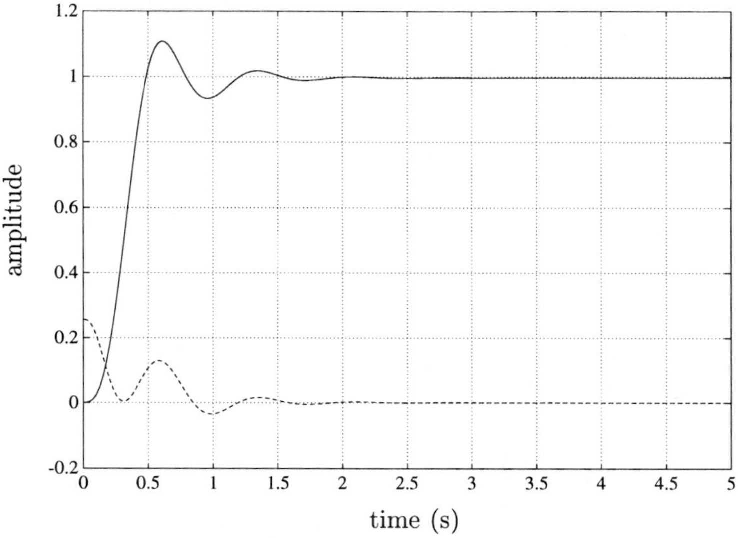

Figure 8.5: Closed-loop step responses, $\dot{\Theta}_2$ (solid) and e (dashed).

8.5 Notes and References

It has been known for some time that the $\mathcal{H}_\infty$ generalized regulator problem could be reduced to an approximation or "general distance" problem known as the four-block problem [52, 36, 65]. A solution based on Davis, Kahan and Weinberger [39] involved a reduction to the classical Nehari extension problem, the solution of which is given by Adamjan, Arov and Krein [1, 2]. A state-space solution to the Nehari (and other) approximation problems given by Glover [71] completed this solution method.

Unfortunately, the cumbersome chain of factorizations required in this methodology involves Riccati equations of increasing dimension and the procedure was slow, unreliable, and resulted in controllers which tended to have high state dimension. The prospect of a simpler solution was raised by Limebeer and Hung [134], Limebeer and Halikias [132] and Limebeer and Anderson [129], who showed that optimal controllers of degree one less than that of the generalized plant could be found (for one- and two-block problems).[4] Explicit solutions to some specific $\mathcal{H}_\infty$ optimization problems, such as Glover [73] and Kwakernaak [123], also supported the view

[4]The generator of all solutions to the suboptimal synthesis problem has degree equal to the degree of the generalized plant. In the optimal case, which is considered in Chapter 11, we will see that the generator of all optimal solutions may have lower degree.

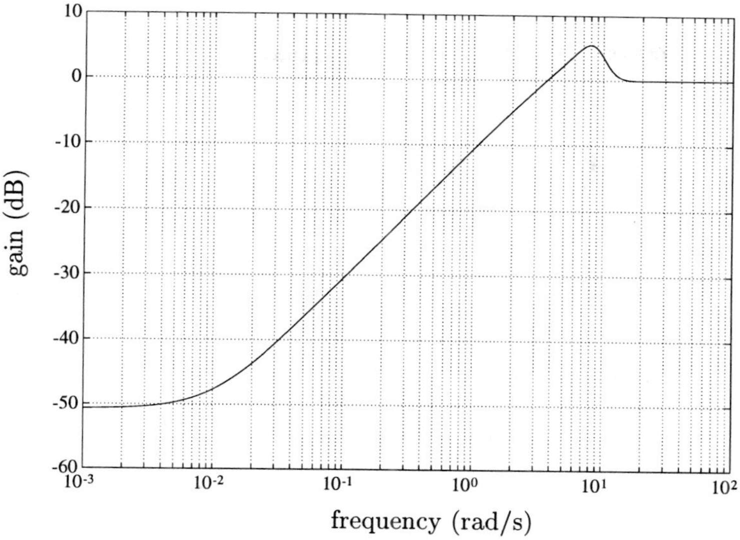

Figure 8.6: Magnitude frequency response of the tracking error transfer function.

that a simpler and more elegant solution to the $\mathcal{H}_\infty$ generalized regulator problem might exist. The work of Ball and Cohen [23] provided the first reasonably simple solution, based on J-spectral factorization ideas, involving three Riccati equations.

The "two Riccati equation" solution to the $\mathcal{H}_\infty$ generalized regulator problem was first presented in Glover and Doyle [76]. The proof based on the four-block problem is due to Glover, Limebeer, Doyle, Kasenally, Jaimoukha and Safonov [78, 135]. Independently, Hung [97, 98] obtained a solution in terms of two Riccati equations based on a model matching problem.

The approach using full-information $\mathcal{H}_\infty$ control and an $\mathcal{H}_\infty$ filter estimating the full-information controller is due to Doyle, Glover, Khargonekar and Francis [54]. Since the controller formulas in this work were already known, the substantive contribution is the methodology, which precipitated a move away from algebraic methods that offer little control engineering insight. The paper provides intuitive remarks concerning "a worst-case input for the full information problem" and it points out that the measurement feedback controller "is actually the optimal filter ... for estimating the full information control input, in the presence of this worst-case input" ([54], page 838; see also page 840). Their solution is based on the theory of mixed Hankel-plus-Toeplitz operators; they use some of the language of game theory, but not its methods.

Tadmor [204] obtained a solution to the infinite-horizon problem based on the maximum principle.

The solution of the time-varying problem was developed using the theory of linear quadratic differential games by Limebeer, Anderson, Khargonekar and Green [130] and Ravi, Nagpal and Khargonekar [169].

The long-established connection between $\mathcal{H}_\infty$ optimization and J-spectral factorization (see Francis [65]) suggested that this approach might also yield the "two Riccati equation" formulas (Glover and Doyle [76]). This J-spectral factorization approach was developed in Green, Glover, Limebeer and Doyle [85] and Green [84]. There are close connections between this approach and the separation arguments of Doyle, Glover, Khargonekar and Francis [54]. Since the J-spectral factorization approach is based on transfer function matrices, the discrete-time case is easily handled with almost no additional effort (Green [84]). We will have more to say about the discrete-time case in Appendix B. Kwakernaak [124] has developed a polynomial approach to $\mathcal{H}_\infty$ control based on J-spectral factorization. Another approach closely related to the J-spectral factorization methods is the J-lossless conjugation method of Kimura, Lu and Kawatani [120].

Extensions of the theory to singular problems were given by Stoorvogel [199], while problems involving imaginary axis zeros were treated by Scherer [193].

The monographs by Başar and Bernhard [20], which concentrates on the discrete-time case, and Stoorvogel [201] contain expository treatments of $\mathcal{H}_\infty$ controller synthesis theory.

8.6 Problems

Problem 8.1.

1. Show that $\rho(A) < 1$ implies $I - A$ is nonsingular.
2. Suppose $A \geq 0$. Show that

$$\rho(A(I+A)^{-1}) = \rho(A)/(1+\rho(A)).$$

Problem 8.2. Define

$$H_Y = \begin{bmatrix} \bar{A}' & -(C_2'C_2 - \gamma^{-2}C_1'C_1) \\ -\bar{B}\bar{B}' & -\bar{A} \end{bmatrix}$$

and

$$H_Z = \begin{bmatrix} A_z' & -(C_{2z}'C_{2z} - \gamma^{-2}F_\infty'F_\infty) \\ -\bar{B}\bar{B}' & -A_z \end{bmatrix}.$$

1. Suppose X_∞ is the stabilizing solution to (8.3.2). Show that

$$\begin{bmatrix} I & \gamma^{-2}X_\infty \\ 0 & I \end{bmatrix} H_Z \begin{bmatrix} I & -\gamma^{-2}X_\infty \\ 0 & I \end{bmatrix} = H_Y. \tag{8.6.1}$$

2. Show that the stabilizing solution to (8.3.9) exists if Y_∞, the stabilizing solution to (8.3.12), exists and satisfies $\rho(X_\infty Y_\infty) < \gamma^2$. Show that in this case $Z_\infty = Y_\infty(I - \gamma^{-2}X_\infty Y_\infty)^{-1}$ is the stabilizing solution to (8.3.9).
3. Verify (8.3.13).

Problem 8.3. Show that the Riccati differential equation

$$\dot{P} = A'P + PA - PDP + Q, \qquad P(0) = M, \tag{8.6.2}$$

has a solution on [0,T] if and only if there exists an X such that the boundary value problem

$$\begin{bmatrix} P_1 \\ P_2 \end{bmatrix} X - \begin{bmatrix} A & -D \\ -Q & -A' \end{bmatrix} \begin{bmatrix} P_1 \\ P_2 \end{bmatrix} = \frac{d}{dt} \begin{bmatrix} P_1 \\ P_2 \end{bmatrix} \tag{8.6.3}$$

has a solution on $[0, T]$ with P_1 nonsingular for all $t \in [0, T]$ and $P_2(0)P_1^{-1}(0) = M$. In this case, show that $P = P_2P_1^{-1}$ is a solution to (8.6.2) and that

$$\begin{bmatrix} I \\ P \end{bmatrix} (A - DP) - \begin{bmatrix} A & -D \\ -Q & -A' \end{bmatrix} \begin{bmatrix} I \\ P \end{bmatrix} = \begin{bmatrix} 0 \\ \dot{P} \end{bmatrix}.$$

Problem 8.4. Suppose X_∞ satisfies (8.2.4).
1. If Z_∞ satisfies (8.2.15), show that $Y_\infty = Z_\infty(I + \gamma^{-2}X_\infty Z_\infty)^{-1}$ exists and satisfies (8.2.8). Furthermore, show that $\rho(X_\infty Y_\infty) < \gamma^2$.
2. If Y_∞ satisfies (8.2.8) and $\rho(X_\infty Y_\infty) < \gamma^2$, show the Riccati equation (8.2.15) has the solution $Z_\infty = Y_\infty(I - \gamma^{-2}X_\infty Y_\infty)^{-1}$.

Problem 8.5. Verify the decomposition indicated by equation (8.3.7).

Note: The next few problems are concerned with special cases of the generalized regulator problem for which a formula for the optimal infinity norm can be derived—the minimum may be determined via an eigenvalue calculation. The simple measurement feedback problems considered on page 288 have the feature that the objective signal $z = C_1x + u$ can be arbitrarily selected via the choice of u. In addition, the measurement $y = C_2x + w$ enables complete reconstruction of w and x from y and $x(0)$. When the objective and the measurement are both of this simple form, an explicit eigenvalue formula can be obtained for the optimal performance level γ. The dependence of the controller on γ can also be determined explicitly. We consider the finite-horizon case first, followed by the problems of maximizing the robustness margin for additive model errors, complementary sensitivity minimization and sensitivity minimization. We conclude with the general infinite-horizon problem with this special structure.

Problem 8.6. We consider the general "one-block" generalized regulator problem which is characterized by the off-diagonal blocks of the generalized plant being square. By assuming that the loop shifting and scaling transformations described in Section 4.6 have been carried out, we may suppose, without loss of generality, that the generalized plant $\boldsymbol{P}$ is of the form:

$$\begin{bmatrix} \dot{x} \\ z \\ y \end{bmatrix} = \begin{bmatrix} A & B_1 & B_2 \\ C_1 & 0 & I \\ C_2 & I & 0 \end{bmatrix} \begin{bmatrix} x \\ w \\ u \end{bmatrix}. \tag{8.6.4}$$

1. Show that the controller

$$\begin{aligned} \dot{\widehat{x}} &= A\widehat{x} + B_2 u + B_1(y - C_2\widehat{x}) \\ u^* &= -C_1\widehat{x} \end{aligned}$$

makes the closed-loop mapping from w to z identically zero. Now show that $\boldsymbol{U}$ is the closed-loop system mapping w to z generated by the controller

$$\begin{aligned} \begin{bmatrix} \dot{\widehat{x}} \\ u \\ \widehat{w} \end{bmatrix} &= \begin{bmatrix} A - B_1C_2 - B_2C_1 & B_1 & B_2 \\ -C_1 & 0 & I \\ -C_2 & I & 0 \end{bmatrix} \begin{bmatrix} \widehat{x} \\ y \\ u - u^* \end{bmatrix} \\ u - u^* &= \boldsymbol{U}\widehat{w}. \end{aligned}$$

By observing that the controller inverts the plant, conclude that any desired closed loop can be achieved.

2. Show that for any $\gamma \geq 0$, there exists a causal, linear controller such that the closed-loop system $\boldsymbol{R} : w \mapsto z$ satisfies $\|\boldsymbol{R}\|_{[0,T]} \leq \gamma$.
3. In the infinite-horizon problem, we must consider internal stability issues. Show that if $A - B_1C_2$ and $A - B_2C_1$ are asymptotically stable, then there exists a stabilizing controller such that $\|\boldsymbol{R}\|_\infty \leq \gamma$ for any $\gamma \geq 0$. (Hint: Use Lemma 4.1.2 to show that any cancellations which occur between the generalized plant and the controller must be stable.)

Problem 8.7. Consider the feedback loop shown in Figure 8.7. We seek a controller $\boldsymbol{K}$ that stablizes the loop for all stable $\boldsymbol{A}$ such that $\gamma(\boldsymbol{A}) \leq \nu$. ($\gamma(\cdot)$ is the incremental gain.)

1. Show that the generalized plant for this problem is

$$\boldsymbol{P} = \begin{bmatrix} 0 & I \\ I & \boldsymbol{G} \end{bmatrix}.$$

2. Suppose

$$\boldsymbol{G} = \boldsymbol{G}_- + \boldsymbol{G}_+ \stackrel{s}{=} \left[\begin{array}{cc|c} A_- & 0 & B_- \\ 0 & A_+ & B_+ \\ \hline C_- & C_+ & 0 \end{array}\right],$$

in which A_+ and $-A_-$ are asymptotically stable, and (A_-, B_-, C_-) is minimal. If P and Q are the controllability and observability gramians of $\boldsymbol{G}_-$, show that

$$X_\infty = \begin{bmatrix} -P^{-1} & 0 \\ 0 & 0 \end{bmatrix} \quad \text{and} \quad Y_\infty = \begin{bmatrix} -Q^{-1} & 0 \\ 0 & 0 \end{bmatrix}$$

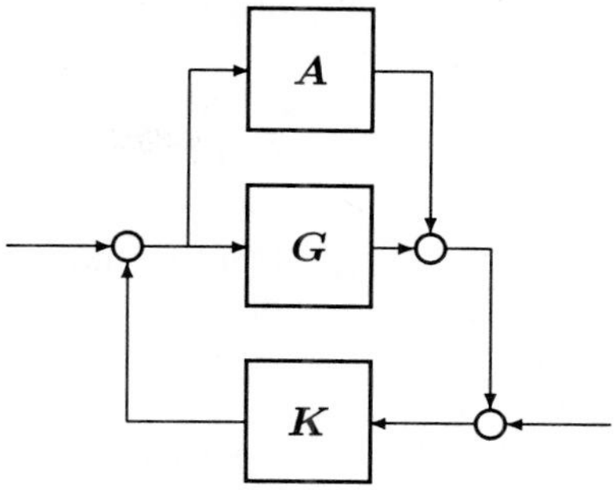

Figure 8.7: Feedback loop with additive model error.

are the stabilizing, nonnegative definite solutions to (8.3.2) and (8.3.12).

3. Conclude that a necessary and sufficient condition for the existence of a controller that achieves the robust stability objective is

$$\nu \le \min_i \{\lambda_i(PQ)\}^{\frac{1}{2}}.$$

4. If $\nu < \min_i\{\lambda_i(PQ)\}^{\frac{1}{2}}$, find a controller that robustly stabilizes the feedback configuration in Figure 8.7 for any stable $\boldsymbol{A}$ such that $\gamma(\boldsymbol{A}) \le \nu$.

Problem 8.8. As an example of the solution to the robust stability synthesis problem given in Problem 8.7, we obtain the controller which optimizes $\|\boldsymbol{k}(1 - \boldsymbol{gk})^{-1}\|_\infty$, with $\boldsymbol{g} = \frac{1}{(s-1)^2}$. The solution was used in Example 2.4.2.

1. If $\boldsymbol{g}$ has realization

$$\boldsymbol{g} \overset{s}{=} \left[\begin{array}{cc|c} 1 & 1 & 0 \\ 0 & 1 & 1 \\ \hline 1 & 0 & 0 \end{array}\right],$$

show that the Riccati equation solutions are

$$X_\infty = 4\begin{bmatrix} 2 & 1 \\ 1 & 1 \end{bmatrix}, \qquad Y_\infty = 4\begin{bmatrix} 1 & 1 \\ 1 & 2 \end{bmatrix}.$$

2. Hence show that

$$\gamma_{opt} = \min_{\boldsymbol{k} \text{ stabilizing}} \|k(1 - gk)^{-1}\|_\infty = 4\sqrt{3 + 2\sqrt{2}}.$$

Problem 8.9. We now consider the complementary sensitivity problem of finding $\gamma_{opt} = \inf_{\boldsymbol{K} \text{ stabilizing}} \|\boldsymbol{GK}(I - \boldsymbol{GK})^{-1}\|_\infty$, which is associated with robust stability with respect to multiplicative model errors and the attenuation of sensor errors.

1. Show that the generalized plant for this problem is

$$\boldsymbol{P} = \begin{bmatrix} 0 & \boldsymbol{G} \\ I & \boldsymbol{G} \end{bmatrix} \stackrel{s}{=} \left[\begin{array}{c|cc} A & 0 & B \\ \hline C & 0 & D \\ C & I & D \end{array}\right].$$

For the remainder of the problem, assume that D is nonsingular.

2. Show that the standard assumption are that (A, B, C) are stabilizable and detectable, and that A and $\tilde{A} = A - BD^{-1}C$ have no eigenvalues on the imaginary axis.
3. Show that the LQG Riccati equations for this problem are

$$\begin{aligned} X\tilde{A} + \tilde{A}'X - X(BD^{-1})(BD^{-1})'X &= 0 \\ AY + YA' - YC'CY &= 0. \end{aligned}$$

4. Show that the $\mathcal{H}_\infty$ Riccati equations for this problem are

$$\begin{aligned} \tilde{A}'X_\infty + X_\infty\tilde{A} - X_\infty(BD^{-1})(BD^{-1})'X_\infty &= 0 \\ AY_\infty + Y_\infty A' - (1-\gamma^{-2})Y_\infty C'CY_\infty &= 0. \end{aligned}$$

Conclude that $X_\infty = X$ and $Y_\infty = Y(1-\gamma^{-2})^{-1}$.

5. What is γ_{opt} when $\boldsymbol{G}$ is stable?
6. When $\boldsymbol{G}$ has at least one closed-right-half-plane pole, show that the lowest achievable infinity norm for the complementary sensitivity problem is $\gamma_{opt} = \sqrt{1+\rho(XY)}$.
7. In the case that $\boldsymbol{G}$ has at least one closed-right-half-plane pole, but has no zeros there, explain why $\gamma_{opt} = 1$.

Problem 8.10. The first $\mathcal{H}_\infty$ control problem to receive widespread attention was the sensitivity minimization problem of finding $\inf_{\boldsymbol{K}} \|(I-\boldsymbol{GK})^{-1}\|_\infty$, in which the infimum is taken over the class of stabilizing controllers.

1. Show that the generalized plant for this problem is

$$\boldsymbol{P} = \begin{bmatrix} I & \boldsymbol{G} \\ I & \boldsymbol{G} \end{bmatrix}.$$

Show that a realization of this generalized plant is

$$\begin{bmatrix} \dot{x} \\ z \\ y \end{bmatrix} = \left[\begin{array}{c|cc} A & 0 & B \\ \hline C & I & D \\ C & I & D \end{array}\right] \begin{bmatrix} x \\ w \\ u \end{bmatrix}.$$

For the rest of the problem assume that D is nonsingular.

2. Consider the controller $\tilde{\boldsymbol{K}} = (I-D\boldsymbol{K})^{-1}$ and the generalized plant $\tilde{\boldsymbol{P}}$ defined by

$$\begin{bmatrix} \dot{x} \\ z \\ \tilde{y} \end{bmatrix} = \begin{bmatrix} \tilde{A} & -BD^{-1} & BD^{-1} \\ 0 & 0 & I \\ C & I & 0 \end{bmatrix} \begin{bmatrix} x \\ w \\ \tilde{u} \end{bmatrix},$$

in which $\tilde{A} = A - BD^{-1}C$. Show that $\mathcal{F}_\ell(\boldsymbol{P},\boldsymbol{K}) = \mathcal{F}_\ell(\tilde{\boldsymbol{P}},\tilde{\boldsymbol{K}})$ and that $\boldsymbol{K}$ stabilizes $\boldsymbol{P}$ if and only if $\tilde{\boldsymbol{K}}$ stabilizes $\tilde{\boldsymbol{P}}$.

3. Show that the standard assumptions are that (A, B, C) are stabilizable and detectable, and that A and $\tilde{A} = A - BD^{-1}C$ have no eigenvalues on the imaginary axis.
4. Show that the Riccati equations associated with the LQG problem of minimizing $\|\mathcal{F}_\ell(\tilde{\boldsymbol{P}},\tilde{\boldsymbol{K}})\|_2$ are

$$\begin{aligned} X\tilde{A} + \tilde{A}'X - X(BD^{-1})(BD^{-1})'X &= 0 \\ AY + YA' - YC'CY &= 0. \end{aligned}$$

5. Show that the Riccati equations associated with the $\mathcal{H}_\infty$ generalized regulator problem $\|\mathcal{F}_\ell(\tilde{\boldsymbol{P}},\tilde{\boldsymbol{K}})\|_\infty < \gamma$ are

$$\begin{aligned} X_\infty\tilde{A} + \tilde{A}'X_\infty - (1-\gamma^{-2})X_\infty(BD^{-1})(BD^{-1})'X_\infty &= 0 \\ AY_\infty + Y_\infty A' - Y_\infty C'CY_\infty &= 0. \end{aligned}$$

Hence show that $Y_\infty = Y$ and that $X_\infty = X(1-\gamma^{-2})^{-1}$.

6. Give two possible reasons why $\gamma_{opt} = 0$ when $\boldsymbol{G}^{-1} \in \mathcal{RH}_\infty$.
7. If $\boldsymbol{G}$ has at least one closed-right-half-plane zero, show that

$$\gamma_{opt} = \sqrt{1+\rho(XY)}.$$

Problem 8.11. We suppose that the generalized plant given in Problem 8.6 is described by the time-invariant realization (8.6.4) and we assume that the standard assumptions hold. Note that, in this case, the full-rank-on-the-axis conditions are equivalent to $\tilde{A} = A - B_2C_1$ and $\bar{A} = A - B_1C_2$ having no eigenvalues on the imaginary axis.

1. Show that the Riccati equations associated with the LQG version of this problem are

$$\begin{aligned} X\tilde{A} + \tilde{A}'X - XB_2B_2'X &= 0 \\ \bar{A}Y + Y\bar{A}' - YC_2'C_2Y &= 0. \end{aligned}$$

Show that the Riccati equations for the $\mathcal{H}_\infty$ version of the problem are

$$\begin{aligned} X_\infty\tilde{A} + \tilde{A}'X_\infty - X_\infty(B_2B_2' - \gamma^{-2}B_1B_1')X_\infty &= 0 \\ \bar{A}Y_\infty + Y_\infty\bar{A}' - Y_\infty(C_2'C_2 - \gamma^{-2}C_1'C_1)Y_\infty &= 0. \end{aligned}$$

2. Show that X is nonsingular if and only if $-\tilde{A}$ is asymptotically stable. In this case, let W be the solution to the linear equation

$$-\tilde{A}W - W\tilde{A}' + B_1B_1' = 0.$$

Show that a stabilizing solution $X_\infty \geq 0$ exists if and only if $\rho(WX) < \gamma^2$.

(Hint: $X_\infty^{-1} = X^{-1} - \gamma^{-2}W$.)
Using a similar analysis for Y_∞, obtain spectral radius condition for the existence of Y_∞ in terms of the solution to the linear equation

$$-V\bar{A} - \bar{A}'V + C_1'C_1 = 0.$$

3. Suppose $-\tilde{A}$ and $-\bar{A}$ are asymptotically stable. Show that there exists a stabilizing controller $\boldsymbol{K}$ such that $\|\mathcal{F}_\ell(\boldsymbol{P}, \boldsymbol{K})\|_\infty < \gamma$ if and only if

$$\Pi(\gamma) = \begin{bmatrix} Y^{-1} - \gamma^{-2}V & \gamma^{-1}I \\ \gamma^{-1}I & X^{-1} - \gamma^{-2}W \end{bmatrix} > 0.$$

Now show that

$$\begin{bmatrix} \gamma^2 I & -\gamma X \\ 0 & \gamma X \end{bmatrix} \Pi(\gamma) \begin{bmatrix} Y & 0 \\ 0 & \gamma I \end{bmatrix} = \gamma^2 \begin{bmatrix} I & 0 \\ 0 & I \end{bmatrix} - \begin{bmatrix} VY + XY & -XW \\ -XY & XW \end{bmatrix}.$$

Conclude that the least value of γ for which a suitable controller exists can be determined via an eigenvalue calculation.
Can you obtain a similar result for the case when $-\tilde{A}$ and $-\bar{A}$ are not assumed to be asymptotically stable?

Problem 8.12. We consider another important controller synthesis problem for which an eigenvalue formula for the optimal performance level can be given. The problem is to find a controller that minimizes the norm of the system mapping $\begin{bmatrix} w' & v' \end{bmatrix}'$ to $\begin{bmatrix} y' & u' \end{bmatrix}'$ in the configuration shown below:

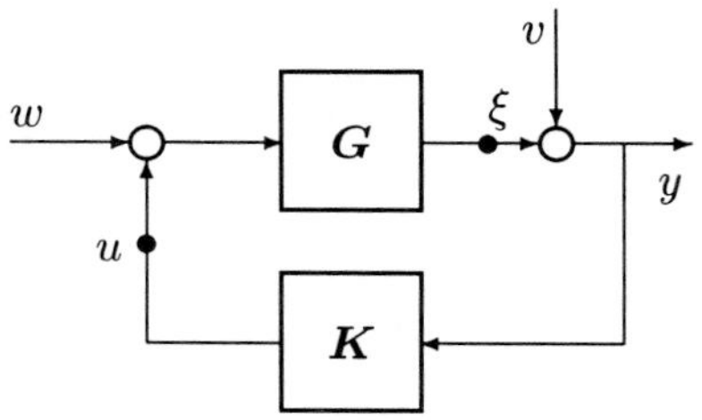

1. Show that the generalized plant is given by

$$\boldsymbol{P} = \left[\begin{array}{cc|c} \boldsymbol{G} & I & \boldsymbol{G} \\ 0 & 0 & I \\ \hline \boldsymbol{G} & I & \boldsymbol{G} \end{array}\right].$$

Show that the closed-loop system is

$$\mathcal{F}_\ell(\boldsymbol{P}, \boldsymbol{K}) = \begin{bmatrix} I \\ \boldsymbol{K} \end{bmatrix} (I - \boldsymbol{G}\boldsymbol{K})^{-1} \begin{bmatrix} \boldsymbol{G} & I \end{bmatrix}.$$

We are therefore interested in finding

$$\gamma_{opt} = \inf_{\boldsymbol{K} \text{ stabilizing}} \left\| \begin{bmatrix} I \\ \boldsymbol{K} \end{bmatrix} (I - \boldsymbol{G}\boldsymbol{K})^{-1} \begin{bmatrix} \boldsymbol{G} & I \end{bmatrix} \right\|_{\infty}.$$

This problem is associated with normalized coprime factor, or gap metric, robustness optimization; $1/\gamma_{opt}$ is the optimal stability margin for the normalized coprime factor model error representation.[5]
Show that when $\boldsymbol{G} = C(sI - A)^{-1}B$, the generalized plant has realization

$$\boldsymbol{P} \stackrel{s}{=} \left[\begin{array}{c|cc} A & \begin{bmatrix} B & 0 \end{bmatrix} & B \\ \hline \begin{bmatrix} C \\ 0 \end{bmatrix} & \begin{bmatrix} 0 & I \\ 0 & 0 \end{bmatrix} & \begin{bmatrix} 0 \\ I \end{bmatrix} \\ C & \begin{bmatrix} 0 & I \end{bmatrix} & 0 \end{array}\right].$$

2. Show that $\gamma_{opt} \geq 1$. (Hint: consider the closed-loop transfer function at infinite frequency.) This means that the stability margin for normalized coprime factor uncertainty must always lie between zero and one. Show also that the 2-norm of $\mathcal{F}_\ell(\boldsymbol{P}, \boldsymbol{K})$ is infinite.
3. Using the loop transformations of Section 4.6, show that $\|\mathcal{F}_\ell(\boldsymbol{P}, \boldsymbol{K})\|_\infty < \gamma$ if and only if $\|\mathcal{F}_\ell(\widehat{\boldsymbol{P}}, \boldsymbol{K})\|_\infty < \gamma$, in which

$$\widehat{\boldsymbol{P}} \stackrel{s}{=} \left[\begin{array}{c|cc} A & \begin{bmatrix} -B & 0 \end{bmatrix} & B \\ \hline \begin{bmatrix} (1-\gamma^{-2})^{-\frac{1}{2}}C \\ 0 \end{bmatrix} & \begin{bmatrix} 0 & 0 \\ 0 & 0 \end{bmatrix} & \begin{bmatrix} 0 \\ I \end{bmatrix} \\ (1-\gamma^{-2})^{-\frac{1}{2}}C & \begin{bmatrix} 0 & -I \end{bmatrix} & 0 \end{array}\right].$$

4. Show that the standard assumptions reduce to (A, B, C) stabilizable and detectable, and that the the Riccati equations associated with the sysnthesis of controllers $\boldsymbol{K}$ such that $\|\mathcal{F}_\ell(\widehat{\boldsymbol{P}}, \boldsymbol{K})\|_\infty < \gamma$ are

$$\begin{aligned} X_\infty A + A'X_\infty - (1-\gamma^{-2})X_\infty BB'X_\infty + (1-\gamma^{-2})^{-1}C'C &= 0 \\ AY_\infty + Y_\infty A' - Y_\infty C'CY_\infty + BB' &= 0. \end{aligned}$$

5. Show that the LQG Riccati equations associated with the problem of minimizing the 2-norm of the closed-loop system mapping $\begin{bmatrix} w' & v' \end{bmatrix}'$ to $\begin{bmatrix} \xi' & u' \end{bmatrix}'$ are

$$\begin{aligned} XA + A'X - XBB'X + C'C &= 0 \\ AY + YA' - YC'CY + BB' &= 0. \end{aligned}$$

[5]The normalized coprime factor robustness problem is discussed in Chapter 12; see also [206, 79, 148, 70].

6. Show that $X_\infty = X(1-\gamma^{-2})^{-1}$ and $Y_\infty = Y$ and hence deduce that

$$\gamma_{opt} = \sqrt{1+\rho(XY)}.$$

7. For $\gamma > \gamma_{opt}$, show that the controller given by the descriptor system

$$\begin{aligned} W\dot{\widehat{x}} &= (W(A-BB'X) - \gamma^2 YC'C)\widehat{x} + \gamma^2 YC'y \\ u &= -B'X\widehat{x}, \end{aligned}$$

in which $W = (\gamma^2-1)I - YX$, achieves the objective $\|\mathcal{F}_\ell(\boldsymbol{P},\boldsymbol{K})\|_\infty < \gamma$.
8. In the case that $\boldsymbol{g} = \frac{1}{s}$, show that $\gamma_{opt} = \sqrt{2}$. This problem is the robust stabilization of an integrator in the gap metric or normalized coprime factor sense. It shows that the optimal stability margin for normalized coprime factor model error representation is $1/\sqrt{2}$. Show that the optimal controller is $\boldsymbol{k} = -1$ (*i.e.*, $u = -y$) and that the singular values of the optimal closed-loop transfer function are $\sqrt{2}$ and zero, for all frequencies.

Problem 8.13. Using suitable computer software[6] verify the optimal controllers given in Section 8.4 and Example 2.4.2.

Problem 8.14. Consider the generalized plant $\boldsymbol{P}$ described by

$$\boldsymbol{P} \stackrel{s}{=} \left[\begin{array}{c|cc} A & B_1 & B_2 \\ \hline C_1 & D_{11} & D_{12} \\ C_2 & D_{21} & D_{22} \end{array}\right].$$

It is assumed that (A, B_2, C_2) is stabilizable and detectable, but no other assumptions are imposed.

Show that $\boldsymbol{K}$ is admissible for $\boldsymbol{P}$ and $\|\mathcal{F}_\ell(\boldsymbol{P},\boldsymbol{K})\|_\infty < \gamma$ if and only if $\boldsymbol{K}$ is admissible for $\boldsymbol{P}_a$ and $\|\mathcal{F}_\ell(\boldsymbol{P}_a,\boldsymbol{K})\|_\infty < \gamma$, for some

$$\boldsymbol{P}_a \stackrel{s}{=} \left[\begin{array}{c|cc} A & B_{1a} & B_2 \\ \hline C_{1a} & D_{11a} & D_{12a} \\ C_2 & D_{21a} & D_{22} \end{array}\right]$$

that satisfies the standard assumptions.

(Hint: See Section 6.3.4.)

[6]The Robust Control Toolbox (see [35]) and MATLAB, for example. MATLAB is a registered trademark of The MathWorks, Inc.

9

Model Reduction by Truncation

9.1 Introduction

The approximation of high-order plant and controller models by models of lower-order is an integral part of control system design. Until relatively recently model reduction was often based on physical intuition. For example, chemical engineers often assume that mixing is instantaneous and that packed distillation columns may be modelled using discrete trays. Electrical engineers represent transmission lines and the eddy currents in the rotor cage of induction motors by lumped circuits. Mechanical engineers remove high-frequency vibration modes from models of aircraft wings, turbine shafts and flexible structures. It may also be possible to replace high-order controllers by low-order approximations with little sacrifice in performance.

The next three chapters develop several procedures which seek to automate the model reduction process. Suppose a high-order, linear, time-invariant model $\boldsymbol{G}$ is given, then the prototype $\mathcal{L}_\infty$ model reduction problem is to find a low-order approximation $\widehat{\boldsymbol{G}}$ of $\boldsymbol{G}$ such that $\|\boldsymbol{G} - \widehat{\boldsymbol{G}}\|_\infty$ is small. In Chapter 11, we consider the more difficult problem of selecting $\widehat{\boldsymbol{G}}$ such that $\|\boldsymbol{W}_1(\boldsymbol{G}-\widehat{\boldsymbol{G}})\boldsymbol{W}_2\|_\infty$ is small; the weighting functions $\boldsymbol{W}_1$ and $\boldsymbol{W}_2$ are used to frequency shape the model reduction error. For example, one might select the weights so that the modelling error is small in the unity gain range of frequencies.

Truncation methods of model reduction seek to remove, or truncate, unimportant states from state-space models. If a state-space model has its A-matrix in Jordan canonical form, state-space truncation will amount to classical modal truncation. For example, one may truncate all those states that correspond to "fast modes"—eigenvalues with a large negative real part. One's interpretation of "fast" will obviously depend on the application, but this could mean modes outside the control system bandwidth. Since the poles of the truncated model are a subset of the poles of the original high-order model, any low-order modal approximation of a stable high-order model is guaranteed to be stable. As we will show later, it is also possible to get a bound on $\|\boldsymbol{G} - \widehat{\boldsymbol{G}}\|_\infty$ for modal truncation. Because any transfer function can be realized in terms of an infinite number of state-space models, there are, in principle, also an infinite number of candidate truncation schemes. For a truncation scheme to be useful, it must preserve stability and carry with it a guaranteed error bound. The aim of this chapter is to develop the balanced truncation method of model reduction, which satisfies an infinity norm bound on the absolute approximation error.

It is well known that the modes of a realization that are either uncontrollable or unobservable do not appear in the corresponding system transfer function matrix. It is therefore natural to conjecture that the modes that are almost uncontrollable and unobservable can be omitted from the realization with little effect on the input-output characteristics of the model. The balanced realization has the property that mode i is equally controllable and observable, with these properties measured in terms of a number $\sigma_i \geq 0$. As σ_i increases, the corresponding level of controllability and observability increases. In Chapter 10 we will show that these σ_i's are the singular values of the Hankel operator associated with the transfer function matrix $\boldsymbol{G}$. The model reduction method that applies the truncation operation to a balanced realization is known as balanced truncation. For this algorithm the absolute error is guaranteed to satisfy the twice-the-sum-of-the-tail bound

$$\|\boldsymbol{G} - \widehat{\boldsymbol{G}}\|_\infty \leq 2(\sigma_{r+1} + \ldots + \sigma_n),$$

in which n is the McMillan degree of $\boldsymbol{G}$ and r is the McMillan degree of $\widehat{\boldsymbol{G}}$.

Example 9.1.1. The transfer function

$$\boldsymbol{g} = \frac{1}{(s+1)(s+2)}$$

has modal realization $\boldsymbol{g} = C_m(sI - A_m)^{-1}B_m$, in which

$$\begin{aligned} A_m &= \begin{bmatrix} -1 & 0 \\ 0 & -2 \end{bmatrix}, \quad B_m = \begin{bmatrix} 1 \\ -1 \end{bmatrix}, \\ C_m &= \begin{bmatrix} 1 & 1 \end{bmatrix}. \end{aligned}$$

If we truncate the fast mode we obtain the reduced-order system

$$\boldsymbol{g}_m = \frac{1}{s+1}.$$

The norm of the error is

$$\|\boldsymbol{g} - \boldsymbol{g}_m\|_\infty = \|\frac{1}{s+2}\|_\infty = \frac{1}{2}.$$

The transfer function g also has realization $g = C_b(sI - A_b)^{-1}B_b$, in which

$$\begin{aligned} A_b &= \begin{bmatrix} -0.40859 & -0.970143 \\ 0.970143 & -2.59141 \end{bmatrix}, \qquad B_b = \begin{bmatrix} 0.492479 \\ -0.492479 \end{bmatrix}, \\ C_b &= \begin{bmatrix} 0.492479 & 0.492479 \end{bmatrix}. \end{aligned}$$

This realization is balanced because the controllability and observability gramians are both equal and diagonal:

$$\Sigma = \begin{bmatrix} 0.296796 & 0 \\ 0 & 0.0467961 \end{bmatrix},$$

so that $\sigma_1 = 0.296796$ and $\sigma_2 = 0.0467961$. If we truncate this realization, we obtain the reduced-order system

$$g_b = \frac{(0.492479)^2}{s + 0.40859},$$

which is stable and the norm of the error is

$$\begin{aligned} \|g - g_b\|_\infty &= 0.0935921 \\ &= 2\sigma_2. \end{aligned}$$

The point to note is that, in this case, the error associated with balanced truncation is considerably smaller than that associated with modal truncation. The generally good performance of balanced truncation has led to its widespread popularity. ∇

Another well known model order reduction method is the singular perturbation approximation. This technique is usually associated with a fast-slow decomposition of the state space, with the approximation achieved by setting the "fast" states to their steady-state values. Since the singular perturbation approximation is related to state-space truncation by the frequency inversion transformation $s \to 1/s$, it is also considered to be a truncation method. Our main interest is in balanced singular perturbation approximation, in which the singular perturbation method is applied to a balanced realization. In this method, states corresponding to small σ_i's are set to their steady-state values.

Although the error bounds for balanced truncation and balanced singular perturbation approximation are identical, the resulting models have different high- and low-frequency characteristics. Direct truncation gives a good model match at high frequency, while singular perturbation methods have superior low-frequency properties. We will develop most of our theory for direct truncation because of its notational simplicity.

9.2 State-space truncation

Consider a linear, time-invariant system with the realization

$$\begin{aligned} \dot{x}(t) &= Ax(t) + Bu(t), \qquad x(0) = x_0, \\ y(t) &= Cx(t) + Du(t) \end{aligned} \tag{9.2.1}$$

and divide the state vector x into components to be retained and components to be discarded:

$$x(t) = \begin{bmatrix} x_1(t) \\ x_2(t) \end{bmatrix}. \tag{9.2.2}$$

The r-vector $x_1(t)$ contains the components to be retained, while the $(n-r)$-vector x_2 contains the components to be discarded. Now partition the matrices A, B and C conformably with x to obtain

$$\begin{aligned} A &= \begin{bmatrix} A_{11} & A_{12} \\ A_{21} & A_{22} \end{bmatrix}, \qquad B = \begin{bmatrix} B_1 \\ B_2 \end{bmatrix}, \\ C &= \begin{bmatrix} C_1 & C_2 \end{bmatrix}. \end{aligned} \tag{9.2.3}$$

By omitting the states and dynamics associated with $x_2(t)$, we obtain the lower-order system

$$\begin{aligned} \dot{p}(t) &= A_{11}p(t) + B_1u(t) \qquad p(0) = p_0, \\ q(t) &= C_1p(t) + Du(t). \end{aligned}$$

The rth-order *truncation* of the realization (A, B, C, D) is given by

$$\mathcal{T}_r(A, B, C, D) = (A_{11}, B_1, C_1, D). \tag{9.2.4}$$

In general, very little can be said about the relationship between x and p, y and q or the transfer function matrices $\boldsymbol{G}$ and $\widehat{\boldsymbol{G}}$ associated with (A, B, C, D) and (A_{11}, B_1, C_1, D). In particular, the truncated system may be unstable even if the full-order system is stable, and the truncated system realization may be nonminimal even if the full-order realization is minimal. One thing that clearly does hold is

$$\widehat{\boldsymbol{G}}(\infty) = \boldsymbol{G}(\infty),$$

which means that all reduced-order models obtained by truncation have perfect matching at infinite frequency.

Example 9.2.1. (Modal Truncation). The truncation of modal realizations is common in engineering practise, because it is often the case that high-frequency modes may be neglected on physical grounds, or because the phenomena resulting in such modes only play a secondary role in determining the model's essential characteristics.

Let $\boldsymbol{G}$ be a transfer function matrix with an asymptotically stable modal realization

$$\begin{aligned} A &= \begin{bmatrix} \lambda_1 & 0 & 0 \\ 0 & \ddots & 0 \\ 0 & 0 & \lambda_m \end{bmatrix}, \qquad B = \begin{bmatrix} B_1 \\ \vdots \\ B_m \end{bmatrix}, \\ C &= \begin{bmatrix} C_1 & \dots & C_m \end{bmatrix} \end{aligned}$$

For simplicity, we assume that each of the eigenvalues λ_i of the A-matrix has a simple Jordan structure. If the modes with a fast decay rate may be omitted from the model, the eigenvalues should be ordered so that $|\mathrm{R}_e(\lambda_i)|$ is nondecreasing with increasing i. Alternatively, if one is to omit the high-frequency modes, the eigenvalues should be ordered so that $|\mathrm{I}_m(\lambda_i)|$ is nondecreasing with increasing i. As a combination of these two, one might order the modes so that $|\lambda_i|$ is nondecreasing with increasing i, so that those modes with the highest "natural" frequency are deleted.

The error incurred in modal truncation depends not only on the λ_i's, but also on the size of the residues C_iB_i. If modes labeled $r+1$ to n are omitted by truncation to obtain $\widehat{\boldsymbol{G}}$, we have

$$\boldsymbol{G} - \widehat{\boldsymbol{G}} = \sum_{i=r+1}^{n} \frac{C_iB_i}{s-\lambda_i}$$

and therefore that

$$\|\boldsymbol{G} - \widehat{\boldsymbol{G}}\|_\infty \leq \sum_{i=r+1}^{n} \frac{\|C_iB_i\|}{|\mathrm{R}_e\lambda_i|}.$$

Since the error associated with deleting a mode depends on the ratio $\|C_iB_i\|/|\mathrm{R}_e\lambda_i|$ and not $|\mathrm{R}_e\lambda_i|$ alone, the modal decay rate is not a reliable guide as to whether a particular mode should be included in the reduced-order model.

The main features of modal truncation are:

1. It is conceptually simple.
2. The poles of the reduced-order model are a subset of the poles of the original model. In addition, the poles of the reduced-order model retain their physical interpretation, because one knows, for example, that certain vibration modes are being retained while others are being omitted.
3. It is computationally cheap, because the main calculation is an eigenvalue decomposition of A. ∇

9.2.1 The truncation error

To help us with later work, in which we develop bounds for the error incurred by model reduction based on truncation, we develop some of the basic properties of the error system.

Lemma 9.2.1 *Suppose (A, B, C, D) is a realization of order n partitioned as in (9.2.3) and let $\boldsymbol{G} = D + C(sI - A)^{-1}B$ and $\widehat{\boldsymbol{G}} = D + C_1(sI - A_{11})^{-1}B_1$. Define*

$$\begin{aligned} \tilde{\boldsymbol{A}}(s) &= A_{22} + A_{21}(sI - A_{11})^{-1}A_{12} \\ \tilde{\boldsymbol{B}}(s) &= B_2 + A_{21}(sI - A_{11})^{-1}B_1 \\ \tilde{\boldsymbol{C}}(s) &= C_2 + C_1(sI - A_{11})^{-1}A_{12}. \end{aligned} \qquad (9.2.5)$$

Then:

1. $\det(sI - A) = \det(sI - A_{11})\det(sI - \tilde{\boldsymbol{A}}(s))$.
2. *The truncation error system satisfies*

$$\boldsymbol{G}(s) - \widehat{\boldsymbol{G}}(s) = \tilde{\boldsymbol{C}}(s)(sI - \tilde{\boldsymbol{A}}(s))^{-1}\tilde{\boldsymbol{B}}(s). \tag{9.2.6}$$

3. *If* $AP + PA' + BB' = 0$ *and* $P = \begin{bmatrix} P_1 & 0 \\ 0 & P_2 \end{bmatrix}$, *in which the partitioning is conformable with (9.2.3), then*

$$\begin{aligned} A_{11}P_1 + P_1A_{11}' + B_1B_1' &= 0 && (9.2.7)\\ \tilde{\boldsymbol{A}}(s)P_2 + P_2\tilde{\boldsymbol{A}}^{\sim}(s) + \tilde{\boldsymbol{B}}(s)\tilde{\boldsymbol{B}}^{\sim}(s) &= 0. && (9.2.8)\end{aligned}$$

   If (A, B) *is controllable, then* $\begin{bmatrix} sI - \tilde{\boldsymbol{A}}(s) & \tilde{\boldsymbol{B}}(s) \end{bmatrix}$ *has full row rank for all* s.

4. *If* $A'Q + QA + C'C = 0$ *and* $Q = \begin{bmatrix} Q_1 & 0 \\ 0 & Q_2 \end{bmatrix}$, *in which the partitioning is conformable with (9.2.3), then*

$$\begin{aligned} A_{11}'Q_1 + Q_1A_{11} + C_1'C_1 &= 0 && (9.2.9)\\ \tilde{\boldsymbol{A}}^{\sim}(s)Q_2 + Q_2\tilde{\boldsymbol{A}}(s) + \tilde{\boldsymbol{C}}^{\sim}(s)\tilde{\boldsymbol{C}}(s) &= 0. && (9.2.10)\end{aligned}$$

   If (A, C) *is observable, then* $\begin{bmatrix} sI - \tilde{\boldsymbol{A}}(s) \\ \tilde{\boldsymbol{C}}(s) \end{bmatrix}$ *has full column rank for all* s.

Proof. Write $\boldsymbol{\Phi}(s) = (sI - A_{11})^{-1}$ and note that

$$\begin{aligned} sI - A &= \begin{bmatrix} I & 0 \\ -A_{21}\boldsymbol{\Phi}(s) & I \end{bmatrix}\begin{bmatrix} sI - A_{11} & 0 \\ 0 & sI - \tilde{\boldsymbol{A}}(s) \end{bmatrix}\\ &\quad \times \begin{bmatrix} I & -\boldsymbol{\Phi}(s)A_{12} \\ 0 & I \end{bmatrix}. \end{aligned} \tag{9.2.11}$$

1. This follows directly from (9.2.11).
2. From (9.2.11), we have

$$\begin{aligned} &C(sI - A)^{-1}B \\ &= \begin{bmatrix} C_1 & C_2 \end{bmatrix}\begin{bmatrix} I & \boldsymbol{\Phi}(s)A_{12} \\ 0 & I \end{bmatrix}\begin{bmatrix} \boldsymbol{\Phi}(s) & 0 \\ 0 & (sI - \tilde{\boldsymbol{A}}(s))^{-1} \end{bmatrix}\\ &\quad \times \begin{bmatrix} I & 0 \\ A_{21}\boldsymbol{\Phi}(s) & I \end{bmatrix}\begin{bmatrix} B_1 \\ B_2 \end{bmatrix}\\ &= C_1\boldsymbol{\Phi}(s)B_1 + \tilde{\boldsymbol{C}}(s)(sI - \tilde{\boldsymbol{A}}(s))^{-1}\tilde{\boldsymbol{B}}(s), \end{aligned}$$

   which proves (9.2.6).

3. Equation (9.2.7) is immediate from the assumed block diagonal structure of P. To prove (9.2.8), write

$$BB' = (sI - A)P + P(-sI - A)'.$$

Now use (9.2.11) to obtain

$$\begin{bmatrix} B_1 \\ \tilde{\boldsymbol{B}}(s) \end{bmatrix} \begin{bmatrix} B_1' & \tilde{\boldsymbol{B}}'(-s) \end{bmatrix}$$

$$= \begin{bmatrix} sI - A_{11} & -A_{12} \\ 0 & sI - \tilde{\boldsymbol{A}}(s) \end{bmatrix} \begin{bmatrix} P_1 & P_1\boldsymbol{\Phi}'(-s)A_{21}' \\ 0 & P_2 \end{bmatrix}$$

$$+ \begin{bmatrix} P_1 & 0 \\ A_{21}\boldsymbol{\Phi}(s)P_1 & P_2 \end{bmatrix} \begin{bmatrix} -sI - A_{11}' & 0 \\ -A_{12}' & -sI - \tilde{\boldsymbol{A}}'(-s) \end{bmatrix}.$$

The $(2,2)$-block of this equation is (9.2.8). We also note that if x is such that

$$x^* \begin{bmatrix} sI - \tilde{\boldsymbol{A}}(s) & \tilde{\boldsymbol{B}}(s) \end{bmatrix} = 0$$

for some s, then

$$\begin{bmatrix} 0 & x^* \end{bmatrix} \begin{bmatrix} I & 0 \\ A_{21}\boldsymbol{\Phi}(s) & I \end{bmatrix} \begin{bmatrix} sI - A & B \end{bmatrix} = 0$$

and we see that (A, B) controllable implies $x = 0$. Hence $\begin{bmatrix} sI - \tilde{\boldsymbol{A}}(s) & \tilde{\boldsymbol{B}}(s) \end{bmatrix}$ has full row rank when (A, B) is controllable.

4. This follows from calculations which are dual to those given in Item 3. ■

9.2.2 Singular perturbation approximation

The steady-state error associated with state-space truncation is given by

$$\boldsymbol{G}(0) - \widehat{\boldsymbol{G}}(0) = C_1 A_{11}^{-1} B_1 - CA^{-1}B.$$

In applications requiring good low-frequency models this may be unacceptably large. In these cases, it is appropriate to use a singular perturbation approximation in preference to state-space truncation because of its greatly improved low-frequency model reduction characteristics.

Consider the full-order model given by

$$\begin{aligned} \dot{x}(t) &= Ax(t) + Bu(t), \qquad x(0) = x_0, \\ y(t) &= Cx(t) + Du(t), \end{aligned}$$

which is partitioned as in (9.2.2) and (9.2.3). If $x_2(t)$ represents the fast dynamics of the system, we may approximate the low-frequency behavior by setting $\dot{x}_2(t) = 0$. This gives

$$0 = A_{21}x_1(t) + A_{22}x_2(t) + B_2u(t),$$

which yields the quasi-steady-state solution

$$x_2(t) = -A_{22}^{-1}(A_{21}x_1(t) + B_2u(t)) \tag{9.2.12}$$

provided A_{22} is nonsingular. Eliminating x_2 from the remaining equations using (9.2.12) yields

$$\begin{aligned}\dot{p}(t) &= (A_{11} - A_{12}A_{22}^{-1}A_{21})p(t) + (B_1 - A_{12}A_{22}^{-1}B_2)u(t)\\ q(t) &= (C_1 - C_2A_{22}^{-1}A_{21})p(t) + (D - C_2A_{22}^{-1}B_2)u(t).\end{aligned}$$

The rth-order *singular perturbation approximation* (SPA) is given by

$$\mathcal{S}_r(A, B, C, D) = (\widehat{A}_{11}, \widehat{B}_1, \widehat{C}_1, \widehat{D}), \tag{9.2.13}$$

in which

$$\begin{aligned}\widehat{A}_{11} &= A_{11} - A_{12}A_{22}^{-1}A_{21}, & \widehat{B}_1 &= B_1 - A_{12}A_{22}^{-1}B_2,\\ \widehat{C}_1 &= C_1 - C_2A_{22}^{-1}A_{21}, & \widehat{D} &= D - C_2A_{22}^{-1}B_2.\end{aligned} \tag{9.2.14}$$

The following result shows that SPA is equivalent to: (a) setting $\boldsymbol{H}(w) = \boldsymbol{G}(w^{-1})$; (b) performing a state-space truncation of $\boldsymbol{H}(w)$ to obtain $\widehat{\boldsymbol{H}}(w)$; and (c) defining the reduced-order model as $\widehat{\boldsymbol{G}}(s) = \widehat{\boldsymbol{H}}(s^{-1})$.

Lemma 9.2.2 *Let $\boldsymbol{G}(s) = D + C(sI - A)^{-1}B$, in which A is nonsingular, and let $\boldsymbol{H}(w) = \boldsymbol{G}(w^{-1})$. Then:*

1. $\boldsymbol{H}(w) = D - CA^{-1}B - CA^{-1}(wI - A^{-1})^{-1}A^{-1}B.$
2. *The realizations of $\boldsymbol{G}(s)$ and $\boldsymbol{H}(w)$ have the same controllability and observability gramians (when they exist).*
3. *Suppose that A_{22} is nonsingular, that $\boldsymbol{G}_r(s)$ is the rth-order SPA of $\boldsymbol{G}(s)$ and that $\boldsymbol{H}_r(w)$ is the rth-order system obtained by truncation of the realization of $\boldsymbol{H}(w)$ defined in Item 1. Then $\boldsymbol{G}_r(s) = \boldsymbol{H}_r(s^{-1})$.*

Proof.

1. This follows from the identity

$$(w^{-1}I - A)^{-1} = -A^{-1} - A^{-1}(wI - A^{-1})^{-1}A^{-1}.$$

2. Suppose P and Q are the controllability and observability gramians of the realization of $\boldsymbol{G}$ satisfying

$$\begin{aligned}AP + PA' + BB' &= 0\\ A'Q + QA + C'C &= 0.\end{aligned}$$

Multiplying by A^{-1} and $(A^{-1})'$ gives

$$\begin{aligned}A^{-1}P + P(A^{-1})' + (A^{-1}B)(A^{-1}B)' &= 0\\ QA^{-1} + (A^{-1})'Q + (CA^{-1})'(CA^{-1}) &= 0.\end{aligned}$$

3. Writing

$$A = \begin{bmatrix} I & A_{12}A_{22}^{-1} \\ 0 & I \end{bmatrix} \begin{bmatrix} \widehat{A}_{11} & 0 \\ 0 & A_{22} \end{bmatrix} \begin{bmatrix} I & 0 \\ A_{22}^{-1}A_{21} & I \end{bmatrix}$$

gives

$$A^{-1} = \begin{bmatrix} I & 0 \\ -A_{22}^{-1}A_{21} & I \end{bmatrix} \begin{bmatrix} \widehat{A}_{11}^{-1} & 0 \\ 0 & A_{22}^{-1} \end{bmatrix} \begin{bmatrix} I & -A_{12}A_{22}^{-1} \\ 0 & I \end{bmatrix}.$$

Now truncate the realization of $\boldsymbol{H}(w)$:

$$\begin{aligned} \begin{bmatrix} I & 0 \end{bmatrix} A^{-1} \begin{bmatrix} I \\ 0 \end{bmatrix} &= \widehat{A}_{11}^{-1} \\ \begin{bmatrix} I & 0 \end{bmatrix} A^{-1}B &= \widehat{A}_{11}^{-1}\widehat{B}_1 \\ -CA^{-1} \begin{bmatrix} I \\ 0 \end{bmatrix} &= -\widehat{C}_1\widehat{A}_{11}^{-1} \\ D - CA^{-1}B &= \widehat{D} - \widehat{C}_1\widehat{A}_{11}^{-1}\widehat{B}_1. \end{aligned}$$

Applying Item 1 to the realization of $\boldsymbol{G}_r$ given in (9.2.13), $\boldsymbol{H}_r(w) = \boldsymbol{G}_r(w^{-1})$, which is equivalent to $\boldsymbol{G}_r(s) = \boldsymbol{H}_r(s^{-1})$. ■

Since the singular perturbation and truncation operations are related in a straightforward way, it suffices to develop all our theoretical results for state-space truncation. When the low-frequency fidelity of the approximation is important, the singular perturbation approximation is the method of choice. Conversely, direct truncation should be preferred when good high-frequency modelling is the central concern.

Main points of the section

1. State-space truncation is a simple but general procedure for generating reduced-order models. The properties of the reduced-order model will depend on the realization selected for truncation. For example, reduced-order models obtained from the truncation of balanced and modal realizations (of the same full-order system) will generally be quite different.
2. State-space truncation produces zero error at infinite frequency.
3. Since the singular perturbation method of model reduction is related to state-space truncation by the bilinear transform $s \to 1/s$, singular perturbation approximations have zero steady-state error.

9.3 Balanced realization

The aim of this section is to introduce balanced realizations, which are of interest because they have good absolute-error truncation properties.

9.3.1 Model reduction motivation

Suppose we are given a $\boldsymbol{G} \in \mathcal{RH}_\infty$ and our aim is to produce a reduced-order model $\widehat{\boldsymbol{G}} \in \mathcal{RH}_\infty$ that approximates $\boldsymbol{G}$. A natural criterion with which to measure the absolute error is $\|\boldsymbol{G} - \widehat{\boldsymbol{G}}\|_\infty$.

If we drive $\boldsymbol{G}$ and $\widehat{\boldsymbol{G}}$ with the same input u, we get

$$y = \boldsymbol{G}u, \qquad \widehat{y} = \widehat{\boldsymbol{G}}u$$

and therefore that

$$\|\boldsymbol{G} - \widehat{\boldsymbol{G}}\|_\infty = \sup_{u \in \mathcal{L}_2} \frac{\|y - \widehat{y}\|_2}{\|u\|_2}. \tag{9.3.1}$$

If $\boldsymbol{G} = D + C(sI - A)^{-1}B$, then

$$\begin{aligned} \dot{x} &= Ax + Bu \\ y &= Cx + Du. \end{aligned}$$

We assume that A is asymptotically stable (*i.e.*, $\mathrm{R}_e\lambda_i(A) < 0$). For $\|\boldsymbol{G} - \widehat{\boldsymbol{G}}\|_\infty$ to be small, the identity given in (9.3.1) suggests we should delete those components of the state-vector x that are least involved in the energy transfer from the input u to the output y. This observation leads us to consider two closely related questions:

1. What is the output energy resulting from a given initial state $x(0) = x_0$?
2. What is the minimum input energy required to bring the state from zero to the given initial state $x(0) = x_0$?

The solutions are well known:

1. Suppose $x(0) = x_0$ is given and that $u(t) = 0$ for $t \geq 0$. By Theorem 3.1.1, the $\mathcal{L}_2[0, \infty)$ norm of y is given by $\|y\|_2^2 = x_0'Qx_0$, in which Q is the observability gramian.
2. Consider the LQ problem

$$\min_{u \in \mathcal{L}_2(-\infty, 0]} \int_{-\infty}^{0} u'(t)u(t)dt$$

subject to $\dot{x} = Ax + Bu$ with $x(0) = x_0$. This is equivalent to

$$\min_{v \in \mathcal{L}_2[0, \infty)} \int_{0}^{\infty} v'(\tau)v(\tau)\, d\tau$$

subject to

$$\frac{d}{d\tau}p(\tau) = -Ap(\tau) - Bv(\tau), \qquad p(0) = x_0,$$

with $\tau = -t$, $p(\tau) = x(t)$ and $v(\tau) = u(t)$. By standard LQ theory (see Chapter 5), the optimal control is $v(\tau) = B'Xp(\tau)$ and

$$\min_v \int_0^\infty v'(\tau)v(\tau)\,d\tau = x_0'Xx_0,$$

in which X is the solution to

$$-XA - A'X - XBB'X = 0$$

such that $-A - BB'X$ is asymptotically stable.

If (A, B) is controllable and P is the controllability gramian satisfying

$$AP + PA' + BB' = 0,$$

then P is invertible and

$$-P^{-1}A - A'P^{-1} - P^{-1}BB'P^{-1} = 0.$$

Furthermore $-A-BB'P^{-1} = PA'P^{-1}$, which is asymptotically stable. Hence $X = P^{-1}$ and we conclude that the optimal control is $u(t) = B'P^{-1}x(t)$ and that

$$\min_{u\in\mathcal{L}_2(-\infty,0]:x(0)=x_0} \int_{-\infty}^0 u(t)'u(t)\,dt = x_0'P^{-1}x_0.$$

Combining the answers to our two questions we get

$$\begin{aligned}\max_{u\in\mathcal{L}_2(-\infty,0]:x(0)=x_0} \frac{\int_0^\infty y'(t)y(t)\,dt}{\int_{-\infty}^0 u'(t)u(t)\,dt} &= \frac{x_0'Qx_0}{x_0'P^{-1}x_0} \\ &= \frac{\alpha'P^{\frac{1}{2}}QP^{\frac{1}{2}}\alpha}{\alpha'\alpha}, \qquad x_0 = P^{\frac{1}{2}}\alpha.\end{aligned} \tag{9.3.2}$$

These calculations suggest that in order to keep $\|\boldsymbol{G}-\widehat{\boldsymbol{G}}\|_\infty$ small, the state-space for the truncated system should be the space spanned by the eigenvectors corresponding to the larger eigenvalues of $P^{\frac{1}{2}}QP^{\frac{1}{2}}$. That is, we should truncate a realization in which $P^{\frac{1}{2}}QP^{\frac{1}{2}}$ is diagonal, with the eigenvalues ordered in descending order.

9.3.2 Balanced realization

In the last section we argued that an appropriate realization for absolute-error model reduction is one in which $P^{\frac{1}{2}}QP^{\frac{1}{2}}$ is diagonal. We now show that these realizations, known as a balanced realizations, always exist for asymptotically stable minimal realizations. The following is the most commonly used definition of a balanced realization:

Definition 9.3.1 *A realization (A, B, C) is balanced if A is asymptotically stable and*

$$A\Sigma + \Sigma A' + BB' = 0 \tag{9.3.3}$$
$$A'\Sigma + \Sigma A + C'C = 0, \tag{9.3.4}$$

in which

$$\Sigma = \begin{bmatrix} \sigma_1 I_{r_1} & 0 & 0 \\ 0 & \ddots & 0 \\ 0 & 0 & \sigma_m I_{r_m} \end{bmatrix}, \quad \sigma_i \neq \sigma_j, i \neq j \text{ and } \sigma_i > 0 \; \forall i. \tag{9.3.5}$$

Note that $n = r_1 + \ldots + r_m$ is the McMillan degree of $C(sI - A)^{-1}B$ and that r_i is the multiplicity of σ_i.

We say that the realization is an ordered balanced realization if, in addition, $\sigma_1 > \sigma_2 > \ldots > \sigma_m > 0$.

In a balanced realization, the basis for the state space is such that each basis vector is equally controllable and observable, with its "degree" of controllability and observability given by the corresponding diagonal entry of Σ.

Suppose (A, B, C) is a balanced realization and the initial condition x_0 is partitioned as $x_0 = \begin{bmatrix} x_1' & \cdots & x_m' \end{bmatrix}'$ with x_i an $r_i \times 1$ vector. It follows from (9.3.2) that

$$\max_{u \in \mathcal{L}_2(-\infty,0]: x(0)=x_0} \frac{\int_0^\infty y'(t)y(t)\,dt}{\int_{-\infty}^0 u'(t)u(t)\,dt} = \sum_{i=1}^m \sigma_i^2 x_i' x_i.$$

This shows that σ_i^2 is a measure of the extent to which the corresponding r_i dimensional subspace of the state space is involved in the transfer of energy from past inputs to future outputs.

The next result is concerned with the existence and uniqueness of balanced realizations.

Lemma 9.3.1 *A given realization (A, B, C) can be transformed by a state transformation to a balanced realization if and only if it is asymptotically stable and minimal. Furthermore, a balanced realization obtained from such an (A, B, C) is unique up to: (a) the ordering of the σ_i's and (b) an orthogonal matrix S satisfying*

$$S\Sigma = \Sigma S.$$

When the σ_i have multiplicity one (i.e., $r_i = 1$ for all i), S is a diagonal matrix with diagonal elements ± 1.

When (A, B, C) is asymptotically stable and minimal, (TAT^{-1}, TB, CT^{-1}) is balanced if $T = \Sigma^{\frac{1}{2}} U' R^{-1}$. When defining T, $P = RR'$ is a Cholesky factorization of P and $R'QR = U\Sigma^2 U'$ is a singular value decomposition of $R'QR$, in which P and Q are the controllability and observability gramians, which satisfy

$$AP + PA' + BB' = 0 \tag{9.3.6}$$
$$A'Q + QA + C'C = 0. \tag{9.3.7}$$

Proof. To begin we note that if P and Q satisfy (9.3.6) and (9.3.7), then for any nonsingular T,

$$(TAT^{-1})(TPT') + (TPT')(TAT^{-1})' + (TB)(TB)' = 0$$

and

$$((T')^{-1}QT^{-1})(TAT^{-1}) + (TAT^{-1})'((T')^{-1}QT^{-1}) + (CT^{-1})'(CT^{-1}) = 0.$$

If (A, B, C) is balanced, it is asymptotically stable by assumption and $\Sigma > 0$ implies minimality. If (A, B, C) is asymptotically stable and minimal is has positive definite controllability and observability gramians P and Q satisfying (9.3.6) and (9.3.7) respectively. Setting $T = \Sigma^{\frac{1}{2}}U'R^{-1}$ gives

$$TPT' = (\Sigma^{\frac{1}{2}}U'R^{-1})RR'((R')^{-1}U\Sigma^{\frac{1}{2}}) = \Sigma$$

and

$$(T')^{-1}QT^{-1} = (\Sigma^{-\frac{1}{2}}U'R')Q(RU\Sigma^{-\frac{1}{2}}) = \Sigma.$$

Clearly, we may re-label the state components in a balanced realization to obtain another balanced realization. To determine the nonuniqueness that is possible while maintaining the same Σ, let S be a transformation that preserves the ordering of the σ_i in some balanced realization. Under this assumption we have $\Sigma = S\Sigma S'$ and $\Sigma = (S^{-1})'\Sigma S^{-1}$. This gives $S\Sigma^2 = \Sigma^2 S$, which implies that $S\Sigma = \Sigma S$ since $\sigma_i > 0$. It now follows that $\Sigma = S\Sigma S' = \Sigma SS'$, so that $I = SS'$ as required. ■

Main points of the section

1. A balanced realization is an asymptotically stable and minimal realization in which the controllability and observability gramians are equal and diagonal.
2. Any stable transfer function matrix has a balanced realization. The balanced realization is unique up to ordering of the numbers σ_i and an orthogonal transformation that commutes with Σ.
3. An analysis of the extent to which states are involved in energy transfer from past inputs to future outputs motivates the consideration of the balanced realization as an appropriate realization for absolute-error model reduction.

9.4 Balanced truncation

Model reduction by balanced truncation simply applies the truncation operation to a balanced realization (A, B, C, D) of a system $\boldsymbol{G}$.

Suppose (A, B, C) is a balanced realization as described in Definition 9.3.1 and partition Σ as

$$\Sigma = \begin{bmatrix} \Sigma_1 & 0 \\ 0 & \Sigma_2 \end{bmatrix} \tag{9.4.1}$$

with

$$\Sigma_1 = \begin{bmatrix} \sigma_1 I_{r_1} & 0 & 0 \\ 0 & \ddots & 0 \\ 0 & 0 & \sigma_l I_{r_l} \end{bmatrix}, \quad \Sigma_2 = \begin{bmatrix} \sigma_{l+1} I_{r_{l+1}} & 0 & 0 \\ 0 & \ddots & 0 \\ 0 & 0 & \sigma_m I_m \end{bmatrix}. \tag{9.4.2}$$

We never "split" states corresponding to a σ_i with multiplicity greater that one. If (A, B, C) is partitioned as in (9.2.3) conformably with Σ, we obtain $\widehat{\boldsymbol{G}}$ with realization (A_{11}, B_1, C_1, D), which is a balanced truncation of $\boldsymbol{G}$.

We will show that (A_{11}, B_1, C_1, D) is itself a balanced realization, which implies that $\widehat{\boldsymbol{G}}$ is stable, has McMillan degree $r = r_1 + \ldots + r_l$ and that the approximation error satisfies the twice-the-sum-of-the-tail infinity norm bound

$$\|\boldsymbol{G} - \widehat{\boldsymbol{G}}\|_\infty \leq 2(\sigma_{l+1} + \ldots + \sigma_m).$$

9.4.1 Stability

Lemma 9.4.1 *Suppose (A, B, C) is a balanced realization as described in Definition 9.3.1 and that (A_{11}, B_1, C_1, D) is a balanced truncation of (A, B, C, D). Then (A_{11}, B_1, C_1) is a balanced realization. In particular, A_{11} is asymptotically stable and (A_{11}, B_1, C_1) is minimal.*

Note that by a trivial re-ordering argument (A_{22}, B_2, C_2, D) is also a balanced realization.

Proof. From (9.3.3) and (9.3.4) we have

$$A_{11}\Sigma_1 + \Sigma_1 A_{11}' + B_1 B_1' = 0 \tag{9.4.3}$$
$$A_{11}'\Sigma_1 + \Sigma_1 A_{11} + C_1' C_1 = 0. \tag{9.4.4}$$

If we can show that $\mathrm{R}_e \lambda_i(A_{11}) < 0$, then it is immediate that (A_{11}, B_1, C_1) is a balanced realization because $\Sigma_1 > 0$.

Since $\Sigma_1 > 0$, we have $\mathrm{R}_e \lambda_i(A_{11}) \leq 0$, but we still need to show that there can be no imaginary axis eigenvalues. Suppose, to obtain a contradiction, that there is a real ω such that $j\omega I - A_{11}$ is singular. Let V be a basis for the kernel of $j\omega I - A_{11}$:

$$(j\omega I - A_{11})V = 0. \tag{9.4.5}$$

Multiplying (9.4.4) on the left by V^* and on the right by V, and then multiplying just on the right by V, we obtain

$$C_1 V = 0, \qquad (j\omega I + A_{11}')\Sigma_1 V = 0.$$

Multiplying (9.4.3) on the left by $V^*\Sigma_1$ and on the right by $\Sigma_1 V$, and then multiplying just on the right by $\Sigma_1 V$, we obtain

$$B_1'\Sigma_1 V = 0, \qquad (j\omega I - A_{11})\Sigma_1^2 V = 0.$$

Therefore $\Sigma_1^2 V$ is also a basis for the right nullspace of $j\omega I - A_{11}$ and hence

$$\Sigma_1^2 V = V\overline{\Sigma}_1^2$$

for some matrix $\overline{\Sigma}_1^2$, which will have eigenvalues which are a subset of the eigenvalues of Σ_1^2. (In fact, since $(j\omega I - A_{11})(VT) = 0$ and $\Sigma_1^2(VT) = (VT)(T^{-1}\overline{\Sigma}_1^2 T)$ for any nonsingular T, we can assume V is such that $\overline{\Sigma}_1^2$ is diagonal—it will have diagonal entries that are a subset of those in Σ_1^2.)

Now consider

$$\begin{aligned} A_{21}\Sigma_1 + \Sigma_2 A_{12}' + B_2 B_1' &= 0 & (9.4.6)\\ A_{12}'\Sigma_1 + \Sigma_2 A_{21} + C_2' C_1 &= 0, & (9.4.7) \end{aligned}$$

which come from the $(2,1)$-blocks of (9.3.3) and (9.3.4). Multiplying (9.4.6) on the right by $\Sigma_1 V$ and multiplying (9.4.7) on the left by Σ_2 and on the right by V, we obtain

$$\begin{aligned} A_{21}\Sigma_1^2 V + \Sigma_2 A_{12}'\Sigma_1 V &= 0\\ \Sigma_2^2 A_{21} V + \Sigma_2 A_{12}'\Sigma_1 V &= 0. \end{aligned}$$

Subtracting these gives

$$\Sigma_2^2 A_{21} V = A_{21}\Sigma_1^2 V = A_{21} V\overline{\Sigma}_1^2,$$

which we may write as

$$\begin{bmatrix} \overline{\Sigma}_1^2 & 0 \\ 0 & \Sigma_2^2 \end{bmatrix}\begin{bmatrix} I \\ A_{21}V \end{bmatrix} = \begin{bmatrix} I \\ A_{21}V \end{bmatrix}\overline{\Sigma}_1^2.$$

Since $\overline{\Sigma}_1^2$ and Σ_2^2 have no eigenvalues in common, $\begin{bmatrix} I & (A_{21}V)' \end{bmatrix}'$ must be a basis for the eigenspace of $\begin{bmatrix} \overline{\Sigma}_1^2 & 0 \\ 0 & \Sigma_2^2 \end{bmatrix}$ corresponding to the eigenvalues $\overline{\Sigma}_1^2$. That is, we have

$$\begin{bmatrix} I \\ A_{21}V \end{bmatrix} = \begin{bmatrix} I \\ 0 \end{bmatrix},$$

which amounts to $A_{21}V = 0$. Combining this with (9.4.5) we obtain

$$(j\omega I - A)\begin{bmatrix} V \\ 0 \end{bmatrix} = 0,$$

which contradicts the asymptotic stability of A. ■

Notice that Lemma 9.4.1 does not assume that the balanced realization is ordered in any way. The only assumption is that the partitioning of Σ does not split the states associated with a multiple σ_i.

9.4.2 Error bound for "one-step" truncation

Our next result determines the infinity norm of the error that occurs when deleting the state(s) associated with *one* of the σ_i's.

Lemma 9.4.2 *Let $\tilde{\boldsymbol{A}}(s)$, $\tilde{\boldsymbol{B}}(s)$ and $\tilde{\boldsymbol{C}}(s)$ be proper real rational transfer function matrices, without poles on the imaginary axis, such that $\tilde{\boldsymbol{A}}(j\omega) - j\omega I$ is nonsingular for all real ω. Suppose that*

$$
\begin{aligned}
\sigma(\tilde{\boldsymbol{A}}(s) + \tilde{\boldsymbol{A}}^{\sim}(s)) + \tilde{\boldsymbol{B}}(s)\tilde{\boldsymbol{B}}^{\sim}(s) &= 0 \qquad (9.4.8)\\
\sigma(\tilde{\boldsymbol{A}}(s) + \tilde{\boldsymbol{A}}^{\sim}(s)) + \tilde{\boldsymbol{C}}^{\sim}(s)\tilde{\boldsymbol{C}}(s) &= 0 \qquad (9.4.9)
\end{aligned}
$$

for some $\sigma > 0$. Then $\boldsymbol{E}(s) = \tilde{\boldsymbol{C}}(s)(sI - \tilde{\boldsymbol{A}}(s))^{-1}\tilde{\boldsymbol{B}}(s)$ satisfies $\|\boldsymbol{E}\|_\infty = 2\sigma$. Moreover, if $\tilde{\boldsymbol{A}}(s)$ has odd dimension, then $\overline{\sigma}(\boldsymbol{E}(0)) = 2\sigma$.

Proof. The proof is divided into two steps: first we show that $\|\boldsymbol{E}\|_\infty \leq 2\sigma$ and then that equality holds. In establishing the equality, we observe that $\overline{\sigma}(\boldsymbol{E}(0)) = 2\sigma$ when $\tilde{\boldsymbol{A}}(s)$ has odd dimension. In the proof, we shall assume that the number of rows of $\tilde{\boldsymbol{C}}(s)(j\omega)$ is greater than or equal to the number of columns of $\tilde{\boldsymbol{B}}(s)(j\omega)$; when this is not the case, we may consider a dual argument based on $\boldsymbol{E}^*$ rather than $\boldsymbol{E}$.

Choose any real ω. From (9.4.8) and (9.4.9), we have

$$\tilde{\boldsymbol{B}}(j\omega)\tilde{\boldsymbol{B}}^*(j\omega) = \tilde{\boldsymbol{C}}^*(j\omega)\tilde{\boldsymbol{C}}(j\omega),$$

so there exists a matrix $\tilde{\boldsymbol{U}}(j\omega)$ such that

$$\tilde{\boldsymbol{U}}^*(j\omega)\tilde{\boldsymbol{U}}(j\omega) = \sigma^2 I, \qquad \sigma\tilde{\boldsymbol{B}}(j\omega) + \tilde{\boldsymbol{C}}^*(j\omega)\tilde{\boldsymbol{U}}(j\omega) = 0. \qquad (9.4.10)$$

(see Problem 9.1.) Now note that

$$
\begin{aligned}
&(\tilde{\boldsymbol{U}}(j\omega) + \boldsymbol{E}(j\omega))^*(\tilde{\boldsymbol{U}}(j\omega) + \boldsymbol{E}(j\omega))\\
&= (\tilde{\boldsymbol{U}}^* + \tilde{\boldsymbol{B}}^*(j\omega I - \tilde{\boldsymbol{A}})^{-*}\tilde{\boldsymbol{C}}^*)(\tilde{\boldsymbol{U}} + \tilde{\boldsymbol{C}}(j\omega I - \tilde{\boldsymbol{A}})^{-1}\tilde{\boldsymbol{B}})\\
&= \sigma^2 I - \sigma\tilde{\boldsymbol{B}}^*(j\omega I - \tilde{\boldsymbol{A}})^{-*}\Big((j\omega I - \tilde{\boldsymbol{A}}) + (j\omega I - \tilde{\boldsymbol{A}})^*\\
&\qquad + (\tilde{\boldsymbol{A}} + \tilde{\boldsymbol{A}}^*)\Big)(j\omega I - \tilde{\boldsymbol{A}})^{-1}\tilde{\boldsymbol{B}}\\
&= \sigma^2 I.
\end{aligned}
$$

Hence

$$
\begin{aligned}
\|\boldsymbol{E}\|_\infty &= \sup_\omega \overline{\sigma}(\boldsymbol{E}(j\omega))\\
&= \sup_\omega \overline{\sigma}(\tilde{\boldsymbol{U}}(j\omega) + \boldsymbol{E}(j\omega) - \tilde{\boldsymbol{U}}(j\omega))\\
&\leq \sup_\omega \overline{\sigma}(\tilde{\boldsymbol{U}}(j\omega) + \boldsymbol{E}(j\omega)) + \sup_\omega \overline{\sigma}(\tilde{\boldsymbol{U}}(j\omega))\\
&= 2\sigma.
\end{aligned}
$$

We now show that there is a frequency ω_0 such that $\overline{\sigma}\big(\boldsymbol{E}(j\omega_0)\big) = 2\sigma$. Define

$$\tilde{\boldsymbol{\Phi}}(j\omega) = \tilde{\boldsymbol{A}}(j\omega) - j\omega I, \qquad \boldsymbol{X}(j\omega) = \tilde{\boldsymbol{\Phi}}(j\omega) - \tilde{\boldsymbol{\Phi}}^*(j\omega)$$

and note that $\boldsymbol{X}(j\omega)$ is skew-Hermitian since

$$\boldsymbol{X}(j\omega) + \boldsymbol{X}^*(j\omega) = 0. \tag{9.4.11}$$

If $\boldsymbol{X}(j\omega)x = \lambda x$, $x \neq 0$, it follows from (9.4.11) that $(\lambda + \overline{\lambda})x^*x = 0$, so that $\lambda + \overline{\lambda} = 0$. That is, every eigenvalue of $\boldsymbol{X}(j\omega)$ is on the imaginary axis. Now $\boldsymbol{X}(0)$ is real, so it has an equal number of eigenvalues with positive and negative imaginary part. For sufficiently large ω, all the eigenvalues of $\boldsymbol{X}(j\omega)$ have negative imaginary part, since $\boldsymbol{X}(j\omega) \to -j2\omega I$ as $\omega \to \infty$. Since the eigenvalues of a matrix are continuous functions of the matrix entries, it follows that there is a frequency, ω_0, such that $\boldsymbol{X}(j\omega_0)$ is singular (*i.e.*, has a zero eigenvalue). If $\boldsymbol{X}$ has odd dimension, $\boldsymbol{X}(0)$ must be singular, since it is a real matrix of odd dimension with all its eigenvalues on the imaginary axis, so we may take $\omega_0 = 0$ in this case.

Let $x \neq 0$ and ω_0 be selected so that $\boldsymbol{X}(j\omega_0)x = 0$. Then

$$\begin{aligned}
0 &= \frac{1}{2}\boldsymbol{X}(j\omega_0)x \\
&= \frac{1}{2}(\tilde{\boldsymbol{\Phi}}(j\omega_0) - \tilde{\boldsymbol{\Phi}}^*(j\omega_0))x \\
&= \tilde{\boldsymbol{\Phi}}(j\omega_0)x - \frac{1}{2}(\tilde{\boldsymbol{\Phi}}(j\omega_0) + \tilde{\boldsymbol{\Phi}}^*(j\omega_0))x \\
&= \tilde{\boldsymbol{\Phi}}(j\omega_0)x + \frac{1}{2\sigma}\tilde{\boldsymbol{B}}(j\omega_0)\tilde{\boldsymbol{B}}^*(j\omega_0)x \qquad \text{by (9.4.8)} \\
&= \tilde{\boldsymbol{\Phi}}(j\omega_0)x + \tilde{\boldsymbol{B}}(j\omega_0)u,
\end{aligned}$$

in which $u = \frac{1}{2\sigma}\tilde{\boldsymbol{B}}^*(j\omega_0)x$. Note that $u \neq 0$, since otherwise we would have $\tilde{\boldsymbol{\Phi}}(j\omega_0)x = 0$, which is banned by assumption. Now using (9.4.10) we have

$$-2\tilde{\boldsymbol{U}}(j\omega_0)u = \tilde{\boldsymbol{C}}(j\omega_0)x,$$

giving

$$\begin{bmatrix} \tilde{\boldsymbol{\Phi}}(j\omega_0) & \tilde{\boldsymbol{B}}(j\omega_0) \\ \tilde{\boldsymbol{C}}(j\omega_0) & 0 \end{bmatrix} \begin{bmatrix} x \\ u \end{bmatrix} = \begin{bmatrix} 0 \\ -2\tilde{\boldsymbol{U}}(j\omega_0)u \end{bmatrix}.$$

Hence

$$\boldsymbol{E}(j\omega_0)u = -2\tilde{\boldsymbol{U}}(j\omega_0)u, \qquad u \neq 0.$$

Since $\tilde{\boldsymbol{U}}^*(j\omega_0)\tilde{\boldsymbol{U}}(j\omega_0) = \sigma^2 I$, we see that $\overline{\sigma}\big(\boldsymbol{E}(j\omega_0)\big) = 2\sigma$. ■

Consider the situation in which the state(s) associated with one σ_i are deleted by balanced truncation and define $\tilde{\boldsymbol{A}}(s)$, $\tilde{\boldsymbol{B}}(s)$ and $\tilde{\boldsymbol{C}}(s)$ as in Lemma 9.2.1. Then by Lemma 9.4.1 the assumptions of Lemma 9.4.2 are satisfied and we conclude that the infinity norm of the error associated with this special "one-step" balanced truncation is exactly 2σ. Moreover, if the associated multiplicity r of σ is odd, then the maximum error (as measured by the maximum singular value) occurs at $\omega = 0$.

9.4.3 The error bound for balanced truncation

Lemma 9.4.2 provides an infinity norm bound on the absolute error associated with the truncation of the state(s) associated with a single σ_i in a balanced realization. To determine a bound that is applicable when the states associated with several σ_i's are deleted, we simply remove the σ_i's one at a time and allow the error to accumulate. This procedure yields the twice-the-sum-of-the-tail error bound.

Theorem 9.4.3 *Let $\boldsymbol{G} = D + C(sI - A)^{-1}B$, in which (A, B, C, D) is a balanced realization partitioned as in (9.4.1). Let $r = r_1 + \ldots + r_l$, $(A_{11}, B_1, C_1, D) = \mathcal{T}_r(A, B, C, D)$ and $\widehat{\boldsymbol{G}} = D + C_1(sI - A_{11})^{-1}B_1$. Then*

$$\|\boldsymbol{G} - \widehat{\boldsymbol{G}}\|_\infty \leq 2(\sigma_{l+1} + \ldots + \sigma_m). \tag{9.4.12}$$

In the case that $l = m - 1$ equality holds, and $\overline{\sigma}\big(\boldsymbol{G}(0) - \widehat{\boldsymbol{G}}(0)\big) = 2\sigma_m$ if r_m is odd.

Proof. Truncating the states associated with $\sigma_{l+1}, \ldots, \sigma_m$ may be achieved by a succession of one-step truncation operations. At the kth step we delete the states associated with σ_{m-k+1}, $k = 1 \ldots m - l$, to obtain $\boldsymbol{G}_k$ from $\boldsymbol{G}_{k-1}$ where $\boldsymbol{G}_0 = \boldsymbol{G}$. Each truncation step preserves the balanced realization and each step incurs an error of $\boldsymbol{E}_k = \boldsymbol{G}_{k-1} - \boldsymbol{G}_k$ with $\|\boldsymbol{E}_k\|_\infty = 2\sigma_{m-k+1}$. The last of these steps gives $\boldsymbol{G}_{m-l} = \widehat{\boldsymbol{G}}$. Now write

$$\begin{aligned} \boldsymbol{G} - \widehat{\boldsymbol{G}} &= (\boldsymbol{G}_0 - \boldsymbol{G}_1) + \ldots + (\boldsymbol{G}_{m-l-1} - \boldsymbol{G}_{m-l}) \\ &= \boldsymbol{E}_1 + \ldots + \boldsymbol{E}_{m-l} \end{aligned} \tag{9.4.13}$$

and observe that the triangle inequality gives

$$\|\boldsymbol{G} - \widehat{\boldsymbol{G}}\|_\infty \leq \|\boldsymbol{E}_1\|_\infty + \ldots + \|\boldsymbol{E}_{m-l}\|_\infty.$$

Since $\|\boldsymbol{E}_k\|_\infty = 2\sigma_{m-k+1}$, we obtain the error bound (9.4.12). ■

By considering the case when *all* the states are deleted, the bound (9.4.12) yields

$$\|\boldsymbol{G} - \boldsymbol{G}(\infty)\|_\infty \leq 2(\sigma_1 + \ldots + \sigma_m).$$

Hence,

$$\begin{aligned} \|\boldsymbol{G}\|_\infty &= \|\boldsymbol{G} - \boldsymbol{G}(\infty) + \boldsymbol{G}(\infty)\|_\infty \\ &\leq \|\boldsymbol{G}(\infty)\| + 2(\sigma_1 + \ldots + \sigma_m). \end{aligned}$$

Tightness of the bound

We have already established that the infinity norm error bound for one-step truncation is tight. In the case of multi-step truncation the situation is less clear cut—one can find examples for which the error bound is close to the true error and there are also cases for which it is conservative.

It is natural to suspect that because the twice-the-sum-of-the-tail bound arises by repeated application of the triangle inequality, it gets weaker and weaker as more and more states are deleted. Although this is usually the case, the bound may remain tight however many states are deleted. The next example illustrates this point.

Example 9.4.1. Consider the transfer function

$$\boldsymbol{g}_n = \sum_{i=1}^{n} \frac{\alpha^i}{s+\alpha^i} \qquad \alpha > 0, \quad \alpha \neq 1$$

which may be realized as

$$A = \begin{bmatrix} -\alpha & 0 & 0 \\ 0 & \ddots & 0 \\ 0 & 0 & -\alpha^n \end{bmatrix} \qquad B = \begin{bmatrix} \sqrt{\alpha} \\ \vdots \\ \sqrt{\alpha^n} \end{bmatrix} \qquad C = B'.$$

It is easily verified that the controllability and observability gramians are equal and the (i,j) entry of the controllability gramian is

$$P_{ij} = \frac{\sqrt{\alpha^{i-j}}}{\alpha^{i-j}+1} \qquad i,j = 1,\ldots,n.$$

Since $P = Q$, we have

$$\sigma_i = \sqrt{\lambda_i(PQ)} = \lambda_i(P), \qquad i = 1,\ldots,n,$$

giving

$$\begin{aligned} 2(\sigma_1 + \ldots + \sigma_n) &= 2 \times \operatorname{trace}(P) \\ &= 2 \times \frac{n}{2} \\ &= n. \end{aligned}$$

Therefore (9.4.13) implies $\|\boldsymbol{g}_n\|_\infty \leq n$. Since $\boldsymbol{g}(0) = n$, equality must hold. ▽

Systems of the form given in the above example have interlaced poles and zeros on the negative real axis (Problem 9.4). The bound is tight for such systems. At the other extreme, for systems that have interlaced poles and zeros on the imaginary axis, the bound exceeds the true error by a factor that is approximately twice the number of states that are deleted—see Enns [57].

Frequency dependence of the error

The error bounds given in Theorem 9.4.3 says nothing about the way the true error varies as a function of frequency. Since the full-order system $\boldsymbol{G}$ and the reduced-order system $\widehat{G}$ match each other exactly at infinite frequency, one would expect good high-frequency fidelity from the reduced order model. Apart from the guaranteed satisfaction of the error bound, little can be said about the variation of the error at low and intermediate frequencies. In most cases, the σ_i's will have unit multiplicity and the truncation of $n-r$ states will be achieved via $n-r$ truncations of one state. Since one is odd, each of these truncations incurs a maximum error at zero frequency. One would therefore expect the largest truncation error to occur at low frequency.

Main points of the section

1. Any truncation of a balanced realization that does not "split" the states associated with a single singular value is called balanced truncation.
2. Balanced truncation preserves stability and minimality, and the approximation error satisfies the twice-the-sum-of-the-tail infinity norm error bound.
3. The infinity norm of a strictly proper transfer function matrix is bounded above by twice the sum of the σ_i in its balanced realization.

9.5 Balanced singular perturbation approximation

The fact that balanced truncation generally incurs the greatest approximation error in the low-frequency region is undesirable in many applications. An algorithm which produces zero error at zero frequency may be obtained via an easy modification to the basic balanced truncation algorithm. The idea is to simply replace s with $1/s$ as follows:

1. Set $\boldsymbol{H}(w) = \boldsymbol{G}(1/w)$.
2. Let $\boldsymbol{H}_r(w)$ be an rth-order balanced truncation of $\boldsymbol{H}(w)$.
3. Set $\boldsymbol{G}_r(s) = \boldsymbol{H}(1/s)$.

This algorithm will have exact matching at zero frequency, thereby leading to prefect steady-state performance; it is a singular perturbation version of balanced truncation, which we call balanced singular perturbation approximation (BSPA).

Since singular perturbation and truncation are connected by the simple frequency inversion $s \to 1/s$, the infinity norm error bounds will still hold. Secondly, since frequency inversion preserves stability, both algorithms will produce reduced-order models with the same stability properties. Finally, since frequency inversion preserves the controllability and observability gramians and hence a balanced realization, we obtain the following result:

Theorem 9.5.1 *Assume the hypotheses of Theorem 9.4.3 and define* $\widehat{G} = \widehat{D} + \widehat{C}_1(sI - \widehat{A}_{11})^{-1}\widehat{B}_1$, *in which* $(\widehat{A}_{11}, \widehat{B}_1, \widehat{C}_1, \widehat{D}) = \mathcal{S}_r(A, B, C, D)$. *Then:*

1. *The realization* $(\widehat{A}_{11}, \widehat{B}_1, \widehat{C}_1, \widehat{D})$ *is balanced with its controllability and observability gramians given by* $\Sigma_l = diag(\sigma_1 I_{r_1}, \ldots, \sigma_l I_{r_l})$. *In particular,* $\widehat{A}_{11}$ *is stable,* $(\widehat{A}_{11}, \widehat{B}_1)$ *is controllable and* $(\widehat{C}_1, \widehat{A}_{11})$ *is observable.*
2. $\|G - \widehat{G}\|_\infty \leq 2(\sigma_{l+1} + \ldots + \sigma_m)$, *and equality holds if* $l = m - 1$.
3. $\widehat{G}(0) = G(0)$.
4. $\|G - G(0)\|_\infty \leq 2(\sigma_1 + \ldots + \sigma_m)$.

Proof. Since (A, B, C) is balanced, A is stable and therefore nonsingular. By Lemma 9.4.1, A_{22} is also stable and hence is nonsingular. Thus $(\widehat{A}_{11}, \widehat{B}_1, \widehat{C}_1, \widehat{D})$ given by (9.2.14) are well defined and the assumptions of Lemma 9.2.2 hold. All the items now follow directly from their balanced truncation counterparts by using Lemma 9.2.2. ■

Main point of the section

The stability and infinity norm properties of any model reduction procedure will be preserved by a change of variables that maps the left-half plane into itself. The balanced singular perturbation approximation, which is equivalent to balanced truncation of the system obtained by setting $w = 1/s$, has the same infinity norm error as balanced truncation, but has zero steady-state error. In general, its performance at low frequencies is superior to that of balanced truncation.

9.6 Example

We illustrate the model reduction methods described above with an eighth-order model of a flexible structure [58]. The model is

$$g = \sum_{i=1}^{4} k_i \frac{\omega_i^2}{s^2 + 2\zeta_i \omega_i s + \omega_i^2},$$

in which

i	ω_i	ζ_i	k_i
1	0.56806689746895	0.00096819582773	0.01651378989774
2	3.94093897440699	0.00100229920475	0.00257034576009
3	10.58229653714164	0.00100167293203	0.00002188016252
4	16.19234386986640	0.01000472824082	0.00027927762861

The controllability and observability gramians of a balanced realization for this system are

$$\Sigma = \text{diag}\begin{bmatrix} 4.26819 & 4.25994 & 0.641754 & 0.640469 \\ 0.069856 & 0.0697163 & 0.00546623 & 0.00545529 \end{bmatrix}.$$

By making use of the error bound given in Theorem 9.4.3, we see that if two states are eliminated, the infinity norm of the error is less than 0.0218431. If four states are eliminated, the error bound increases to 0.300988 and so on.

Eliminating four states by balanced truncation gives

$$\widehat{\boldsymbol{g}} \stackrel{s}{=} \left[\begin{array}{cccc|c} -0.000550222 & -0.568066 & 0.000993291 & 0.00134457 & 0.068534 \\ 0.568066 & -0.000549776 & 0.00134607 & 0.000994008 & -0.0684399 \\ 0.000993291 & -0.00134607 & -0.00394544 & -3.94093 & -0.0711619 \\ -0.00134457 & 0.000994008 & 3.94093 & -0.00395455 & 0.0711725 \\ \hline 0.068534 & 0.0684399 & -0.0711619 & -0.0711725 & 0 \end{array}\right].$$

Figure 9.1 shows the gain of the full-order model $\boldsymbol{g}$, the fourth-order balanced

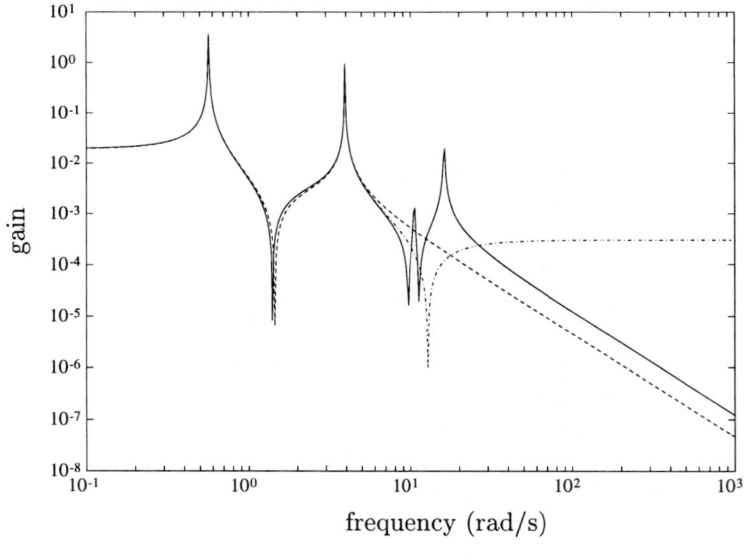

Figure 9.1: Flexible structure models: full-order $\boldsymbol{g}$ (solid), balanced truncation $\widehat{\boldsymbol{g}}$ (dashed) and balanced singular perturbation (dash-dot).

truncation model $\widehat{\boldsymbol{g}}$ and the fourth-order balanced singular perturbation model.

The gains of the error incurred by each method, along with the error bound, are shown in Figure 9.2. The solid line is the error bound, the dashed line is the balanced truncation error and the dash-dot line is the balanced singular perturbation error. Notice that the actual error is an order of magnitude less than the error bound. This

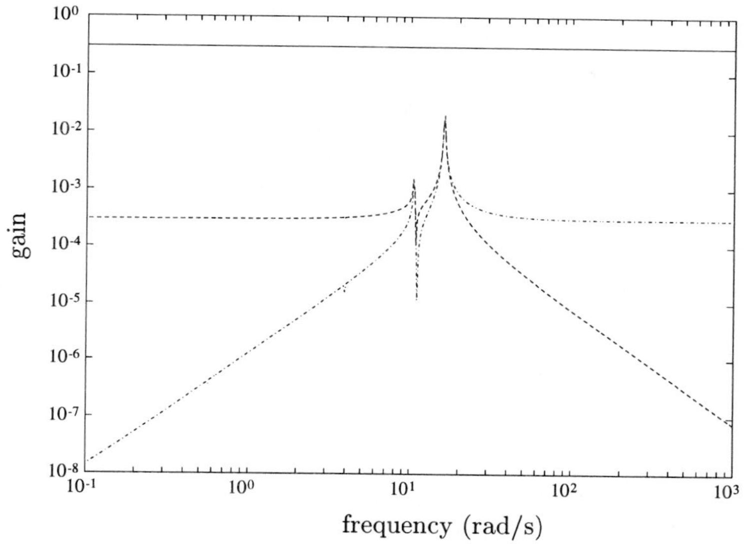

Figure 9.2: Model reduction errors: error bound (solid), balanced truncation (dashed) and balanced singular perturbation (dash-dot).

is not unexpected for this type of system because its poles and zeros are interlaced and close to the imaginary axis.

It is also worth noting that the balanced truncation reduced-order model is virtually identical to the fourth-order model obtained by deleting the two high-frequency modes. The main difference is that the balanced truncation reduced-order model has an additional zero at -3980.19.

9.7 Notes and References

Balanced realizations first appeared with the work of Mullis and Roberts [153], who were interested in realizations of digital filters that are optimal with respect to round-off errors in the state update calculations. These issues are developed extensively in the book by Williamson [212].

The balanced truncation method of model reduction is due to Moore, who argued that the method is sensible on system theoretic grounds. He also proved a weak version of the stability result. The asymptotic stability result, Lemma 9.4.1, is due to Pernebo and Silverman [162]. The twice-the-sum-of-the-tail infinity norm error bound for balanced truncation is due to Enns [57], who also proposed a frequency weighted generalization. He introduced formula (9.2.6) for the truncation error system and proved that the error for "one-step" truncation is 2σ when the multiplicity of σ is one. Our new proof shows that no matter what the multiplicity of σ is, the infinity norm of the error is exactly 2σ. The twice-the-sum-of-the-tail error bound was also proved by Glover [71] using a different approach.

The balanced singular perturbation approximation method was introduced by Fernando and Nicholson [62]. Liu and Anderson [140] showed that it was related to balanced truncation by the transformation $s \to 1/s$.

Numerical algorithms for computing balanced realizations have been considered by Laub, Heath, Page and Ward [128]. Tombs and Postlethwaite [152], and Safonov and Chiang [180] have developed various algorithms that compute balanced truncation approximations without computing balanced realizations. None of these procedures eliminate the need to compute the controllability and observability gramians, which is a serious problem when large-scale models need to be reduced. Jaimoukha, Kasenally and Limebeer [104] have developed algorithms for computing approximate solutions to Lyapunov equations using Krylov subpace methods that can be effective even for models containing many hundreds of states.

A relative error based truncation method of model reduction is the balanced stochastic truncation method of Desai and Pal [45]. Green derived an infinity norm bound for the relative error associated with this method [83]; the bound was subsequently improved by Wang and Safonov [208]. Another feature of the algorithm is that it preserves the closed-right-half-plane zeros of the model and will therefore produce a minimum phase approximation of a minimum phase system [82].

Discrete-time versions of the results in this chapter (see Problem 9.6) have been proved by Al-Saggaf and Franklin [5].

9.8 Problems

Problem 9.1. Let B and C be complex matrices such that $BB^* = C^*C$.

1. If the number of rows of C is greater than or equal to the number of columns of B, show that for any nonzero real number σ, there exists a matrix U such that $\sigma B + C^*U = 0$ and $U^*U = \sigma^2 I$.
   (Hint: Write a singular value decomposition of C and infer the form of the singular value decomposition of B; see Lemma 3.5 of [71].)
2. Show that for any nonzero real number σ, there exists a matrix U such that $\sigma B + C^*U = 0$ and $U^*U \leq \sigma^2 I$. Show further that the nonzero singular values of U are all equal to σ.

Problem 9.2. Suppose (A_{ii}, B_i, C_i), $i = 1, 2$ are two balanced realizations with controllability/observability gramians Σ_1 and Σ_2 respectively. Suppose also that

Σ_1 and Σ_2 have no eigenvalues in common. Construct the unique matrices A_{21} and A_{12} such that

$$\begin{aligned} A &= \begin{bmatrix} A_{11} & A_{12} \\ A_{21} & A_{22} \end{bmatrix}, \qquad B = \begin{bmatrix} B_1 \\ B_2 \end{bmatrix}, \\ C &= \begin{bmatrix} C_1 & C_2 \end{bmatrix} \end{aligned}$$

is a balanced realization with controllability/observability gramian $\begin{bmatrix} \Sigma_1 & 0 \\ 0 & \Sigma_2 \end{bmatrix}$.

Problem 9.3. Assume the hypotheses of Lemma 9.4.2. Using the bounded real lemma (Theorem 3.7.1), prove that

$$\sup_{\omega} \overline{\sigma}\big(\tilde{C}(j\omega)(j\omega I - \tilde{\boldsymbol{A}}(j\omega))^{-1}\tilde{B}(j\omega)\big) \leq 2\sigma.$$

Problem 9.4. Show that the poles and zeros of the system $\boldsymbol{g}_n$ defined in Example 9.4.1 have an interlacing property—between any two poles there is exactly one zero. If $\boldsymbol{g}_n$ is the impedance of a linear circuit, explain why this interlacing property implies that the circuit is passive.

Problem 9.5. Let (A, B, C, D) be any realization such that A is asymptotically stable and let P and Q satisfy

$$\begin{aligned} AP + PA' + BB' &= 0 \\ A'Q + QA + C'C &= 0. \end{aligned}$$

Show that the following procedure computes the rth-order balanced truncation approximation to $\boldsymbol{G} = D + C(sI - A)^{-1}B$:

a. Let $P = U_P S_P U_P'$ and $Q = U_Q S_Q U_Q'$ be ordered singular value decompositions of P and Q.
b. Let $S_Q^{\frac{1}{2}} U_Q' U_P S_P^{\frac{1}{2}}$ have (ordered) singular value decomposition $V\Sigma U'$.
c. Partition the matrices V, Σ and U as

$$V = \begin{bmatrix} V_1 & V_2 \end{bmatrix}, \quad \Sigma = \begin{bmatrix} \Sigma_1 & 0 \\ 0 & \Sigma_2 \end{bmatrix}, \quad U = \begin{bmatrix} U_1 & U_2 \end{bmatrix},$$

in which Σ_1 is $r \times r$.

d. Define

$$L = U_Q S_Q^{\frac{1}{2}} V_1 \Sigma_1^{-\frac{1}{2}}, \qquad M = U_P S_P^{\frac{1}{2}} U_1 \Sigma_1^{-\frac{1}{2}}.$$

e. Define $A_r = L'AM$, $B_r = L'B$ and $C_r = CM$.
f. Define $\widehat{\boldsymbol{G}} = D + C_r(sI - A_r)^{-1}B_r$.

Problem 9.6. [5] A realization (A, B, C, D) of a discrete-time system $\boldsymbol{G}(z) = D + C(zI - A)^{-1}B$ is balanced if $|\lambda_i(A)| < 1$ for all i and there exists a positive definite diagonal matrix of the form given in (9.3.5) such that

$$\begin{aligned} A\Sigma A' - \Sigma + BB' &= 0 \\ A'\Sigma A - \Sigma + C'C &= 0. \end{aligned}$$

1. Show that a given realization of a discrete-time system can be transformed into a discrete-time balanced realization if and only if it is stable and minimal.
2. Suppose that (A, B, C, D) is a discrete-time balanced realization which is partitioned as in (9.2.3) and (9.3.5). Show that A_{11} is asymptotically stable ($|\lambda_i(A_{11})| < 1$ for all i).
3. Define

$$\begin{aligned} \tilde{\boldsymbol{A}}(\theta) &= A_{22} + A_{21}(e^{j\theta}I - A_{11})^{-1}A_{12} \\ \tilde{\boldsymbol{B}}(\theta) &= B_2 + A_{21}(e^{j\theta}I - A_{11})^{-1}B_1 \\ \tilde{\boldsymbol{C}}(\theta) &= C_2 + C_1(e^{j\theta}I - A_{11})^{-1}A_{12}. \end{aligned}$$

   Show that

$$\begin{aligned} \tilde{\boldsymbol{A}}(\theta)\Sigma_2\tilde{\boldsymbol{A}}^*(\theta) - \Sigma_2 + \tilde{\boldsymbol{B}}(\theta)\tilde{\boldsymbol{B}}^*(\theta) &= 0 \\ \tilde{\boldsymbol{A}}^*(\theta)\Sigma_2\tilde{\boldsymbol{A}}(\theta) - \Sigma_2 + \tilde{\boldsymbol{C}}^*(\theta)\tilde{\boldsymbol{C}}(\theta) &= 0. \end{aligned}$$

4. Suppose that A is asymptotically stable $|\lambda_i(A)| < 1$ for all i and that

$$\begin{aligned} AA^* - I + BB^* &= 0 \\ A^*A - I + C^*C &= 0. \end{aligned}$$

   Show that $\overline{\sigma}[C(e^{j\theta}I - A)^{-1}B] < 2$.
5. Show that $(A_{11}, \begin{bmatrix} A_{12}\Sigma_2^{\frac{1}{2}} & B_1 \end{bmatrix}, \begin{bmatrix} A_{21}\Sigma_2^{\frac{1}{2}} \\ C_1 \end{bmatrix})$ is a balanced realization.
6. Suppose that $G(z) = D + C(zI - A)^{-1}B$, in which (A, B, C, D) is a discrete-time balanced realization. Let (A_{11}, B_1, C_1, D) be an rth-order balanced truncation of (A, B, C, D) and let $\widehat{\boldsymbol{G}}(z) = D + C_1(zI - A_{11})^{-1}B_1$. Show that

$$\|\boldsymbol{G} - \widehat{\boldsymbol{G}}\|_\infty < 2(\sigma_{r+1} + \ldots + \sigma_n).$$

Problem 9.7. [91, 6] Let (A, B, C, D) be a balanced realization of a continuous-time system and let α be a nonnegative number. Define

$$\begin{aligned} \widehat{A} &= A_{11} + A_{12}(\alpha I - A_{22})^{-1}A_{21} \\ \widehat{B} &= B_1 + A_{12}(\alpha I - A_{22})^{-1}B_2 \\ \widehat{C} &= C_1 + C_2(\alpha I - A_{22})^{-1}A_{21} \\ \widehat{D} &= D + C_2(\alpha I - A_{22})^{-1}B_2, \end{aligned}$$

in which (A, B, C, D) are partioned as in (9.2.3) conformably with a partioning of Σ in (9.4.2). The generalized singular perturbation approximation (GSPA) is defined by $\mathcal{GS}_r(A, B, C, D) = (\widehat{A}, \widehat{B}, \widehat{C}, \widehat{D})$.

1. Show that the GSPA reduced-order model results from replacing the dynamics associated with x_2 by the exponential system $\dot{x}_2 = \alpha x_2$.
2. Show that the GSPA approximant has zero error at $s = \alpha$.
3. Suppose that $0 < \alpha < \infty$ and define the linear fractional transformation $z = \frac{\alpha+s}{\alpha-s}$, which maps the left-half plane to the unit circle. Suppose also that we consider the equivalent discrete-time system defined by $\boldsymbol{F}(z) = \boldsymbol{G}(\frac{\alpha(z-1)}{z+1})$. Show that $\boldsymbol{F} = \tilde{D} + \tilde{C}(zI - \tilde{A})^{-1}\tilde{B}$, in which

$$\begin{aligned}
\tilde{A} &= (\alpha I + A)(\alpha I - A)^{-1} = (\alpha I - A)^{-1}(\alpha I + A) \\
\tilde{B} &= \sqrt{2\alpha}(\alpha I - A)^{-1}B \\
\tilde{C} &= \sqrt{2\alpha}C(\alpha I - A)^{-1} \\
\tilde{D} &= D + C(\alpha I - A)^{-1}B.
\end{aligned}$$

   Show that this realization of $\boldsymbol{F}$ is a discrete-time balanced realization.
4. Show that for $0 < \alpha < \infty$, GSPA is equivalent to: (a) mapping to discrete-time via $z = \frac{\alpha+s}{\alpha-s}$; (b) discrete-time balanced truncation (see Problem 9.6) and (c) mapping back to continuous-time via $s = \frac{\alpha(z-1)}{z+1}$.
5. For $0 \leq \alpha \leq \infty$, show that reduced-order models obtained by GSPA enjoy the same stability and infinity norm error bound properties as balanced truncation and SPA.

10

Optimal Model Reduction

10.1 Introduction

The motivation for the balanced truncation method of model reduction came from energy transmission arguments. If a high-order model $\boldsymbol{G}$ maps u to y via $y = \boldsymbol{G}u$, then the idea was to the select a low-order model $\widehat{\boldsymbol{G}}$ of degree r, which maps u to $\widehat{y}$, such that

$$e = \sup_{u \in \mathcal{L}_2(-\infty,0]} \left(\frac{\int_0^\infty (y-\widehat{y})'(y-\widehat{y})\, dt}{\int_{-\infty}^0 u'u\, dt} \right)$$

is small when $u(t) = 0$ for $t > 0$. If $t \leq 0$ represents the past and $t \geq 0$ the future, then this quantity can be thought of as the energy gain from past inputs to future outputs. If the past-input-to-future-output energy gain is indeed a good basis upon which to select a reduced-order model, it seems reasonable to seek to minimize it. That is, choose $\widehat{\boldsymbol{G}}$ of McMillan degree r such that e is minimized. This is optimal Hankel norm approximation and a method for determining $\widehat{\boldsymbol{G}}$ will now be given.

10.2 Hankel operators

The *Hankel operator* of a linear system is the prediction operator that maps (the reflection of) past inputs to future outputs, assuming the future input is zero.[1]

Suppose the system $\boldsymbol{G} \in \mathcal{RH}_\infty$ is defined by the minimal state-space realization

$$\dot{x} = Ax + Bu, \qquad x(-\infty) = 0, \tag{10.2.1}$$

$$y = Cx + Du. \tag{10.2.2}$$

[1]The reflection is introduced so that the Hankel operator is a map from $\mathcal{L}_2[0,\infty)$ to $\mathcal{L}_2[0,\infty)$, rather than from $\mathcal{L}_2(-\infty,0]$ to $\mathcal{L}_2[0,\infty)$.

If $u \in \mathcal{L}_2(-\infty, 0]$, then future outputs are determined by the convolution integral

$$y(t) = \int_{-\infty}^{0} Ce^{A(t-\tau)}Bu(\tau)\,d\tau, \qquad t > 0.$$

If we set $v(t) = u(-t)$, then $y(t) = (\boldsymbol{\Gamma}_G v)(t)$ for $t > 0$, in which $\boldsymbol{\Gamma}_G : \mathcal{L}_2[0, \infty) \mapsto \mathcal{L}_2[0, \infty)$ is the Hankel operator defined by

$$(\boldsymbol{\Gamma}_G v)(t) = \int_{0}^{\infty} Ce^{A(t+\tau)}Bv(\tau)\,d\tau. \tag{10.2.3}$$

We say that $\boldsymbol{\Gamma}_G$ is the Hankel operator with $\boldsymbol{G}$ as its symbol. Notice that because D is not involved in prediction it plays no role in defining the Hankel operator.

If $u \in \mathcal{L}_2(-\infty, 0]$, then $y(t) = Ce^{At}x(0)$, for $t > 0$. The present state is given by $x(0) = \int_{-\infty}^{0} e^{-A\tau}u(\tau)\,d\tau$.[2] Therefore, in order to determine $\boldsymbol{\Gamma}_G v$, we only need to know the present state $x(0)$ that results from driving the system with $u(t)$—all inputs that give rise to the same $x(0)$ produce the same future output. Since (A, B) is controllable, $x(0)$ ranges over $\mathbb{R}^n$ as u ranges over $\mathcal{L}_2(-\infty, 0]$. Since (A, C) is observable, any two linearly independent initial states result in linearly independent future outputs. Thus, the number of linearly independent outputs is n, the dimension of a minimal realization of $\boldsymbol{G}$. We conclude that the rank of the Hankel operator $\boldsymbol{\Gamma}_G$ (*i.e.*, the number of linearly independent outputs) is equal to the McMillan degree of $\boldsymbol{G}$.[3]

10.2.1 The Hankel norm

The *Hankel norm* of a system is the $\mathcal{L}_2[0, \infty)$ induced norm of its associated Hankel operator and we write

$$\|\boldsymbol{G}\|_H = \|\boldsymbol{\Gamma}_G\|.$$

By definition of the induced norm we see that

$$\|\boldsymbol{G}\|_H^2 = \sup_{u \in \mathcal{L}_2(-\infty, 0]} \left(\frac{\int_0^\infty y'y\,dt}{\int_{-\infty}^0 u'u\,dt} \right).$$

Thus the future output energy resulting from any input is at most the Hankel norm squared times the energy of the input, assuming the future input is zero. The optimal Hankel norm model reduction problem is to find a $\widehat{\boldsymbol{G}} \in \mathcal{RH}_\infty$ of McMillan degree $r < n$ that minimizes $\|\boldsymbol{G} - \widehat{\boldsymbol{G}}\|_H$.

We use the arguments of Section 9.3.1 to compute the Hankel norm of a system. Suppose $u \in \mathcal{L}_2(-\infty, 0]$ results in the current state $x(0) = x_0$. Then

$$\int_0^\infty y'(t)y(t)\,dt = x_0'Qx_0 \tag{10.2.4}$$

[2] We think of the time $t = 0$ as the present.

[3] The McMillan degree of a system is defined in books such as [105]—it is equal to the dimension of a minimal state-space realization.

and

$$\int_{-\infty}^{0} u'u\,dt \geq x_0'P^{-1}x_0, \tag{10.2.5}$$

in which P and Q are the controllability and observability gramians satisfying

$$\begin{aligned} AP + PA' + BB' &= 0 & (10.2.6)\\ A'Q + QA + C'C &= 0. & (10.2.7)\end{aligned}$$

(See Section 9.3.1 for details.) Note that P^{-1} exists because (A, B) is controllable. Since the input $u = B'e^{-A't}P^{-1}x_0$ satisfies (10.2.5) with equality, we conclude that

$$\begin{aligned} \|\boldsymbol{G}\|_H^2 &= \sup_{x_0} \frac{x_0'Qx_0}{x_0'P^{-1}x_0} \\ &= \overline{\sigma}(PQ). & (10.2.8)\end{aligned}$$

The Hankel norm of a system is bounded above by its infinity norm, because for an arbitrary unit energy input in $\mathcal{L}_2(-\infty, 0]$, $\|\boldsymbol{G}\|_H^2$ is the least upper bound on the energy of the future output and $\|\boldsymbol{G}\|_\infty^2$ is the least upper bound on the energy of the total output.

To explore this connection in a little further, note that if $\boldsymbol{F}$ is any anticausal system and $u \in \mathcal{L}_2(-\infty, 0]$, then $(\boldsymbol{F}u)(t)$ is zero for $t > 0$.[4] Thus the future output is unaffected by the addition of any anticausal system $\boldsymbol{F}$ and it is immediate that the inequality

$$\|\boldsymbol{G}\|_H \leq \|\boldsymbol{G} - \boldsymbol{F}\|_\infty \tag{10.2.9}$$

is satisfied for any anticausal $\boldsymbol{F}$. This simple observation is the cornerstone of the solution to the optimal Hankel norm model reduction problem. Nehari's theorem, which is presented in detail later, shows that

$$\|\boldsymbol{G}\|_H = \min_{\boldsymbol{F} \in \mathcal{H}_\infty^-} \|\boldsymbol{G} - \boldsymbol{F}\|_\infty.$$

It follows from the Paley-Wiener theorem that $\boldsymbol{F} \in \mathcal{H}_\infty^-$ implies that $\boldsymbol{F}$ is anticausal.

10.2.2 Hankel singular values and the Schmidt decomposition

The *Schmidt decomposition* is the singular value decomposition of $\boldsymbol{\Gamma}_G$:

$$\boldsymbol{\Gamma}_G(u) = \sum_{i=1}^{n} \sigma_i \langle u, v_i \rangle w_i, \tag{10.2.10}$$

in which $v_i \in \mathcal{L}_2[0, \infty)$ and $w_i \in \mathcal{L}_2[0, \infty)$ are sets of orthonormal functions.[5] The numbers $\sigma_i > 0$, which we will also denote $\sigma_i(\boldsymbol{G})$, are the singular values of the

[4] A system is anticausal if it is causal in reverse time.

[5] That is, $\langle v_i, v_j \rangle = 0$ and $\langle w_i, w_j \rangle = 0$ for $i \neq j$ with $\|v_i\|_2 = 1$ and $\|w_i\|_2 = 1$ for all i.

Hankel operator $\boldsymbol{\Gamma}_G$ and they are called the *Hankel singular values* of $\boldsymbol{G}$. The largest Hankel singular value is equal to the Hankel norm and we shall assume that the Hankel singular values are ordered in descending order of magnitude. The multiplicity of a Hankel singular value σ_i is the number of Hankel singular values that are equal to σ_i. Generically, each Hankel singular value has unit multiplicity.

The pair (v_i, w_i), corresponding to the Hankel singular value σ_i, is called a *Schmidt pair*. It follows from the orthogonality of the v_i's and the w_i's that

$$\begin{aligned}\boldsymbol{\Gamma}_G v_i &= \sigma_i w_i\\ \boldsymbol{\Gamma}_G^{\sim} w_i &= \sigma_i v_i,\end{aligned}$$

in which $\boldsymbol{\Gamma}_G^{\sim}$ is the adjoint operator.

We will now determine the Hankel singular values and the Schmidt pairs in terms of a minimal realization (A, B, C, D) of the system $\boldsymbol{G}$. Consider $v(t) = B'e^{A't}P^{-1}x_0$. Then

$$\begin{aligned}(\boldsymbol{\Gamma}_G v)(t) &= Ce^{At}\left(\int_0^\infty e^{A\tau}BB'e^{A'\tau}\,d\tau\right)P^{-1}x_0\\ &= Ce^{At}x_0,\end{aligned}$$

since $P = \int_0^\infty e^{A\tau}BB'e^{A'\tau}\,d\tau$. In the same way, if $w(t) = Ce^{At}x_0$, then

$$\begin{aligned}(\boldsymbol{\Gamma}_G^{\sim} w)(t) &= \int_0^\infty B'e^{A'(t+\tau)}C'w(\tau)\,d\tau\\ &= B'e^{A't}\left(\int_0^\infty e^{A'\tau}C'Ce^{A\tau}\,d\tau\right)x_0\\ &= B'e^{A't}Qx_0.\end{aligned}$$

Therefore, $\boldsymbol{\Gamma}_G^{\sim}\boldsymbol{\Gamma}_G v = \sigma^2 v$ if $Qx_0 = \sigma^2 P^{-1}x_0$ and we conclude that the Hankel singular values σ_i of $\boldsymbol{G}$ are given by

$$\sigma_i = \lambda_i^{\frac{1}{2}}(PQ), \qquad i = 1, \ldots, n.$$

For notational convenience, we also define $\sigma_0 = \infty$ and $\sigma_{n+1} = 0$. To determine the Schmidt vector corresponding to $\sigma_i = \lambda_i^{\frac{1}{2}}(PQ)$, we need to choose an $x_i \in \mathbb{R}^n$ such that $Qx_i = \sigma_i^2 P^{-1}x_i$, with the norm of x_i scaled so that $v_i(t) = B'e^{A't}P^{-1}x_i$ has unit $\mathcal{L}_2[0, \infty)$ norm. Now

$$\begin{aligned}\|v_i\|_2^2 &= x_i'P^{-1}\left(\int_0^\infty e^{A\tau}BB'e^{A'\tau}\,d\tau\right)P^{-1}x_i\\ &= x_i'P^{-1}x_i\\ &= \frac{x_i'Qx_i}{\sigma_i^2}.\end{aligned}$$

Hence, if $x_i \in \mathbb{R}^n$ satisfies $PQx_i = \sigma_i^2 x_i$ and $x_i' Q x_i = \sigma_i^2$, then

$$\begin{aligned} v_i(t) &= \sigma_i^{-2} B' e^{A't} Q x_i, & i = 1, \ldots, n \\ w_i(t) &= \sigma_i^{-1} C e^{At} x_i, & i = 1, \ldots, n \end{aligned}$$

is a Schmidt pair corresponding to σ_i. The Schmidt decomposition (10.2.10) is therefore obtained by selecting a set of orthogonal vectors $x_i \in \mathbb{R}^n$ such that $PQx_i = \sigma_i^2 x_i$, $x_i' Q x_i = \sigma_i^2$. If the realization (A, B, C, D) is a balanced realization (see Definition 9.3.1), then

$$P = Q = \Sigma = \begin{bmatrix} \sigma_1 & 0 & 0 \\ 0 & \ddots & 0 \\ 0 & 0 & \sigma_n \end{bmatrix}$$

and $x_i = \sqrt{\sigma_i} e_i$, with e_i the ith standard basis vector.

10.2.3 A lower bound on the approximation error

We now show that $\sigma_{r+1}(\boldsymbol{G})$ is a lower bound on the Hankel norm of the error incurred when approximating $\boldsymbol{G}$ by a stable system of McMillan degree r. It is a consequence of this and the definition of the Hankel norm that the energy in the prediction error signal is at least σ_{r+1}^2 times the input energy, assuming the future input is zero. In a later section, we will show that this lower bound can be attained.

Lemma 10.2.1 *Suppose $\boldsymbol{G} \in \mathcal{RH}_\infty$ has Hankel singular values $\sigma_1, \ldots, \sigma_n$ and let $\widehat{\boldsymbol{G}} \in \mathcal{RH}_\infty$ have McMillan degree less than or equal to $r < n$. Then*

$$\|\boldsymbol{G} - \widehat{\boldsymbol{G}}\|_H \geq \sigma_{r+1}. \tag{10.2.11}$$

If equality holds and $\sigma_r > \sigma_{r+1}$, then $\boldsymbol{\Gamma}_{\widehat{G}} v_j = 0$ for every Schmidt vector v_j corresponding to any Hankel singular value $\sigma_j = \sigma_{r+1}$.

Proof. Let $\widehat{\boldsymbol{G}} \in \mathcal{RH}_\infty$ have McMillan degree less than or equal to $r < n$ and let (v_i, w_i), $i = 1 \ldots n$ be the Schmidt pairs of $\boldsymbol{G}$. Consider inputs of the form

$$v = \sum_{i=1}^{r+1} \alpha_i v_i.$$

Since $v_1, \cdots, v_{r+1}$ span an $r+1$ dimensional space and the Hankel operator $\boldsymbol{\Gamma}_{\widehat{G}}$ has rank less than or equal to r, we can select the α_i's, not all zero, such that $\boldsymbol{\Gamma}_{\widehat{G}} v = 0$. For such a v,

$$\begin{aligned} \|(\boldsymbol{\Gamma}_G - \boldsymbol{\Gamma}_{\widehat{G}})v\|_2^2 &= \|\boldsymbol{\Gamma}_G v\|_2^2 \\ &= \|\sum_{i=1}^{r+1} \alpha_i \sigma_i w_i\|_2^2 \end{aligned}$$

$$
\begin{aligned}
&= \sum_{i=1}^{r+1} \alpha_i^2 \sigma_i^2 \\
&\geq \sigma_{r+1}^2 \sum_{i=1}^{r+1} \alpha_i^2 \\
&= \sigma_{r+1}^2 \|v\|_2^2. \qquad (10.2.12)
\end{aligned}
$$

Hence $\|\mathbf{\Gamma}_G - \mathbf{\Gamma}_{\widehat{G}}\| \geq \sigma_{r+1}$.

If equality holds in (10.2.11), then equality also holds in (10.2.12). If $\sigma_r > \sigma_{r+1}$, then $\sigma_i > \sigma_{r+1}$ for $i = 1, \ldots, r$ and we conclude that $\alpha_i = 0$ for $i = 1, \ldots, r$. Since the α's are not all zero, σ_{r+1} cannot be zero and we must have $\mathbf{\Gamma}_{\widehat{G}} v_{r+1} = 0$. Since the labelling is arbitrary, we conclude $\mathbf{\Gamma}_{\widehat{G}} v_j = 0$ for any i such that $\sigma_j = \sigma_{r+1}$. ■

Since the infinity norm is never smaller than the Hankel norm, it follows from Lemma 10.2.1 that any $\widehat{\boldsymbol{G}} \in \mathcal{RH}_\infty$ of McMillan degree r satisfies

$$\|\boldsymbol{G} - \widehat{\boldsymbol{G}}\|_\infty \geq \sigma_{r+1}(\boldsymbol{G}).$$

Thus σ_{r+1} is also a lower bound on the infinity norm of the error incurred in approximating $\boldsymbol{G}$ by $\widehat{\boldsymbol{G}}$.

Main points of the section

1. The Hankel operator maps inputs that are nonzero only in negative time to the future part of the output. The rank of the Hankel operator $\mathbf{\Gamma}_G$ is equal to the McMillan degree of its symbol $\boldsymbol{G}$. The Hankel norm is the square root of the energy gain from inputs that are only nonzero in negative time to the future part of the output.
2. The Hankel norm is no greater than the infinity norm. Indeed,

   $$\|\boldsymbol{G}\|_H \leq \|\boldsymbol{G} - \boldsymbol{F}\|_\infty$$

   for any anticausal system $\boldsymbol{F}$. If $\boldsymbol{F} \in \mathcal{RH}_\infty^-$, then $\boldsymbol{F}$ is anticausal.
3. The singular values of the Hankel operator $\mathbf{\Gamma}_G$ are given by

   $$\sigma_i(\boldsymbol{G}) = \lambda_i^{\frac{1}{2}}(PQ),$$

   in which P and Q are the controllability and observability gramians of a minimal realization of $\boldsymbol{G}$.
4. The Schmidt decomposition is a singular value decomposition of the Hankel operator $\mathbf{\Gamma}_G$. The Schmidt vectors are easily determined from a state-space realization of $\boldsymbol{G}$.
5. The Hankel norm of the error incurred in approximating $\boldsymbol{G}$ by a system $\widehat{\boldsymbol{G}}$ of McMillan degree r is at least as large as $\sigma_{r+1}(\boldsymbol{G})$. If this lower bound is attained, $\mathbf{\Gamma}_G v_{r+1} = 0$ for any Schmidt vector v_{r+1} corresponding to $\sigma_{r+1}(\boldsymbol{G})$.

10.3 Suboptimal Hankel norm approximations

The construction we will use for the solution of the optimal Hankel norm model reduction problem involves embedding $\boldsymbol{G}$ in an allpass system with dimensions exceeding those of $\boldsymbol{G}$. To motivate this construction, suppose we can find a $\widehat{\boldsymbol{G}} \in \mathcal{RH}_\infty$ of McMillan degree r and an anticausal system $\boldsymbol{F}$ such that $\gamma^{-1}(\boldsymbol{G}-\widehat{\boldsymbol{G}}-\boldsymbol{F})$ is allpass. Then $\|\boldsymbol{G}-\widehat{\boldsymbol{G}}-\boldsymbol{F}\|_\infty = \gamma$ and we conclude from inequality (10.2.9) that $\|\boldsymbol{G}-\widehat{\boldsymbol{G}}\|_H \leq \gamma$. We shall see that the construction can be performed for any value of $\gamma > \sigma_{r+1}(\boldsymbol{G})$, which shows that the lower bound of Lemma 10.2.1 is the infimal error. A greater level of sophistication is required to show that this infimum can be achieved (*i.e.*, the infimum is a minimum); we postpone a consideration of this case to Section 10.4.

10.3.1 Allpass embedding

Assume that $\boldsymbol{G} \in \mathcal{RH}_\infty$ is $p \times m$ with minimal realization (A, B, C, D). It is important to note that this implies that A is asymptotically stable. Now write the augmented system

$$\begin{aligned} \boldsymbol{G}_a &= \begin{bmatrix} \boldsymbol{G} & 0 \\ 0 & 0 \end{bmatrix} \\ &\overset{s}{=} \left[\begin{array}{c|cc} A & B & 0 \\ \hline C & D & 0 \\ 0 & 0 & 0 \end{array}\right] = \left[\begin{array}{c|c} A & B_a \\ \hline C_a & D_a \end{array}\right], \end{aligned} \tag{10.3.1}$$

in which the dimensions of the zero blocks will be fixed at a later stage. In the next phase of the construction we use Theorem 3.2.1 to find a system $\boldsymbol{Q}_a$ such that the error system

$$\boldsymbol{E}_a = \boldsymbol{G}_a - \boldsymbol{Q}_a$$

satisfies

$$\boldsymbol{E}_a^\sim \boldsymbol{E}_a = \gamma^2 I. \tag{10.3.2}$$

If $\boldsymbol{Q}_a$ has realization

$$\boldsymbol{Q}_a \overset{s}{=} \left[\begin{array}{c|c} \widehat{A} & \widehat{B} \\ \hline \widehat{C} & \widehat{D} \end{array}\right],$$

$\boldsymbol{E}_a$ is given by

$$\boldsymbol{E}_a \overset{s}{=} \left[\begin{array}{cc|c} A & 0 & B_a \\ 0 & \widehat{A} & \widehat{B} \\ \hline C_a & -\widehat{C} & D_a - \widehat{D} \end{array}\right] = \left[\begin{array}{c|c} A_e & B_e \\ \hline C_e & D_e \end{array}\right]. \tag{10.3.3}$$

By Theorem 3.2.1, $\boldsymbol{E}_a$ satisfies (10.3.2) if there exists a nonsingular Q_e such that

$$A_e' Q_e + Q_e A_e + C_e' C_e = 0 \tag{10.3.4}$$

$$\begin{aligned} D_e'C_e + B_e'Q_e &= 0 \qquad (10.3.5)\\ D_e'D_e &= \gamma^2 I. \qquad (10.3.6) \end{aligned}$$

Our aim is to construct matrices $\widehat{A}$, $\widehat{B}$, $\widehat{C}$, $\widehat{D}$ and a matrix Q_e to satisfy these all-pass equations. Before we begin the main construction, we determine a connection between Q_e defined by (10.3.4) and the controllability gramian P_e defined by

$$A_eP_e + P_eA_e' + B_eB_e' = 0. \qquad (10.3.7)$$

Subtract Q_e(10.3.7)Q_e from $\gamma^2\times$(10.3.4) while making use of (10.3.5) to obtain

$$Q_eA_e(\gamma^2 I - P_eQ_e) + (\gamma^2 I - Q_eP_e)A_e'Q_e + C_e'(\gamma^2 I - D_eD_e')C_e = 0.$$

At this point we fix the dimensions of the zero blocks in (10.3.1) so that D_a and D_e are square. If we make D_e $(p+m)\times(m+p)$, then the satisfaction of (10.3.6) requires $\gamma^{-2}D_e' = D_e^{-1}$. Choosing $\gamma^{-1}D_e$ to be any $(p+m)\times(m+p)$ orthogonal matrix, we see that

$$Q_eA_e(\gamma^2 I - P_eQ_e) + (\gamma^2 I - Q_eP_e)A_e'Q_e = 0.$$

If $\boldsymbol{E}_a$ is to have bounded infinity norm, it must not have any poles on the imaginary axis. If the realization (A_e, B_e, C_e, D_e) is to be minimal, A_e must not have imaginary axis eigenvalues, Q_e should be nonsingular and P_e and Q_e should satisfy $P_eQ_e = \gamma^2 I$.

By examining the (1,1)-blocks of (10.3.4) and (10.3.7) we see that Q_e and P_e have the form

$$P_e = \begin{bmatrix} P & P_{12} \\ P_{12}' & P_{22} \end{bmatrix}, \qquad Q_e = \begin{bmatrix} Q & Q_{21}' \\ Q_{21} & Q_{22} \end{bmatrix},$$

in which P and Q are the controllability and observability gramians of $\boldsymbol{G}$ (and of $\boldsymbol{G}_a$). From the $(1,1)$-block of $P_eQ_e = \gamma^2 I$ we see that $P_{12}Q_{21} = \gamma^2 I - PQ$. In the suboptimal case that

$$\gamma \neq \sigma_i(\boldsymbol{G}), \qquad i = 1, \ldots, n, \qquad (10.3.8)$$

it is clear that $P_{12}Q_{21}$ must have rank n, since γ^2 is not an eigenvalue of PQ, which shows that the dimension of $\widehat{A}$ must be at least n. In order that $\boldsymbol{Q}_a$ has the least possible degree, we choose the dimension of $\widehat{A}$ to be n. This means that P_{12} and Q_{21} are square and nonsingular. Since the basis for the state-space of $\boldsymbol{Q}_a$ is arbitrary, we may use this freedom to scale the nonsingular matrix P_{12} to be the identity matrix. Therefore $Q_{21} = \gamma^2 I - PQ$ and the $(2,2)$-blocks of P_e and Q_e are now determined from $P_eQ_e = \gamma^2 I$. Summarizing, we have

$$P_e = \begin{bmatrix} P & I \\ I & E^{-1}Q \end{bmatrix}, \qquad Q_e = \begin{bmatrix} Q & -E \\ -E' & PE \end{bmatrix}, \qquad (10.3.9)$$

in which

$$E = QP - \gamma^2 I. \qquad (10.3.10)$$

The matrices $\widehat{A}$, $\widehat{B}$ and $\widehat{C}$ are now easily determined. The (1,1)-block of (10.3.5) gives

$$\widehat{B} = E^{-1}(QB_a + C_a' D_e), \tag{10.3.11}$$

while the (1,1)-block of $D_e(10.3.5)P_e$ yields

$$\widehat{C} = D_e B_a' + C_a P. \tag{10.3.12}$$

Finally, the (2,1)-block of (10.3.7) and the (1,2)-block of (10.3.4) yield

$$\widehat{A} = -A' - \widehat{B}B_a' \tag{10.3.13}$$

and

$$\widehat{A} = -E^{-1}(A'E + C_a'\widehat{C}) \tag{10.3.14}$$

respectively, which are two alternative expressions for $\widehat{A}$. The construction of $\boldsymbol{G}_a$ is completed by choosing any $\widehat{D}$ such that $\gamma^{-1}D_e$ is a $(p+m)\times(m+p)$ orthogonal matrix. The obvious choice is

$$\widehat{D} = \begin{bmatrix} D & \gamma I_p \\ \gamma I_m & 0 \end{bmatrix}. \tag{10.3.15}$$

In summary, we take (A, B, C, D), solve for the controllability and observability gramians P and Q and define $(\widehat{A}, \widehat{B}, \widehat{C}, \widehat{D})$ according to the above equations. Since the allpass equations (10.3.4) to (10.3.6) are satisfied, $\boldsymbol{E}_a$ satisfies (10.3.2) as required. We note also that since $\boldsymbol{E}_a$ is square, we must have $\gamma^{-2}\boldsymbol{E}_a^{\sim} = \boldsymbol{E}_a^{-1}$, which implies that $\boldsymbol{E}_a\boldsymbol{E}_a^{\sim} = \gamma^2 I$.

Before proceeding to apply the allpass embedding to the solution of the Hankel norm model reduction problem, we verify that the realizations (A_e, B_e, C_e, D_e) and $(\widehat{A}, \widehat{B}, \widehat{C}, \widehat{D})$ are minimal. Since Q_e and P_e are nonsingular, the minimality of (A_e, B_e, C_e, D_e) is assured provided A_e has no imaginary axis eigenvalues. Since A_e is block diagonal and A is asymptotically stable, we need to show that $\widehat{A}$ has no imaginary axis eigenvalues. The (2,2)-block of (10.3.4) is

$$PE\widehat{A} + \widehat{A}'PE + \widehat{C}'\widehat{C} = 0. \tag{10.3.16}$$

If $\widehat{A}x = j\omega x$, multiplying (10.3.16) on the left by x^* and on the right by x gives $\widehat{C}x = 0$. From (10.3.14) we obtain $A'Ex = -j\omega Ex$, which implies that $x = 0$ since E is nonsingular and A is asymptotically stable. Thus $\widehat{A}$ has no imaginary axis eigenvalue and we conclude that (A_e, B_e, C_e, D_e) is minimal. From the structure of the realization (A_e, B_e, C_e, D_e), we conclude that $(\widehat{A}, \widehat{B}, \widehat{C}, \widehat{D})$ is also minimal, thereby establishing that the McMillan degree of $\boldsymbol{Q}_a$ is n.

10.3.2 One solution to the model reduction problem

The allpass embedding we have constructed has a number of properties we shall need in order to solve the model reduction problem. In the first place, it is clearly important to know about the number of poles of $\boldsymbol{Q}_a$ in the left-half plane.

We now show that the dimension of the asymptotically stable subspace of $\widehat{A}$ is the number of Hankel singular values of $\boldsymbol{G}$ that are larger than γ. Let V_1 be a (real) basis for the asymptotically stable subspace of $\widehat{A}$ and let $\widehat{A}V_1 = V_1\Lambda$. Then $V_1'(10.3.16)V_1$ yields

$$(V_1'PEV_1)\Lambda + \Lambda'(V_1'PEV_1) + (\widehat{C}V_1)'(\widehat{C}V_1) = 0.$$

Since Λ is asymptotically stable and $(\Lambda, \widehat{C}V_1)$ is observable (since $(\widehat{A}, \widehat{C})$ is observable), we conclude that $V_1'PEV_1 > 0$. Similarly, if V_2 is a (real) basis for the antistable subspace of $\widehat{A}$, then $V_2'PEV_2 < 0$.

If $\gamma > \sigma_1$, then $PE = P(QP - \gamma^2 I)$ is negative definite and we conclude that all the eigenvalues of $\widehat{A}$ are in the open-right-half plane. If $\gamma < \sigma_n$, then PE is positive definite and we conclude that $\widehat{A}$ is asymptotically stable. Finally, if

$$\sigma_r(\boldsymbol{G}) > \gamma > \sigma_{r+1}(\boldsymbol{G}), \qquad r = 1, \ldots, n$$

then PE has r positive and $n - r$ negative eigenvalues and we conclude that $\widehat{A}$ has r eigenvalues in the open-left-half plane and $n - r$ eigenvalues in the open-right-half plane. It is convenient to introduce the notation $\mathcal{RH}_\infty^-(r)$ for a transfer function matrix in $\mathcal{RL}_\infty$ that has at most r poles in the open-left-half plane. Thus $\sigma_r(\boldsymbol{G}) > \gamma > \sigma_{r+1}(\boldsymbol{G})$ implies that $\boldsymbol{Q}_a \in \mathcal{RH}_\infty^-(r)$.

The next property concerns the zeros of the $(1,2)$- and $(2,1)$-blocks of $\boldsymbol{Q}_a$, which we will call $\boldsymbol{Q}_{a12}$ and $\boldsymbol{Q}_{a21}$ respectively. The realization of $\boldsymbol{Q}_a$ has the form

$$\boldsymbol{Q}_a \stackrel{s}{=} \left[\begin{array}{c|cc} \widehat{A} & \widehat{B}_1 & \widehat{B}_2 \\ \hline \widehat{C}_1 & D & \gamma I_p \\ \widehat{C}_2 & \gamma I_m & 0 \end{array}\right].$$

From the definitions in (10.3.13) to (10.3.15) we obtain

$$\begin{aligned} \begin{bmatrix} \widehat{A} - \lambda I & \widehat{B}_1 \\ \widehat{C}_2 & \gamma I \end{bmatrix} &= \begin{bmatrix} -A' - \lambda I & \widehat{B}_1 \\ 0 & \gamma I \end{bmatrix} \begin{bmatrix} I & 0 \\ -B' & I \end{bmatrix} \\ \begin{bmatrix} \widehat{A} - \lambda I & \widehat{B}_2 \\ \widehat{C}_1 & \gamma I \end{bmatrix} &= \begin{bmatrix} I & -E^{-1}C' \\ 0 & I \end{bmatrix} \begin{bmatrix} -E^{-1}A'E - \lambda I & 0 \\ \widehat{C}_1 & \gamma I \end{bmatrix}. \end{aligned}$$

It is now clear that the zeros of $\boldsymbol{Q}_{a12}$ and $\boldsymbol{Q}_{a21}$, along with any uncontrollable or unobservable modes, are all in the open-right-half plane since A is asymptotically stable.

The allpass embedding and Lemma 10.2.1 establish the following result, which gives one solution to the suboptimal Hankel norm model reduction problem.

Theorem 10.3.1 *If $\boldsymbol{G} \in \mathcal{RH}_\infty$, there exists a $\widehat{\boldsymbol{G}} \in \mathcal{RH}_\infty$ of McMillan degree at most r and an $\boldsymbol{F} \in \mathcal{H}_\infty^-$ such that $\|\boldsymbol{G} - \widehat{\boldsymbol{G}} - \boldsymbol{F}\|_\infty < \gamma$ if and only if $\gamma > \sigma_{r+1}(\boldsymbol{G})$.*

Proof. If $\|\boldsymbol{G} - \widehat{\boldsymbol{G}} - \boldsymbol{F}\|_\infty < \gamma$, then

$$\gamma > \|\boldsymbol{G} - \widehat{\boldsymbol{G}} - \boldsymbol{F}\|_\infty \geq \|\boldsymbol{G} - \widehat{\boldsymbol{G}}\|_H \geq \sigma_{r+1}(\boldsymbol{G}).$$

Conversely, for any $\gamma > \sigma_{r+1}(\boldsymbol{G})$, $\gamma \neq \sigma_i(\boldsymbol{G})$, the construction given in Section 10.3.1 results in $\boldsymbol{Q}_a \in \mathcal{RH}_\infty^-(r)$ such that $\|\boldsymbol{G}_a - \boldsymbol{Q}_a\|_\infty = \gamma$. Since $\boldsymbol{Q}_{a12}$ and $\boldsymbol{Q}_{a21}$ have no zeros on the imaginary axis, we must have $\|\boldsymbol{G} - \boldsymbol{Q}_{a11}\|_\infty < \gamma$. Therefore, $\widehat{\boldsymbol{G}}$ and $\boldsymbol{F}$ are obtained from a stable/unstable decomposition of $\boldsymbol{Q}_{a11}$. ■

The reduced-order model we seek is any stable part of $\boldsymbol{Q}_{a11}$.[6] The choice of the direct feedthrough term of the stable part is arbitrary because it is irrelevant to the Hankel norm. It is of interest when we consider the infinity norm in Section 10.5.

10.3.3 All solutions to the model reduction problem

The allpass embedding described in Section 10.3.1 actually captures all solutions to the Hankel norm model reduction problem. The proof uses the "small gain" results for contractive linear fractional transformations from Chapter 4 .

Theorem 10.3.2 *Let $\boldsymbol{G} \in \mathcal{RH}_\infty$ and γ be given such that $\sigma_r(\boldsymbol{G}) > \gamma > \sigma_{r+1}(\boldsymbol{G})$. Then every $\boldsymbol{Q} \in \mathcal{RH}_\infty^-(r)$ that satisfies*

$$\|\boldsymbol{G} - \boldsymbol{Q}\|_\infty < \gamma \tag{10.3.17}$$

is generated by

$$\boldsymbol{Q} = \mathcal{F}_\ell(\boldsymbol{Q}_a, \boldsymbol{U}), \qquad \boldsymbol{U} \in \mathcal{RH}_\infty^-, \quad \|\boldsymbol{U}\|_\infty < 1/\gamma. \tag{10.3.18}$$

Proof. Suppose $\boldsymbol{Q}$ is any function such that (10.3.17) holds. Since $\boldsymbol{Q}_{a12}$ and $\boldsymbol{Q}_{a21}$ are nonsingular on the imaginary axis and $\boldsymbol{Q}_{a22}(\infty) = 0$, there exists a $\boldsymbol{U} \in \mathcal{RL}_\infty$ such that $\boldsymbol{Q} = \mathcal{F}_\ell(\boldsymbol{Q}_a, \boldsymbol{U})$ (just solve this equation for $\boldsymbol{U}$). Thus

$$\boldsymbol{G} - \boldsymbol{Q} = \mathcal{F}_\ell(\boldsymbol{G}_a - \boldsymbol{Q}_a, \boldsymbol{U}) = \mathcal{F}_\ell(\boldsymbol{E}_a, \boldsymbol{U}),$$

in which $\gamma^{-1}\boldsymbol{E}_a$ is allpass. It now follows from Theorem 4.3.2 that $\|\boldsymbol{U}\|_\infty < \gamma^{-1}$. If $\boldsymbol{Q} \in \mathcal{RH}_\infty^-(r)$, the proven properties of $\boldsymbol{Q}_a$ and Lemma 4.3.4 imply that $\boldsymbol{U} \in \mathcal{RH}_\infty^-$.

Conversely, if $\boldsymbol{Q}$ is given by (10.3.18), the result is immediate from Theorem 4.3.2 and Lemma 4.3.4. ■

We obtain all solutions to the Hankel norm model reduction problem, *i.e.*, all $\widehat{\boldsymbol{G}} \in \mathcal{RH}_\infty$ of degree at most r satisfying $\|\boldsymbol{G} - \widehat{\boldsymbol{G}}\|_H < \gamma$, by selecting any stable part of any system $\boldsymbol{Q} \in \mathcal{RH}_\infty^-(r)$ that is generated by (10.3.18).

---

[6] A stable part of $\boldsymbol{Q}_{a11} \in \mathcal{RL}_\infty$ is any $\widehat{\boldsymbol{G}} \in \mathcal{RH}_\infty$ such that $\boldsymbol{Q}_{a11} - \widehat{\boldsymbol{G}} \in \mathcal{RH}_\infty^-$. A stable part is unique up to the direct feedthrough or D-matrix of the system. By the Paley-Wiener theorem, this is equivalent to a causal/anticausal decomposition of the system and the nonuniqueness arises because the present is considered part of the past and part of the future.

Main points of the section

1. Provided $\gamma \neq \sigma_i(\boldsymbol{G})$, there exists a $\boldsymbol{Q}_a$ such that $\gamma^{-1}(\boldsymbol{G}_a - \boldsymbol{Q}_a)$ is square and allpass.
2. The system $\boldsymbol{Q}_a$ has no poles on the imaginary axis. The number of poles of $\boldsymbol{Q}_a$ in the open-left (-right)-half plane is exactly the number of Hankel singular values of $\boldsymbol{G}$ that are larger (smaller) than γ.
3. There exists a $\widehat{\boldsymbol{G}} \in \mathcal{RH}_\infty$ of McMillan degree r or less such that $\|\boldsymbol{G}-\widehat{\boldsymbol{G}}\|_H < \gamma$ if and only if $\gamma > \sigma_{r+1}(\boldsymbol{G})$. In this case one solution is the stable part of $\boldsymbol{Q}_{a11}$ as constructed in Section 10.3.1.
4. If $\sigma_r(\boldsymbol{G}) > \gamma > \sigma_{r+1}(\boldsymbol{G})$, then every solution to the suboptimal Hankel norm model reduction problem of finding $\widehat{\boldsymbol{G}}$ of McMillan degree (at most) r such that $\|\boldsymbol{G} - \widehat{\boldsymbol{G}}\|_H < \gamma$ is generated by taking the stable part of the linear fractional transformation $\mathcal{F}_\ell(\boldsymbol{Q}_a, \boldsymbol{U})$, in which $\boldsymbol{Q}_a$ is constructed as shown in Section 10.3.1. The parameter $\boldsymbol{U} \in \mathcal{RH}_\infty^-$ must satisfy $\|\boldsymbol{U}\|_\infty < \gamma^{-1}$.

10.4 Optimal Hankel norm approximation

We will now extend our analysis to the optimal case in which we seek a $\widehat{\boldsymbol{G}} \in \mathcal{RH}_\infty$ of McMillan degree at most r such that $\|\boldsymbol{G} - \widehat{\boldsymbol{G}}\|_H = \sigma_{r+1}(\boldsymbol{G})$. This is the optimal case, because $\sigma_{r+1}(\boldsymbol{G})$ is the greatest lower bound on the achievable Hankel norm (Theorem 10.3.1). In order to show that this lower bound is in fact achievable, we reconsider the construction of the allpass embedding in Section 10.3.1.

10.4.1 Optimal allpass embedding

We return to the construction of Section 10.3.1 and instead of making the assumption (10.3.8), which says that γ is not a Hankel singular value of $\boldsymbol{G}$, we assume that

$$\gamma = \sigma_{r+1}(\boldsymbol{G}). \tag{10.4.1}$$

Since $\gamma = \sigma_{r+1}(\boldsymbol{G})$ and $P_{12}Q_{21} = \gamma^2 I - PQ$, $P_{12}Q_{21}$ must have rank $n - l$ where l is the multiplicity of $\sigma_{r+1}(\boldsymbol{G})$.

Suppose the realization of $\boldsymbol{G}_a$ is chosen so that

$$P = \begin{bmatrix} P_1 & 0 \\ 0 & \sigma_{r+1}I_l \end{bmatrix}, \qquad Q = \begin{bmatrix} Q_1 & 0 \\ 0 & \sigma_{r+1}I_l \end{bmatrix}. \tag{10.4.2}$$

To see that this is always possible, we need only recall that an appropriately ordered balanced realization of $\boldsymbol{G}_a$ has this form. By choosing the dimension of $\widehat{A}$ to be $n-l$, we see that P_{12} and Q_{21} are full column rank and full row rank respectively and that we may use our freedom to choose the basis for the state space in the realization of $\boldsymbol{Q}_a$ to obtain $P_{12} = \begin{bmatrix} I & 0 \end{bmatrix}'$. It now follows from the various partitions of $P_e Q_e = \gamma^2 I$ that

$$P_e = \begin{bmatrix} P_1 & 0 & I \\ 0 & \gamma I & 0 \\ I & 0 & E_1^{-1} Q_1 \end{bmatrix}, \qquad Q_e = \begin{bmatrix} Q_1 & 0 & -E_1 \\ 0 & \gamma I & 0 \\ -E_1' & 0 & P_1 E_1 \end{bmatrix}, \tag{10.4.3}$$

in which

$$E_1 = Q_1 P_1 - \gamma^2 I_{n-l}. \tag{10.4.4}$$

In order to determine the matrices $\widehat{A}$, $\widehat{B}$ and $\widehat{C}$, we begin by partitioning A, B, C conformably with P and Q, to get

$$\begin{aligned} A &= \begin{bmatrix} A_{11} & A_{12} \\ A_{21} & A_{22} \end{bmatrix}, \qquad B = \begin{bmatrix} B_1 \\ B_2 \end{bmatrix}, \\ C &= \begin{bmatrix} C_1 & C_2 \end{bmatrix}. \end{aligned} \tag{10.4.5}$$

The $(1,1)$-block of $D_e(10.3.5)P_e$ gives

$$\widehat{B} = E_1^{-1}(Q_1 \begin{bmatrix} B_1 & 0 \end{bmatrix} + \begin{bmatrix} C_1' & 0 \end{bmatrix} D_e), \tag{10.4.6}$$

and as before the (1,1)-block of (10.3.5) yields

$$\widehat{C} = D_e \begin{bmatrix} B_1' \\ 0 \end{bmatrix} + \begin{bmatrix} C_1 \\ 0 \end{bmatrix} P_1. \tag{10.4.7}$$

The $(3,1)$-block of (10.3.7) gives

$$\widehat{A} = -A_{11}' - \widehat{B} \begin{bmatrix} B_1' \\ 0 \end{bmatrix} \tag{10.4.8}$$

while the $(1,3)$-block of (10.3.4) yields the alternative expression

$$\widehat{A} = -E_1^{-1}(A_{11}' E_1 + \begin{bmatrix} C_1' & 0 \end{bmatrix} \widehat{C}). \tag{10.4.9}$$

As part of the process of determining D_e, we note from the $(1,2)$-blocks of (10.3.5) that in addition to (10.3.6), D_e must satisfy

$$\begin{bmatrix} C_2' & 0 \end{bmatrix} D_e + \gamma \begin{bmatrix} B_2 & 0 \end{bmatrix} = 0. \tag{10.4.10}$$

To see that such a D_e exists, we note from the $(2,2)$-blocks of (10.3.4) and (10.3.7) that $B_2 B_2' = C_2' C_2$. From this fact we obtain the following lemma.

Lemma 10.4.1 *Suppose $B_2 \in \mathbb{R}^{l \times m}$ and $C_2 \in \mathbb{R}^{p \times l}$ satisfy $B_2 B_2' = C_2' C_2$ and let $\ell = \operatorname{rank}(B_2 B_2')$. Then there exists a $(p+m-\ell) \times (m+p-\ell)$ matrix D_e satisfying (10.3.6) and (10.4.10). Moreover, the $(m-\ell) \times (p-\ell)$ $(2,2)$-block of D_e can be chosen to be zero.*

Proof. Since $B_2B_2' = C_2'C_2$ there exists a $p \times m$ constant matrix U such that $B_2 = C_2'U$ with $U'U \leq I$ and all the singular values of U either one or zero.[7] If B_2B_2' has rank ℓ, U has singular value decomposition

$$U = \begin{bmatrix} Y_1 & Y_2 \end{bmatrix} \begin{bmatrix} I_\ell & 0 \\ 0 & 0 \end{bmatrix} \begin{bmatrix} Z_1' \\ Z_2' \end{bmatrix}.$$

Some routine algebra shows that

$$D_e = -\gamma \begin{bmatrix} U & Y_2 \\ Z_2' & 0 \end{bmatrix}$$

has the required properties. ■

Since $\widehat{D} = D_a - D_e$, we obtain

$$\widehat{D} = \begin{matrix} p \\ m-\ell \end{matrix} \overset{\begin{matrix} m & \quad m-\ell \end{matrix}}{\begin{bmatrix} D + \gamma U & \gamma Y_2 \\ \gamma Z_2' & 0 \end{bmatrix}} \tag{10.4.11}$$

as a suitable selection for $\widehat{D}$. The dimensions of the augmented realizations are fixed and the construction of $\boldsymbol{Q}_a$ is complete. The augmented systems have ℓ fewer rows and columns than they did in the suboptimal case with $1 \leq \ell \leq \min(l, m, p)$. In the single-input or single-output case $\ell = 1$ and one of the dimensions of the augmented systems is the same as the corresponding dimension of $\boldsymbol{G}$.

In order to establish the minimality of the realization of $\boldsymbol{Q}_a$ and $\boldsymbol{E}_a$, we must show that $\widehat{A}$ has no imaginary axis eigenvalues. It is easy to check that $\widehat{A}$ and $\widehat{C}$ satisfy

$$\widehat{A}'P_1E_1 + P_1E_1\widehat{A} + \widehat{C}'\widehat{C} = 0. \tag{10.4.12}$$

Hence $\widehat{A}x = j\omega x$ implies that $\widehat{C}x = 0$ and multiplying (10.3.4) by $\begin{bmatrix} 0 & x' \end{bmatrix}'$ yields

$$(j\omega I + A')\begin{bmatrix} E_1 \\ 0 \end{bmatrix} x = 0.$$

Since E_1 is nonsingular and A is asymptotically stable, x must be zero and we conclude that $\widehat{A}$ has no imaginary axis eigenvalue. It follows from the nonsingularity of Q_e and P_e that (A_e, B_e, C_e, D_e) is minimal and consequently that $(\widehat{A}, \widehat{B}, \widehat{C}, \widehat{D})$ is minimal also.

10.4.2 One optimal Hankel norm approximant

We exhibit one solution to the optimal problem by following the approach used in the suboptimal case. Arguments that are identical to those presented in the

[7] See Problem 9.1 or Lemma 3.5 in [71].

suboptimal case show that the number of eigenvalues of $\widehat{A}$ in the open-left-half plane is exactly the number of positive eigenvalues of P_1E_1. That is, the number poles of $\boldsymbol{Q}_a$ in the open-left-half plane is the number of Hankel singular values of $\boldsymbol{G}$ that are larger than $\gamma = \sigma_{r+1}(\boldsymbol{G})$.

We have established the following result:

Theorem 10.4.2 *If $\boldsymbol{G} \in \mathcal{RH}_\infty$, there exists a $\widehat{\boldsymbol{G}} \in \mathcal{RH}_\infty$ of McMillan degree at most r and an $\boldsymbol{F} \in \mathcal{H}_\infty^-$ such that $\|\boldsymbol{G} - \widehat{\boldsymbol{G}} - \boldsymbol{F}\|_\infty \leq \gamma$ if and only if $\gamma \geq \sigma_{r+1}(\boldsymbol{G})$.*

Proof. If $\|\boldsymbol{G} - \widehat{\boldsymbol{G}} - \boldsymbol{F}\|_\infty \leq \gamma$, then

$$\gamma \geq \|\boldsymbol{G} - \widehat{\boldsymbol{G}} - \boldsymbol{F}\|_\infty \geq \|\boldsymbol{G} - \widehat{\boldsymbol{G}}\|_H \geq \sigma_{r+1}(\boldsymbol{G}).$$

Conversely, if $\gamma = \sigma_{r+1}(\boldsymbol{G})$ then the construction given in Section 10.4.1 results in $\boldsymbol{Q}_a \in \mathcal{RH}_\infty^-(r)$ such that $\|\boldsymbol{G}_a - \boldsymbol{Q}_a\|_\infty = \gamma$. Letting $\widehat{\boldsymbol{G}}$ be any stable part of $\boldsymbol{Q}_{a11}$ and $\boldsymbol{F} = \boldsymbol{Q}_{a11} - \boldsymbol{G}$, we have that $\|\boldsymbol{G} - \widehat{\boldsymbol{G}} - \boldsymbol{F}\|_\infty \leq \gamma$. ■

An optimal solution to the Hankel norm model reduction problem is obtained by taking any stable part of $\boldsymbol{Q}_{a11}$ as constructed in Section 10.4.1.

10.4.3 All optimal approximants

Capturing all solutions to the optimal Hankel norm model reduction problem is more complicated than in its suboptimal counterpart described in Section 10.3.3. The added difficulty comes from the fact that $\boldsymbol{Q}_{a12}$ and $\boldsymbol{Q}_{a21}$ are no longer square. As a result, a linear fractional map of the form $\mathcal{F}_\ell(\boldsymbol{Q}_a, \boldsymbol{U})$ does not generate the whole of $\mathcal{RH}_\infty^-(r)$. Nevertheless, as we will now demonstrate, it does still capture all solutions. The proof relies on three facts. Firstly, $\boldsymbol{Q}_{a12}$ and $\boldsymbol{Q}_{a21}$ have full rank in the closed-left-half plane. Secondly, the difference between any two error systems, $\boldsymbol{E}_1 = \boldsymbol{G} - \boldsymbol{Q}_1$ and $\boldsymbol{E}_2 = \boldsymbol{G} - \boldsymbol{Q}_2$ say, have the properties

$$(\boldsymbol{E}_1 - \boldsymbol{E}_2)\boldsymbol{V}_{r+1}(-s) = 0$$

and

$$(\boldsymbol{E}_1 - \boldsymbol{E}_2)^\sim \boldsymbol{W}_{r+1}(s) = 0,$$

in which the columns of $\boldsymbol{V}_{r+1}$ and $\boldsymbol{W}_{r+1}$ are the Laplace transforms of the Schmidt vectors of $\boldsymbol{\Gamma}_G$ corresponding to $\sigma_{r+1}(\boldsymbol{G})$. As a consequence, and this is the third point,

$$\mathcal{F}_\ell\left(\begin{bmatrix} 0 & \boldsymbol{Q}_{a12} \\ \boldsymbol{Q}_{a21} & \boldsymbol{Q}_{a22} \end{bmatrix}, \boldsymbol{U}\right)$$

generates the difference between every solution and the solution $\boldsymbol{Q}_{a11}$. We will now prove these claims.

As we have already shown, $\boldsymbol{Q}_a$ has a realization of the form

$$\boldsymbol{Q}_a \stackrel{s}{=} \left[\begin{array}{c|cc} \widehat{A} & \widehat{B}_1 & \widehat{B}_2 \\ \hline \widehat{C}_1 & \widehat{D}_{11} & \widehat{D}_{12} \\ \widehat{C}_2 & \widehat{D}_{21} & 0 \end{array}\right].$$

The definitions of these matrices, as given in (10.4.8) to (10.4.11), may be used to show that

$$\begin{aligned} \begin{bmatrix} \widehat{A}-\lambda I & \widehat{B}_1 \\ \widehat{C}_2 & \widehat{D}_{21} \end{bmatrix} &= \begin{bmatrix} -A_{11}'-\lambda I & \widehat{B}_1 \\ 0 & \widehat{D}_{21} \end{bmatrix} \begin{bmatrix} I & 0 \\ -B_1' & I \end{bmatrix} \\ \begin{bmatrix} \widehat{A}-\lambda I & \widehat{B}_2 \\ \widehat{C}_1 & \widehat{D}_{12} \end{bmatrix} &= \begin{bmatrix} I & -E_1^{-1}C_1' \\ 0 & I \end{bmatrix} \begin{bmatrix} -E_1^{-1}A_{11}'E_1-\lambda I & 0 \\ \widehat{C}_1 & \widehat{D}_{12} \end{bmatrix}. \end{aligned}$$

From the decomposition in (10.4.2), it follows that A_{11} is asymptotically stable (see Lemma 9.4.1). We therefore conclude that $\boldsymbol{Q}_{a12}$ and $\boldsymbol{Q}_{a21}$ have full column rank and full row rank respectively, except at the eigenvalues of $-A_{11}$, which are in the open-right-half plane.

With P and Q as in (10.4.2), the Schmidt pairs of $\boldsymbol{G}_a$ corresponding to the l Hankel singular values that equal σ_{r+1} are the columns of

$$\begin{aligned} V_a(t) &= \frac{1}{\sqrt{\sigma_{r+1}}} B_a' e^{A't} \begin{bmatrix} 0 \\ I_l \end{bmatrix}, \qquad t \geq 0 \\ W_a(t) &= \frac{1}{\sqrt{\sigma_{r+1}}} C_a e^{At} \begin{bmatrix} 0 \\ I_l \end{bmatrix}, \qquad t \geq 0. \end{aligned}$$

The Schmidt vectors of $\boldsymbol{G}$ corresponding to the Hankel singular values that equal σ_{r+1} are obtained by dropping the subscript a.

Lemma 10.4.3 *Suppose $\boldsymbol{G} \in \mathcal{RH}_\infty$ has Hankel singular values σ_i with $\sigma_r > \sigma_{r+1}$. Suppose also that*

$$u(t) = \begin{cases} v_j(-t) & t \leq 0 \\ 0 & t > 0 \end{cases},$$

in which v_j is a Schmidt vector corresponding to any Hankel singular value $\sigma_j = \sigma_{r+1}$. If $\boldsymbol{Q} \in \mathcal{RH}_\infty^-(r)$ and

$$\|\boldsymbol{G}-\boldsymbol{Q}\|_\infty \leq \sigma_{r+1}, \tag{10.4.13}$$

then

$$(\boldsymbol{G}-\boldsymbol{Q})u(t) = \begin{cases} 0 & t < 0 \\ \sigma_{r+1} w_j(t) & t \geq 0. \end{cases}$$

If $\boldsymbol{v}_j(s)$ and $\boldsymbol{w}_j(s)$ denote the Laplace transforms of v_j and w_j, an equivalent statement is

$$(\boldsymbol{G}-\boldsymbol{Q})\boldsymbol{v}_j(-s) = \sigma_{r+1}\boldsymbol{w}_j(s).$$

By applying this result to the system $\boldsymbol{G}'$, we obtain the dual relationship

$$(\boldsymbol{G}-\boldsymbol{X})^{\sim}\boldsymbol{w}_j(s)=\sigma_{r+1}\boldsymbol{v}_j(-s).$$

Proof. Let $\boldsymbol{E}=\boldsymbol{G}-\boldsymbol{Q}$ and divide the output $y=\boldsymbol{E}u$ into $y_+\in\mathcal{L}_2[0,\infty)$ and $y_-\in\mathcal{L}_2(-\infty,0]$. By (10.4.13) and (10.2.9), any stable part of $\boldsymbol{Q}$ is an optimal degree r Hankel norm approximation of $\boldsymbol{G}$. Since y_+ is only affected by the stable part of $\boldsymbol{Q}$, we conclude from Lemma 10.2.1 that $y_+=\sigma_{r+1}w_j$. To see that $y_-=0$, we note that since $\|u\|_2=1$ and $\|\boldsymbol{E}\|_\infty\le\sigma_{r+1}$, we have

$$\sigma_{r+1}^2\ge\|y\|_2^2=\|y_+\|_2^2+\|y_-\|_2^2=\sigma_{r+1}^2+\|y_-\|_2^2.$$

Hence $y_-=0$. ■

Remark 10.4.1. As a direct consequence of this lemma, if $\boldsymbol{Q}_1\in\mathcal{RH}_\infty^-(r)$ and $\boldsymbol{Q}_2\in\mathcal{RH}_\infty^-(r)$ both satisfy (10.4.13), then

$$\begin{aligned}(\boldsymbol{Q}_1-\boldsymbol{Q}_2)\boldsymbol{v}_j(-s) &= 0\\ (\boldsymbol{Q}_1-\boldsymbol{Q}_2)^{\sim}\boldsymbol{w}_j(s) &= 0.\end{aligned}$$

This fact is essential in showing that $\mathcal{F}_\ell(\widehat{\boldsymbol{Q}}_a,\boldsymbol{U})$ generates all optimal solutions.

Remark 10.4.2. We may apply Lemma 10.4.3 to the system $\boldsymbol{G}_a$, with the system $\boldsymbol{Q}_a$ taking the role of $\boldsymbol{Q}$, to obtain

$$\boldsymbol{E}_a(s)\boldsymbol{V}_a(-s) = \sigma_{r+1}\boldsymbol{W}_a(s) \qquad (10.4.14)$$

$$\boldsymbol{E}_a^{\sim}\boldsymbol{W}_a(-s) = \sigma_{r+1}\boldsymbol{V}_a(s), \qquad (10.4.15)$$

in which

$$\begin{aligned}\boldsymbol{V}_a(s) &= \frac{1}{\sqrt{\sigma_{r+1}}}B_a'(sI-A')^{-1}\begin{bmatrix}0\\ I_l\end{bmatrix},\\ \boldsymbol{W}_a(s) &= \frac{1}{\sqrt{\sigma_{r+1}}}C_a(sI-A)^{-1}\begin{bmatrix}0\\ I_l\end{bmatrix}\end{aligned}$$

are the Laplace transforms of the Schmidt pairs associated with the Hankel singular values that are equal to $\sigma_{r+1}(\boldsymbol{G})$. Since we have explicit formulas for $\boldsymbol{E}_a$, these identities can be verified by direct calculation as requested in Problem 10.3.

Lemma 10.4.4 *Let $\boldsymbol{P}$ be a proper rational matrix partitioned such that*

$$\boldsymbol{P}=\begin{matrix} & m_1 & m_2\\ p_1 & \boldsymbol{P}_{11} & \boldsymbol{P}_{12}\\ p_2 & \boldsymbol{P}_{21} & \boldsymbol{P}_{22}\end{matrix},$$

in which $p_1 \geq m_2$ *and* $m_1 \geq p_2$ *and let* $\boldsymbol{X}$ *be a* $p_1 \times m_1$ *rational tranfer function matrix. Suppose that* $\boldsymbol{P}_{12}$ *has a proper left inverse* $\boldsymbol{P}_{12}^L$*, that* $\boldsymbol{P}_{21}$ *has a proper right inverse* $\boldsymbol{P}_{21}^R$ *and that* $\boldsymbol{P}_{22}(\infty) = 0$*. Then*

$$\boldsymbol{X} = \mathcal{F}_\ell(\boldsymbol{P}, \boldsymbol{\Phi}) \tag{10.4.16}$$

for some proper rational matrix $\boldsymbol{\Phi}$ *if and only if there exists a rational* $\boldsymbol{R}$ *such that* $\operatorname{rank}(\boldsymbol{R}) \geq p_1 - m_2$ *for almost all* s *and a rational* $\boldsymbol{S}$ *with* $\operatorname{rank}(\boldsymbol{S}) \geq m_1 - p_2$ *for almost all* s *such that*

$$\begin{aligned} \boldsymbol{R}\begin{bmatrix} \boldsymbol{X} - \boldsymbol{P}_{11} & \boldsymbol{P}_{12} \end{bmatrix} &= 0, & (10.4.17)\\ \begin{bmatrix} \boldsymbol{X} - \boldsymbol{P}_{11} \\ \boldsymbol{P}_{21} \end{bmatrix}\boldsymbol{S} &= 0. & (10.4.18) \end{aligned}$$

Proof. The assumptions on $\boldsymbol{P}_{12}$ and $\boldsymbol{P}_{21}$ ensure the existence of an $\boldsymbol{R}$ with $\operatorname{rank}(\boldsymbol{R}) \geq p_1 - m_2$ and an $\boldsymbol{S}$ with $\operatorname{rank}(\boldsymbol{S}) \geq m_1 - p_2$ such that $\boldsymbol{R}\boldsymbol{P}_{12} = 0$ and $\boldsymbol{P}_{21}\boldsymbol{S} = 0$. For such an $\boldsymbol{R}$ and $\boldsymbol{S}$, any $\boldsymbol{X}$ generated by (10.4.16) satisfies (10.4.17) and (10.4.18), since $\mathcal{F}_\ell(\boldsymbol{P}, \boldsymbol{\Phi}) = \boldsymbol{P}_{11} + \boldsymbol{P}_{12}(I - \boldsymbol{P}_{22}\boldsymbol{\Phi})^{-1}\boldsymbol{P}_{21}$. Note that $\boldsymbol{P}_{22}(\infty) = 0$ ensures that $\mathcal{F}_\ell(\boldsymbol{P}, \boldsymbol{\Phi})$ is proper.

Conversely, if $\boldsymbol{R}$ and $\boldsymbol{S}$ exist, we can choose a right inverse $\boldsymbol{R}^R$ and a left inverse $\boldsymbol{S}^L$ such that

$$\begin{bmatrix} \boldsymbol{P}_{12}^L \\ \boldsymbol{R} \end{bmatrix}\begin{bmatrix} \boldsymbol{P}_{12} & \boldsymbol{R}^R \end{bmatrix} = \begin{bmatrix} I_{m_2} & 0 \\ 0 & I_{p_1 - m_2} \end{bmatrix}$$

and

$$\begin{bmatrix} \boldsymbol{P}_{21} \\ \boldsymbol{S}^L \end{bmatrix}\begin{bmatrix} \boldsymbol{P}_{21}^R & \boldsymbol{S} \end{bmatrix} = \begin{bmatrix} I_{p_2} & 0 \\ 0 & I_{m_1 - p_2} \end{bmatrix}.$$

Hence

$$\begin{aligned} \boldsymbol{X} - \boldsymbol{P}_{11} &= \begin{bmatrix} \boldsymbol{P}_{12} & \boldsymbol{R}^R \end{bmatrix}\begin{bmatrix} \boldsymbol{P}_{12}^L \\ \boldsymbol{R} \end{bmatrix}(\boldsymbol{X} - \boldsymbol{P}_{11})\begin{bmatrix} \boldsymbol{P}_{21}^R & \boldsymbol{S} \end{bmatrix}\begin{bmatrix} \boldsymbol{P}_{21} \\ \boldsymbol{S}^L \end{bmatrix} \\ &= \boldsymbol{P}_{12}\boldsymbol{P}_{12}^L(\boldsymbol{X} - \boldsymbol{P}_{11})\boldsymbol{P}_{21}^R\boldsymbol{P}_{21}, \end{aligned}$$

in which the second equality follows from $\boldsymbol{R}(\boldsymbol{X} - \boldsymbol{P}_{11})\boldsymbol{S} = 0$. Defining $\boldsymbol{\Psi} = \boldsymbol{P}_{12}^L(\boldsymbol{X} - \boldsymbol{P}_{11})\boldsymbol{P}_{21}^R$ and $\boldsymbol{\Phi} = \boldsymbol{\Psi}(I + \boldsymbol{P}_{22}\boldsymbol{\Psi})^{-1}$, which is proper since $\boldsymbol{P}_{22}(\infty) = 0$, we see that (10.4.16) is satisfied. ∎

Theorem 10.4.5 *Let* $\boldsymbol{G} \in \mathcal{RH}_\infty$ *and* γ *be given such that* $\sigma_r > \gamma = \sigma_{r+1}(\boldsymbol{G})$*. Then every* $\boldsymbol{Q} \in \mathcal{RH}_\infty^-(r)$ *that satisfies*

$$\|\boldsymbol{G} - \boldsymbol{Q}\|_\infty \leq \gamma$$

is generated by

$$\boldsymbol{Q} = \mathcal{F}_\ell(\boldsymbol{Q}_a, \boldsymbol{U}), \qquad \boldsymbol{U} \in \mathcal{RH}_\infty^-, \quad \|\boldsymbol{U}\|_\infty \leq \sigma_{r+1}^{-1}. \tag{10.4.19}$$

The system $\boldsymbol{Q}_a$ *is as defined in Section 10.4.1, with* $\gamma = \sigma_{r+1}$.

Proof. If Q is given by (10.4.19), Theorem 4.3.2 an the allpass nature of E_a imply that $\|G - Q\|_\infty \leq \gamma$. Furthermore, Lemma 4.3.4 and the established rank properties of Q_{a12} and Q_{a21} imply that $Q \in \mathcal{RH}_\infty^-(r)$.

Conversely, if $Q \in \mathcal{RH}_\infty^-(r)$ and $\|G - Q\|_\infty \leq \gamma$, then Lemma 10.4.4, together with the Schmidt vector properties given in Lemma 10.4.3, show that there exists a proper rational U such that $Q = \mathcal{F}_\ell(Q_a, U)$. Since $Q_{a22}(\infty) = 0$, $\det(I - Q_{a22}U)(\infty) = 1$ and Theorem 4.3.2 implies that $\|U\|_\infty \leq \sigma_{r+1}^{-1}(G)$. Finally, Theorem 4.3.4 together with the rank properties of Q_{a12} and Q_{a21} prove that $U \in \mathcal{RH}_\infty^-$. ■

Remark 10.4.3. In the optimal case the dimension of Q_a drops from $(p+m) \times (p+m)$ to $(p+m-\ell) \times (p+m-\ell)$. This has the knock on effect of reducing the dimension of the free parameter U from $p \times m$ to $(p-\ell) \times (m-\ell)$. Since $1 \leq \ell \leq \min(l, m, p)$, it is clear that the optimal solution will be unique in the single-input or single-output case.

An important special case of this result is Nehari's theorem, which is given next.

10.4.4 Nehari's theorem

Theorem 10.4.6 *Suppose $G \in \mathcal{RH}_\infty$. Then*

$$\|G\|_H = \min_{F \in \mathcal{RH}_\infty^-} \|G - F\|_\infty.$$

Every $F \in \mathcal{RH}_\infty^-$ such that $\|G - F\|_\infty = \sigma_1(G)$ is generated by

$$F = \mathcal{F}_\ell(Q_a, U), \qquad U \in \mathcal{RH}_\infty^-, \quad \|U\|_\infty \leq \sigma_1^{-1}(G),$$

in which Q_a is as constructed as in Section 10.4.1 with $\gamma = \sigma_1(G)$.

Proof. This is immediate from Theorem 10.4.5 by setting $r = 0$. ■

The system F is often referred to as a *Nehari extension* of G.

Main points of the section

1. The allpass embedding of Section 10.3.1 can be carried out even if $\gamma = \sigma_{r+1}$ for some r. In this case, the dimensions of the augmented system drop from $(p+m) \times (p+m)$ to $(p+m-\ell) \times (p+m-\ell)$ with $1 \leq \ell \leq \min(l, m, p)$.
2. The number of poles of Q_a in the open-left (right)-half plane is exactly the number of Hankel singular values of G that are strictly larger (smaller) than $\gamma = \sigma_{r+1}(G)$.
3. There exists a $\widehat{G}$ of McMillan degree r such that $\|G - \widehat{G}\|_H \leq \gamma$ if and only if $\gamma \geq \sigma_{r+1}(G)$. In this case, a suitable $\widehat{G}$ is (any) stable part of the (1,1)-block of the system Q_a as constructed in Section 10.4.1 with $\gamma = \sigma_{r+1}(G)$.

4. Provided $\sigma_r(\boldsymbol{G}) > \sigma_{r+1}(\boldsymbol{G})$, every $\widehat{\boldsymbol{G}}$ of McMillan degree r (or less) that satisfies $\|\boldsymbol{G}-\widehat{\boldsymbol{G}}\|_H \leq \sigma_{r+1}$ is generated by taking (any) stable part of the linear fractional transformation $\mathcal{F}_\ell(\boldsymbol{Q}_a, \boldsymbol{U})$, in which $\sigma_{r+1}\boldsymbol{U} \in \mathcal{RH}_\infty^-$ is contractive. In the single input or single output case, the optimal reduced-order system is unique up to a constant.
5. There exists an anticausal system $\boldsymbol{F}$ such that

$$\|\boldsymbol{G}-\boldsymbol{F}\|_\infty = \|\boldsymbol{G}\|_H.$$

This is known as Nehari's theorem.

10.5 The infinity norm error bound

Because reduced-order models are often used for robust controller design, it is natural to ask if minimizing the Hankel norm of the error will result in a good approximation in the infinity norm sense. This section develops a model reduction algorithm which is optimal in the Hankel norm and which has an infinity norm error bound equal to "the sum of the tail". A bound of this type is therefore half the "twice the sum of the tail" bound obtained for balanced truncation model reduction.

The basic connection between the infinity norm and the Hankel norm is Nehari's theorem, which says that

$$\|\boldsymbol{G}-\widehat{\boldsymbol{G}}\|_H = \|\boldsymbol{G}-\widehat{\boldsymbol{G}}-\boldsymbol{F}\|_\infty$$

for some $\boldsymbol{F} \in \mathcal{RH}_\infty^-$. This gives

$$\begin{aligned}\|\boldsymbol{G}-\widehat{\boldsymbol{G}}\|_\infty &= \|\boldsymbol{G}-\widehat{\boldsymbol{G}}-\boldsymbol{F}+\boldsymbol{F}\|_\infty \\ &\leq \|\boldsymbol{G}-\widehat{\boldsymbol{G}}-\boldsymbol{F}\|_\infty + \|\boldsymbol{F}\|_\infty \\ &= \|\boldsymbol{G}-\widehat{\boldsymbol{G}}\|_H + \|\boldsymbol{F}\|_\infty. \end{aligned} \tag{10.5.1}$$

Since we already know how to minimize $\|\boldsymbol{G}-\widehat{\boldsymbol{G}}\|_H$, it only remains for us to say something about the size of $\|\boldsymbol{F}\|_\infty$.

We can always choose $\boldsymbol{F}(\infty) = 0$ without affecting $\|\boldsymbol{G}-\widehat{\boldsymbol{G}}\|_H$ and we know from the results of Chapter 9 that $\|\boldsymbol{F}\|_\infty = \|\boldsymbol{F}^\sim\|_\infty$ is no larger than twice the sum of the distinct Hankel singular values of $\boldsymbol{F}^\sim$. As we will show, the removal of the factor of two comes from making full use of the procedure for calculating optimal Hankel norm approximations and of their properties.

10.5.1 Hankel singular values of optimal error systems

The improvement in the error bound follows from the properties of the Hankel singular values of allpass systems, which we now derive. This result will be used to relate the Hankel singular of $\widehat{\boldsymbol{G}}$ and $\boldsymbol{F}_a^\sim$ in the stable/antistable decomposition of $\boldsymbol{Q}_a = \widehat{\boldsymbol{G}}_a + \boldsymbol{F}_a$.

Lemma 10.5.1 *Suppose* $\boldsymbol{E} \overset{s}{=} \left[\begin{array}{c|c} A & B \\ \hline C & D \end{array}\right]$ *is square and satisfies the allpass equations of Theorem 3.2.1. Suppose also that* A *has dimension* $(n_1+n_2)\times(n_1+n_2)$*, has* n_1 *eigenvalues in the open-left-half plane and has* n_2 *eigenvalues in the open-right-half plane, with* $n_1 > n_2$*. If* $\boldsymbol{E} = \boldsymbol{G} + \boldsymbol{F}$ *with* $\boldsymbol{G}, \boldsymbol{F}^{\sim} \in \mathcal{RH}_\infty$*, then*

$$\sigma_i(\boldsymbol{G}) = \begin{cases} 1 & i = 1, \cdots, n_1 - n_2 \\ \sigma_{i-(n_1-n_2)}(\boldsymbol{F}^{\sim}) & i = n_1 - n_2 + 1, \cdots, n_1. \end{cases}$$

Proof. Transform the given realization of $\boldsymbol{E}$ to the form

$$\boldsymbol{E} \overset{s}{=} \left[\begin{array}{cc|c} A_1 & 0 & B_1 \\ 0 & A_2 & B_2 \\ \hline C_1 & C_2 & D \end{array}\right] \quad \text{with } \mathrm{R_e}\lambda_i(A_1) < 0 \text{ and } \mathrm{R_e}\lambda_i(A_2) > 0.$$

Therefore, for some matrix X,

$$\boldsymbol{G} \overset{s}{=} \left[\begin{array}{c|c} A_1 & B_1 \\ \hline C_1 & D - X \end{array}\right] \quad \text{and } \boldsymbol{F} \overset{s}{=} \left[\begin{array}{c|c} A_2 & B_2 \\ \hline C_2 & X \end{array}\right].$$

Let P and Q be the controllability and observability gramians of $\boldsymbol{E}$ and partition them as

$$P = \begin{bmatrix} P_1 & P_2 \\ P_2' & P_3 \end{bmatrix}, \qquad Q = \begin{bmatrix} Q_1 & Q_2' \\ Q_2 & Q_3 \end{bmatrix}.$$

Since $PQ = I$, $P_1Q_1 = I - P_2Q_2$ and since $QP = I$, $Q_2P_2 = I - Q_3P_3$. Hence

$$\begin{aligned} \det(\lambda I - P_1Q_1) &= \det\big(\lambda I - (I - P_2Q_2)\big) \\ &= \det\big((\lambda - 1)I + P_2Q_2\big) \\ &= (\lambda - 1)^{n_1-n_2}\det\big((\lambda - 1)I + Q_2P_2\big) \\ &= (\lambda - 1)^{n_1-n_2}\det(\lambda I - Q_3P_3). \end{aligned}$$

The result now follows from $\sigma_i^2(\boldsymbol{G}) = \lambda_i(P_1Q_1)$ and $\sigma_i^2(\boldsymbol{F}^{\sim}) = \lambda_i(P_3Q_3)$. ■

We now apply this result to the optimal error system.

Lemma 10.5.2 *Assume* $\sigma_r(\boldsymbol{G}) > \sigma_{r+1}(\boldsymbol{G})$ *and let* $\boldsymbol{G}_a$ *and* $\boldsymbol{Q}_a$ *be as constructed in Section 10.4.1. Let* $\boldsymbol{Q}_a = \widehat{\boldsymbol{G}}_a + \boldsymbol{F}_a$ *with* $\widehat{\boldsymbol{G}}_a, \boldsymbol{F}_a^{\sim} \in \mathcal{RH}_\infty$*. Then*

$$\begin{aligned} \sigma_i(\boldsymbol{G}_a - \widehat{\boldsymbol{G}}_a) &= \sigma_{r+1}(\boldsymbol{G}_a), \qquad i = 1, \cdots, 2r + l & (10.5.2) \\ \sigma_i(\boldsymbol{F}_a^{\sim}) &= \sigma_{i+2r+l}(\boldsymbol{G}_a - \widehat{\boldsymbol{G}}_a), \qquad i = 1, \cdots, n - r - l & (10.5.3) \\ &\le \sigma_{i+r+l}(\boldsymbol{G}_a), \qquad i = 1, \cdots, n - r - l. & (10.5.4) \end{aligned}$$

Proof. The construction of $\boldsymbol{E}_a = \boldsymbol{G}_a - \boldsymbol{Q}_a$ ensures that $\gamma^{-1}\boldsymbol{E}_a$ satisfies the allpass equations of Theorem 3.2.1, with $\gamma = \sigma_{r+1}(\boldsymbol{G}_a)$. Furthermore, A_e is a $(2n-l)\times(2n-l)$ dimensional matrix which has $n+r$ eigenvalues in the open-left-half plane and $n-r-l$ eigenvalues in the open-right-half plane. Applying Lemma 10.5.1 to $\gamma^{-1}\boldsymbol{E}_a$, we obtain equations (10.5.2) and (10.5.3). The inequality in (10.5.4) comes from our optimal Hankel norm approximation results (see Theorem 10.4.2)—for any $j \geq r+1$

$$\begin{aligned}\sigma_j(\boldsymbol{G}_a - \widehat{\boldsymbol{G}}_a) &= \inf_{\boldsymbol{K}_1 \in \mathcal{RH}_\infty^-(j-1)} \|\boldsymbol{G}_a - \widehat{\boldsymbol{G}}_a - \boldsymbol{K}_1\|_\infty \\ &\leq \inf_{\boldsymbol{K}_2 \in \mathcal{RH}_\infty^-(j-r-1)} \|\boldsymbol{G}_a - \boldsymbol{K}_2\|_\infty \\ &= \sigma_{j-r}(\boldsymbol{G}_a).\end{aligned}$$

(Use the fact that $\boldsymbol{K}_1 \in \mathcal{RH}_\infty^-(j-1)$ implies $\widehat{\boldsymbol{G}}_a + \boldsymbol{K}_1$ has at least $j-1-r$ stable poles.) ■

10.5.2 The error bound

In Chapter 9 we showed that $\|\boldsymbol{G}-\boldsymbol{G}(\infty)\|_\infty$ is no greater than twice the sum of the distinct Hankel singular values of $\boldsymbol{G}$. In the scalar case, this means that the Nyquist diagram of $\boldsymbol{g}$ is within a circle centered at $\boldsymbol{g}(\infty)$ and with radius no greater than twice the sum of the distinct Hankel singular values of $\boldsymbol{g}$. The next result shows that the Nyquist diagram infact remains inside a circle centered on some point in the complex plane and with radius no greater the sum of the distinct Hankel singular values of $\boldsymbol{g}$—the factor of two has been removed. This result is essential to proving the "sum of the tail" error bound and is also of interest in its own right.

Example 10.5.1. Consider

$$\boldsymbol{g} = \frac{2}{s+1} \stackrel{s}{=} \left[\begin{array}{c|c} -1 & \sqrt{2} \\ \hline \sqrt{2} & 0 \end{array}\right].$$

The observability and controllability gramians are 1, so $\|\boldsymbol{g}\|_H = 1$ and $\boldsymbol{g}(\infty) = 0$. Therefore, the Nyquist diagram of $\boldsymbol{g}$ never strays outside the origin centered circle of radius 2. The Nyquist diagram of $\boldsymbol{g}$ is actually a circle of radius 1 centered on 1. It is no accident that

$$\frac{2}{s+1} - 1 = \frac{1-s}{1+s}$$

is allpass. ▽

Lemma 10.5.3 *If $\boldsymbol{G} \in \mathcal{RH}_\infty$, there exists a constant matrix $\tilde{D}$ such that $\|\boldsymbol{G}-\tilde{D}\|_\infty$ is no larger than the sum of the distinct Hankel singular values of $\boldsymbol{G}$.*

Proof. Set $\gamma = \sigma_n$ and construct $\boldsymbol{Q}_a \in \mathcal{RH}_\infty$ as in Section 10.4.1. The system $\boldsymbol{Q}_a$ has McMillan degree $n-l_1$, in which l_1 is the multiplicity of σ_n and $\|\boldsymbol{G}_a - \boldsymbol{Q}_a\| = \sigma_n$.

Furthermore, the Hankel singular values of $\boldsymbol{Q}_a$ are given by $\sigma_i(\boldsymbol{G})$, $i = 1, \ldots, n - l_1$, since

$$\begin{aligned}\sigma_i^2(\boldsymbol{Q}) &= \lambda_i(P_1 E_1 (E_1)^{-1} Q_1) \\ &= \lambda_i(P_1 Q_1) \\ &= \sigma_i^2(\boldsymbol{G}), \qquad i = 1, \ldots, n - l_1\end{aligned}$$

with P_1, Q_1 and E_1 defined in Section 10.4.1.

Now set $\gamma = \sigma_{n-l_1}$ and construct an approximation for $\boldsymbol{Q}_a$, with error σ_{n-l_1}, degree $n - l_1 - l_2$ and Hankel singular values σ_i, $i = 1, \ldots, n - l_1 - l_2$, with l_2 the multiplicity of σ_{n-l_1}. Now continue this process until only a constant $\tilde{D}_a$ remains and define $\tilde{D}$ to be the $p \times m$ (1,1)-block of $\tilde{D}_a$. The final bound follows from the error incurred at each step of the reduction and the triangle inequality. ■

We are now in a position to prove the main result.

Theorem 10.5.4 *Suppose* $\boldsymbol{G} \in \mathcal{RH}_\infty$ *has Hankel singular values* σ_i *and let* r *be such that* $\sigma_r > \sigma_{r+1}$. *Then there exists a* $\widehat{\boldsymbol{G}} \in \mathcal{RH}_\infty$ *of McMillan degree* r *such that* $\|\boldsymbol{G} - \widehat{\boldsymbol{G}}\|_\infty$ *is no larger than the sum of the distinct Hankel singular values of* $\boldsymbol{G}$ *that are strictly smaller than* σ_r.

If all the Hankel singular values smaller than σ_r *are distinct, then*

$$\|\boldsymbol{G} - \widehat{\boldsymbol{G}}\|_\infty \le \sigma_{r+1} + \ldots + \sigma_n.$$

The proof contains a constructive procedure for obtaining such a $\widehat{\boldsymbol{G}}$.

Proof. Set $\gamma = \sigma_{r+1}$ and construct $\boldsymbol{Q}_a$ as in Section 10.4.1. Divide $\boldsymbol{Q}_a$ into stable and unstable parts so that $\boldsymbol{Q}_a = \widehat{\boldsymbol{G}}_a + \boldsymbol{F}_a$ and note that $\widehat{\boldsymbol{G}}_a$ has McMillan degree r. For any such decomposition,

$$\begin{aligned}\|\boldsymbol{G}_a - \widehat{\boldsymbol{G}}_a\|_\infty &= \|\boldsymbol{G}_a - \boldsymbol{Q}_a + \boldsymbol{F}_a\|_\infty \\ &\le \|\boldsymbol{G}_a - \boldsymbol{Q}_a\|_\infty + \|\boldsymbol{F}_a\|_\infty \\ &= \sigma_{r+1} + \|\boldsymbol{F}_a\|_\infty.\end{aligned}$$

By Lemma 10.5.2, the Hankel singular values of $\boldsymbol{F}_a^\sim$ are less than or equal to the Hankel singular values of $\boldsymbol{G}_a$ that are strictly smaller than σ_{r+1} . We can use the construction described in Lemma 10.5.3 to choose $\widehat{D} = \widehat{\boldsymbol{G}}_a(\infty)$ in such a way that $\|\boldsymbol{F}_a\|_\infty$ is no larger than the sum of the Hankel singular values of $\boldsymbol{G}$ that are strictly smaller than σ_{r+1}. Hence, for such a decomposition, $\|\boldsymbol{G}_a - \widehat{\boldsymbol{G}}_a\|_\infty$ is no greater than the sum of the Hankel singular values of $\boldsymbol{G}$ that are strictly smaller than σ_r. We now choose $\widehat{\boldsymbol{G}}$ to be the $(1,1)$-block of such a $\widehat{\boldsymbol{G}}_a$. ■

Main points of the section

1. Suppose $\boldsymbol{Q}_a$ is as constructed in Section 10.4.1 and that it is decomposed as $\boldsymbol{Q}_a = \widehat{\boldsymbol{G}}_a + \boldsymbol{F}_a$, in which $\widehat{\boldsymbol{G}}_a \in \mathcal{RH}_\infty$ and $\boldsymbol{F}_a \in \mathcal{RH}_\infty^-$. The Hankel singular values of $\boldsymbol{F}_a^\sim$ are less than or equal to the Hankel singular values of $\boldsymbol{G}$ that are strictly smaller than $\sigma_{r+1}(\boldsymbol{G})$.
2. There exists a constant matrix $\tilde{D}$ such that $\|\boldsymbol{G} - \tilde{D}\|_\infty$ is less than or equal to the sum of the distinct Hankel singular values of $\boldsymbol{G}$.
3. There exists a system $\widehat{\boldsymbol{G}} \in \mathcal{RH}_\infty$ of McMillan degree (at most) r such that $\|\boldsymbol{G} - \widehat{\boldsymbol{G}}\|_\infty$ is no greater than the sum of the distinct Hankel singular values of $\boldsymbol{G}$ that are strictly smaller than σ_r. Such a $\widehat{\boldsymbol{G}}$ may be constructed by taking a particular stable part of $\boldsymbol{Q}_{a11}$ as constructed in Section 10.4.1.

10.6 Example

This example illustrates the optimal Hankel norm model reduction of the flexible structure model described in [58]. We used the same model to illustrate balanced truncation model reduction in Section 9.6.

The four lightly damped modes and eight Hankel singular values of the model $\boldsymbol{g}$ are given in Section 9.6. Since the fifth Hankel singular value of $\boldsymbol{g}$ is $\sigma_5 = 0.069856$, the Hankel norm of the error incurred in approximating $\boldsymbol{g}$ by a system with at most four stable poles is at least 0.06985. Because the infinity norm cannot be less than the Hankel norm, the infinity norm of the approximation error must also be at least this large. The sum of the Hankel singular values smaller than σ_4 is $\sigma_5 + \ldots + \sigma_8 = 0.1505$, so there is a stable fourth-order system $\widehat{\boldsymbol{g}}$ such that $\|\boldsymbol{g} - \widehat{\boldsymbol{g}}\|_\infty \leq 0.1505$. One such $\widehat{\boldsymbol{g}}$ is given by the realization[8]

$$\widehat{\boldsymbol{g}} \stackrel{s}{=} \left[\begin{array}{cccc|c} 0.0095755 & -1.1342323 & -0.5729631 & 0.6037008 & 0.0825993 \\ 0.28458172 & -0.0106736 & 0.0499715 & 0.0963557 & -0.0008078 \\ 0.0000000 & 0.0000000 & -1.0700576 & -9.7441671 & 0.0067206 \\ 0.0000000 & 0.0000000 & 1.7099590 & 1.0627683 & -0.1219712 \\ \hline -0.0051978 & 0.5471814 & 0.0267315 & -0.0236216 & 0.0002923 \end{array}\right].$$

If the direct feedthrough term is set to zero rather than 0.0002923, the resulting reduced-order system satisfies the error bound $2(\sigma_5 + \ldots + \sigma_8)$. Figure 10.1 shows the magnitude of $\boldsymbol{g}$, $\widehat{\boldsymbol{g}}$ and $\widehat{\boldsymbol{g}} - \widehat{\boldsymbol{g}}(\infty)$.

Figure 10.2 shows the upper bound $\sigma_5 + \ldots + \sigma_8$, $|\boldsymbol{g}(j\omega) - \widehat{\boldsymbol{g}}(j\omega)|$, $|\boldsymbol{g}(j\omega) - (\widehat{\boldsymbol{g}}(j\omega) - \widehat{\boldsymbol{g}}(\infty))|$ and the lower bound σ_5. The lower bound σ_5 is exactly the error that would be incurred if we allowed ourselves to include unstable poles in the reduced-order

[8] This reduced-order model was calculated using the `ohkapp` function in the MATLAB Robust Control Toolbox. (MATLAB is a registered trademark of The MathWorks, Inc.) The direct feedthrough gain was computed by using `ohkapp` recursively on the adjoint of the anticausal part.

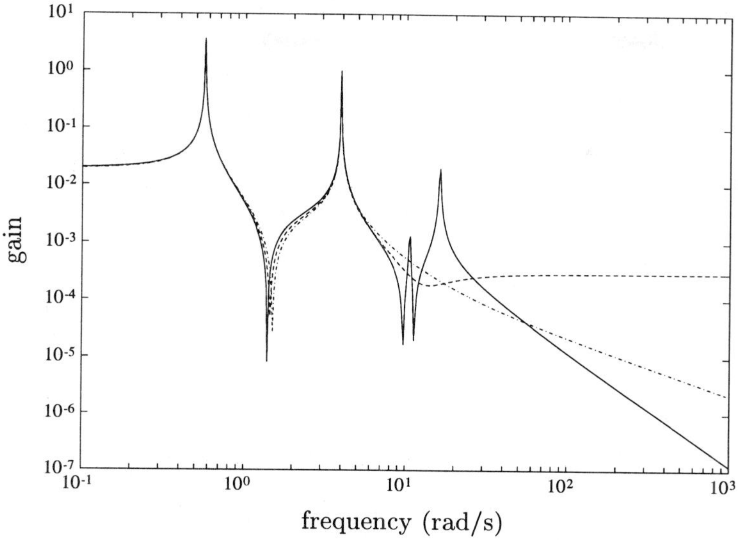

Figure 10.1: Flexible structure models. Full-order model $\boldsymbol{g}$ (solid), a nonstrictly proper optimal Hankel norm approximant $\widehat{\boldsymbol{g}}$ (dashed) and a strictly proper optimal Hankel norm approximant $\widehat{\boldsymbol{g}} - \widehat{\boldsymbol{g}}(\infty)$ (dash-dot).

model. Comparing Figure 10.2 with Figure 9.2, we observe that although the bound for optimal Hankel norm approximation is half the balanced truncation bound, the actual performance of the two methods is comparable on this example.

Notice that the σ_5 lower bound is a result of the optimal Hankel norm theory. It is important because it provides an absolute standard against which the performance of any particular reduced-order model can be assessed. No model with at most four stable poles can better the infinity norm performance of the approximations computed by the optimal Hankel norm or balanced truncation methods by more than a factor of about 1.8 (5.1 dB) on this flexible structure.

10.7 Notes and References

Twentieth-century functional analysts and operator theorists have had a continuing interest in extension and interpolation problems. Interestingly, problems such as Nevanlinna-Pick interpolation and the Nehari extension are equivalent. The interconnectedness and long history of this work means that we are only able to give those references most directly related to the material covered in this chapter.

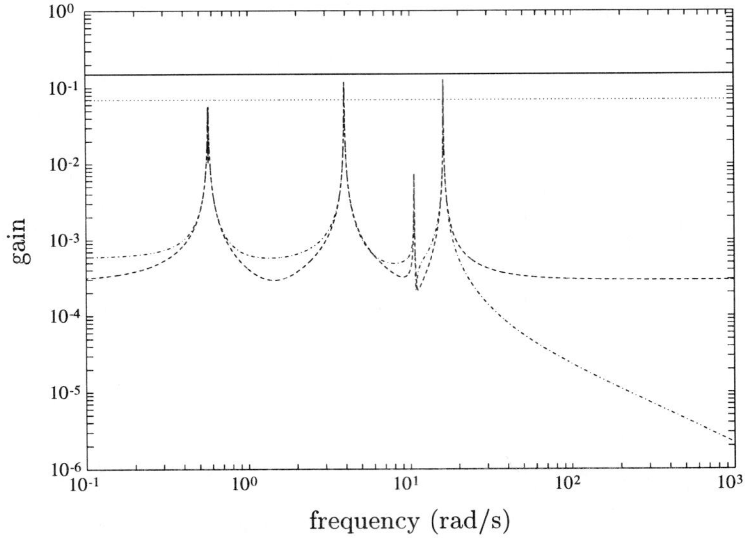

Figure 10.2: Model reduction error and bounds. Sum-of-the-tail upper bound (solid), nonstrictly proper approximation error $|\boldsymbol{g}(j\omega) - \widehat{\boldsymbol{g}}(j\omega)|$ (dashed), strictly proper approximation error $\widehat{\boldsymbol{g}} - \widehat{\boldsymbol{g}}(\infty)$ (dash-dot) and lower bound σ_5 (dotted).

Nehari [155] was interested in obtaining necessary and sufficient conditions for the boundedness of a bilinear form. His main result, Nehari's theorem, states that a bilinear form $\gamma(u,v) = \sum_{k=0}^{\infty}\sum_{m=0}^{\infty}\gamma_{k+m}u_k v_m$ is bounded by M (*i.e.*, $|\gamma(u,v)| \leq M$ for arbitrary sequences u, v such that $\sum_{k=0}^{\infty}|u_k|^2 = 1$, $\sum_{m=0}^{\infty}|v_m|^2 = 1$) if and only if the sequence γ_n, $n = 0, 1, \ldots$ admits an extension γ_n, $n = -1, -2 \ldots$ such that the numbers γ_n are the Fourier coefficients of a function $\boldsymbol{f}(e^{j\theta})$ in $\mathcal{L}_2$ (on the unit circle) such that $|\boldsymbol{f}(e^{j\theta})| \leq M$ for (almost all) $\theta \in [0, 2\pi)$. As a corollary, Nehari also showed that the boundedness of the form $\gamma(u,v)$ by M is equivalent to the existence of a function $\boldsymbol{q}(z)$, analytic in $|z| < 1$, such that $|\boldsymbol{\gamma}(z)^* + \boldsymbol{q}(z)| \leq M$ for $|z| < 1$, in which $\boldsymbol{\gamma}(z) = \sum_{n=0}^{\infty}\gamma_n^* z^n$, which is a statement of Nehari's theorem that looks more like Theorem 10.4.6.

Adamjan, Arov and Krein published several papers dealing with infinite Hankel matrices and approximation problems associated with them. Reference [1] contains a version of Theorem 10.4.5 for the case of scalar $\mathcal{L}_\infty$ functions on the unit disc including a linear fractional parametrization of all solutions.

Multivariable generalizations of these interpolation and extension problems were considered by Adamjan, Arov and Krein [2], Sarason [191] and Szokefalvi-Nagy and

Foias [203] during the late 1960s. The work of Nehari, Adamjan, Arov and Krein, Sarason and Szokefalvi-Nagy and Foias is not restricted to the rational case. A brief treatment of these results may be found in the book by Young [222] and an extended coverage is given in the books of Power [168] and Partington [161].

Nehari's theorem and Nevanlinna-Pick interpolation became known to the system theory and control community through work on the synthesis of passive circuits by Youla and Saito [221], the broadband matching problem by Helton [90], optimal prediction by Dewilde, Vieira and Kailath [48] and optimal sensitivity synthesis by Zames [227].

Nehari's theorem formed the basis of a solution to $\mathcal{H}_\infty$ control problems of the one-block type (see Doyle [52], Francis [65] and Limebeer and Hung [134]).[9] For such problems, perfect control can always be achieved if the closed-loop stability constraint is ignored.[10] The optimal performance level that can be achieved by a stable closed loop is determined by how well a possibly unstable system can be approximated by a stable one. It follows from this and Nehari's theorem that the optimal performance level for any one-block problem is determined by a Hankel norm calculation.

The state-space construction of the allpass embedding and the infinity norm bounds for optimal Hankel norm approximation are due to Glover [71, 75]. The infinity norm bounds put Hankel norm model reduction on an honest footing and the computational and theoretical simplicity of the state-space approach has led to a widespread appreciation and application of these results. The state-space formulas for the calculation of Nehari extensions are at the center of the four-block approach to the computation of $\mathcal{H}_\infty$ optimal controllers [52, 65].

The free parameter $\boldsymbol{U}$ in the parametrization of all solutions to Nehari's problem, or the optimal Hankel norm model reduction problem, may be used to satisfy additional performance criteria. One suggestion is to choose $\boldsymbol{U}$ to minimize an entropy integral, which leads to the very satisfying choice of $\boldsymbol{U} = 0$ [134, 80]. An alternative, introduced by Young [223], is to minimize not only the maximum singular value (*i.e.*, the infinity norm) of the error, but also all subsequent singular values of the error. This is the superoptimal Hankel norm approximation problem and a state-space approach is considered in Limebeer, Halikias and Glover [133].

A state-space theory of Nehari and Adamjan, Arov and Krein extensions for discrete-time is due to Ball and Ran [25]. These results have been generalized by Al-Hussari, Jaimoukha and Limebeer [4] to the optimal case by considering the problem in a descriptor system framework.

Despite the motivation for the Hankel norm criterion as a sensible basis for model reduction, our real interest is in the infinity norm. The only known methods of tackling the optimal infinity norm model reduction problem are based on nonconvex parameter optimization. Because the cost function (the infinity norm

[9]A one-block $\mathcal{H}_\infty$ control problem is one in which the off-diagonal blocks of the generalized plant are square. This means that all the constraints are analytic in nature and are a result of the closed-loop stability requirement.

[10]Just set $\boldsymbol{K} = -(I - \boldsymbol{P}_{12}^{-1}\boldsymbol{P}_{11}\boldsymbol{P}_{21}^{-1}\boldsymbol{P}_{22})^{-1}\boldsymbol{P}_{12}^{-1}\boldsymbol{P}_{11}\boldsymbol{P}_{21}^{-1}$.

of the error) is expensive to compute and may contain multiple local minima, it is important to have a good initial guess at what the optimal infinity norm approximant might be. Obvious candidates for the initial guess are the balanced truncation or optimal Hankel norm approximations. The improvement over the initial guess obtainable by parameter optimization, however, may not represent a worthwhile saving. We know that the infinity norm of the error in approximating G by a system of McMillan degree r will exceed σ_{r+1} and we also know that an optimal Hankel norm approximant can achieve an infinity norm error that does not exceed $\sigma_{r+1} + \ldots + \sigma_n$.

10.8 Problems

Problem 10.1. This problem considers the decomposition of a system into a sum of stable and antistable subsystems or, equivalently, causal and anticausal subsystems.

1. Show that $F \in \mathcal{RH}_\infty^-$ implies $F\mathcal{H}_2^- \subset \mathcal{H}_2^-$. Conclude that $F \in \mathcal{RH}_\infty^-$ defines an anticausal system (*i.e.*, one that is causal in reverse time).
2. Show that if $G \in \mathcal{RL}_\infty$, then a stable/antistable decomposition $G = G_+ + G_-$, with $G_+ \in \mathcal{RH}_\infty$ and $G_- \in \mathcal{RH}_\infty^-$, is equivalent to a causal/anticausal decomposition of the system.
3. Give a state-space algorithm for determining a causal/anticausal decomposition of a system $G \in \mathcal{RL}_\infty$.

Problem 10.2. Suppose (A, B, C, D) is a minimal realization of a square system G. Show that G satisfies $G^\sim G = I$ if and only if

$$\begin{aligned} QA + A'Q + C'C &= 0 \\ D'C + B'Q &= 0 \\ D'D &= I. \end{aligned}$$

(Hint: Sufficiency may be established by direct calculation. For necessity use the fact that $G^\sim = G^{-1}$ and then observe that a minimal realization is unique up to a state-space co-ordinate transformation.) Conclude that the Hankel singular values of any square, stable allpass system are unity.

Problem 10.3. Verify equations (10.4.14) and (10.4.15) by direct calculation.

Problem 10.4. Suppose $g \in \mathcal{RH}_\infty$ is a scalar transfer function. Show that the unique $q \in \mathcal{RH}_\infty^-(r)$ such that $\|g - q\|_\infty = \sigma_{r+1}$ is given by

$$q = g - \sigma_{r+1}\frac{w_{r+1}(s)}{v_{r+1}(-s)},$$

in which $v_{r+1}(s)$ and $w_{r+1}(s)$ are the (Laplace transforms of) the Schmidt vectors associated with $\sigma_{r+1}(g)$. Conclude that optimal degree r Hankel norm approximants $\widehat{g} \in \mathcal{RH}_\infty$ differ only by a constant.

Problem 10.5. Consider the generalized plant with state-space realization

$$\begin{bmatrix} \boldsymbol{P}_{11} & \boldsymbol{P}_{12} \\ \boldsymbol{P}_{21} & \boldsymbol{P}_{22} \end{bmatrix} \stackrel{s}{=} \left[\begin{array}{c|cc} A & B_1 & B_2 \\ \hline C_1 & 0 & I \\ C_2 & I & 0 \end{array}\right],$$

in which (A, B_2) is stabilizable and (C_2, A) is detectable. We shall find the optimal solution to this one-block $\mathcal{H}_\infty$ controller synthesis problem using Nehari's theorem.

1. Using the parametrization of all stabilizing controllers in Appendix A, show that
$$\mathcal{F}_\ell(\boldsymbol{P}, \boldsymbol{K}) = \boldsymbol{T}_{11} + \boldsymbol{T}_{12}\boldsymbol{Q}\boldsymbol{T}_{21}$$
for some $\boldsymbol{Q} \in \mathcal{RH}_\infty$. Give state-space formulas for the $\boldsymbol{T}_{ij}$'s in terms of the realization of $\boldsymbol{P}$ and two matrices F and H such that $A - B_2F$ and $A - HC_2$ are asymptotically stable.
2. Suppose $A - B_2C_1$ and $A - B_1C_2$ have no eigenvalues on the imaginary axis and let X and Y be the stabilizing solutions to the Riccati equations
$$\begin{aligned} X(A - B_2C_1) + (A - B_2C_1)'X - XB_2B_2'X &= 0 \\ (A - B_1C_2)Y + Y(A - B_1C_2)' - YC_2'C_2Y &= 0. \end{aligned}$$
If $F = C_1 + B_2'X$ and $H = B_1 + YC_2'$, show that the systems $\boldsymbol{T}_{12}$ and $\boldsymbol{T}_{21}$ in Item 1 are square and allpass. Conclude that for this choice of F and H
$$\|\mathcal{F}_\ell(\boldsymbol{P}, \boldsymbol{K})\|_\infty = \|\boldsymbol{R} + \boldsymbol{Q}\|_\infty,$$
in which $\boldsymbol{R} = \boldsymbol{T}_{12}^\sim \boldsymbol{T}_{11} \boldsymbol{T}_{21}^\sim \in \mathcal{RH}_\infty^-$.
3. Use Nehari's theorem to conclude that $\|(\boldsymbol{R}^\sim)_+\|_H$ is the infimal norm that can be achieved with a stabilizing controller. By calculating a realization of $\boldsymbol{R}$, show that $(\boldsymbol{R}^\sim)_+ = \boldsymbol{R}^\sim$ and conclude that $\|\boldsymbol{R}^\sim\|_H$ is the infimal norm that can be achieved with a stabilizing controller.
4. Describe how a state-space formula for all $\mathcal{H}_\infty$ optimal controllers could be obtained.

Problem 10.6. (Glover [73]) A simple one-block problem is the additive robustness margin problem in which we seek a controller $\boldsymbol{K}$ that stabilizes all plants of the form $\boldsymbol{G} + \boldsymbol{\Delta}$, that have the same number of unstable poles as $\boldsymbol{G}$, and which satisfy $\|\boldsymbol{\Delta}\|_\infty \le \epsilon$. In Chapter 2 it was shown that this requires us to choose $\boldsymbol{K}$ so $\|\boldsymbol{K}(I - \boldsymbol{G}\boldsymbol{K})^{-1}\|_\infty < \frac{1}{\epsilon}$.[11]

1. Suppose $\boldsymbol{G}$ has no stable poles (*i.e.*, $\boldsymbol{G} \in \mathcal{RH}_\infty^-$) and let ϵ_0 be the smallest Hankel singular value of $\boldsymbol{G}^\sim$. Show that there is a $\widehat{\boldsymbol{G}} \in \mathcal{RH}_\infty^-$ with (strictly) fewer poles than $\boldsymbol{G}$ such that $\|\boldsymbol{G} - \widehat{\boldsymbol{G}}\|_\infty \le \epsilon$ if and only if $\epsilon \ge \epsilon_0$. Show that if

[11] Assume that any indicated LFT is well posed; *i.e.*, you may assume that $I - \boldsymbol{G}(\infty)\boldsymbol{K}(\infty)$ and $I - \widehat{\boldsymbol{G}}(\infty)\widehat{\boldsymbol{K}}(\infty)$ are nonsingular.

$\epsilon > \epsilon_0$, then for some matrix M, some $l > 0$ and all $0 < \delta < \delta_0 = (\epsilon - \epsilon_0)/\|M\|$ the family of plants

$$G + \Delta = \widehat{G} + \frac{\delta M}{(s-1)^l}$$

has the same number of poles in the right-half plane as G, satisfies $\|\Delta\|_\infty < \epsilon$ and cannot be stabilized by a single controller. Conclude that $\inf \|K(I - GK)^{-1}\|_\infty \geq 1/\epsilon_0$, where the infimim is taken over the class of stabilizing controllers.

2. Suppose $G = G_+ + G_-$, in which $G_+ \in \mathcal{RH}_\infty$ and $G_- \in \mathcal{RH}_\infty^-$. Show that $K = \widehat{K}(I + G_+\widehat{K})^{-1}$ results in

$$K(I - GK)^{-1} = \widehat{K}(I - G_-\widehat{K})^{-1}.$$

Show further that K stabilizes G if and only if $\widehat{K}$ stabilizes G_-. Conclude that $\inf \|K(I - GK)^{-1}\|_\infty$, where the infimum is taken over the class of stabilizing controllers, is greater than or equal to the inverse of the smallest Hankel singular value of $G_-^\sim$.

Hence the optimal (additive) stability margin is no greater (and in fact is equal to) the smallest Hankel singular value of $G_-^\sim$. (This means that systems whose unstable part is easy to approximate—$\sigma_{\min}[G_-^\sim]$ small—have little robustness to additive uncertainty.)

3. Show that the generalized plant for this problem is

$$\begin{bmatrix} P_{11} & P_{12} \\ P_{21} & P_{22} \end{bmatrix} \stackrel{s}{=} \left[\begin{array}{c|cc} A & 0 & B \\ \hline 0 & 0 & I \\ C & I & 0 \end{array}\right],$$

in which $(A, B, C, 0)$ is a realization of G. Explain why $G(\infty) = 0$ can be assumed without loss of generality.

Use your answer to Problem 10.5 to show that $\inf \|K(I - GK)^{-1}\|_\infty$, where the infimum is taken over the class of stabilizing controllers, is equal to the inverse of the smallest Hankel singular value of $G_-^\sim$. (Assume that A has no eigenvalue on the imaginary axis.)

Problem 10.7. The Hankel operator associated with a discrete-time system is defined to be the operator that maps (the reflection of) the past input to the future output, assuming the future input is zero. Now consider the strictly causal, discrete-time, scalar convolution system

$$y_n = \sum_{k=-\infty}^{n-1} h_{n-k} u_k.$$

1. Show that the Hankel operator associated with the system may be represented by the semi-infinite Hankel matrix

$$\mathbf{\Gamma} = \begin{bmatrix} h_1 & h_2 & h_3 & \cdots \\ h_2 & h_3 & h_4 & \cdots \\ h_3 & h_4 & h_5 & \cdots \\ \vdots & \vdots & \vdots & \ddots \end{bmatrix}.$$

2. Nehari's bounded linear form is the inner product $v^*\mathbf{\Gamma}u$, in which $\{u\}_{k=1}^{\infty}$ and $\{v\}_{k=1}^{\infty}$ are ℓ_2 sequences. The problem is to find the least number M such that $|v^*\mathbf{\Gamma}u| \leq M\|v\|_2\|u\|_2$. In other words, the problem is to find $\|\mathbf{\Gamma}\|$, the ℓ_2-induced norm of $\mathbf{\Gamma}$. Nehari's theorem, in its original form, states that $|v^*\mathbf{\Gamma}u| \leq M\|v\|_2\|u\|_2$ if and only if there exists a function in $\boldsymbol{f} \in \mathcal{L}_2$ (on the unit circle) such that

$$h_k = \frac{1}{2\pi}\int_0^{2\pi} \boldsymbol{f}(e^{j\theta})e^{jk\theta}\,d\theta, \qquad k = 1, 2, \ldots$$

and $|\boldsymbol{f}(e^{j\theta})| \leq M$ for (almost) all θ.
Consider Hilbert's Hankel matrix

$$\mathbf{\Gamma}_H = \begin{bmatrix} 1 & \frac{1}{2} & \frac{1}{3} & \cdots \\ \frac{1}{2} & \frac{1}{3} & \frac{1}{4} & \cdots \\ \frac{1}{3} & \frac{1}{4} & \frac{1}{5} & \cdots \\ \vdots & \vdots & \vdots & \ddots \end{bmatrix}$$

(*i.e.*, $h_n = \frac{1}{n}$, $n = 1, 2, \ldots$). It is not at all clear whether $\|\mathbf{\Gamma}_H\|$ is finite and even if it is, it would appear to be far from obvious what the value of $\|\mathbf{\Gamma}_H\|$ is. Use Nehari's theorem to show that $\|\mathbf{\Gamma}_H\| \leq \pi$ by considering the function $\boldsymbol{f}(e^{j\theta}) = j(\theta - \pi)$.[12] Show that this implies the inequality

$$\left|\sum_{k=1}^{\infty}\sum_{m=1}^{\infty} \frac{\bar{v}_k u_k}{k+m-1}\right| \leq \pi\left\{\sum_1^{\infty}|v_k|^2\right\}^{\frac{1}{2}}\left\{\sum_1^{\infty}|u_k|^2\right\}^{\frac{1}{2}},$$

which is known as Hilbert's inequality.

3. One application of Nehari's theorem is in finite impulse response approximation (Kootsookos, Bitmead and Green [121]). Suppose we are given a possibly infinite number of filter coefficients $h_0, h_1, h_2, \ldots$ and we seek a finite number of coefficients $\widehat{h}_0, \widehat{h}_2, \ldots, \widehat{h}_{N-1}$ such that $|\boldsymbol{f}(e^{j\theta}) - \widehat{\boldsymbol{f}}(e^{j\theta})| \leq M$ for all θ, in which

$$\boldsymbol{f}(e^{j\theta}) = \sum_{k=0}^{\infty} h_k e^{-jk\theta} \quad \text{and} \quad \widehat{\boldsymbol{f}}(e^{j\theta}) = \sum_{k=0}^{N-1} \widehat{h}_k e^{-jk\theta}$$

[12] Hilbert showed that $\|\mathbf{\Gamma}_H\|$ was bounded; it was Schur [194] who showed that $\|\mathbf{\Gamma}_H\| = \pi$.

are the frequency responses of the filters. Show that this is possible only if $\|\boldsymbol{t}_N\|_H \leq M$, in which $\boldsymbol{t}_N(z) = z^{N-1}\sum_{k=N}^{\infty} h_k z^{-k}$ is the "tail" function. ($\|\boldsymbol{t}_N\|_H$ denotes the Hankel norm, *i.e.*, the norm of the matrix $\boldsymbol{\Gamma}_{km} = h_{k+m+N-2}$.)

Problem 10.8. In the case of rational discrete-time systems, the Hankel norm is easy to compute. If $H_i = CA^{i-1}B$, $i = 1, 2, \ldots$, show that the Hankel operator $\boldsymbol{\Gamma}$ associated with the discrete-time convolution system

$$y_n = \sum_{k=-\infty}^{n-1} H_{n-k} u_k.$$

can be written as $\boldsymbol{\Gamma} = \mathcal{O}\mathcal{C}$, in which

$$\mathcal{C} = \begin{bmatrix} B & AB & A^2B & \ldots \end{bmatrix}, \qquad \mathcal{O} = \begin{bmatrix} C \\ CA \\ CA^2 \\ \vdots \end{bmatrix}.$$

Conclude that the Hankel singular values are given by

$$\sigma_i^2 = \lambda_i(PQ),$$

in which $P = \mathcal{C}\mathcal{C}'$ and $Q = \mathcal{O}'\mathcal{O}$ are the controllability and observability gramians, respectively, associated with the realization (A, B, C).

Problem 10.9. (Glover [71]) In this problem another algorithm for finding a reduced-order system that satisfies a "sum of the tail" error bound is considered.

1. Suppose $\boldsymbol{G} \in \mathcal{RH}_\infty$ has Hankel singular values σ_i, $i = 1, \ldots, n$ and let σ_n have multiplicity l. Show that there exists a $\widehat{\boldsymbol{G}} \in \mathcal{RH}_\infty$ of McMillan degree $n - l$ such that
$$\|\boldsymbol{G} - \widehat{\boldsymbol{G}}\|_\infty = \sigma_n.$$
2. Show that the $\widehat{\boldsymbol{G}}$ in Item 1 may be chosen so that its Hankel singular values are the first $n - l$ Hankel singular value of $\boldsymbol{G}$.
3. By iterating the results of Items 1 and 2, conclude that there exists a $\widehat{\boldsymbol{G}}$ of McMillan r such that $\|\boldsymbol{G} - \widehat{\boldsymbol{G}}\|_\infty$ is less than or equal to the sum of the distinct Hankel singular values of $\boldsymbol{G}$ that are strictly smaller than σ_r.
4. Let $\widehat{\boldsymbol{G}}$ be the one-step approximant of $\boldsymbol{G}$ constructed in Item 1 and let $\tilde{\boldsymbol{G}}$ be the balanced truncation approximation of $\boldsymbol{G}$ of the same degree as $\widehat{\boldsymbol{G}}$. Show that $\sigma_n^{-1}(\tilde{\boldsymbol{G}}_a - \boldsymbol{Q}_a)$ is allpass ($\tilde{\boldsymbol{G}}_a$ is an augmentation of $\tilde{\boldsymbol{G}}$ and $\boldsymbol{Q}_a$ is the optimal allpass embedding constructed from $\boldsymbol{G}_a$ with $\gamma = \sigma_n$). Use this to show that $\|\boldsymbol{G} - \tilde{\boldsymbol{G}}\|_\infty \leq 2\sigma_n$.

11

The Four-Block Problem

11.1 Introduction

An early example of a four-block problem comes from work on extension theorems for Hankel operators. Suppose a square summable sequence of complex numbers $a = (a_1, a_2, \cdots)$ is given and that we define the Hankel operator via the semi-infinite matrix representation

$$\mathbf{\Gamma} = \begin{bmatrix} \ddots & \vdots & \vdots & \vdots \\ \cdots & \ddots & \vdots & a_3 \\ \cdots & \cdots & a_3 & a_2 \\ \cdots & a_3 & a_2 & a_1 \end{bmatrix}.$$

Is it possible to extend this sequence and the associated Hankel operator without increasing the norm $\|\mathbf{\Gamma}\|$? The famous answer to this question is yes. A modern proof follows from the one-step-ahead extension problem of finding

$$\inf_x \left\| \left[\begin{array}{ccc|c} \ddots & \vdots & \vdots & \vdots \\ \cdots & \ddots & \vdots & a_2 \\ \cdots & \cdots & a_2 & a_1 \\ \hline \cdots & a_2 & a_1 & x \end{array} \right] \right\|,$$

which is an example of a four-block problem. A more general problem of this type was studied by Parrott, who considered the problem of finding

$$\inf_Q \left\| \begin{bmatrix} A & B \\ C & Q \end{bmatrix} \right\|,$$

in which each of the four entries are linear operators on Hilbert space. It turns out that

$$\inf_{Q} \left\| \begin{bmatrix} A & B \\ C & Q \end{bmatrix} \right\| = \max \left\{ \left\| \begin{bmatrix} A \\ C \end{bmatrix} \right\|, \left\| \begin{bmatrix} A & B \end{bmatrix} \right\| \right\},$$

which is known as Parrott's theorem. In the matrix case, the infimizing Q is hardly ever unique and Parrott gave a representation formula for all the minimizing Q's.

We shall consider this problem for the case of rational transfer function matrices, with additional restrictions imposed on Q. For example, we might insist that the Q's are stable.

Problem statement

Suppose the transfer function matrices $R_{ij} \in \mathcal{RL}_\infty$ are given and that we seek a $Q \in \mathcal{RL}_\infty$ such that

$$\left\| \begin{bmatrix} R_{11} & R_{12} \\ R_{21} & R_{22} - Q \end{bmatrix} \right\|_\infty < 1. \qquad (11.1.1)$$

The dimensions of each of the R_{ij}'s is specified by

$$\begin{matrix} & m_1 & m_2 \\ p_1 & R_{11} & R_{12} \\ p_2 & R_{21} & R_{22} \end{matrix},$$

with Q of dimension $p_2 \times m_2$. There are a number of different versions of this problem that are of interest. The differences relate to the assumptions on the transfer function matrix Q.

An early solution to the generalized regulator problem uses the parametrization of all stabilizing controllers to reduce the controller synthesis problem to one of the form given in (11.1.1). The transfer function matrices R_{ij} turn out to be completely unstable, while Q is required to be stable (*i.e.*, an element of $\mathcal{RH}_\infty$). This requirement on Q is equivalent to the requirement that the controller is internally stabilizing.

A four-block problem also arises in the solution of the frequency weighted model reduction problem, in which we seek a stable $\widehat{G}$ of McMillan degree r such that

$$\|W_1^{-1}(G - \widehat{G})W_2^{-1}\|_\infty$$

is small. The transfer function matrices W_i are frequency dependent weighting functions. In this case, the matrices R_{ij} in (11.1.1) turn out to be stable and we seek a Q that has no more than r stable poles. That is, $R_{ij} \in \mathcal{RH}_\infty$ and we seek a $Q \in \mathcal{RH}_\infty^-(r)$.

Although one of our problems places a restriction on the number of left-half-plane poles, while the other places a restriction on the number of right-half-plane poles, the theory of the four-block problem may be developed for only one of these formulations. This follows since the change of complex variable $s \to -s$ renders them mathematically identical.[1] Our aim is to find necessary and sufficient conditions for the existence of a $\boldsymbol{Q} \in \mathcal{RH}_{\infty}^{-}(r)$ such that (11.1.1) is satisfied. When such $\boldsymbol{Q}$ exist, we would like a parametrization of all of them.

The requirement that strict inequality holds in (11.1.1) relieves us from the technically difficult optimal case in which

$$\inf_{\boldsymbol{Q}\in\mathcal{RH}_{\infty}^{-}(r)} \left\| \begin{bmatrix} \boldsymbol{R}_{11} & \boldsymbol{R}_{12} \\ \boldsymbol{R}_{21} & \boldsymbol{R}_{22} - \boldsymbol{Q} \end{bmatrix} \right\|_{\infty} = 1.$$

A complete solution of the optimal case has appeared in the literature—this is the only method that has dealt comprehensively with the synthesis of $\mathcal{H}_{\infty}$ optimal controllers. Towards the end of this chapter we will show how a generalized state-space representation may be used to perform the calculations associated with the synthesis of optimal controllers, but no proofs will be supplied.

11.2 The constant matrix problem

As a preliminary step to the solution of the four-block problem, we solve the constant matrix problem of finding every D such that

$$\left\| \begin{bmatrix} D_{11} & D_{12} \\ D_{21} & D \end{bmatrix} \right\| < 1. \qquad (11.2.1)$$

Here, $\|\cdot\|$ denotes the matrix norm induced by the Euclidean norm, which is given by the maximum singular value of the matrix. Necessary conditions for the existence of a solution are

$$\left\| \begin{bmatrix} D_{11} & D_{12} \end{bmatrix} \right\| < 1 \qquad (11.2.2)$$

$$\left\| \begin{bmatrix} D_{11} \\ D_{21} \end{bmatrix} \right\| < 1, \qquad (11.2.3)$$

since the induced norm of any submatrix cannot exceed that of the whole matrix. It is much harder to see that these conditions are also sufficient. We shall do this by showing that conditions (11.2.2) and (11.2.3) facilitate the construction of the dilated matrix

$$D_{aa} = \begin{array}{c} \\ p_1 \\ p_2 \\ m_1 \\ m_2 \end{array} \begin{array}{c} \begin{array}{cccc} m_1 & m_2 & p_1 & p_2 \end{array} \\ \begin{bmatrix} D_{11} & D_{12} & D_{13} & 0 \\ D_{21} & D_{22} & D_{23} & D_{24} \\ D_{31} & D_{32} & D_{33} & D_{34} \\ 0 & D_{42} & D_{43} & 0 \end{bmatrix} \end{array}, \qquad (11.2.4)$$

[1] If the $\boldsymbol{R}_{ij}$ are not in $\mathcal{RH}_{\infty}$, pre-multiplication and post-multiplication by suitable (norm preserving) allpass transfer function matrices will give $\boldsymbol{R}_{11}, \boldsymbol{R}_{12}, \boldsymbol{R}_{21} \in \mathcal{RH}_{\infty}$. Also, any component of $\boldsymbol{R}_{22} \in \mathcal{RH}_{\infty}^{-}$ may be absorbed into $\boldsymbol{Q}$.

which has the property $D'_{aa}D_{aa} = I$. Notice that $D'_{aa}D_{aa} = I$ implies that

$$\begin{bmatrix} D_{11} & D_{12} \\ D_{21} & D_{22} \end{bmatrix}' \begin{bmatrix} D_{11} & D_{12} \\ D_{21} & D_{22} \end{bmatrix} \leq I.$$

Equality cannot hold if $\begin{bmatrix} D_{31} & D_{32} \\ 0 & D_{42} \end{bmatrix}$ is nonsingular—we shall show that this is the case—and we may therefore conclude that $D = D_{22}$ is one solution to (11.2.1). We will also show that the construction of D_{aa} will actually enable us to parametrize all solutions D that satisfy (11.2.1).

Construction of the dilation

We now turn to the construction of the dilation D_{aa}. The condition (11.2.2) can be written as

$$I_{p_1} - \begin{bmatrix} D_{11} & D_{12} \end{bmatrix} \begin{bmatrix} D_{11} & D_{12} \end{bmatrix}' > 0.$$

This implies that there is a nonsingular $p_1 \times p_1$ matrix D_{13}, which may be found by Cholesky factorization, such that

$$D_{11}D'_{11} + D_{12}D'_{12} + D_{13}D'_{13} = I_{p_1}.$$

Similarly, condition (11.2.3) ensures the existence of a nonsingular $m_1 \times m_1$ matrix D_{31} such that

$$D'_{11}D_{11} + D'_{21}D_{21} + D'_{31}D_{31} = I_{m_1}.$$

Since D_{13} is nonsingular, the rank of $\begin{bmatrix} D_{12} & D_{13} \end{bmatrix}$ is p_1 and the right null space of $\begin{bmatrix} D_{12} & D_{13} \end{bmatrix}$ has rank m_2. Let $\begin{bmatrix} D_{42} & D_{43} \end{bmatrix}'$, in which D_{42} is $m_2 \times m_2$, be an orthogonal basis for the right nullspace of $\begin{bmatrix} D_{12} & D_{13} \end{bmatrix}$. From

$$\begin{bmatrix} D_{12} & D_{13} \end{bmatrix} \begin{bmatrix} D'_{42} \\ D'_{43} \end{bmatrix} = 0$$

we obtain

$$D'_{43} = -D_{13}^{-1}D_{12}D'_{42},$$

which shows that the rank of D'_{42} is equal to the rank of $\begin{bmatrix} D_{42} & D_{43} \end{bmatrix}'$, which is m_2. This means that D_{42} is nonsingular. Similarly, the nonsingularity of D_{31} guarantees the existence of the orthogonal basis $\begin{bmatrix} D'_{24} & D'_{34} \end{bmatrix}$ for the left null space of $\begin{bmatrix} D'_{21} & D'_{31} \end{bmatrix}'$ such that D_{24} is nonsingular.

It remains to find the central 2×2 block matrix of D_{aa}. By ordering the rows and columns of D_{aa} as $1, 4, 2, 3$, we see that all the unknowns are in the bottom-right 2×2 block matrix. That is, we have the problem of finding X such that

$$\begin{bmatrix} A' & C' \\ B' & X' \end{bmatrix} \begin{bmatrix} A & B \\ C & X \end{bmatrix} = \begin{bmatrix} I & 0 \\ 0 & I \end{bmatrix},$$

with B and C square. If $\|A\| < 1$, then C is nonsingular and it follows from the $(1,2)$-block that

$$X = -(C')^{-1}A'B.$$

Returning to our original problem, we see that $A = \begin{bmatrix} D_{11} & 0 \\ 0 & 0 \end{bmatrix}$ and either of the conditions (11.2.2) or (11.2.3) implies that $\|A\| < 1$. Hence $C = \begin{bmatrix} D_{21} & D_{24} \\ D_{31} & D_{34} \end{bmatrix}$ is nonsingular and

$$\begin{bmatrix} D_{22} & D_{23} \\ D_{32} & D_{33} \end{bmatrix} = -\begin{bmatrix} D_{21}' & D_{31}' \\ D_{24}' & D_{34}' \end{bmatrix}^{-1} \begin{bmatrix} D_{11}' & 0 \\ 0 & 0 \end{bmatrix} \begin{bmatrix} D_{12} & D_{13} \\ D_{42} & D_{43} \end{bmatrix}.$$

This completes the construction of D_{aa}.

To generate all solutions D to (11.2.1), we note that if D is any $p_2 \times m_2$ matrix, then the linear fractional transformation $\mathcal{F}_\ell(D_{aa}, \begin{bmatrix} 0 & 0 \\ 0 & \Phi \end{bmatrix})$, with $\Phi = D_{24}^{-1}(D - D_{22})D_{42}^{-1}$, gives

$$\begin{aligned} \mathcal{F}_\ell\left(D_{aa}, \begin{bmatrix} 0 & 0 \\ 0 & \Phi \end{bmatrix}\right) &= \begin{bmatrix} D_{11} & D_{12} \\ D_{21} & D_{22} + D_{24}\Phi D_{42} \end{bmatrix} \\ &= \begin{bmatrix} D_{11} & D_{12} \\ D_{21} & D \end{bmatrix}. \end{aligned} \qquad (11.2.5)$$

By invoking Theorem 4.3.1, we conclude that D satisfies (11.2.1) if and only if $\|\Phi\| < 1$.

Main points of the section

1. A necessary condition for the existence of a solution to the four-block problem for constant matrices is that the norm of each of the known submatrices is less than unity.
2. The necessary condition is sufficient. This may be established by considering an allpass dilation, which also enables us to generate all solutions.
3. Extending the results to the case of transfer function matrices in $\mathcal{RL}_\infty$ is straightforward, since we may replace the Cholesky factorizations with spectral factorizations. As mentioned in the introduction, Parrott showed that the result holds for linear operators on Hilbert spaces.

11.3 Suboptimal solutions

With the treatment of the constant matrix problem behind us, we now seek necessary and sufficient conditions for the existence of a $\boldsymbol{Q} \in \mathcal{RH}_\infty^-(r)$ satisfying

$$\left\| \begin{bmatrix} \boldsymbol{R}_{11} & \boldsymbol{R}_{12} \\ \boldsymbol{R}_{21} & \boldsymbol{R}_{22} - \boldsymbol{Q} \end{bmatrix} \right\|_\infty < 1. \tag{11.3.1}$$

In (11.3.1), each of the transfer function matrices $\boldsymbol{R}_{ij}$ is in $\mathcal{RH}_\infty$. The strict inequality in (11.3.1) avoids the need to consider the optimal cases. The treatment of the optimal Hankel norm approximation problem in Chapter 10 provides some insight into the complexity of treating optimal cases, but we will not consider these intricacies in the four-block case.

We begin by considering necessary conditions, and a state-space dilation. The necessary conditions are then shown to be sufficient by an allpass embedding construction reminiscent of that used in Section 10.3.1.

11.3.1 The necessary conditions

Suppose that there exists a $\boldsymbol{Q} \in \mathcal{RH}_\infty^-(r)$ satisfying (11.3.1). Since the infinity norm of a submatrix can never exceed the infinity norm of the whole matrix, we obtain the following necessary conditions:

$$\left\| \begin{bmatrix} \boldsymbol{R}_{11} & \boldsymbol{R}_{12} \end{bmatrix} \right\|_\infty < 1, \qquad \left\| \begin{bmatrix} \boldsymbol{R}_{11} \\ \boldsymbol{R}_{21} \end{bmatrix} \right\|_\infty < 1. \tag{11.3.2}$$

It follows from Parrott's theorem that these conditions are also sufficient for the existence of a $\boldsymbol{Q} \in \mathcal{RL}_\infty$ that satisfies (11.3.1), but additional conditions come into play when we also require that $\boldsymbol{Q} \in \mathcal{RH}_\infty^-(r)$.

A further necessary condition may be obtained from the results of Chapter 10, in which it is shown that there exists a $\tilde{\boldsymbol{Q}} \in \mathcal{RH}_\infty^-(r)$ such that $\|\boldsymbol{R} - \tilde{\boldsymbol{Q}}\|_\infty < 1$ if and only if $\sigma_{r+1}(\boldsymbol{R}) < 1$. It follows that

$$\sigma_{r+1}\left(\begin{bmatrix} \boldsymbol{R}_{11} & \boldsymbol{R}_{12} \\ \boldsymbol{R}_{21} & \boldsymbol{R}_{22} \end{bmatrix} \right) < 1 \tag{11.3.3}$$

is necessary for the existence of $\boldsymbol{Q} \in \mathcal{RH}_\infty^-(r)$ satisfying (11.3.1). The conditions (11.3.2) and (11.3.3) are not, however, sufficient for the existence of $\boldsymbol{Q} \in \mathcal{RH}_\infty^-(r)$. In this section we develop a necessary condition in terms of the Hankel singular values of a partial dilation of the original problem. The dilation can be constructed whenever the necessary condition (11.3.2) holds. It turns out that this more sophisticated Hankel singular value condition is also sufficient.

The dilated Hankel singular value condition

We now construct a dilated system that will provide a Hankel singular value condition for the existence of a $\boldsymbol{Q} \in \mathcal{RH}_\infty^-(r)$ satisfying (11.3.1).

Theorem 11.3.1 *Suppose* $\begin{bmatrix} \boldsymbol{R}_{11} & \boldsymbol{R}_{12} \\ \boldsymbol{R}_{21} & \boldsymbol{R}_{22} \end{bmatrix} \in \mathcal{RH}_\infty$ *and that there exists a* $\boldsymbol{Q} \in \mathcal{RH}_\infty^-(r)$ *such that* $\boldsymbol{E}_{22} = \boldsymbol{R}_{22} - \boldsymbol{Q}$ *satisfies*

$$\left\| \begin{bmatrix} \boldsymbol{R}_{11} & \boldsymbol{R}_{12} \\ \boldsymbol{R}_{21} & \boldsymbol{E}_{22} \end{bmatrix} \right\|_\infty < 1. \tag{11.3.4}$$

Then:

1. *Condition (11.3.2) holds. Consequently there exists a* $p_1 \times p_1$ *transfer function matrix* $\boldsymbol{R}_{13} \in \mathcal{RH}_\infty$ *such that* $\boldsymbol{R}_{13}^{-1} \in \mathcal{RH}_\infty$ *and*

$$\boldsymbol{R}_{11}\boldsymbol{R}_{11}^\sim + \boldsymbol{R}_{12}\boldsymbol{R}_{12}^\sim + \boldsymbol{R}_{13}\boldsymbol{R}_{13}^\sim = I. \tag{11.3.5}$$

Also, there exists a $m_1 \times m_1$ *transfer function matrix* $\boldsymbol{R}_{31} \in \mathcal{RH}_\infty$ *such that* $\boldsymbol{R}_{31}^{-1} \in \mathcal{RH}_\infty$ *and*

$$\boldsymbol{R}_{11}^\sim\boldsymbol{R}_{11} + \boldsymbol{R}_{21}^\sim\boldsymbol{R}_{21} + \boldsymbol{R}_{31}^\sim\boldsymbol{R}_{31} = I. \tag{11.3.6}$$

2. *The transfer function matrix* $\boldsymbol{E}_a$ *defined by*

$$\boldsymbol{E}_a = (\boldsymbol{T}_1^{-1})^\sim \boldsymbol{T}_2 (\boldsymbol{T}_3^{-1})^\sim \tag{11.3.7}$$

has the form

$$\boldsymbol{E}_a = \begin{bmatrix} \boldsymbol{R}_{11} & \boldsymbol{R}_{12} & \boldsymbol{R}_{13} \\ \boldsymbol{R}_{21} & \boldsymbol{E}_{22} & \boldsymbol{E}_{23} \\ \boldsymbol{R}_{31} & \boldsymbol{E}_{32} & \boldsymbol{E}_{33} \end{bmatrix}, \tag{11.3.8}$$

and satisfies $\|\boldsymbol{E}_a\| = 1$. *In (11.3.7),*

$$\begin{aligned} \boldsymbol{T}_1 &= \begin{bmatrix} I & 0 & \boldsymbol{R}_{11} \\ 0 & I & \boldsymbol{R}_{21} \\ 0 & 0 & \boldsymbol{R}_{31} \end{bmatrix}, \\ \boldsymbol{T}_2 &= \begin{bmatrix} \boldsymbol{R}_{11} & \boldsymbol{R}_{12} & I \\ \boldsymbol{R}_{21} & \boldsymbol{E}_{22} & 0 \\ I & 0 & \boldsymbol{R}_{11}^\sim \end{bmatrix}, \\ \boldsymbol{T}_3 &= \begin{bmatrix} I & 0 & 0 \\ 0 & I & 0 \\ \boldsymbol{R}_{11} & \boldsymbol{R}_{12} & \boldsymbol{R}_{13} \end{bmatrix}. \end{aligned}$$

3. *Define* $\boldsymbol{R}_a \in \mathcal{RH}_\infty$ *to be*

$$\boldsymbol{R}_a = \left\{ (\boldsymbol{T}_1^{-1})^\sim \begin{bmatrix} \boldsymbol{R}_{11} & \boldsymbol{R}_{12} & 0 \\ \boldsymbol{R}_{21} & \boldsymbol{R}_{22} & 0 \\ 0 & 0 & 0 \end{bmatrix} (\boldsymbol{T}_3^{-1})^\sim \right\}_+ , \tag{11.3.9}$$

in which $(\cdot)_+$ *denotes any stable part.*[2] *Then* $\sigma_{r+1}(\boldsymbol{R}_a) < 1$.

Proof. Condition (11.3.2) is seen to be necessary by noting that the induced norm of a submatrix can never exceed the induced norm of the matrix it forms part of. To see this, one may consider the dynamic problem on a frequency-by-frequency basis. The existence of the transfer function matrices $\boldsymbol{R}_{13}$ and $\boldsymbol{R}_{31}$ then follows from standard spectral factorization theory (see Section 3.7).

Now construct $\boldsymbol{E}_a$ according to the definition (11.3.7). The structure of $\boldsymbol{E}_a$ given in (11.3.8) can be verified by direct calculation. To show that $\|\boldsymbol{E}_a\|_\infty = 1$, we first establish that $\|\boldsymbol{E}_a\|_\infty \leq 1$ and then show that equality holds. The inequality $\|\boldsymbol{E}_a\|_\infty \leq 1$ is equivalent to $I - \boldsymbol{E}_a\boldsymbol{E}_a^\sim \geq 0$. Multiplying this inequality on the left by $\boldsymbol{T}_1^\sim$ and on the right by $\boldsymbol{T}_1$ we see that $\|\boldsymbol{E}_a\|_\infty \leq 1$ is equivalent to the inequality

$$\boldsymbol{T}_1^\sim\boldsymbol{T}_1 - \boldsymbol{T}_2(\boldsymbol{T}_3^{-1})^\sim(\boldsymbol{T}_3^{-1})\boldsymbol{T}_2^\sim \geq 0.$$

Multiplying this out, we see that all but one of the nine blocks are zero and the nonzero block shows that $\|\boldsymbol{E}_a\|_\infty \leq 1$ is equivalent to the inequality

$$I - \boldsymbol{R}_{21}\boldsymbol{R}_{21}^\sim - \boldsymbol{E}_{22}\boldsymbol{E}_{22}^\sim - \boldsymbol{E}_{23}\boldsymbol{E}_{23}^\sim \geq 0.$$

We now verify that this inequality is satisfied. From (11.3.4), we see that

$$I - \begin{bmatrix} \boldsymbol{R}_{11} & \boldsymbol{R}_{12} \\ \boldsymbol{R}_{21} & \boldsymbol{E}_{22} \end{bmatrix} \begin{bmatrix} \boldsymbol{R}_{11}^\sim & \boldsymbol{R}_{21}^\sim \\ \boldsymbol{R}_{12}^\sim & \boldsymbol{E}_{22}^\sim \end{bmatrix} > 0.$$

Substituting for $I - \boldsymbol{R}_{11}\boldsymbol{R}_{11}^\sim + \boldsymbol{R}_{12}\boldsymbol{R}_{12}^\sim$ using (11.3.5) and noting that

$$\boldsymbol{R}_{21}\boldsymbol{R}_{11}^\sim + \boldsymbol{E}_{22}\boldsymbol{R}_{12}^\sim + \boldsymbol{E}_{23}\boldsymbol{R}_{13}^\sim = 0$$

by definition of $\boldsymbol{E}_{23}$, we obtain the inequality

$$\begin{bmatrix} \boldsymbol{R}_{13}\boldsymbol{R}_{13}^\sim & \boldsymbol{R}_{13}\boldsymbol{E}_{23}^\sim \\ \boldsymbol{E}_{23}\boldsymbol{R}_{13}^\sim & I - \boldsymbol{R}_{21}\boldsymbol{R}_{21}^\sim - \boldsymbol{E}_{22}\boldsymbol{E}_{22}^\sim \end{bmatrix} > 0.$$

Taking the Schur complement with respect to the (1,1)-block now yields the desired inequality

$$I - \boldsymbol{R}_{21}\boldsymbol{R}_{21}^\sim - \boldsymbol{E}_{22}\boldsymbol{E}_{22}^\sim - \boldsymbol{E}_{23}\boldsymbol{E}_{23}^\sim > 0.$$

The fact that $\|\boldsymbol{E}_a\|_\infty = 1$ follows from

$$\begin{bmatrix} \boldsymbol{R}_{11} & \boldsymbol{R}_{12} & \boldsymbol{R}_{13} \\ \boldsymbol{R}_{21} & \boldsymbol{E}_{22} & \boldsymbol{E}_{23} \\ \boldsymbol{R}_{31} & \boldsymbol{E}_{32} & \boldsymbol{E}_{33} \end{bmatrix} \begin{bmatrix} I \\ 0 \\ 0 \end{bmatrix} = \begin{bmatrix} \boldsymbol{R}_{11} \\ \boldsymbol{R}_{21} \\ \boldsymbol{R}_{31} \end{bmatrix},$$

[2] A stable part of $\boldsymbol{G} \in \mathcal{RL}_\infty$ is any $\boldsymbol{G}_+ \in \mathcal{RH}_\infty$ such that $\boldsymbol{G} - \boldsymbol{G}_+ \in \mathcal{RH}_\infty^-$. A stable part is unique up to the direct feedthrough or D-matrix of the system. By the Paley-Wiener theorem, this is equivalent to a causal/anticausal decomposition of the system and the nonuniqueness arises because the present is considered part of the past and part of the future.

since the infinity norm of the right-hand side is unity by (11.3.6).

To prove the Hankel singular value condition, we decompose $\boldsymbol{E}_a$ as

$$\boldsymbol{E}_a = \boldsymbol{R}_a + \left\{ (\boldsymbol{T}_1^{-1})^\sim \begin{bmatrix} \boldsymbol{R}_{11} & \boldsymbol{R}_{12} & 0 \\ \boldsymbol{R}_{21} & \boldsymbol{R}_{22} & 0 \\ 0 & 0 & 0 \end{bmatrix} (\boldsymbol{T}_3^{-1})^\sim \right\}_- + (\boldsymbol{T}_1^{-1})^\sim \begin{bmatrix} 0 & 0 & I \\ 0 & \boldsymbol{Q} & 0 \\ I & 0 & \boldsymbol{R}_{11}^\sim \end{bmatrix} (\boldsymbol{T}_3^{-1})^\sim.$$

The second term is in $\mathcal{RH}_\infty^-$ by definition (it is the antistable part of something) and the third term is in $\mathcal{RH}_\infty^-(r)$, since $(\boldsymbol{T}_1^{-1})^\sim$, $(\boldsymbol{T}_3^{-1})^\sim$ and $\boldsymbol{R}_{11}^\sim$ are all terms in $\mathcal{RH}_\infty^-$ and $\boldsymbol{Q} \in \mathcal{RH}_\infty^-(r)$. Since $\|\boldsymbol{E}_a\|_\infty = 1$, the Hankel norm approximation results of Chapter 10 ensure that $\sigma_{r+1}(\boldsymbol{R}_a) \leq 1$ (see Lemma 10.2.1 or Theorem 10.4.2). We now show that strict inequality holds using a contradiction argument involving Schmidt vectors.

Suppose, to obtain a contradiction, that $\sigma_{r+1}(\boldsymbol{R}_a) = 1$. Let $\boldsymbol{v} \in \mathcal{RH}_2$ and $\boldsymbol{w} \in \mathcal{RH}_2$ be the Laplace transforms of the Schmidt pair associated with $\sigma_{r+1}(\boldsymbol{R}_a) = 1$. Since $\|\boldsymbol{E}_a\|_\infty = 1$, $\boldsymbol{E}_a$ is an optimal Hankel norm extension of $\boldsymbol{R}_a$. Therefore, by Lemma 10.4.3, we have

$$\boldsymbol{E}_a \boldsymbol{v}(-s) = \boldsymbol{w}(s). \qquad (11.3.10)$$

Indeed, if we construct $\boldsymbol{E}_a(\boldsymbol{\Delta})$ by replacing $\boldsymbol{T}_2$ in (11.3.7) by

$$\boldsymbol{T}_2(\boldsymbol{\Delta}) = \begin{bmatrix} \boldsymbol{R}_{11} & \boldsymbol{R}_{12} & I \\ \boldsymbol{R}_{21} & \boldsymbol{E}_{22} - \boldsymbol{\Delta} & 0 \\ I & 0 & \boldsymbol{R}_{11}^\sim \end{bmatrix},$$

then $\boldsymbol{\Delta} \in \mathcal{RH}_\infty^-$ implies $\boldsymbol{Q} + \boldsymbol{\Delta} \in \mathcal{RH}_\infty^-(r)$ and

$$\|\boldsymbol{\Delta}\|_\infty < 1 - \left\| \begin{bmatrix} \boldsymbol{R}_{11} & \boldsymbol{R}_{12} \\ \boldsymbol{R}_{21} & \boldsymbol{E}_{22} \end{bmatrix} \right\|_\infty \qquad (11.3.11)$$

implies that $\|\boldsymbol{E}_a(\boldsymbol{\Delta})\|_\infty = 1$. Thus $\boldsymbol{E}_a(\boldsymbol{\Delta})$ is also an optimal Hankel norm extension of $\boldsymbol{R}_a$ and therefore

$$(\boldsymbol{E}_a(\boldsymbol{\Delta}) - \boldsymbol{E}_a)\boldsymbol{v}(-s) = 0.$$

Multiplying by $\boldsymbol{T}_1^\sim$ we obtain

$$\begin{bmatrix} 0 & 0 & 0 \\ 0 & \boldsymbol{\Delta} & 0 \\ 0 & 0 & 0 \end{bmatrix} (\boldsymbol{T}_3^{-1})^\sim \boldsymbol{v}(-s) = 0.$$

Since this is true for arbitrary $\boldsymbol{\Delta} \in \mathcal{RH}_\infty^-$ satisfying (11.3.11), we see that

$$\begin{bmatrix} 0 & I & 0 \end{bmatrix} (\boldsymbol{T}_3^{-1})^\sim \boldsymbol{v}(-s) = 0.$$

That is, the second block-row of $(\boldsymbol{T}_3^{-1})^\sim \boldsymbol{v}(-s)$ is zero. Thus

$$\boldsymbol{T}_2(\boldsymbol{T}_3^{-1})^\sim \boldsymbol{v}(-s) = \begin{bmatrix} \boldsymbol{R}_{11} & 0 & (I - \boldsymbol{R}_{11}\boldsymbol{R}_{11}^\sim)(\boldsymbol{R}_{13}^{-1})^\sim \\ \boldsymbol{R}_{21} & 0 & -\boldsymbol{R}_{21}\boldsymbol{R}_{11}^\sim(\boldsymbol{R}_{13}^{-1})^\sim \\ I & 0 & 0 \end{bmatrix} \boldsymbol{v}(-s).$$

Examining the last row of (11.3.10) now gives

$$(\boldsymbol{R}_{31}^{-1})^\sim \begin{bmatrix} -\boldsymbol{R}_{11}^\sim & -\boldsymbol{R}_{21}^\sim & I \end{bmatrix} \begin{bmatrix} \boldsymbol{R}_{11} & 0 & (I - \boldsymbol{R}_{11}\boldsymbol{R}_{11}^\sim)(\boldsymbol{R}_{13}^{-1})^\sim \\ \boldsymbol{R}_{21} & 0 & -\boldsymbol{R}_{21}\boldsymbol{R}_{11}^\sim(\boldsymbol{R}_{13}^{-1})^\sim \\ I & 0 & 0 \end{bmatrix} \boldsymbol{v}(-s)$$
$$= \begin{bmatrix} 0 & 0 & I \end{bmatrix} \boldsymbol{w}(s).$$

Simplifying the left-hand side using (11.3.6), we obtain

$$\begin{bmatrix} I & 0 & -\boldsymbol{R}_{11}^\sim(\boldsymbol{R}_{13}^{-1})^\sim \end{bmatrix} \boldsymbol{v}(-s) = \begin{bmatrix} 0 & 0 & \boldsymbol{R}_{31}^{-1} \end{bmatrix} \boldsymbol{w}(s).$$

Since the left-hand side of this equality is in $\mathcal{RH}_2^-$ and the right-hand side is in $\mathcal{RH}_2$, we conclude that both sides must be zero. This shows that that the first block-row of $(\boldsymbol{T}_3^{-1})^\sim \boldsymbol{v}(-s)$ is zero. Examining the implications of this on (11.3.10), we obtain

$$\begin{bmatrix} 0 & 0 & (\boldsymbol{R}_{13}^{-1})^\sim \end{bmatrix} \boldsymbol{v}(-s) = \begin{bmatrix} I & 0 & 0 \end{bmatrix} \boldsymbol{w}(s).$$

Once again, the left-hand side of this equality is in $\mathcal{RH}_2^-$ and the right-hand side is in $\mathcal{RH}_2$, so both sides are zero. This means that third block-row of $(\boldsymbol{T}_3^{-1})^\sim \boldsymbol{v}(-s)$ is zero. That is, we have now shown that $(\boldsymbol{T}_3^{-1})^\sim \boldsymbol{v}(-s) = 0$. Hence $\boldsymbol{v} = 0$ and $\boldsymbol{w} = 0$, which is a contradiction, since Schmidt pairs cannot be zero. This means that $\boldsymbol{R}_a$ has no Schmidt pair corresponding to a Hankel singular value $\sigma_{r+1}(\boldsymbol{R}_a) = 1$ and we conclude that $\sigma_{r+1}(\boldsymbol{R}_a) < 1$. ■

It is important to note that the dilated system $\boldsymbol{R}_a$ can be constructed without knowing $\boldsymbol{Q} \in \mathcal{RH}_\infty^-(r)$. Thus, a check of the necessary conditions involves checking (11.3.2) and, if this test is passed, we construct $\boldsymbol{R}_a$ and check the Hankel singular value condition. This can be done via an explicit state-space construction of $\boldsymbol{R}_a$.

11.3.2 State-space construction of the dilation

The aim of this section is to construct the dilated transfer function $\boldsymbol{R}_a$ given in (11.3.9) in the state-space. This requires a state-space construction of the two spectral factors $\boldsymbol{R}_{13}$ and $\boldsymbol{R}_{31}$, which involves two Riccati equations. This construction leads to a simple re-statement of the necessary conditions in terms of state-space quantities.

Lemma 11.3.2 *Suppose*

$$\begin{bmatrix} \boldsymbol{R}_{11} & \boldsymbol{R}_{12} \\ \boldsymbol{R}_{21} & \boldsymbol{R}_{22} \end{bmatrix} \stackrel{s}{=} \left[\begin{array}{c|cc} A & B_1 & B_2 \\ \hline C_1 & D_{11} & D_{12} \\ C_2 & D_{21} & * \end{array}\right],$$

in which A is an $n \times n$ matrix that is asymptotically stable ($\mathrm{R}_e\lambda_i(A) < 0$). Then the condition (11.3.2) holds if and only if there exists a nonsingular matrix D_{31} and a matrix $Y \geq 0$ satisfying

$$\begin{aligned} YA + A'Y + \begin{bmatrix} C_1' & C_2' \end{bmatrix}\begin{bmatrix} C_1' & C_2' \end{bmatrix}' + C_3'C_3 &= 0 \qquad (11.3.12)\\ \begin{bmatrix} D_{11}' & D_{21}' \end{bmatrix}\begin{bmatrix} C_1' & C_2' \end{bmatrix}' + D_{31}'C_3 + B_1'Y &= 0 \qquad (11.3.13)\\ D_{11}'D_{11} + D_{21}'D_{21} + D_{31}'D_{31} &= I \end{aligned}$$

such that $A - B_1D_{31}^{-1}C_3$ is asymptotically stable, and there exists a nonsingular matrix D_{13} and a matrix $X \geq 0$ satisfying

$$\begin{aligned} AX + XA' + \begin{bmatrix} B_1 & B_2 \end{bmatrix}\begin{bmatrix} B_1 & B_2 \end{bmatrix}' + B_3B_3' &= 0 \qquad (11.3.14)\\ \begin{bmatrix} B_1 & B_2 \end{bmatrix}\begin{bmatrix} D_{11} & D_{12} \end{bmatrix}' + B_3D_{13}' + XC_1' &= 0 \qquad (11.3.15)\\ D_{11}D_{11}' + D_{12}D_{12}' + D_{13}D_{13}' &= I \end{aligned}$$

such that $A - B_3D_{13}^{-1}C_1$ asymptotically stable.

In this case, the system $\boldsymbol{R}_a$ defined in (11.3.9) has a state-space realization of the form

$$\boldsymbol{R}_a \stackrel{s}{=} \left[\begin{array}{c|ccc} A & B_1 & B_2 & B_3 \\ \hline C_1 & D_{11} & D_{12} & D_{13} \\ C_2 & D_{21} & * & * \\ C_3 & D_{31} & * & * \end{array}\right], \qquad (11.3.16)$$

and the Hankel singular values of $\boldsymbol{R}_a$ are given by

$$\sigma_{r+1}(\boldsymbol{R}_a) = \sqrt{\lambda_{r+1}(XY)}, \qquad r = 0, 1, 2, \ldots, n-1.$$

Consequently, there exists a $\boldsymbol{Q} \in \mathcal{RH}_\infty^-(r)$ satisfying

$$\left\| \begin{bmatrix} \boldsymbol{R}_{11} & \boldsymbol{R}_{12} \\ \boldsymbol{R}_{21} & \boldsymbol{R}_{22} + \boldsymbol{Q} \end{bmatrix} \right\|_\infty < 1$$

if and only if D_{13}, D_{31}, X and Y as above exist and $\lambda_{r+1}(XY) < 1$.

Proof. The two infinity norm inequalities of (11.3.2) are equivalent to the existence of D_{13}, D_{31}, X and Y as stated by the bounded real lemma (Theorem 3.7.1). See, in particular, the spectral factorization proof of the bounded real lemma. The spectral factors $\boldsymbol{R}_{13}$ and $\boldsymbol{R}_{31}$ are given by

$$\boldsymbol{R}_{13} \stackrel{s}{=} \left[\begin{array}{c|c} A & B_3 \\ \hline C_1 & D_{13} \end{array}\right], \qquad \boldsymbol{R}_{31} \stackrel{s}{=} \left[\begin{array}{c|c} A & B_1 \\ \hline C_3 & D_{31} \end{array}\right].$$

Now expand $\boldsymbol{R}_a$ in (11.3.9) as

$$\boldsymbol{R}_a = \left\{ \begin{bmatrix} \boldsymbol{R}_{11} & \boldsymbol{R}_{12} & \boldsymbol{R}_{13} \\ \boldsymbol{R}_{21} & \boldsymbol{R}_{22} & (2,3) \\ \boldsymbol{R}_{31} & (3,2) & (3,3) \end{bmatrix} \right\}_+,$$

in which

$$\begin{aligned}
(2,3) &= -\begin{bmatrix} \boldsymbol{R}_{21} & \boldsymbol{R}_{22} \end{bmatrix}\begin{bmatrix} \boldsymbol{R}_{11}^{\sim} \\ \boldsymbol{R}_{12}^{\sim} \end{bmatrix}(\boldsymbol{R}_{13}^{-1})^{\sim} \\
(3,2) &= -(\boldsymbol{R}_{31}^{-1})^{\sim}\begin{bmatrix} \boldsymbol{R}_{11}^{\sim} & \boldsymbol{R}_{21}^{\sim} \end{bmatrix}\begin{bmatrix} \boldsymbol{R}_{12} \\ \boldsymbol{R}_{22} \end{bmatrix} \\
(3,3) &= (\boldsymbol{R}_{31}^{-1})^{\sim}\begin{bmatrix} \boldsymbol{R}_{11}^{\sim} & \boldsymbol{R}_{21}^{\sim} \end{bmatrix}\begin{bmatrix} \boldsymbol{R}_{12} \\ \boldsymbol{R}_{22} \end{bmatrix}\boldsymbol{R}_{12}^{\sim}(\boldsymbol{R}_{13}^{-1})^{\sim} - \boldsymbol{R}_{31}\boldsymbol{R}_{11}^{\sim}(\boldsymbol{R}_{13}^{-1})^{\sim}.
\end{aligned}$$

The realization in (11.3.16) therefore matches $\boldsymbol{R}_a$ in the $\boldsymbol{R}_{11}$, $\boldsymbol{R}_{12}$, $\boldsymbol{R}_{13}$, $\boldsymbol{R}_{21}$, $\boldsymbol{R}_{31}$ and $\boldsymbol{R}_{22}$ locations; it remains for us to verify that the (3,2), (2,3) and (3,3) locations of (11.3.16) match the corresponding entries in (11.3.9).

Direct calculations, which are facilitated by using the state-space interconnection formulas of Problem 3.6, give

$$(\boldsymbol{R}_{31}^{-1})^{\sim}\begin{bmatrix} \boldsymbol{R}_{11}^{\sim} & \boldsymbol{R}_{21}^{\sim} \end{bmatrix} \stackrel{s}{=} \left[\begin{array}{c|c} -(A - B_1 D_{31}^{-1} C_3)' & C_3'(D_{31}^{-1})'\begin{bmatrix} D_{11}' & D_{21}' \end{bmatrix} - \begin{bmatrix} C_1' & C_2' \end{bmatrix} \\ \hline (D_{31}^{-1})'B_1' & (D_{31}^{-1})'\begin{bmatrix} D_{11}' & D_{21}' \end{bmatrix} \end{array}\right]$$

and

$$\begin{bmatrix} \boldsymbol{R}_{11}^{\sim} \\ \boldsymbol{R}_{12}^{\sim} \end{bmatrix}(\boldsymbol{R}_{13}^{-1})^{\sim} = \left[\begin{array}{c|c} -(A - B_3 D_{13}^{-1} C_1)' & C_1'(D_{13}^{-1})' \\ \hline \begin{bmatrix} D_{11}' \\ D_{12}' \end{bmatrix}(D_{13}^{-1})'B_3' - \begin{bmatrix} B_1' \\ B_2' \end{bmatrix} & \begin{bmatrix} D_{11}' \\ D_{12}' \end{bmatrix}(D_{13}^{-1})' \end{array}\right].$$

Equations (11.3.13) and (11.3.12) give

$$\begin{aligned}
&(\boldsymbol{R}_{31}^{-1})^{\sim}\begin{bmatrix} \boldsymbol{R}_{11}^{\sim} & \boldsymbol{R}_{21}^{\sim} \end{bmatrix}\begin{bmatrix} C_1 \\ C_2 \end{bmatrix}(sI - A)^{-1} \\
&= -C_3(sI - A)^{-1} + \{\text{terms analytic in } \mathrm{R}_e(s) > 0\}.
\end{aligned}$$

And (11.3.15) and (11.3.14) give

$$\begin{aligned}
&(sI - A)^{-1}\begin{bmatrix} B_1 & B_2 \end{bmatrix}\begin{bmatrix} \boldsymbol{R}_{11}^{\sim} \\ \boldsymbol{R}_{12}^{\sim} \end{bmatrix}(\boldsymbol{R}_{13}^{-1})^{\sim} \\
&= -(sI - A)^{-1}B_3 + \{\text{terms analytic in } \mathrm{R}_e(s) > 0\}.
\end{aligned}$$

From these calculations, we see that the (2,3)- and (3,2)-blocks of $\boldsymbol{R}_a$ are indeed as given in (11.3.16). Now observe that

$$\begin{aligned}
\{(3,3)\}_+ &= -\left\{\begin{bmatrix} \boldsymbol{R}_{31} & \boldsymbol{R}_{32} \end{bmatrix}\begin{bmatrix} \boldsymbol{R}_{11}^{\sim} \\ \boldsymbol{R}_{21}^{\sim} \end{bmatrix}(\boldsymbol{R}_{13}^{-1})^{\sim}\right\}_+ \\
&= C_3(sI - A)^{-1}B_3 + \{\text{a constant matrix}\},
\end{aligned}$$

which shows that the (3,3)-block of $\boldsymbol{R}_a$ is also of the form given in (11.3.16). (The details of these state-space calculations are left as an exercise.)

To conclude the proof, we observe from (11.3.14) and (11.3.12) that X and Y are the controllability and observability gramians respectively of the realization in (11.3.16). Therefore, $\sqrt{\lambda_{r+1}(XY)}$ are the Hankel singular values of $\boldsymbol{R}_a$. Combining this information with Theorem 11.3.1, we have the desired state-space conditions for necessity. ■

11.3.3 The sufficient conditions

In this section, we show that the necessary conditions given in Theorem 11.3.1 are also sufficient. In doing so, we shall construct every $\boldsymbol{Q} \in \mathcal{RH}_\infty^-(r)$ such that

$$\left\| \begin{bmatrix} \boldsymbol{R}_{11} & \boldsymbol{R}_{12} \\ \boldsymbol{R}_{21} & \boldsymbol{R}_{11} - \boldsymbol{Q} \end{bmatrix} \right\|_\infty < 1. \tag{11.3.17}$$

We shall establish sufficiency via an allpass embedding in which we assemble a transfer function matrix of the form

$$\boldsymbol{E}_{aa} = \begin{bmatrix} \boldsymbol{R}_{11} & \boldsymbol{R}_{12} & \boldsymbol{R}_{13} & 0 \\ \boldsymbol{R}_{21} & \boldsymbol{E}_{22} & \boldsymbol{E}_{23} & -\boldsymbol{Q}_{24} \\ \boldsymbol{R}_{31} & \boldsymbol{E}_{32} & \boldsymbol{E}_{33} & -\boldsymbol{Q}_{34} \\ 0 & -\boldsymbol{Q}_{42} & -\boldsymbol{Q}_{43} & -\boldsymbol{Q}_{44} \end{bmatrix}$$

such that $\boldsymbol{E}_{aa}$ is allpass, which generalizes the construction used in the constant matrix case in Section 11.2. Each of the entries $\boldsymbol{E}_{ij}$ may be decomposed as $\boldsymbol{E}_{ij} = \boldsymbol{R}_{ij} - \boldsymbol{Q}_{ij}$, with $\boldsymbol{R}_{ij} \in \mathcal{RH}_\infty$, and

$$\boldsymbol{Q}_{aa} = \begin{bmatrix} 0 & 0 & 0 & 0 \\ 0 & \boldsymbol{Q}_{22} & \boldsymbol{Q}_{23} & \boldsymbol{Q}_{24} \\ 0 & \boldsymbol{Q}_{32} & \boldsymbol{Q}_{33} & \boldsymbol{Q}_{34} \\ 0 & \boldsymbol{Q}_{42} & \boldsymbol{Q}_{43} & \boldsymbol{Q}_{44} \end{bmatrix} \in \mathcal{RH}_\infty^-(r). \tag{11.3.18}$$

As in the constant matrix case, the allpass nature of $\boldsymbol{E}_{aa}$ ensures that the inequality (11.3.17) holds, provided that at least one of the off-diagonal 2×2 blocks of $\boldsymbol{E}_{aa}$ is nonsingular. The construction of $\boldsymbol{E}_{aa}$ from $\boldsymbol{R}_a$ will be accomplished using state-space arguments familiar from Section 10.3.1.

Construction of the allpass embedding

Adding an extra block-row and block-column to $\boldsymbol{R}_a$ gives

$$\boldsymbol{R}_{aa} = \begin{bmatrix} \boldsymbol{R}_a & 0 \\ 0 & 0 \end{bmatrix} \stackrel{s}{=} \left[\begin{array}{c|c} A & B_{aa} \\ \hline C_{aa} & 0 \end{array}\right],$$

in which

$$\begin{aligned} B_{aa} &= \begin{bmatrix} B_1 & B_2 & B_3 & 0 \end{bmatrix} \\ C'_{aa} &= \begin{bmatrix} C'_1 & C'_2 & C'_3 & 0 \end{bmatrix}. \end{aligned}$$

We seek

$$\boldsymbol{Q}_{aa} \stackrel{s}{=} \left[\begin{array}{c|c} \widehat{A} & \widehat{B}_{aa} \\ \hline \widehat{C}_{aa} & D_{aa} \end{array}\right]$$

such that $\widehat{A}$ has no more than r eigenvalues in the left-half plane, and such that the resulting $\boldsymbol{E}_{aa} = \boldsymbol{R}_{aa} - \boldsymbol{Q}_{aa}$ satisfies $\boldsymbol{E}_{aa}^{\sim}\boldsymbol{E}_{aa} = I$.

Assuming that $\lambda_i(XY) \neq 1$ for all i, we apply the construction of Section 10.3.1 to $\boldsymbol{R}_{aa}$ given by the realization (11.3.16) to obtain

$$\widehat{B}_{aa} = Z^{-1}(YB_{aa} + C'_{aa}D_{aa}) \tag{11.3.19}$$
$$\widehat{C}_{aa} = D_{aa}B'_{aa} + C_{aa}X, \tag{11.3.20}$$

and

$$\widehat{A} = -A' - \widehat{B}_{aa}B'_{aa}. \tag{11.3.21}$$

In the above,

$$Z = YX - I,$$

which is nonsingular because we have assumed that no Hankel singular value of $\boldsymbol{R}_a$ is unity. The matrix $\widehat{A}$ has no eigenvalues on the imaginary axis, and the number of eigenvalues of $\widehat{A}$ in the left-half plane is precisely the number of Hankel singular values of $\boldsymbol{R}_a$ that are larger than unity. Thus, if $\sigma_{r+1}(\boldsymbol{R}_a) < 1$ and $\sigma_r(\boldsymbol{R}_a) > 1$, then $\widehat{A}$ has exactly r eigenvalues in the left-half plane—these facts are immediate from the allpass embedding construction of Section 10.3.1. The new twist is that we choose D_{aa} as given in (11.2.4) in the construction of all solutions to the constant matrix problem.

In order to show that $\boldsymbol{Q}_{aa}$ is zero in the first block-row and block-column, as indicated in (11.3.18), partition $\widehat{C}_{aa}$ and $\widehat{B}_{aa}$ as

$$\begin{aligned} \widehat{B}_{aa} &= \begin{bmatrix} \widehat{B}_1 & \widehat{B}_2 & \widehat{B}_3 & \widehat{B}_4 \end{bmatrix} \\ \widehat{C}'_{aa} &= \begin{bmatrix} \widehat{C}'_1 & \widehat{C}'_2 & \widehat{C}'_3 & \widehat{C}'_4 \end{bmatrix}. \end{aligned}$$

We now show that $\widehat{C}_1 = 0$ and $\widehat{B}_1 = 0$. From the definition of $\widehat{B}_{aa}$ in (11.3.19) and (11.3.13), we have

$$\widehat{B}_1 = Z^{-1}(YB_1 + \begin{bmatrix} C'_1 & C'_2 & C'_3 \end{bmatrix} \begin{bmatrix} D_{11} \\ D_{21} \\ D_{31} \end{bmatrix}) = 0.$$

Similarly, it follows from (11.3.20) and (11.3.15) that

$$\widehat{C}_1 = C_1 X + \begin{bmatrix} D_{11} & D_{12} & D_{31} \end{bmatrix} \begin{bmatrix} B_1' \\ B_2' \\ B_3' \end{bmatrix} = 0.$$

Theorem 11.3.3 *Suppose A is asymptotically stable and $\boldsymbol{R} \in \mathcal{RH}_\infty$ is given by*

$$\begin{bmatrix} \boldsymbol{R}_{11} & \boldsymbol{R}_{12} \\ \boldsymbol{R}_{21} & \boldsymbol{R}_{22} \end{bmatrix} \stackrel{s}{=} \left[\begin{array}{c|cc} A & B_1 & B_2 \\ \hline C_1 & D_{11} & D_{12} \\ C_2 & D_{21} & * \end{array}\right]. \tag{11.3.22}$$

If

$$\left\| \begin{bmatrix} \boldsymbol{R}_{11} & \boldsymbol{R}_{12} \end{bmatrix} \right\|_\infty < 1, \qquad \left\| \begin{bmatrix} \boldsymbol{R}_{11} \\ \boldsymbol{R}_{21} \end{bmatrix} \right\|_\infty < 1,$$

and $\sigma_{r+1}(\boldsymbol{R}_a) < 1$, then there exists a $\boldsymbol{Q} \in \mathcal{RH}_\infty^-(r)$ such that

$$\left\| \begin{bmatrix} \boldsymbol{R}_{11} & \boldsymbol{R}_{12} \\ \boldsymbol{R}_{21} & \boldsymbol{R}_{22} - \boldsymbol{Q} \end{bmatrix} \right\|_\infty < 1. \tag{11.3.23}$$

When $\sigma_{r+1}(\boldsymbol{R}_a) < 1 < \sigma_r(\boldsymbol{R}_a)$, every $\boldsymbol{Q} \in \mathcal{RH}_\infty^-(r)$ satisfying (11.3.23) is given by

$$\boldsymbol{Q} = \mathcal{F}_\ell\left(\begin{bmatrix} \boldsymbol{Q}_{22} & \boldsymbol{Q}_{24} \\ \boldsymbol{Q}_{42} & \boldsymbol{Q}_{44} \end{bmatrix}, \boldsymbol{U} \right) \tag{11.3.24}$$

for some $\boldsymbol{U} \in \mathcal{RH}_\infty^-$ such that $\|\boldsymbol{U}\|_\infty < 1$. In (11.3.24),

$$\begin{bmatrix} \boldsymbol{Q}_{22} & \boldsymbol{Q}_{24} \\ \boldsymbol{Q}_{42} & \boldsymbol{Q}_{44} \end{bmatrix} \stackrel{s}{=} \left[\begin{array}{c|cc} \widehat{A} & \widehat{B}_2 & \widehat{B}_4 \\ \hline \widehat{C}_2 & D_{22} & D_{24} \\ \widehat{C}_4 & D_{42} & 0 \end{array}\right].$$

The D_{ij}'s are as in (11.2.4), and the remaining matrices are given by the appropriate partitions of (11.3.19), (11.3.20) and (11.3.21).

Proof. We prove the existence of a $\boldsymbol{Q} \in \mathcal{RH}_\infty^-(r)$ satisfying (11.3.23) using the construction of $\boldsymbol{E}_{aa}$ in this section. Assume that no Hankel singular value of $\boldsymbol{R}_a$ is unity. Construct $\boldsymbol{E}_{aa}$ and note that $\boldsymbol{Q}_{aa} \in \mathcal{RH}_\infty^-(r)$, since no more than r Hankel singular values of $\boldsymbol{R}_a$ are larger than unity. Since $\boldsymbol{E}_{aa}$ is allpass,

$$\left\| \begin{bmatrix} \boldsymbol{R}_{11} & \boldsymbol{R}_{12} \\ \boldsymbol{R}_{21} & \boldsymbol{R}_{22} - \boldsymbol{Q}_{22} \end{bmatrix} \right\|_\infty \leq 1.$$

In order to show that strict inequality holds, rather than simply inequality, we need to show that $\boldsymbol{Q}_{42}$ is nonsingular on the imaginary axis, since we already known that

$\boldsymbol{R}_{31}$ is nonsingular on the imaginary axis. We shall in fact show that $\boldsymbol{Q}_{42}^{-1}$ (and $\boldsymbol{Q}_{24}^{-1}$) are in $\mathcal{RH}_\infty^-$. The A-matrix of $\boldsymbol{Q}_{42}^{-1}$ is given by

$$\begin{aligned}\widehat{A} - \widehat{B}_2 D_{42}^{-1}\widehat{C}_4 &= -A' - \widehat{B}_{aa}B_{aa}' - \widehat{B}_2 D_{42}^{-1}(D_{42}B_2' + D_{43}B_3')\\ &= -A' - (\widehat{B}_3 - \widehat{B}_2 D_{42}^{-1}D_{34})B_3'.\end{aligned}$$

Since D_{aa} is orthogonal, we have $D_{42}^{-1}D_{43} = -D_{12}'(D_{13}^{-1})'$ (see Problem 11.4), giving

$$\begin{aligned}\widehat{B}_3 - \widehat{B}_2 D_{42}^{-1}D_{34} &= \begin{bmatrix} \widehat{B}_2 & \widehat{B}_3 \end{bmatrix}\begin{bmatrix} D_{12}' \\ D_{13}' \end{bmatrix}(D_{13}^{-1})'\\ &= \widehat{B}_{aa}D_{aa}'\begin{bmatrix} I \\ 0 \\ 0 \\ 0 \end{bmatrix}(D_{13}^{-1})'\\ &= (Z^{-1})'(YB_{aa}D_{aa}'\begin{bmatrix} I \\ 0 \\ 0 \\ 0 \end{bmatrix} - C_1')(D_{13}^{-1})' \qquad \text{by (11.3.19)}\\ &= Z^{-1}(I - YX)C_1'(D_{13}^{-1})' \qquad \text{by (11.3.15)}\\ &= -C_1'(D_{13}^{-1})'.\end{aligned}$$

Hence $\widehat{A} - \widehat{B}_2 D_{42}^{-1}\widehat{C}_4 = -(A - B_3 D_{13}^{-1}C_1)'$ and since $A - B_3D_{13}^{-1}C_1$ is asymptotically stable we see that $\boldsymbol{Q}_{42}^{-1} \in \mathcal{RH}_\infty^-$. A similar argument gives $\widehat{A} - \widehat{B}_4 D_{24}^{-1}\widehat{C}_2 = -Z^{-1}(A - B_1D_{31}^{-1}C_3)'Z$ (see Problem 11.5) and hence that $\boldsymbol{Q}_{24}^{-1} \in \mathcal{RH}_\infty^-$. We conclude that $\boldsymbol{Q}_{22} \in \mathcal{RH}_\infty^-(r)$ and that (11.3.23) holds. Thus $\sigma_{r+1}(\boldsymbol{R}_a) < 1$ is sufficient for the existence of a $\boldsymbol{Q} \in \mathcal{RH}_\infty^-(r)$ satisfying (11.3.23).

We now verify that (11.3.24) generates all solutions when $\sigma_{r+1}(\boldsymbol{R}_a) < 1 < \sigma_r(\boldsymbol{R}_a)$. Since $\boldsymbol{Q}_{24}$ and $\boldsymbol{Q}_{42}$ have inverses in $\mathcal{RH}_\infty^-$, any $\boldsymbol{Q} \in \mathcal{RH}_\infty^-(r)$ can be generated by setting

$$\boldsymbol{U} = (I + \boldsymbol{\Psi}\boldsymbol{Q}_{44})^{-1}\boldsymbol{\Psi}, \qquad \boldsymbol{\Psi} = \boldsymbol{Q}_{24}^{-1}(\boldsymbol{Q} - \boldsymbol{Q}_{22})\boldsymbol{Q}_{42}^{-1}.$$

Since

$$\begin{bmatrix} \boldsymbol{R}_{11} & \boldsymbol{R}_{12} \\ \boldsymbol{R}_{21} & \boldsymbol{R}_{22} - \boldsymbol{Q} \end{bmatrix} = \mathcal{F}_\ell(\boldsymbol{E}_{aa}, \begin{bmatrix} 0 & 0 \\ 0 & \boldsymbol{U} \end{bmatrix}),$$

with $\boldsymbol{E}_{aa}$ allpass, Lemma 4.3.2 ensures that (11.3.23) holds if and only if $\|\boldsymbol{U}\|_\infty < 1$. From the allpass nature of $\boldsymbol{E}_{aa}$, we also see that $\|\boldsymbol{Q}_{44}\|_\infty \le 1$, and therefore $\|\boldsymbol{U}\|_\infty < 1$ implies $\|\boldsymbol{Q}_{44}\boldsymbol{U}\|_\infty < 1$. Lemma 4.3.4 now ensures that $\boldsymbol{U} \in \mathcal{RH}_\infty^-$ if and only if $\boldsymbol{Q} \in \mathcal{RH}_\infty^-(r)$. ■

Optimal solution of the four-block problem

The theory of optimal solutions to the four-block problem is intricate, due to the several possible ways in which optimality can occur.

If the Parrott conditions of (11.3.2) hold, there exists a $\boldsymbol{Q} \in \mathcal{RL}_\infty$ that satisfies the norm objective, but it may or may not have only r poles in the left-half plane. Under these conditions, we may construct the dilated matrix $\boldsymbol{R}_a$ and test the Hankel singular value condition $\sigma_{r+1}(\boldsymbol{R}_a) \leq 1$. If equality holds, we have an optimal problem in which the constraint that $\boldsymbol{Q}$ contains only r stable poles is the limiting factor. This type of optimality is easily dealt with by constructing an optimal allpass embedding $\boldsymbol{E}_{aa}$ as in Section 10.4.1 to obtain all optimal solutions.

If one of the Parrott conditions of (11.3.2) holds with equality, the overall solution procedure is similar to the suboptimal case in that we may still construct a dilated matrix $\boldsymbol{R}_a$. However, we cannot demand that $\boldsymbol{R}_{13}$ and $\boldsymbol{R}_{31}$ are nonsingular, which makes a consideration of this case technically difficult. The interested reader will find all these details in [78].

Main points of the section

1. If $\begin{bmatrix} \boldsymbol{R}_{11} & \boldsymbol{R}_{12} \\ \boldsymbol{R}_{21} & \boldsymbol{R}_{22} \end{bmatrix} \in \mathcal{RH}_\infty$, then there exists a $\boldsymbol{Q} \in \mathcal{RH}_\infty^-(r)$ such that

$$\left\| \begin{bmatrix} \boldsymbol{R}_{11} & \boldsymbol{R}_{12} \\ \boldsymbol{R}_{21} & \boldsymbol{R}_{22} - \boldsymbol{Q} \end{bmatrix} \right\|_\infty < 1$$

   if and only if each of the following three conditions hold:

$$\begin{aligned} \left\| \begin{bmatrix} \boldsymbol{R}_{11} & \boldsymbol{R}_{12} \end{bmatrix} \right\|_\infty &< 1; \\ \left\| \begin{bmatrix} \boldsymbol{R}_{11} \\ \boldsymbol{R}_{21} \end{bmatrix} \right\|_\infty &< 1; \\ \sigma_{r+1}(\boldsymbol{R}_a) &< 1. \end{aligned}$$

2. The conditions in Item 1 are equivalent to the existence of the Cholesky factors D_{13} and D_{31}, and stabilizing, nonnegative definite solutions X and Y to the algebraic Riccati equations (11.3.14) and (11.3.12) such that $\lambda_{r+1}(XY) < 1$.
3. When the conditions of Item 1 hold and $\sigma_r(\boldsymbol{R}_a) > 1$, an allpass embedding construction provides an explicit parametrization, given in (11.3.24), of all solutions $\boldsymbol{Q}$.
4. The optimal case, while straightforward in principle, is intricate when the Parrott condition (11.3.2) holds with equality.

11.4 Frequency weighted model reduction

The frequency weighted model reduction problem is concerned with the selection of a $\widehat{\boldsymbol{G}} \in \mathcal{RH}_\infty$ of McMillan degree r such that the frequency weighted error

$$\|\boldsymbol{W}_1^{-1}(\boldsymbol{G} - \widehat{\boldsymbol{G}})\boldsymbol{W}_2^{-1}\|_\infty \tag{11.4.1}$$

is small. In (11.4.1), $\boldsymbol{G} \in \mathcal{RH}_\infty$ is a given system (of McMillan degree $n > r$), and $\boldsymbol{W}_1$ and $\boldsymbol{W}_2$ are given frequency dependent weighting functions. Ideally, we would like to minimize the objective (11.4.1), but at present nonconvex parameter optimization is the only means by which this might be achieved. As noted in Chapter 10, parameter optimization approaches are hampered by the possibility of multiple local minima and the difficulty of computing the infinity norm. It is therefore desirable to have an alternative procedure, even if only to initialize a parameter optimization based solution. Our approach is to find a $\boldsymbol{Q}$ with at most r poles in the left-half plane such that $\|\boldsymbol{W}_1^{-1}(\boldsymbol{G}-\boldsymbol{Q})\boldsymbol{W}_2^{-1}\|_\infty$ is minimized. This problem has a closed-form algebraic solution and we may then choose $\widehat{\boldsymbol{G}}$ to be the stable part of the minimizing $\boldsymbol{Q}$. This results in a lower bound on the minimum value of the criterion (11.4.1), which provides an absolute standard of comparison for any candidate reduced-order model. An upper bound on the criterion (11.4.1) will also be derived.

Frequency weighted model reduction problems arise in many areas of engineering. For example, one may wish to reduce the order of a filter in such a way as to ensure smaller modelling errors in the stop-band than in the pass-band. One method of achieving this is to consider a relative error model reduction criterion instead of the absolute error criterion considered in Chapters 9 and 10. This is a special case of a frequency weighted model reduction problem, in which the magnitude of frequency dependent weighting function matches that of the plant.

As another example, there are many reasons why it might be desirable to implement a simpler, reduced-order approximation to a controller resulting from a LQG or $\mathcal{H}_\infty$ synthesis procedure. In selecting a reduced-order controller, the closed-loop environment in which the controller is to operate should be taken into consideration. For the unity feedback configuration shown in Figure 11.1, a reasonable objective

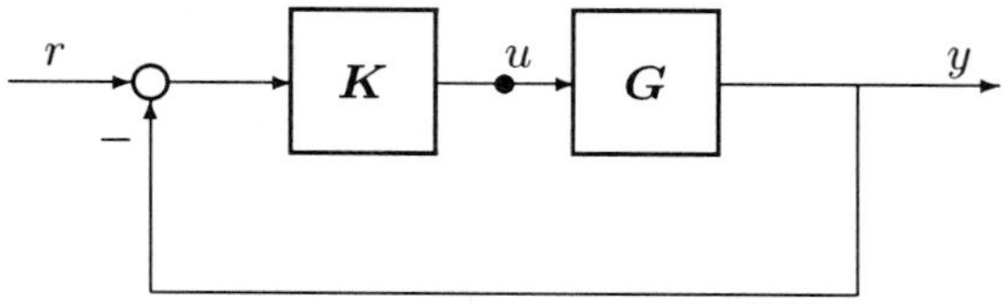

Figure 11.1: Unity feedback configuration.

is that the reduced-order controller match the closed-loop performance of the full-order controller. Since $y = (I+\boldsymbol{GK})^{-1}\boldsymbol{GK}r$, we seek a reduced-order controller $\widehat{\boldsymbol{K}}$ such that

$$\|(I+\boldsymbol{GK})^{-1}\boldsymbol{GK} - (I+\boldsymbol{G}\widehat{\boldsymbol{K}})^{-1}\boldsymbol{G}\widehat{\boldsymbol{K}}\|_\infty$$

is minimized. The difficulties of selecting $\widehat{\boldsymbol{K}}$ are compounded by the fact that $\widehat{\boldsymbol{K}}$ appears nonlinearly in this criterion. To simplify things, we make the assumption that $(I+\boldsymbol{G}\widehat{\boldsymbol{K}})^{-1}$ can be approximated by $(I+\boldsymbol{GK})^{-1}$, which leads to the approximate objective

$$\|(I+GK)^{-1}G(K-\widehat{K})\|_\infty.$$[3]

11.4.1 Problem formulation and a lower bound

Suppose a stable $p\times m$ transfer function G of McMillan degree n is given, together with two frequency dependent weights W_1 of dimension $p\times p$ and W_2 of dimension $m\times m$. Let n_1 and n_2 denote the McMillan degrees of W_1 and W_2 respectively. We would like to find

$$\gamma_{r+1} = \inf_{Q\in\mathcal{RH}_\infty^-(r)} \|W_1^{-1}(G-Q)W_2^{-1}\|_\infty \tag{11.4.2}$$

and all the infimizing Q's.

A lower bound on γ_{r+1} may be determined from the Hankel norm approximation results as follows. Let $M_1\in\mathcal{RH}_\infty$ and $M_2\in\mathcal{RH}_\infty$ be spectral factors satisfying

$$\begin{aligned} M_1^\sim M_1 &= W_1W_1^\sim, & M_1, M_1^{-1}\in\mathcal{RH}_\infty,\\ M_2M_2^\sim &= W_2^\sim W_2, & M_2, M_2^{-1}\in\mathcal{RH}_\infty. \end{aligned}$$

Multiplying the weighted error $W_1^{-1}(G-Q)W_2^{-1}$ by the allpass factors $M_1^{\sim-1}W_1$ and $W_2M_2^{\sim-1}$ gives

$$\begin{aligned} \gamma_{r+1} &= \inf_{Q\in\mathcal{RH}_\infty^-(r)} \|W_1^{-1}(G-Q)W_2^{-1}\|_\infty\\ &= \inf_{Q\in\mathcal{RH}_\infty^-(r)} \|M_1^{\sim-1}(G-Q)M_2^{\sim-1}\|_\infty\\ &\geq \inf_{X\in\mathcal{RH}_\infty^-(r)} \|(M_1^{\sim-1}GM_2^{\sim-1})_+ - X\|_\infty\\ &\geq \sigma_{r+1}(M_1^{\sim-1}GM_2^{\sim-1})_+. \end{aligned}$$

Here, we have used the fact that

$$X = M_1^{\sim-1}QM_2^{\sim-1} - (M_1^{\sim-1}GM_2^{\sim-1})_-$$

is in $\mathcal{RH}_\infty^-(r)$ if and only if Q is. To see that this lower bound is attainable, suppose $X\in\mathcal{RH}_\infty^-(r)$ is an optimal approximant of $(M_1^{\sim-1}GM_2^{\sim-1})_+$ and define

$$Q = M_1^\sim\left(X + (M_1^{\sim-1}GM_2^{\sim-1})_-\right)M_2^\sim.$$

Because $M_1^\sim$ and $M_2^\sim$ are in $\mathcal{RH}_\infty^-$, we see that $Q\in\mathcal{RH}_\infty^-(r)$, and by definition we have

$$\begin{aligned} \|W_1^{-1}(G-Q)W_2^{-1}\|_\infty &= \|(M_1^{\sim-1}GM_2^{\sim-1})_+ - X\|_\infty\\ &= \sigma_{r+1}(M_1^{\sim-1}GM_2^{\sim-1})_+. \end{aligned}$$

[3] Many other formulations of the controller reduction problem are possible. The main idea is that the reduction procedure should take account of the closed-loop environment in which the controller operates.

Hence

$$\gamma_{r+1} = \sigma_{r+1}(\boldsymbol{M}_1^{\sim -1}\boldsymbol{G}\boldsymbol{M}_2^{\sim -1})_+.$$

As in the case of Hankel norm approximation, a stable reduced-order system of McMillan degree r may be obtained from $\boldsymbol{Q} \in \mathcal{RH}_\infty^-(r)$ by taking the stable part. Setting $\boldsymbol{Q} = \widehat{\boldsymbol{G}} + \boldsymbol{F}$ with $\widehat{\boldsymbol{G}} \in \mathcal{RH}_\infty$ and $\boldsymbol{F} \in \mathcal{RH}_\infty^-$, we can then bound the infinity norm error via

$$\|\boldsymbol{W}_1^{-1}(\boldsymbol{G} - \widehat{\boldsymbol{G}})\boldsymbol{W}_2^{-1}\|_\infty \leq \gamma_{r+1} + \|\boldsymbol{W}_1^{-1}\boldsymbol{F}\boldsymbol{W}_2^{-1}\|_\infty.$$

The second term is difficult to bound *a priori* and might be arbitrarily large. Of course, it can always be calculated or bounded *a posteriori*. In what follows, we shall reformulate the frequency weighted model reduction problem as a four-block problem, obtaining all solutions and an easily computable *a priori* bound on the infinity norm (11.4.1).

11.4.2 Reformulation as a four-block problem

To solve the problem in (11.4.2) as a four-block problem, choose $\alpha_1 > \|\boldsymbol{W}_1\|_\infty$, $\alpha_2 > \|\boldsymbol{W}_2\|_\infty$ and define $\boldsymbol{R}_{12}$ and $\boldsymbol{R}_{21}$ via the spectral factorization equations

$$\begin{aligned} \boldsymbol{R}_{21}\boldsymbol{R}_{21}^\sim &= I - \alpha_1^{-2}\boldsymbol{W}_1\boldsymbol{W}_1^\sim, & \boldsymbol{R}_{21}, \boldsymbol{R}_{21}^{-1} \in \mathcal{RH}_\infty \\ \boldsymbol{R}_{12}^\sim\boldsymbol{R}_{12} &= I - \alpha_2^{-2}\boldsymbol{W}_2^\sim\boldsymbol{W}_2, & \boldsymbol{R}_{12}, \boldsymbol{R}_{12}^{-1} \in \mathcal{RH}_\infty. \end{aligned}$$

Setting $\boldsymbol{E} = \boldsymbol{G} - \boldsymbol{Q}$, we have

$$\begin{aligned} & \left\|\boldsymbol{W}_1^{-1}\boldsymbol{E}\boldsymbol{W}_2^{-1}\right\|_\infty < \gamma \\ \Leftrightarrow\ & (\boldsymbol{W}_1^{-1}\boldsymbol{E})^\sim(\boldsymbol{W}_1^{-1}\boldsymbol{E}) < \gamma^2\boldsymbol{W}_2^\sim\boldsymbol{W}_2 \\ \Leftrightarrow\ & \boldsymbol{R}_{12}^\sim\boldsymbol{R}_{12} + (\boldsymbol{W}_1^{-1}\boldsymbol{E})^\sim(\boldsymbol{W}_1^{-1}\boldsymbol{E})/(\gamma^2\alpha_2^2) < I \\ \Leftrightarrow\ & \left\|\begin{bmatrix} \boldsymbol{R}_{12} \\ \boldsymbol{W}_1^{-1}\boldsymbol{E}/(\gamma\alpha_2) \end{bmatrix}\right\|_\infty < 1 \\ \Leftrightarrow\ & \begin{bmatrix} \boldsymbol{R}_{12} \\ \boldsymbol{E}/(\gamma\alpha_2) \end{bmatrix}\begin{bmatrix} \boldsymbol{R}_{12} \\ \boldsymbol{E}/(\gamma\alpha_2) \end{bmatrix}^\sim < \begin{bmatrix} I & 0 \\ 0 & \boldsymbol{W}_1\boldsymbol{W}_1^\sim \end{bmatrix} \\ \Leftrightarrow\ & \begin{bmatrix} 0 \\ \boldsymbol{R}_{21} \end{bmatrix}\begin{bmatrix} 0 & \boldsymbol{R}_{21}^\sim \end{bmatrix} + \begin{bmatrix} \boldsymbol{R}_{12} \\ \boldsymbol{E}/(\gamma\alpha_1\alpha_2) \end{bmatrix}\begin{bmatrix} \boldsymbol{R}_{12} \\ \boldsymbol{E}/(\gamma\alpha_1\alpha_2) \end{bmatrix}^\sim < I \\ \Leftrightarrow\ & \left\|\begin{bmatrix} 0 & \boldsymbol{R}_{12} \\ \boldsymbol{R}_{21} & (\boldsymbol{G} - \boldsymbol{Q})/(\gamma\alpha_1\alpha_2) \end{bmatrix}\right\|_\infty < 1. \end{aligned} \tag{11.4.3}$$

This four-block is of exactly the form studied in Section 11.3. The fact that (1,1)-block is zero and γ affects only the (2,2)-block makes it is possible to obtain an explicit formula for the least γ such that (11.4.3) holds—we already know that a Hankel norm calculation determines γ_{r+1}, the optimal performance level.

11.4.3 Allpass dilation

The four-block theory provides necessary and sufficient conditions under which (11.4.3) has a solution in terms of a dilated operator $\boldsymbol{R}_a$. Although we already have the necessary and sufficient condition $\gamma \geq \sigma_{r+1}(\boldsymbol{M}_1^{\sim -1}\boldsymbol{G}\boldsymbol{M}_2^{\sim -1})_+$, the exercise of constructing the dilation will be useful in developing an upper bound on the infinity norm of the approximation error.

Suppose that $\boldsymbol{G}$ has the state-space realization

$$\boldsymbol{G} \stackrel{s}{=} \left[\begin{array}{c|c} A & B \\ \hline C & 0 \end{array}\right].$$

We may assume that $\boldsymbol{G}(\infty) = 0$ without loss of generality because it can always be absorbed into $\boldsymbol{Q}$. The spectral factorizations that define $\boldsymbol{R}_{12}$ and $\boldsymbol{R}_{21}$ are standard state-space computations (see the spectral factorization proof of the bounded real lemma in Section 3.7) and we therefore assume that they have been calculated to give

$$\boldsymbol{R}_{21} = \left[\begin{array}{c|c} A_1 & B_1 \\ \hline C_1 & D_{21} \end{array}\right], \qquad \boldsymbol{R}_{12} = \left[\begin{array}{c|c} A_2 & B_2 \\ \hline C_2 & D_{12} \end{array}\right].$$

Thus, our four-block problem is characterized by the state-space system

$$\left[\begin{array}{cc} 0 & \boldsymbol{R}_{12} \\ \boldsymbol{R}_{21} & \boldsymbol{R}_{22} \end{array}\right] = \left[\begin{array}{ccc|cc} A_1 & 0 & 0 & B_1 & 0 \\ 0 & A_2 & 0 & 0 & B_2 \\ 0 & 0 & A & 0 & \epsilon B \\ \hline 0 & C_2 & 0 & 0 & D_{12} \\ C_1 & 0 & \epsilon C & D_{21} & 0 \end{array}\right], \tag{11.4.4}$$

in which $\epsilon = (\alpha_1\alpha_2\gamma)^{-1/2}$.

We can now apply Theorem 11.3.3 to determine conditions for the existence of a solution. Since $\|\boldsymbol{R}_{12}\|_\infty < 1$ and $\|\boldsymbol{R}_{21}\|_\infty < 1$ by construction, there exists a solution to (11.4.3) if and only if $\lambda_{r+1}\left(X(\epsilon)Y(\epsilon)\right) < 1$, with $X(\epsilon)$ and $Y(\epsilon)$ being the stabilizing, nonnegative definite solutions to the Riccati equations (11.3.14) and (11.3.12). Examining (11.3.14), we find that

$$X(\epsilon) = \left[\begin{array}{ccc} X_{11} & 0 & 0 \\ 0 & X_{22} & \epsilon X_{23} \\ 0 & \epsilon X_{23}' & \epsilon^2 X_{33} \end{array}\right], \qquad B_3 = \left[\begin{array}{c} 0 \\ B_{32} \\ \epsilon B_{33} \end{array}\right],$$

in which:

1. X_{11} is the solution to the Lyapunov equation

$$A_1X_{11} + X_{11}A_1' + B_1B_1' = 0.$$

2. X_{22} is the stabilizing, nonnegative definite solution to the Riccati equation

$$A_2X_{22} + X_{22}A_2' + B_2B_2' + B_{32}B_{32}' = 0 \tag{11.4.5}$$

and

$$B_{32} = -(B_2D_{12}' + X_{22}C_2')(D_{13}^{-1})'. \tag{11.4.6}$$

3. X_{23} is the solution to the linear equation

$$(A_2 - B_{32}D_{13}^{-1}C_2)X_{23} + X_{23}A' + (B_2 - B_{32}D_{13}^{-1}D_{12})B' = 0.$$

There is a unique solution to this equation, since A and $A_2 - B_{32}D_{13}^{-1}C_2$ are asymptotically stable (X_{22} is the stabilizing solution to (11.4.5)).

4. B_{33} is given by

$$B_{33} = -(BD_{12}' + X_{23}'C_2')(D_{13}^{-1})'.$$

5. X_{33} is the solution to the Lyapunov equation

$$AX_{33} + X_{33}A' + BB' + B_{33}B_{33}' = 0.$$

Similarly, it may be observed that $Y(\epsilon)$ and C_3 have the form

$$Y(\epsilon) = \begin{bmatrix} Y_{11} & 0 & \epsilon Y_{13} \\ 0 & Y_{22} & 0 \\ \epsilon Y_{13}' & 0 & \epsilon^2 Y_{33} \end{bmatrix}, \qquad C_3 = \begin{bmatrix} C_{31} & 0 & \epsilon C_{33} \end{bmatrix},$$

in which the various matrices may be obtained from an examination of (11.3.12).

The minimum value of γ is attained when $\lambda_{r+1}\big(X(\epsilon)Y(\epsilon)\big) = 1$. We therefore consider the characteristic equation $\det\big(I - X(\epsilon)Y(\epsilon)\big) = 0$. Defining

$$Z = \begin{bmatrix} Z_{11} & 0 & Z_{13} \\ Z_{21} & Z_{22} & Z_{23} \\ Z_{31} & Z_{32} & Z_{33} \end{bmatrix} = \begin{bmatrix} X_{11}Y_{11} & 0 & \epsilon^{-3}X_{11}Y_{13} \\ \epsilon^2 X_{23}Y_{13}' & X_{22}Y_{22} & \epsilon^{-1}X_{23}Y_{33} \\ \epsilon^3 X_{33}Y_{13}' & \epsilon X_{23}'Y_{22} & X_{33}Y_{33} \end{bmatrix},$$

we have

$$\begin{aligned} &\det\left(I - X(\epsilon)Y(\epsilon)\right) \\ &= \epsilon^4 \det\left(\begin{bmatrix} I & 0 & 0 \\ 0 & I & 0 \\ 0 & 0 & \epsilon^{-4}I \end{bmatrix} - \begin{bmatrix} Z_{11} & 0 & Z_{13} \\ Z_{21} & Z_{22} & Z_{23} \\ Z_{31} & Z_{32} & Z_{33} \end{bmatrix} \right). \end{aligned} \tag{11.4.7}$$

In order to proceed, we need to show that $I - Z_{11}$ and $I - Z_{22}$ are nonsingular. To see this, we note that $\boldsymbol{R}_{21}^{\sim}\boldsymbol{R}_{21} + \boldsymbol{R}_{31}^{\sim}\boldsymbol{R}_{31} = I$. Thus

$$\left\| \begin{bmatrix} \boldsymbol{R}_{21} \\ \boldsymbol{R}_{31} \end{bmatrix} \right\|_\infty = 1$$

and, since the Hankel norm never exceeds the infinity norm, we have the Hankel norm inequality

$$\left\| \begin{bmatrix} \boldsymbol{R}_{21} \\ \boldsymbol{R}_{31} \end{bmatrix} \right\|_H \leq 1.$$

If equality holds, then $\begin{bmatrix} \boldsymbol{R}_{21} \\ \boldsymbol{R}_{31} \end{bmatrix}$ is its own optimal Nehari extension, which implies (Lemma 10.4.3) that there exist Schmidt vectors $\boldsymbol{v}$ and $\boldsymbol{w}$ in $\mathcal{RH}_2$ such that

$$\begin{bmatrix} \boldsymbol{R}_{21} \\ \boldsymbol{R}_{31} \end{bmatrix} \boldsymbol{v}(-s) = \boldsymbol{w}(s).$$

But $\boldsymbol{R}_{21}\boldsymbol{R}_{31}^{-1}$ is a coprime factorization, since $\boldsymbol{R}_{31}^{-1} \in \mathcal{RH}_\infty$, which implies (see Appendix A) there exist $\boldsymbol{U}$ and $\boldsymbol{V}$ in $\mathcal{RH}_\infty$ such that $\boldsymbol{U}\boldsymbol{R}_{21} + \boldsymbol{V}\boldsymbol{R}_{31} = I$. Consequently

$$\boldsymbol{v}(-s) = \begin{bmatrix} \boldsymbol{U} & \boldsymbol{V} \end{bmatrix} \boldsymbol{w}(s),$$

which is a contradiction, since the left-hand side is in $\mathcal{RH}_2^-$ and the right-hand side is in $\mathcal{RH}_2$. Thus

$$\left\| \begin{bmatrix} \boldsymbol{R}_{21} \\ \boldsymbol{R}_{31} \end{bmatrix} \right\|_H < 1.$$

Since X_{11} and Y_{11} are, respectively, the controllability and observability gramians of

$$\begin{bmatrix} \boldsymbol{R}_{21} \\ \boldsymbol{R}_{31} \end{bmatrix} \stackrel{s}{=} \left[\begin{array}{c|c} A_1 & B_1 \\ \hline C_1 & D_{21} \\ C_{31} & D_{31} \end{array} \right],$$

we conclude that $\rho(X_{11}Y_{11}) < 1$, which implies that $I - Z_{11} = I - X_{11}Y_{11}$ is nonsingular. A similar argument using $\boldsymbol{R}_{12}$ and $\boldsymbol{R}_{13}$ shows that $I - Z_{22} = I - X_{22}Y_{22}$ is also nonsingular (see Problems 11.9 and 11.10). We may therefore take Schur complements with respect to the upper-left 2×2 block in (11.4.7) to obtain the characteristic equation

$$0 = \det\left(\epsilon^{-4}I - Z_{33} - \begin{bmatrix} Z_{31} & Z_{32} \end{bmatrix} \begin{bmatrix} I - Z_{11} & 0 \\ -Z_{21} & I - Z_{22} \end{bmatrix}^{-1} \begin{bmatrix} Z_{13} \\ Z_{23} \end{bmatrix} \right).$$

This shows that ϵ^{-4} is an eigenvalue of the matrix

$$Z_{33} + \begin{bmatrix} Z_{31} & Z_{32} \end{bmatrix} \begin{bmatrix} I - Z_{11} & 0 \\ -Z_{21} & I - Z_{22} \end{bmatrix}^{-1} \begin{bmatrix} Z_{13} \\ Z_{23} \end{bmatrix} = \mathcal{F}_u\left(Z, I_{n_1+n_2}\right),$$

in which $\mathcal{F}_u(\cdot,\cdot)$ denotes the upper linear fractional transformation. Indeed, since Z is the product of two nonnegative definite matrices, the number of positive eigenvalues of $\left(\begin{bmatrix} I & 0 \\ 0 & \epsilon^{-4}I \end{bmatrix} - Z \right)$ is monotonically increasing as ϵ decreases, from which we conclude that

$$\alpha_1\alpha_2\gamma_{r+1} = \lambda_{r+1}^{1/2}\left(\mathcal{F}_u(Z, I_{n_1+n_2})\right).$$

We leave it as an exercise for the reader to show that

$$\sigma_{r+1}(\boldsymbol{M}_1^{\sim -1}\boldsymbol{G}\boldsymbol{M}_2^{\sim -1})_+ = \frac{1}{\alpha_1\alpha_2}\lambda_{r+1}^{1/2}\big(\mathcal{F}_u\left(Z, I_{n_1+n_2}\right)\big),$$

which means that the two necessary and sufficient conditions we have derived are indeed identical. For any $\gamma > \gamma_{r+1}$, every $\boldsymbol{Q}$ satisfying (11.4.3) can be generated by Theorem 11.3.3 and the corresponding state-space manipulations.

In the case of the special four-block problem (11.4.3) associated with the frequency weighted model reduction problem, the optimal case is quite easy to treat. This is because the optimal level is always determined by the Hankel singular value condition, since the Parrott conditions (11.3.2) are satisfied by construction. This means that all optimal solutions can be obtained by applying Theorem 10.4.5 to the dilated system $\boldsymbol{R}_a$. This construction may be found in [77].

11.4.4 Infinity norm error bounds

In the last section we showed how one might find every $\boldsymbol{Q} \in \mathcal{RH}_\infty^-(r)$ that satisfies $\|\boldsymbol{W}_1^{-1}(\boldsymbol{G}-\boldsymbol{Q})\boldsymbol{W}_2^{-1}\|_\infty \le \gamma$ with γ minimized. The minimum level γ_{r+1} can be determined by an eigenvalue calculation. For any $\boldsymbol{Q}$ that attains the minimum level γ_{r+1}, set $\boldsymbol{Q} = \widehat{\boldsymbol{G}} + \boldsymbol{F}$ with $\widehat{\boldsymbol{G}} \in \mathcal{RH}_\infty$ and $\boldsymbol{F} \in \mathcal{RH}_\infty^-$. The triangle inequality gives

$$\|\boldsymbol{W}_1^{-1}(\boldsymbol{G}-\widehat{\boldsymbol{G}})\boldsymbol{W}_2^{-1}\|_\infty \le \gamma_{r+1} + \|\boldsymbol{W}_1^{-1}\boldsymbol{F}\boldsymbol{W}_2^{-1}\|_\infty. \tag{11.4.8}$$

In order to bound $\|\boldsymbol{W}_1^{-1}(\boldsymbol{G}-\widehat{\boldsymbol{G}})\boldsymbol{W}_2^{-1}\|_\infty$, we seek a bound for $\|\boldsymbol{W}_1^{-1}\boldsymbol{F}\boldsymbol{W}_2^{-1}\|_\infty$.

It follows from the material in Section 11.3.3 that the allpass error system corresponding to (11.4.3) is of the form

$$\begin{aligned}\boldsymbol{E}_{aa} &= \boldsymbol{R}_{aa}(\gamma_{r+1}) - \boldsymbol{Q}_{aa}\\ &= \begin{bmatrix} 0 & \boldsymbol{R}_{12} & \boldsymbol{R}_{13} & 0\\ \boldsymbol{R}_{21} & \gamma_{r+1}^{-1}\boldsymbol{R}_{22} & \boldsymbol{R}_{23} & 0\\ \boldsymbol{R}_{31} & \boldsymbol{R}_{32} & \boldsymbol{R}_{33} & 0\\ 0 & 0 & 0 & 0\end{bmatrix} - \begin{bmatrix} 0 & 0 & 0 & 0\\ 0 & \boldsymbol{Q}_{22} & \boldsymbol{Q}_{23} & \boldsymbol{Q}_{24}\\ 0 & \boldsymbol{Q}_{32} & \boldsymbol{Q}_{33} & \boldsymbol{Q}_{34}\\ 0 & \boldsymbol{Q}_{42} & \boldsymbol{Q}_{43} & \boldsymbol{Q}_{44}\end{bmatrix},\end{aligned}$$

with $\boldsymbol{R}_{22} = \boldsymbol{G}/\alpha_1\alpha_2$. Now decompose $\boldsymbol{Q}_{aa}$ as

$$\begin{aligned}\boldsymbol{Q}_{aa} &= \widehat{\boldsymbol{G}}_{aa} + \boldsymbol{F}_{aa}\\ &= \begin{bmatrix} 0 & 0 & 0 & 0\\ 0 & \widehat{\boldsymbol{G}}_{22} & \widehat{\boldsymbol{G}}_{23} & \widehat{\boldsymbol{G}}_{24}\\ 0 & \widehat{\boldsymbol{G}}_{32} & \widehat{\boldsymbol{G}}_{33} & \widehat{\boldsymbol{G}}_{34}\\ 0 & \widehat{\boldsymbol{G}}_{42} & \widehat{\boldsymbol{G}}_{43} & \widehat{\boldsymbol{G}}_{44}\end{bmatrix} + \begin{bmatrix} 0 & 0 & 0 & 0\\ 0 & \boldsymbol{F}_{22} & \boldsymbol{F}_{23} & \boldsymbol{F}_{24}\\ 0 & \boldsymbol{F}_{32} & \boldsymbol{F}_{33} & \boldsymbol{F}_{34}\\ 0 & \boldsymbol{F}_{42} & \boldsymbol{F}_{43} & \boldsymbol{F}_{44}\end{bmatrix},\end{aligned}$$

in which the matrix $\widehat{\boldsymbol{G}}_{aa} \in \mathcal{RH}_\infty$ is of degree r and $\boldsymbol{F}_{aa} \in \mathcal{RH}_\infty^-$ is of degree $\le n + n_1 + n_2 - r - l$, with l being the multiplicity of $\sigma_{r+1}\big(\boldsymbol{R}_a(\gamma_{r+1})\big)$. Applying Lemma 10.5.2 to $\boldsymbol{R}_{aa}(\gamma_{r+1})$ we see that the Hankel singular values of $\boldsymbol{F}_{aa}^\sim$ are less than or equal to the Hankel singular values of $\boldsymbol{R}_{aa}(\gamma_{r+1})$ that are strictly smaller than $\sigma_{r+1}\big(\boldsymbol{R}_{aa}(\gamma_{r+1})\big)$. Iterative allpass embedding arguments that parallel those in Section 10.5 establish the following theorem:

Theorem 11.4.1 *Suppose $\boldsymbol{R}_{aa}$ and $\boldsymbol{Q}_{aa}$ are as above and $\alpha_1\alpha_2\gamma_{r+1}\boldsymbol{Q}_{22} = \widehat{\boldsymbol{G}} + \boldsymbol{F}$, with $\widehat{\boldsymbol{G}} \in \mathcal{RH}_\infty$ of McMillan degree r and $\boldsymbol{F} \in \mathcal{RH}_\infty^-$. Then*

1. *$\|\boldsymbol{W}_1^{-1}(\boldsymbol{G} - \widehat{\boldsymbol{G}})\boldsymbol{W}_2^{-1}\|_\infty$ is bounded above by γ_{r+1} plus twice the sum of the distinct Hankel singular values of $\boldsymbol{M}_2^{-1}\boldsymbol{F}^\sim\boldsymbol{M}_1^{-1}$. If all the Hankel singular values of $\boldsymbol{M}_2^{-1}\boldsymbol{F}^\sim\boldsymbol{M}_1^{-1}$ are distinct, we have*

$$\|\boldsymbol{W}_1^{-1}(\boldsymbol{G} - \widehat{\boldsymbol{G}})\boldsymbol{W}_2^{-1}\|_\infty \leq \gamma_{r+1} + 2\sum_{i=1}^{n+n_1+n_2-r-l}\sigma_i(\boldsymbol{M}_2^{-1}\boldsymbol{F}^\sim\boldsymbol{M}_1^{-1}).$$

2. *There exists a D such that $\|\boldsymbol{W}_1^{-1}\big(\boldsymbol{G} - (\widehat{\boldsymbol{G}} + D)\big)\boldsymbol{W}_2^{-1}\|_\infty$ is bounded above by γ_{r+1} plus $\|\boldsymbol{W}_1^{-1}\|_\infty\|\boldsymbol{W}_2^{-1}\|_\infty$ times the sum of the distinct Hankel singular values of $\boldsymbol{R}_{aa}$ that are strictly smaller than γ_{r+1}. For the case when all these Hankel singular values are distinct, we have*

$$\begin{aligned}&\|\boldsymbol{W}_1^{-1}\big(\boldsymbol{G} - (\widehat{\boldsymbol{G}} + D)\big)\boldsymbol{W}_2^{-1}\|_\infty \\ &\quad\leq \gamma_{r+1} + \|\boldsymbol{W}_1^{-1}\|_\infty\|\boldsymbol{W}_2^{-1}\|_\infty\sum_{i=1}^{n+n_1+n_2-r-l}\sigma_{i+r+l}\big(\boldsymbol{R}_{aa}(\gamma_{r+1})\big).\end{aligned}$$

11.4.5 Relative error model reduction

In many cases, it is desirable that the model reduction process produces a model that is a good relative error approximation to the full-order model. This is achieved by choosing a weighting function whose magnitude matches the magnitude of the full-order model. We now briefly indicate how this problem may be tackled using the techniques of Section 11.3.

Suppose $\boldsymbol{G} \in \mathcal{RH}_\infty$ is given and α is such that $\|\boldsymbol{G}\|_\infty < \alpha$. We seek $\widehat{\boldsymbol{G}} \in \mathcal{RH}_\infty$ of McMillan degree r such that

$$\widehat{\boldsymbol{G}} = (\boldsymbol{\Delta} + I)\boldsymbol{G}, \qquad (11.4.9)$$

with $\|\boldsymbol{\Delta}\|_\infty$ small. If $\boldsymbol{G}$ has full column rank (almost everywhere), there exists a spectral factor $\boldsymbol{M} \in \mathcal{RH}_\infty$ with $\boldsymbol{M}^{-1} \in \mathcal{RH}_\infty$ such that $\boldsymbol{G}^\sim\boldsymbol{G} = \boldsymbol{M}\boldsymbol{M}^\sim$. If $\widehat{\boldsymbol{G}}$ is given by (11.4.9), then

$$\begin{aligned}\|(\boldsymbol{G} - \widehat{\boldsymbol{G}})\boldsymbol{M}^{\sim -1}\|_\infty &= \|\boldsymbol{\Delta}\boldsymbol{G}\boldsymbol{M}^{\sim -1}\|_\infty \\ &\leq \|\boldsymbol{\Delta}\|_\infty.\end{aligned}$$

Conversely, for any $\widehat{G}$, defining $\Delta = (\widehat{G} - G)(G^{\sim}G)^{-1}G^{\sim}$ gives $\widehat{G} = (\Delta + I)G$ and

$$\begin{aligned} \|\Delta\|_\infty &= \|(G - \widehat{G})M^{\sim -1}M^{-1}G^{\sim}\|_\infty \\ &\le \|(G - \widehat{G})M^{\sim -1}\|_\infty. \end{aligned}$$

Therefore, (11.4.9) with $\|\Delta\|_\infty \le \gamma$ is equivalent to

$$\|(G - \widehat{G})M^{\sim -1}\|_\infty \le \gamma. \tag{11.4.10}$$

Since $\widehat{G}M^{\sim -1} \in \mathcal{RH}_\infty^-(r)$, we have that

$$\|(G - \widehat{G})M^{\sim -1}\|_\infty \ge \sigma_{r+1}(GM^{\sim -1})_+ \tag{11.4.11}$$

by the results of Chapter 10. The matrix $GM^{\sim -1}$ is known as the phase matrix associated with the system G.

The problem (11.4.10) is also equivalent to the two-block problem

$$\left\| \begin{bmatrix} R_{12} \\ \epsilon(G - \widehat{G}) \end{bmatrix} \right\|_\infty \le 1, \tag{11.4.12}$$

in which

$$R_{12}^{\sim}R_{12} = I - \alpha^{-2}G^{\sim}G$$

and $\epsilon = (\alpha\gamma)^{-1}$. Using the bounded real lemma to determine R_{12}, we see that

$$R_{12} \stackrel{s}{=} \left[\begin{array}{c|c} A & B \\ \hline \bar{C} & D_{12} \end{array}\right],$$

in which $Y = Y' \ge 0$, $\bar{C}$ and D_{12} satisfy

$$\begin{bmatrix} A'Y + YA + \alpha^{-2}C'C & YB + \alpha^{-2}C'D \\ B'Y + \alpha^{-2}D'C & -I + \alpha^{-2}D'D \end{bmatrix} = -\begin{bmatrix} \bar{C}' \\ D_{12}' \end{bmatrix} \begin{bmatrix} \bar{C} & D_{12} \end{bmatrix}$$

and $A - BD_{12}^{-1}\bar{C}$ is asymptotically stable.

We now construct the dilated operator associated with the two-block problem (11.4.12). Since $\|R_{12}\|_\infty < 1$, the bounded real lemma implies that there exists an $X = X' \ge 0$, a $\bar{B}$ and D_{13} such that

$$\begin{bmatrix} AX + XA' + BB' & X\bar{C}' + BD_{12} \\ \bar{C}X + D_{12}B' & -I + D_{12}D_{12}' \end{bmatrix} = -\begin{bmatrix} \bar{B} \\ D_{13} \end{bmatrix} \begin{bmatrix} \bar{B}' & D_{13}' \end{bmatrix},$$

with $A - \bar{B}D_{13}^{-1}\bar{C}$ asymptotically stable. Therefore, the dilated operator corresponding to the relative error model reduction problem is given by

$$R_a = \begin{bmatrix} R_{12} & R_{13} \\ \epsilon G & R_{23} \end{bmatrix} \stackrel{s}{=} \left[\begin{array}{c|cc} A & B & \bar{B} \\ \hline \bar{C} & D_{12} & D_{13} \\ \epsilon C & \epsilon D & 0 \end{array}\right]. \tag{11.4.13}$$

Since $\boldsymbol{R}_{12}\boldsymbol{R}_{12}^{\sim} + \boldsymbol{R}_{13}\boldsymbol{R}_{13}^{\sim} = I$, $\boldsymbol{R}_{12}^{-1}\boldsymbol{R}_{13}$ is a normalized left coprime factorization, and it follows that $\| \begin{bmatrix} \boldsymbol{R}_{12} & \boldsymbol{R}_{13} \end{bmatrix} \|_H < 1$. If Z is the observability gramian of $\boldsymbol{G}$, then some elementary algebra shows that the observability gramian of

$$\begin{bmatrix} \boldsymbol{R}_{12} & \boldsymbol{R}_{13} \end{bmatrix} \stackrel{s}{=} \left[\begin{array}{c|cc} A & B & \bar{B} \\ \hline \bar{C} & D_{12} & D_{13} \end{array}\right] \tag{11.4.14}$$

is given by $Y - \alpha^{-2}Z$. Since X is the controllability gramian of (11.4.14), we see that $\rho\big((Y - \alpha^{-2}Z)X\big) < 1$. Arguments paralleling those given in Section 11.4.3 show that the lowest achievable value of $\|\boldsymbol{\Delta}\|_\infty$ in (11.4.9) are given by

$$\gamma_{r+1} = \lambda_{r+1}^{1/2}\left(\mathcal{F}_\ell\left(\begin{bmatrix} 0 & \alpha^{-2}Z \\ I & Y - \alpha^{-2}Z \end{bmatrix}, X\right)\right). \tag{11.4.15}$$

The number γ_{r+1} can be shown to be equal to $\sigma_{r+1}\big((\boldsymbol{G}\boldsymbol{M}^{\sim -1})_+\big)$, so the bounds (11.4.11) and (11.4.15) are identical.

11.4.6 Example

We conclude this section with an example illustrating the frequency weighted Hankel norm model reduction of an eighth-order elliptic filter. An absolute error method of model reduction will destroy the stop-band performance of the filter; some frequency weighting that insists that the errors must be small compared with the magnitude of the filter needs to be introduced. A relative error criterion is perhaps a natural choice, but this is fraught with difficulties because elliptic filters have all their zeros on the imaginary axis. It can be shown that this results in the phase matrix $\boldsymbol{G}\boldsymbol{M}^{\sim -1}$ being a stable allpass matrix, which implies that all its Hankel singular values are unity (see Lemma 10.5.1), so the relative error incurred is at least unity. We are therefore forced to consider the general frequency weighted problem. We aim to retain both the pass-band and stop-band behavior of the filter. The importance of the transition-band, however, will be de-emphasized.

The frequency weights we have chosen for this example are given by

$$\boldsymbol{W}_1 = \frac{0.014(s+1)^2(s+2)^2}{(s^2+0.2s+1.45)(s^2+0.2s+0.65)}, \qquad \boldsymbol{W}_2 = I; \tag{11.4.16}$$

the scaling term in $\boldsymbol{W}_1$ was introduced to ensure that $\|\boldsymbol{W}_1\|_\infty < 1$. The Bode magnitude plot for this weight is illustrated in Figure 11.2 and it is clear from this diagram that the model reduction error between roughly 0.6 rad/s and 1.5 rad/s will be de-emphasized in the reduction process. A computation shows that the γ_r's for this example are given by the values in Table 11.1. For the purpose of illustration, we have selected a reduced model order of five, and the corresponding Hankel singular values of $\boldsymbol{R}_a(\gamma_6)$ are given in Table 11.2. Figure 11.3 shows plots of $|\boldsymbol{W}_1^{-1}(j\omega)|$ and $|(\boldsymbol{G} - \widehat{\boldsymbol{G}})(j\omega)|$, and it is clear that the frequency response of $|(\boldsymbol{G} - \widehat{\boldsymbol{G}})(j\omega)|$ is being modulated by $|\boldsymbol{W}_1^{-1}(j\omega)|$ in the required manner.

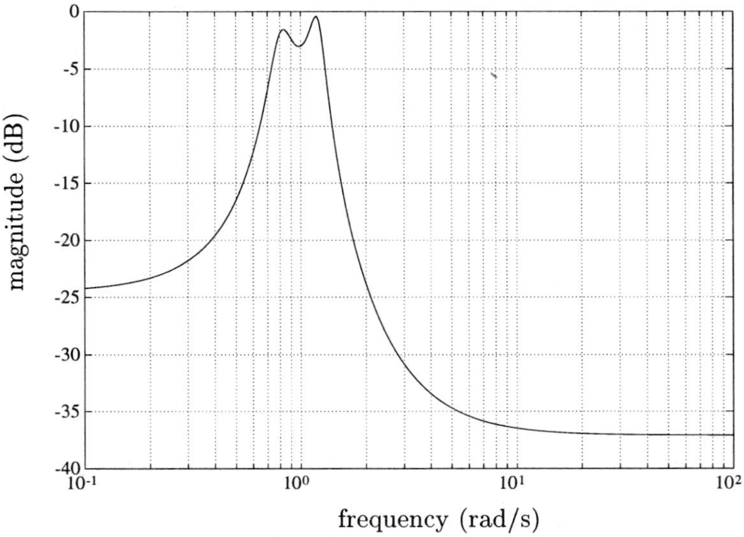

Figure 11.2: The frequency weight magnitude response.

Figure 11.4 shows the Bode magnitude plots of the eighth-order elliptic filter, the frequency weighted fifth-order approximation and an unweighted fifth-order optimal Hankel approximation. The unweighted reduced-order model is an inferior approximation, as compared with the frequency weighted approximation, in the frequency ranges 0 to 0.7 rad/s, and 1.5 rad/s to high frequency. This is consistent with the fact that the weight has been chosen in a way that de-emphasizes the transition region behavior of the weighted approximation. A Bode magnitude plot of $\boldsymbol{W}_1^{-1}(\boldsymbol{G}-\widehat{\boldsymbol{G}})(j\omega)$ is shown in Figure 11.5, and we see that the weighted error peaks at about $-4.96\ dB$ at 2.21 rad/s. Finally, it follows from further computation that

$$-10.736\ dB \leq \|\boldsymbol{W}_1^{-1}(\boldsymbol{G}-\widehat{\boldsymbol{G}})\|_\infty = -4.96\ dB \leq 2.073\ dB.$$

7.9132	2.5924	1.3073	0.9718
0.5860	0.2905	0.0969	0.0536

Table 11.1: Hankel singular values of $(\boldsymbol{G}\boldsymbol{W}^{-1})_+$.

7.5336	2.3394	1.2074	0.9401	0.5557	0.2905
0.1431	0.1207	0.0701	0.0451	0.0148	0.0134

Table 11.2: Hankel singular values of $\boldsymbol{R}_a(\gamma_6)$.

The lower bound is γ_6 (in dB) while the upper bound follows from inequality given in Item 1 of Theorem 11.4.1. Notice that the upper and lower bounds are about a factor of two (6 dB) higher and lower than the true frequency weighted error. In general, it is difficult to deduce whether the bounds are overly conservative or whether a different approximation scheme could more closely approach the lower bound.

Main points of the section

1. The frequency weighted model reduction problem may be solved using the Hankel norm approximation theory of Chapter 10. The minimum achievable Hankel norm is determined by a Hankel singular value calculation.
2. The frequency weighted model reduction problem may be solved by recasting it as a four-block problem via two spectral factorizations. This four-block problem has a special structure, which enables an eigenvalue formula for the minimum achievable Hankel norm to be given.
3. The allpass embedding solution of the four-block problem provides a parametrization of all solutions to the frequency weighted model reduction problem and *a priori* computable upper bounds on the infinity norm of the weighted approximation error.
4. The relative error model reduction problem, which is a special case of the frequency weighted model reduction, may be recast as a two-block problem.

11.5 All $\mathcal{H}_\infty$ optimal controllers

Theorem 8.3.2 gives a representation formula for all internally-stabilizing controllers that satisfy an $\mathcal{H}_\infty$ norm constraint of the form $\|\mathcal{F}_\ell(\boldsymbol{P}, \boldsymbol{K})\|_\infty < \gamma$. This is known as the suboptimal case, because γ cannot be equal to the minimum achievable norm if strict inequality is imposed. One derivation of this result, which uses the theory of linear quadratic differential games, is developed in Chapters 6 to 8. In its present form this approach does not yield a solution of the optimal problem in which equality is permitted. An alternative approach is based on reducing the controller

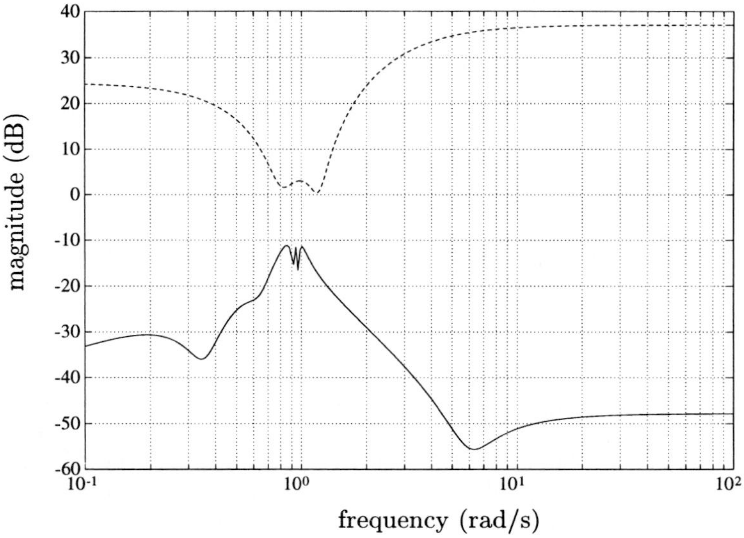

Figure 11.3: $\boldsymbol{W}^{-1}(j\omega)$ (dashed line) and $(\boldsymbol{G}-\widehat{\boldsymbol{G}})(j\omega)$ (solid line).

synthesis problem to a four-block problem. This approach uses the parametrization of all stabilizing controllers (see Appendix A) to show that

$$\mathcal{F}_\ell(\boldsymbol{P},\boldsymbol{K}) = \boldsymbol{T}_{11} + \boldsymbol{T}_{12}\boldsymbol{Q}\boldsymbol{T}_{21},$$

in which $\boldsymbol{Q} \in \mathcal{RH}_\infty$ and the $\boldsymbol{T}_{ij}$'s are also in $\mathcal{RH}_\infty$. Selecting the nominal controller (*i.e.*, the controller corresponding to $\boldsymbol{Q} = 0$) to be the LQG optimal controller results in $\boldsymbol{T}_{12}^\sim\boldsymbol{T}_{12} = I$ and $\boldsymbol{T}_{21}\boldsymbol{T}_{21}^\sim = I$. We then write

$$\mathcal{F}_\ell(\boldsymbol{P},\boldsymbol{K}) = \boldsymbol{T}_{11} + \begin{bmatrix} \widehat{\boldsymbol{T}}_{12} & \boldsymbol{T}_{12} \end{bmatrix} \begin{bmatrix} 0 & 0 \\ 0 & \boldsymbol{Q} \end{bmatrix} \begin{bmatrix} \widehat{\boldsymbol{T}}_{21} \\ \boldsymbol{T}_{21} \end{bmatrix},$$

in which $\widehat{\boldsymbol{T}}_{12}$ and $\widehat{\boldsymbol{T}}_{21}$ are such that $\begin{bmatrix} \widehat{\boldsymbol{T}}_{12} & \boldsymbol{T}_{12} \end{bmatrix}$ and $\begin{bmatrix} \widehat{\boldsymbol{T}}_{21}^\sim & \boldsymbol{T}_{21}^\sim \end{bmatrix}^\sim$ are square and allpass. Since multiplication by an allpass system does not change the norm, we have

$$\begin{aligned} \|\mathcal{F}_\ell(\boldsymbol{P},\boldsymbol{K})\|_\infty &= \left\| \begin{bmatrix} \widehat{\boldsymbol{T}}_{12}^\sim \\ \boldsymbol{T}_{12}^\sim \end{bmatrix} \boldsymbol{T}_{11} \begin{bmatrix} \widehat{\boldsymbol{T}}_{21}^\sim & \boldsymbol{T}_{21}^\sim \end{bmatrix} + \begin{bmatrix} 0 & 0 \\ 0 & \boldsymbol{Q} \end{bmatrix} \right\|_\infty \\ &= \left\| \begin{bmatrix} \boldsymbol{R}_{11} & \boldsymbol{R}_{12} \\ \boldsymbol{R}_{21} & \boldsymbol{R}_{22} + \boldsymbol{Q} \end{bmatrix} \right\|_\infty . \end{aligned}$$

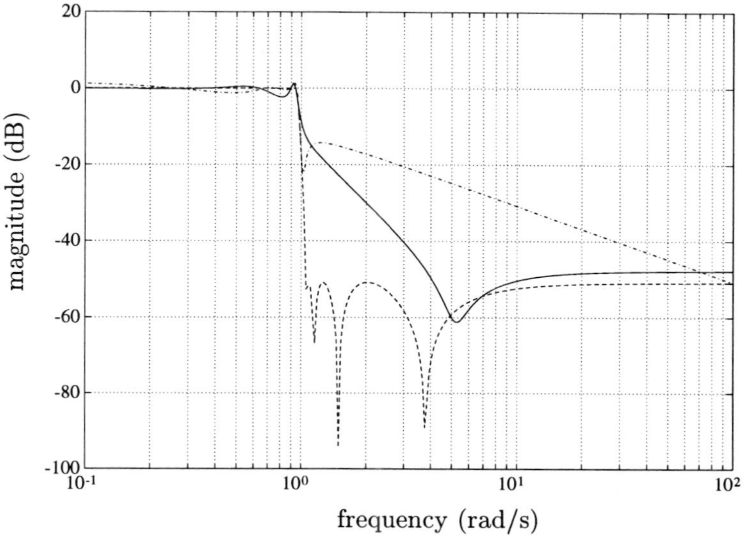

Figure 11.4: Eigth-order elliptic filter (dashed), frequency weighted approximation (solid) and an unweighted approximation (dot-dash).

It turns out that $\begin{bmatrix} \boldsymbol{R}_{11} & \boldsymbol{R}_{12} \\ \boldsymbol{R}_{21} & \boldsymbol{R}_{22} \end{bmatrix} \in \mathcal{RH}_\infty^-$ and we seek $\boldsymbol{Q} \in \mathcal{RH}_\infty$ such that $\|\mathcal{F}_\ell(\boldsymbol{P}, \boldsymbol{K})\|_\infty < \gamma$. This is a four-block problem of the form considered in this chapter, provided we interchange the role of the left and right-half planes, which may be done via the change of variable $s \to -s$. Solving this four-block problem yields all controllers by combining the parametrization of all $\boldsymbol{Q}$'s with the parametrization of all stabilizing controllers. This approach has provided a complete treatment of all the optimal cases, but is too intricate for inclusion in this book. Despite this, we will state the necessary and sufficient conditions for the existence of an $\mathcal{H}_\infty$ optimal controller and the representation formula for all such controllers.

Suppose we are given the generalized plant

$$\boldsymbol{P} = \begin{bmatrix} \boldsymbol{P}_{11} & \boldsymbol{P}_{12} \\ \boldsymbol{P}_{21} & \boldsymbol{P}_{22} \end{bmatrix} \stackrel{s}{=} \left[\begin{array}{c|cc} A & B_1 & B_2 \\ \hline C_1 & D_{11} & D_{12} \\ C_2 & D_{21} & D_{22} \end{array}\right] \tag{11.5.1}$$

and that we require all controllers that internally stabilize $\boldsymbol{P}$ and satisfy

$$\|\mathcal{F}_\ell(\boldsymbol{P}, \boldsymbol{K})\|_\infty \le \gamma. \tag{11.5.2}$$

The assumptions are:

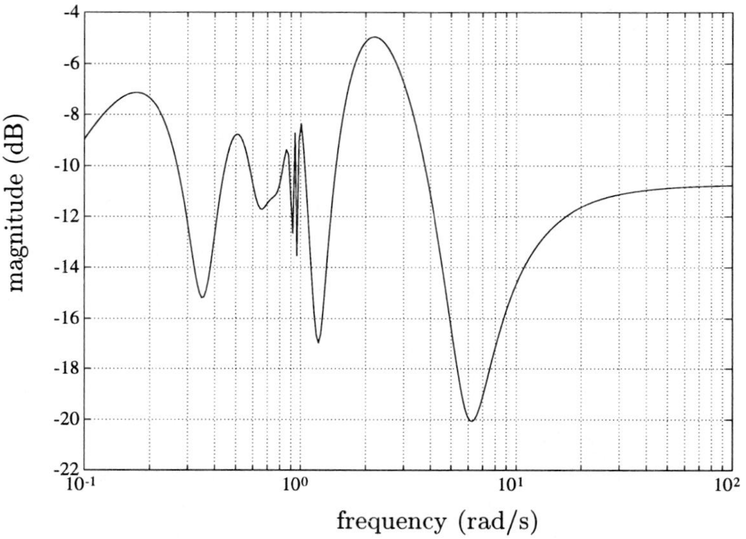

Figure 11.5: Frequency-weighted modelling error magnitude.

1. (A, B_2, C_2) is stabilizable and detectable.
2. The problem has been scaled so that $D_{21}D_{21}' = I_q$ and $D_{12}'D_{12} = I_m$; this assumption clearly pre-supposes that $\text{rank}(D_{12}) = m$ and that $\text{rank}(D_{21}) = q$.
3. $\text{rank}\left(\begin{bmatrix} j\omega I - A & -B_2 \\ C_1 & D_{12} \end{bmatrix}\right) = n + m$ for all real ω.
4. $\text{rank}\left(\begin{bmatrix} j\omega I - A & -B_1 \\ C_2 & D_{21} \end{bmatrix}\right) = n + q$ for all real ω.
5. $D_{11} = 0$ and $D_{22} = 0$. As explained in Chapter 4, this assumption may be removed by loop shifting.

In the following results, we introduce $D_\perp$ and $\tilde{D}_\perp$, which have been chosen so that $\begin{bmatrix} D_\perp & D_{12} \end{bmatrix}$ and $\begin{bmatrix} \tilde{D}_\perp' & D_{21}' \end{bmatrix}$ are orthogonal. The necessary and sufficient conditions for a solution to exist are as follows.

Theorem 11.5.1 *Suppose that $\boldsymbol{P}$ in (11.5.1) is given, and that assumptions (1) to (5) above are satisfied. Then for any $\gamma > 0$ there exists an internally-stabilizing controller such that $\|\mathcal{F}_\ell(\boldsymbol{P}, \boldsymbol{K})\|_\infty \leq \gamma$ if and only if:*

1. *There exists*

$$\begin{bmatrix} X_{\infty 1} \\ X_{\infty 2} \end{bmatrix} \in \mathbb{R}^{2n \times n}$$

of rank n such that:

(i) $H_\infty \begin{bmatrix} X_{\infty 1} \\ X_{\infty 2} \end{bmatrix} = \begin{bmatrix} X_{\infty 1} \\ X_{\infty 2} \end{bmatrix} T_X, \qquad \mathrm{R}_e\lambda_i(T_X) \leq 0$ *for all i, and*

(ii) $X'_{\infty 1}X_{\infty 2} = X'_{\infty 2}X_{\infty 1}$,

where

$$H_\infty = \begin{bmatrix} A - B_2 D'_{12} C_1 & \gamma^{-2} B_1 B'_1 - B_2 B'_2 \\ -C'_1 D_\perp D'_\perp C_1 & -(A - B_2 D'_{12} C_1)' \end{bmatrix}.$$

2. *There exists*

$$\begin{bmatrix} Y_{\infty 1} \\ Y_{\infty 2} \end{bmatrix} \in \mathbb{R}^{2n \times n}$$

of rank n such that:

(i) $J_\infty \begin{bmatrix} Y_{\infty 1} \\ Y_{\infty 2} \end{bmatrix} = \begin{bmatrix} Y_{\infty 1} \\ Y_{\infty 2} \end{bmatrix} T_Y, \qquad$ *with* $\mathrm{R}_e\lambda_i(T_Y) \leq 0$ *for all i, and*

(ii) $Y'_{\infty 1}Y_{\infty 2} = Y'_{\infty 2}Y_{\infty 1}$,

where

$$J_\infty = \begin{bmatrix} (A - B_1 D'_{21} C_2)' & \gamma^{-2} C'_1 C_1 - C'_2 C_2 \\ -B_1 \tilde{D}'_\perp \tilde{D}_\perp B'_1 & -(A - B_1 D'_{21} C_2) \end{bmatrix}.$$

3.

$$\Pi(\gamma) = \begin{bmatrix} X'_{\infty 2} X_{\infty 1} & \gamma^{-1} X'_{\infty 2} Y_{\infty 2} \\ \gamma^{-1} Y'_{\infty 2} X_{\infty 2} & Y'_{\infty 2} Y_{\infty 1} \end{bmatrix} \geq 0. \qquad (11.5.3)$$

Proof. See [78]. ■

In the case that $X_{\infty 1}$ and $Y_{\infty 1}$ are nonsingular, the full-information control and $\mathcal{H}_\infty$ filter Riccati equation solutions X_∞ and Y_∞ are given by

$$X_\infty = X_{\infty 2} X_{\infty 1}^{-1}, \qquad Y_\infty = Y_{\infty 2} Y_{\infty 1}^{-1}.$$

In this case, (11.5.3) holds if and only if

$$\begin{aligned} 0 &\leq \begin{bmatrix} X_\infty & \gamma^{-1} X_\infty Y_\infty \\ \gamma^{-1} Y_\infty X_\infty & Y_\infty \end{bmatrix} \\ &= \begin{bmatrix} I & 0 \\ \gamma^{-1} Y_\infty & I \end{bmatrix} \begin{bmatrix} X_\infty & 0 \\ 0 & Y_\infty (I - \gamma^{-2} X_\infty Y_\infty) \end{bmatrix} \begin{bmatrix} I & \gamma^{-1} Y_\infty \\ 0 & I \end{bmatrix}. \end{aligned}$$

This shows that under these conditions (11.5.3) is equivalent to the three conditions: $X_\infty \geq 0$; $Y_\infty \geq 0$; and $\rho(X_\infty Y_\infty) \leq \gamma^2$. Theorem 8.3.2, which deals with the suboptimal case, shows that a suboptimal solution exists if and only if stabilizing solutions $X_\infty \geq 0$ and $Y_\infty \geq 0$ exist and $\rho(X_\infty Y_\infty) < \gamma^2$.

When designing a controller using an $\mathcal{H}_\infty$ synthesis procedure, it is rarely the case that the first attempt provides a totally satisfactory controller; usually, some adjustment of the design weighting matrices is desirable. In this process, it is helpful to know the limiting design factor. That is, which aspect of the problem is preventing the performance level γ from being decreased. In order to provide some insight into this, we make the following remarks:

- If it is the condition (11.5.3) that prevents γ being reduced, the design is stability limited. That is, the norm objective could be achieved if the controller did not also have to stabilize the system. This means that analytic constraints, such as Bode's conservation of sensitivity theorem, are the limiting factor in the design. Typically, this means that there is insufficient frequency separation between the high-gain objectives and the low-gain objectives.[4]

  The number of negative eigenvalues of the matrix $\Pi(\gamma)$ on the left-hand side of (11.5.3) gives the number of unstable closed-loop poles that must be allowed in order to meet the infinity norm objective. If $X_{\infty 2}' X_{\infty 1} \geq 0$, but $\Pi(\gamma)$ has negative eigenvalues, the problem is limited by the estimation problem; one could achieve the objective with a stabilizing full-information controller, but not with a stabilizing measurement feedback controller. If $X_{\infty 2}' X_{\infty 1}$ has negative eigenvalues, one cannot achieve the objective even with a stabilizing full-information controller.

- If the existence of $\begin{bmatrix} X_{\infty 1}' & X_{\infty 2}' \end{bmatrix}'$ or $\begin{bmatrix} Y_{\infty 1}' & Y_{\infty 2}' \end{bmatrix}'$ is what prevents γ being reduced, the design is norm limited. That is, it is the norm objective associated with Parrott's theorem that is fixing the lower bound on the achievable norm. No controller, stabilizing or otherwise, could achieve the objective. This means that algebraic constraints, such as $\boldsymbol{S} - \boldsymbol{GKS} = I$, in which $\boldsymbol{S} = (I - \boldsymbol{GK})^{-1}$ is the sensitivity operator, are the limiting factor in the design. The situation may be improved by introducing a frequency weighting function to de-emphasize one of the constraints.

  If the existence of $\begin{bmatrix} X_{\infty 1}' & X_{\infty 2}' \end{bmatrix}'$ is the limiting factor, the problem is control limited—even a full-information controller could not achieve the objective.

In our final result, we characterize all the controllers that achieve the objective.

Theorem 11.5.2 *If the three conditions of Theorem 11.5.1 are satisfied, all finite-dimensional, internally-stabilizing controllers $\boldsymbol{K}$ that satisfy $\|\mathcal{F}_\ell(\boldsymbol{P}, \boldsymbol{K})\|_\infty \leq \gamma$ are given by $\boldsymbol{K} = \mathcal{F}_\ell(\boldsymbol{K}_a, \boldsymbol{U})$, in which $\boldsymbol{U} \in \mathcal{RH}_\infty$ with $\|\boldsymbol{U}\|_\infty \leq \gamma$ and $\det(I - \boldsymbol{K}_{22}(\infty)\boldsymbol{U}(\infty)) \neq 0$. The generator of all controllers $\boldsymbol{K}_a$ is given by*

$$\boldsymbol{K}_a = \begin{bmatrix} 0 & I \\ I & 0 \end{bmatrix} + \begin{bmatrix} C_{k1} \\ C_{k2} \end{bmatrix} (sE_k - A_k)^{\#} \begin{bmatrix} B_{k1} & B_{k2} \end{bmatrix}, \tag{11.5.4}$$

[4]As explained in Section 2.5.6, a rapid gain roll-off from high gain to low gain can result in closed-loop instability or a small stability margin.

in which $(\cdot)^{\#}$ *denotes a generalized inverse and*

$$\begin{aligned}
E_k &= Y'_{\infty 1}X_{\infty 1} - \gamma^{-2}Y'_{\infty 2}X_{\infty 2} && (11.5.5)\\
B_{k1} &= Y'_{\infty 1}B_1D'_{21} + Y'_{\infty 2}C'_2 && (11.5.6)\\
B_{k2} &= Y'_{\infty 1}B_2 + \gamma^{-2}Y'_{\infty 2}C'_1D_{12} && (11.5.7)\\
C_{k1} &= -(D'_{12}C_1X_{\infty 1} + B'_2X_{\infty 2}) && (11.5.8)\\
C_{k2} &= -(C_2X_{\infty 1} + \gamma^{-2}D_{21}B'_1X_{\infty 2}) && (11.5.9)\\
A_k &= E_kT_X + B_{k1}C_{k2} && (11.5.10)\\
&= T'_YE_k + B_{k2}C_{k1}.
\end{aligned}$$

Proof. See [78] and Problem 11.6. ■

There are two possible consequences of E_k in (11.5.5) being singular. Firstly, $sE_k - A_k$ may have eigenvalues at infinity—these infinite eigenvalues do not appear as poles of $\boldsymbol{K}_a$. Secondly, $sE_k - A_k$ may be identically singular (singular for all values of s).

We will now outline how to derive a reduced-order controller representation formula when E_k is singular; the state dimension of $\boldsymbol{K}_a$ is reduced by the rank defect of E_k. There is also a reduction in the dimension of the free parameter $\boldsymbol{U}$ and we will show explicitly how this comes about. This reduction in dimension leads to the optimal controller in the single-input-single-output case being unique.

Write $\boldsymbol{K}_a$ as the descriptor system

$$\begin{aligned}
E_k\dot{\zeta} &= A_k\zeta + \begin{bmatrix} B_{k1} & B_{k2} \end{bmatrix}\begin{bmatrix} y \\ r \end{bmatrix}\\
\begin{bmatrix} u \\ s \end{bmatrix} &= \begin{bmatrix} C_{k1} \\ C_{k2} \end{bmatrix}\zeta + \begin{bmatrix} 0 & I \\ I & 0 \end{bmatrix}\begin{bmatrix} y \\ r \end{bmatrix}.
\end{aligned}$$

Let U and V be orthogonal matrices such that

$$UE_kV = \begin{bmatrix} \widehat{E}_k & 0 \\ 0 & 0 \end{bmatrix}, \qquad \det(\widehat{E}_k) \neq 0.$$

Introducing a new state variable $\xi = V'\zeta$ and multiplying the state dynamical equation by U', we obtain

$$\begin{aligned}
\begin{bmatrix} \widehat{E}_k\dot{\xi}_1 \\ 0 \end{bmatrix} &= \begin{bmatrix} \widehat{A}_{k11} & \widehat{A}_{k12} \\ \widehat{A}_{k21} & \widehat{A}_{k22} \end{bmatrix}\begin{bmatrix} \xi_1 \\ \xi_2 \end{bmatrix} + \begin{bmatrix} \widehat{B}_{k11} & \widehat{B}_{k12} \\ \widehat{B}_{k21} & \widehat{B}_{k22} \end{bmatrix}\begin{bmatrix} y \\ r \end{bmatrix}\\
\begin{bmatrix} u_k \\ s_k \end{bmatrix} &= \begin{bmatrix} \widehat{C}_{k11} & \widehat{C}_{k12} \\ \widehat{C}_{k21} & \widehat{C}_{k22} \end{bmatrix}\begin{bmatrix} \xi_1 \\ \xi_2 \end{bmatrix} + \begin{bmatrix} 0 & I \\ I & 0 \end{bmatrix}\begin{bmatrix} y \\ r \end{bmatrix},
\end{aligned}$$

in which

$$\widehat{A}_k = UA_kV = \begin{bmatrix} \widehat{A}_{k11} & \widehat{A}_{k12} \\ \widehat{A}_{k21} & \widehat{A}_{k22} \end{bmatrix},$$

$$\begin{aligned}
\widehat{B}_k &= U\begin{bmatrix} B_{k1} & B_{k2} \end{bmatrix} = \begin{bmatrix} \widehat{B}_{k11} & \widehat{B}_{k12} \\ \widehat{B}_{k21} & \widehat{B}_{k22} \end{bmatrix}, \\
\widehat{C}_k &= \begin{bmatrix} C_{k1} \\ C_{k2} \end{bmatrix} V = \begin{bmatrix} \widehat{C}_{k11} & \widehat{C}_{k12} \\ \widehat{C}_{k21} & \widehat{C}_{k22} \end{bmatrix}.
\end{aligned}$$

(All the partitioning is conformable with that of E_k.) The algebraic equation that determines ξ_2 can always be solved (see [78]) giving

$$\xi_2 = -\widehat{A}_{k22}^{\dagger}(\widehat{A}_{k21}\xi_1 + \begin{bmatrix} \widehat{B}_{k21} & \widehat{B}_{k22} \end{bmatrix}\begin{bmatrix} y \\ r \end{bmatrix}) + \nu,$$

in which $(\cdot)^{\dagger}$ denotes the Moore-Penrose generalized inverse and $\nu \in \ker(\widehat{A}_{k22})$. It can also be shown ([78]) that

$$\ker(\widehat{A}_{k22}) \subset \ker \begin{bmatrix} \widehat{A}_{k12} \\ \widehat{C}_{k12} \\ \widehat{C}_{k22} \end{bmatrix},$$

which means that ν has no effect on the controller transfer function. Thus, eliminating ξ_2, we obtain the state-space representation

$$\begin{aligned}
\dot{\xi}_1 &= A_{kr}\xi_1 + \begin{bmatrix} B_{kr1} & B_{kr2} \end{bmatrix}\begin{bmatrix} y \\ r \end{bmatrix} \\
\begin{bmatrix} u \\ s \end{bmatrix} &= \begin{bmatrix} C_{kr1} \\ C_{kr2} \end{bmatrix}\xi_1 + \begin{bmatrix} D_{kr11} & D_{kr12} \\ D_{kr21} & D_{kr22} \end{bmatrix}\begin{bmatrix} y \\ r \end{bmatrix},
\end{aligned}$$

in which

$$\begin{aligned}
A_{kr} &= \widehat{E}_k^{-1}(\widehat{A}_{k11} - \widehat{A}_{k12}\widehat{A}_{k22}^{\dagger}\widehat{A}_{k21}) \\
\begin{bmatrix} B_{kr1} & B_{kr2} \end{bmatrix} &= \widehat{E}_k^{-1}\begin{bmatrix} I & -\widehat{A}_{k12}\widehat{A}_{k22}^{\dagger} \end{bmatrix}\widehat{B}_k, \\
\begin{bmatrix} C_{kr1} \\ C_{kr2} \end{bmatrix} &= \widehat{C}_k\begin{bmatrix} I \\ -\widehat{A}_{k22}^{\dagger}\widehat{A}_{k12} \end{bmatrix}, \\
\begin{bmatrix} D_{kr11} & D_{kr12} \\ D_{kr21} & D_{kr22} \end{bmatrix} &= \begin{bmatrix} 0 & I \\ I & 0 \end{bmatrix} - \begin{bmatrix} C_{k12} \\ C_{k22} \end{bmatrix}\widehat{A}_{k22}^{\dagger}\begin{bmatrix} B_{k21} & B_{k22} \end{bmatrix}.
\end{aligned}$$

To show explicitly the reduction in dimension of the free parameter, $\boldsymbol{U}$, we select orthogonal matrices Y and Z (which always exist) such that

$$\begin{aligned}
Y\begin{bmatrix} C_{kr2} & D_{kr21} \end{bmatrix} &= \begin{bmatrix} \bar{C}_{kr2} & \bar{D}_{kr21} \\ 0 & 0 \end{bmatrix}, \\
\begin{bmatrix} B_{kr2} \\ D_{kr12} \end{bmatrix} Z &= \begin{bmatrix} \bar{B}_{kr2} & 0 \\ \bar{D}_{kr12} & 0 \end{bmatrix}, \\
YD_{kr22}Z &= \begin{bmatrix} \bar{D}_{kr22} & 0 \\ 0 & \gamma^{-1}I \end{bmatrix}.
\end{aligned}$$

This means that only the (1,1)-block of $\boldsymbol{U}$ has a role to play. We may therefore eliminate the redundant pieces of the controller generator to obtain

$$\bar{\boldsymbol{K}}_a = \begin{bmatrix} D_{kr11} & \bar{D}_{kr12} \\ \bar{D}_{kr21} & \bar{D}_{kr22} \end{bmatrix} + \begin{bmatrix} C_{kr1} \\ \bar{C}_{kr2} \end{bmatrix} (sI - A_{kr})^{-1} \begin{bmatrix} B_{kr1} & \bar{B}_{kr2} \end{bmatrix},$$

which is a reduced degree, reduced dimension generator for all optimal controllers. An example of this optimal behavior is considered in Problem 11.7.

Main points of the section

1. The $\mathcal{H}_\infty$ controller synthesis problem may be recast as a four-block problem using the parametrization of all stabilizing controllers.
2. The optimal solution of the four-block problem enables a complete solution of the optimal $\mathcal{H}_\infty$ controller synthesis problem to be given. The conditions for a solution to exist are in terms of bases for the stable invariant subspaces of two Hamiltonian matrices.
3. In contrast to the one-block problem, which is considered in Chapter 10, there are several mechanisms by which optimality may arise. The stability constraint is the limiting factor if condition (11.5.3) determines the optimal performance level. Otherwise, it is the norm constraint itself that is the limiting factor.
4. A descriptor system representation for all optimal controllers can be given.
5. When E_k in the descriptor system representation of the controller generator is singular, it may always be reduced to a normal state-space system, which has state dimension lower than that of the generalized plant. In these cases, there is also a reduction in the dimensions of the free parameter $\boldsymbol{U}$.

11.6 Notes and References

An early example of a four-block problem may be found in the work of Parrott [160], who was motivated by problems involving the extension and approximation of Hankel operators. The book by Power [168] is a useful reference on the subject and Young's book [222] also contains a nice treatment of Parrott's theorem.

Interest in the four-block problem by the control community dates from the work of Doyle [52]. Motivated by the work of Davis, Kahan and Weinberger [39], he showed that the generalized regulator problem was equivalent to the four-block problem. It was also shown that the four-block problem could be reduced to a classical Nehari problem (see Doyle [52], Chu, Doyle and Lee [36] and Francis [65]).

Although this method provided a complete mathematical solution to the $\mathcal{H}_\infty$ controller synthesis problem, it was not considered satisfactory because of its complexity, a lack of control system insight and a host of numerical and degree inflation problems.

The state-space approach to the four-block problem based on allpass dilation is due to Glover, Limebeer, Doyle, Kasenally and Safonov [78]. This produced an explicit state-space formula for the linear fractional transformation that generates all the controllers in terms of a state-space realization of the generalized plant and the solutions of two algebraic Riccati equations. The simplicity of the final answer suggested that a more insightful and direct approach might be possible, resulting in the separation theory approach of Doyle, Glover, Khargonekar and Francis [54], which is the basis for Chapters 6 to 8.

Other solutions to the four-block problem have been given by Foias and Tannenbaum [64], Ball and Jonckheere [24] and Feintuch and Francis [60].

A solution to the frequency weighted model reduction problem was developed by Anderson and Latham [10, 127] using the optimal Hankel norm approximation techniques of Chapter 10. However, the infinity norm bounds resulting from this approach are rather conservative. Glover, Limebeer and Hung [77] showed that the frequency weighted model reduction problem may be recast as a four-block problem, which could be solved using the allpass dilation arguments developed in [78]. Truncation-based approaches to the frequency weighted model reduction have been given by Enns [57] and Al-Saggaf and Franklin [6].

The relative error model reduction problem was considered by Glover [72] using the optimal Hankel norm approach that Anderson and Latham [10, 127] had developed for the general frequency weighted case. Truncation based methods for relative error approximation have also be developed—see Desai and Pal [45], Green [83] and Safonov and Wang [208].

11.7 Problems

Problem 11.1. Suppose $\begin{bmatrix} C \\ D \end{bmatrix}$ is an orthogonal basis for the right null space of $\begin{bmatrix} A & B \end{bmatrix}$. If B is nonsingular, show that C must be nonsingular also.

Problem 11.2. Let

$$X = \begin{bmatrix} X_{11} & X_{12} \\ X_{21} & X_{22} \end{bmatrix}$$

be a partitioned complex matrix. Show that

$$\begin{aligned} \operatorname{trace}(X^*X) &= \operatorname{trace}(X_{11}^*X_{11}) + \operatorname{trace}(X_{12}^*X_{12}) \\ &\quad + \operatorname{trace}(X_{21}^*X_{21}) + \operatorname{trace}(X_{22}^*X_{22}), \end{aligned}$$

and hence prove that

$$\inf_{X_{22}} \left\| \begin{bmatrix} X_{11} & X_{12} \\ X_{21} & X_{22} \end{bmatrix} \right\|_2 = \left\| \begin{bmatrix} X_{11} & X_{12} \\ X_{21} & 0 \end{bmatrix} \right\|_2,$$

in which $\|X\|_2^2 = \text{trace}(X'X)$.

Problem 11.3. Use equations (11.3.14), (11.3.12) and (11.3.21) to verify that

$$\widehat{A}Y(Z^{-1})' + Z^{-1}Y\widehat{A}' + \widehat{B}_{aa}\widehat{B}'_{aa} = 0.$$

Problem 11.4. Consider the matrix D_{aa} given in (11.2.4). Use the fact that this matrix is orthogonal to prove:

1. $D_{42}^{-1}D_{34} = -D'_{12}(D_{13}^{-1})'$.
2. $D_{34}D_{24}^{-1} = -(D_{31}^{-1})'D'_{21}$.

Problem 11.5. Show that $\boldsymbol{Q}_{24}^{-1}$ is antistable as follows:

1. Show that an alternative expression for $\widehat{A}$ is

$$\widehat{A} = -Z^{-1}(A'Z + C'_{aa}\widehat{C}_{aa}).$$

2. Show that

$$\widehat{A} - \widehat{B}_4 D_{24}^{-1}\widehat{C}_2 = -Z^{-1}\big(A'Z + C'_3(\widehat{C}_3 + (D_{31}^{-1})'D'_{21}\widehat{C}_2)\big).$$

3. Show that

$$\widehat{C}_3 + (D_{31}^{-1})'D'_{21}\widehat{C}_2 = -(D_{31}^{-1})'B'_1 Z.$$

4. Hence, show that

$$\widehat{A} - \widehat{B}_4 D_{24}^{-1}\widehat{C}_2 = -Z^{-1}(A - B_1 D_{31}^{-1}C_3)'Z.$$

Problem 11.6. By substituting $X_\infty = X_{\infty 2}X_{\infty 1}^{-1}$ and $Y_\infty = (Y'_{\infty 1})^{-1}Y'_{\infty 2}$ into Theorem 8.3.2, derive the descriptor representation formula in Theorem 11.5.2.

(Hint: You will need to use the Hamiltonian matrix relationships given in Theorem 11.5.1.)

Problem 11.7. (Kasenally and Limebeer [111]) Consider the mixed sensitivity problem of finding

$$\gamma_{opt} = \inf_{\boldsymbol{K}} \left\| \begin{bmatrix} \boldsymbol{GK}(I - \boldsymbol{GK})^{-1} \\ (I - \boldsymbol{GK})^{-1} \end{bmatrix} \right\|_\infty,$$

in which the infimum is taken over the set of stabilizing controllers.

1. Show that the generalized plant for this problem is

$$\boldsymbol{P} = \left[\begin{bmatrix} 0 \\ I \\ -I \end{bmatrix} \quad \begin{bmatrix} -\boldsymbol{G} \\ \boldsymbol{G} \\ -\boldsymbol{G} \end{bmatrix} \right] \stackrel{s}{=} \left[\begin{array}{c|cc} A & 0 & B \\ \hline \begin{bmatrix} C \\ C \end{bmatrix} & \begin{bmatrix} 0 \\ I \end{bmatrix} & \begin{bmatrix} D \\ D \end{bmatrix} \\ C & I & D \end{array} \right].$$

2. If D is nonsingular, show that D_{12} may be orthogonalized by re-scaling the problem as

$$\tilde{\boldsymbol{P}} \stackrel{s}{=} \left[\begin{array}{c|cc} A & 0 & \frac{1}{\sqrt{2}}BD^{-1} \\ \hline \begin{bmatrix} C \\ C \end{bmatrix} & \begin{bmatrix} 0 \\ I \end{bmatrix} & \begin{bmatrix} \frac{1}{\sqrt{2}}I \\ \frac{1}{\sqrt{2}}I \end{bmatrix} \\ C & I & \frac{1}{\sqrt{2}}I \end{array}\right].$$

3. Show that

$$\left[\begin{array}{cc} D_{12} & D_{\perp} \end{array}\right] = \frac{1}{\sqrt{2}}\begin{bmatrix} I & -I \\ I & I \end{bmatrix}.$$

4. Show that the LQG Riccati equations (5.4.11) and (5.4.12) associated with this problem are

$$(A - BD^{-1}C)'X + X(A - BD^{-1}C) - \frac{1}{2}XB(D'D)^{-1}B'X = 0$$

and

$$AY + YA' - YC'CY = 0.$$

(Note, however, that the LQG cost for this problem is infinite, for any controller, because $D_{\perp}'D_{11} \neq 0$.)

5. Show that the $\mathcal{H}_\infty$ Riccati equations for this problem are

$$(A-BD^{-1}C)'X_\infty+X_\infty(A-BD^{-1}C)-\frac{\gamma^2-1}{2(\gamma^2-1/2)}X_\infty B(D'D)^{-1}B'X_\infty = 0.$$

and

$$Y_\infty A' + AY_\infty - (1-\gamma^{-2})Y_\infty C'CY_\infty.$$

6. By comparing terms, show that

$$X_\infty = \frac{\gamma^2 - \frac{1}{2}}{\gamma^2 - 1}X, \qquad Y_\infty = \frac{\gamma^2}{\gamma^2 - 1}Y.$$

7. Show that $\gamma_{opt} = 1$ when $\boldsymbol{G}$ is either stable or minimum phase (but not both). If $\boldsymbol{G}$ is stable with at least one right-half-plane zero, show that $\lim_{\gamma\to 1}\|X_\infty(\gamma)\| = \infty$. If $\boldsymbol{G}$ is unstable and minimum phase show that $\lim_{\gamma\to 1}\|Y_\infty(\gamma)\| = \infty$.
8. If $\boldsymbol{G}$ is stable and minimum phase show that $\gamma_{opt} = 1/\sqrt{2}$. (Hint: Show that $\boldsymbol{K} = -\rho\boldsymbol{G}^{-1}$ is a stabilizing controller, and then consider

$$\frac{d}{d\rho}\left\|\begin{bmatrix} \boldsymbol{GK}(I-\boldsymbol{GK})^{-1} \\ (I-\boldsymbol{GK})^{-1} \end{bmatrix}\right\|_\infty = 0.)$$

Problem 11.8. A normalized right coprime factorization of a plant $\boldsymbol{G}$ is given by

$$\boldsymbol{G} = \boldsymbol{N}\boldsymbol{D}^{-1},$$

in which $\boldsymbol{N}, \boldsymbol{D} \in \mathcal{RH}_\infty$ satisfy

$$\begin{bmatrix} \boldsymbol{D}^\sim & \boldsymbol{N}^\sim \end{bmatrix} \begin{bmatrix} \boldsymbol{D} \\ \boldsymbol{N} \end{bmatrix} = I.$$

Show that

$$\left\| \begin{bmatrix} \boldsymbol{D} \\ \boldsymbol{N} \end{bmatrix} \right\|_H < 1.$$

(Hint: Exploit the analyticity properties of the maximal Schmidt pair of a Hankel operator [79].)

Problem 11.9. Show that the dilated D-matrix associated with the four block problem (11.4.4) is given by

$$\begin{bmatrix} 0 & D_{12} & D_{13} & 0 \\ D_{21} & 0 & 0 & D_{24} \\ D_{31} & 0 & 0 & D_{34} \\ 0 & D_{42} & D_{43} & 0 \end{bmatrix}.$$

Problem 11.10. For the four-block problem (11.4.4) associated with model reduction, show that

$$A_2'Y_{22} + Y_{22}A_2 + C_2'C_2 = 0$$

and

$$A_2X_{22} + X_{22}A_2' + B_2B_2' + B_{32}B_{32}' = 0$$

and consequently that $\rho(X_{22}Y_{22}) < 1$.

Problem 11.11. Show that the representation formula given in Theorem 11.3.3 may be written in the following generalized state-space form:

$$\begin{bmatrix} \boldsymbol{Q}_{22} & \boldsymbol{Q}_{24} \\ \boldsymbol{Q}_{42} & \boldsymbol{Q}_{44} \end{bmatrix} = \begin{bmatrix} \widehat{C}_2 \\ \widehat{C}_4 \end{bmatrix} (sZ' - A' - YAX + C_{aa}'D_{aa}B_{aa}')^{-1} \begin{bmatrix} \widehat{B}_2 & \widehat{B}_4 \end{bmatrix} + \begin{bmatrix} D_{22} & D_{24} \\ D_{42} & 0 \end{bmatrix},$$

in which

$$\begin{bmatrix} \widehat{C}_2 \\ \widehat{C}_4 \end{bmatrix} = \begin{bmatrix} C_2X \\ 0 \end{bmatrix} + \begin{bmatrix} D_{21} & D_{22} & D_{23} \\ 0 & D_{42} & D_{43} \end{bmatrix} \begin{bmatrix} B_1' \\ B_2' \\ B_3' \end{bmatrix}$$

and

$$\begin{bmatrix} \widehat{B}_2 & \widehat{B}_4 \end{bmatrix} = \begin{bmatrix} YB_2 & 0 \end{bmatrix} + \begin{bmatrix} C_1' & C_2' & C_3' \end{bmatrix} \begin{bmatrix} D_{12} & 0 \\ D_{22} & D_{24} \\ D_{32} & D_{34} \end{bmatrix}.$$

12

Design Case Studies

12.1 Introduction

The generalized regulator theory presupposes the existence of a linear model of the plant and a number of frequency dependent weighting functions, which are selected to represent closed-loop performance specifications. Once the weights and plant model have been chosen, the lowest achievable infinity norm determines if the specifications can be met. If they can, the evaluation of a controller is a fully automated process. Although we have these necessary and sufficient conditions for the existence of a controller, theorems cannot design control systems.

The central difficulty with using the generalized regulator to solve design problems is interfacing the engineering requirements to the mathematical optimization process. The most obvious of these interfacing difficulties concerns the treatment of the discrepancy between the plant and the model we use to represent it. All hardware systems are nonlinear, and as a consequence, any linear model we use to represent them only provides an approximate representation of their true dynamical behavior.[1] The design optimization process must therefore be set up so that the discrepancy between the plant and the model we use to represent it, is taken into account. Precautions must be taken against the possible degradation of the system's performance as one ranges over all possible plant behaviors—the worst type of performance degradation is the onset of closed-loop instability.

To alleviate the design difficulties associated with nonlinearities and changes in the system's characteristics, one might deliberately design the control system so that the plant is constrained to operate in an approximately linear part of the operating regime where the system dynamics are accurately represented by a linear model. The maintenance of system linearity is not always appropriate and may involve a

[1]No model, linear or nonlinear, can completely represent a physical system's behavior.

sacrifice in performance; an example that comes to mind is the design of guidance systems for certain high-performance military missiles, where bang-bang controllers produce much better performance than linear controls. However, we may be forced to take a linear approach because of our inability to design controllers for some truly nonlinear systems.

The attenuation of unknown disturbances is an important design issue, which is dealt with by limiting the gain between the signal's point of entry and the outputs we would like to maintain as disturbance free. Controllers that meet a combination of time-domain and frequency-domain robust performance specifications are often required. One of our case studies shows how a class of these problems may be addressed using two-degree-of-freedom (TDF) controller structures. This study shows how the general theory may be used to produce good results in terms of time-domain specifications.

A problem that is closely related to the plant modelling issue is controller complexity—complex plant models will usually lead to high-order controllers and the difficulties associated with implementing them. On the assumption that we have ways of dealing with the "modelling gap", it would seem reasonable that we consider the possibility of replacing complex plant models with simpler ones. Simple models simplify the process of understanding the design limitations. The controller synthesis computations will be faster, will require less in the way of storage and will be less prone to numerical difficulties. In addition, the implementation of the resulting controller is simplified, because the controller degree is reduced. The model reduction ideas introduced in Chapters 9 to 11 therefore play a central role in the design process.

The objectives of this chapter are relatively modest. We are not going to attempt a survey of contemporary design techniques, or to produce a detailed prescriptive methodology that can be applied to every design problem. It would be a fool's errand to attempt to develop a theory that foresees and encompasses all possible applications. Rather, our aim is to concentrate on a single, simple approach to control system design which uses $\mathcal{H}_\infty$ optimization and which has produced good results on our case studies. When applying these ideas to their own design problems, readers may find it necessary to extend some of the ideas and make modifications that are appropriate to their circumstances. We hope that this book will provide them with the tools necessary to extend and modify the ideas to suit their own purposes and handle their own particular problems.

The next section introduces the theoretical background associated with robust stabilization theory for normalized coprime factor model error representations. After that, we will present two case studies. The first study is concerned with the stabilization of the vertical dynamics of the elongated plasma in a tokamak. It includes a consideration of actuator saturation and bumpless transfer. The second study looks at the design of a product-composition controller for a high-purity distillation column. Our hope is that these case studies will communicate some of the current thinking behind the use of $\mathcal{H}_\infty$ optimization in the solution of design problems.

12.2 Robust stability

A fundamental performance requirement for any feedback control system is its ability to maintain the stability of the closed loop. By closed-loop stability, we mean the stability of an uncertain plant, rather than just the stability of the nominal linear finite-dimensional model used to represent the plant. Designing a controller to stabilize a linear model is trivial provided certain stabilizability and detectability conditions are satisfied. On the other hand, designing a controller to stabilize an uncertain hardware system may be much more difficult, or even impossible.

The design of a robust controller usually proceeds in two steps. First, one seeks to characterize a plant model set $\mathcal{G}$, say, which "contains" the hardware system. A closed-loop system is called robustly stable if it is stable for every plant model $\boldsymbol{G} \in \mathcal{G}$. In the second step one attempts to design a controller that stabilizes every model $\boldsymbol{G} \in \mathcal{G}$.

In Chapter 2, representations of the model set are given in terms of a nominal model $\boldsymbol{G}$ and an additive model error $\boldsymbol{\Delta}_A$ or a multiplicative model error $\boldsymbol{\Delta}_M$. Robust stability results were developed for the the model sets

$$\mathcal{A}_\gamma = \{(\boldsymbol{G}+\boldsymbol{\Delta}_A) : \partial(\boldsymbol{G}) = \partial(\boldsymbol{G}+\boldsymbol{\Delta}_A),\ \|\boldsymbol{\Delta}_A\|_\infty < \gamma^{-1}\} \tag{12.2.1}$$

$$\mathcal{M}_\gamma = \{(I+\boldsymbol{\Delta}_M)\boldsymbol{G} : \partial(\boldsymbol{G}) = \partial((I+\boldsymbol{\Delta}_M)\boldsymbol{G}),\ \|\boldsymbol{\Delta}_M\|_\infty < \gamma^{-1}\}, \tag{12.2.2}$$

in which $\partial(\cdot)$ denotes the number of closed-right-half-plane poles of the transfer function matrix. These representations of model error are handicapped by the side condition on the number of right-half-plane poles. This somewhat artificial constraint was introduced so that simple robustness theorems could be proved using homotopy arguments. To illustrate the limitations of the model sets (12.2.1) and (12.2.2), we consider a system with a pair of poles on the imaginary axis. If the resonant frequencies of these poles are uncertain, the uncertainty cannot be captured by (12.2.1) or (12.2.2) with a perturbation of finite norm.

Example 12.2.1. Consider the two systems

$$\boldsymbol{G} = \frac{2\sqrt{2}}{s^2+1}, \qquad \boldsymbol{G}_\Delta = \frac{2\sqrt{2}}{s^2+1+\alpha}.$$

It can be verified that

$$\boldsymbol{\Delta}_A = -\frac{2\sqrt{2}\alpha}{(s^2+1)(s^2+1+\alpha)}$$

and

$$\boldsymbol{\Delta} = -\frac{\alpha}{(s^2+1+\alpha)},$$

which are both unbounded in the infinity norm for any $\alpha > 0$. ▽

12.2.1 Normalized coprime factor perturbations

This section introduces the normalized coprime factor model error representation, which has no restriction on the number of right-half-plane poles and which is capable of representing a wider class of systems than either (12.2.1) or (12.2.2). If $\boldsymbol{G}$ is a given plant model, then

$$\boldsymbol{G} = \boldsymbol{M}^{-1}\boldsymbol{N}$$

is a *normalized left coprime factorization* of $\boldsymbol{G}$ if $\boldsymbol{M}, \boldsymbol{N} \in \mathcal{H}_\infty$ are coprime (see Appendix A) and satisfy

$$\boldsymbol{M}\boldsymbol{M}^{\sim} + \boldsymbol{N}\boldsymbol{N}^{\sim} = I. \tag{12.2.3}$$

Normalized coprime factorizations have a number of interesting properties that can be found in the references given in the notes at the end of the chapter.

Given such a normalized left coprime factorization, we define the model set

$$\mathcal{G}_\gamma = \left\{ (\boldsymbol{M} - \boldsymbol{\Delta}_M)^{-1}(\boldsymbol{N} + \boldsymbol{\Delta}_N) : \begin{array}{l} \left[\begin{array}{cc} \boldsymbol{\Delta}_N & \boldsymbol{\Delta}_M \end{array} \right] \in \mathcal{H}_\infty, \\ \| \left[\begin{array}{cc} \boldsymbol{\Delta}_N & \boldsymbol{\Delta}_M \end{array} \right] \|_\infty < \gamma^{-1} \end{array} \right\}. \tag{12.2.4}$$

Note that if

$$y = (\boldsymbol{M} - \boldsymbol{\Delta}_M)^{-1}(\boldsymbol{N} + \boldsymbol{\Delta}_N)u,$$

then

$$(\boldsymbol{M} - \boldsymbol{\Delta}_M)y = (\boldsymbol{N} + \boldsymbol{\Delta}_N)u.$$

This may be re-written as

$$\boldsymbol{M}y = \boldsymbol{N}u + \left[\begin{array}{cc} \boldsymbol{\Delta}_N & \boldsymbol{\Delta}_M \end{array} \right] \left[\begin{array}{c} u \\ y \end{array} \right],$$

which is illustrated in Figure 12.1.

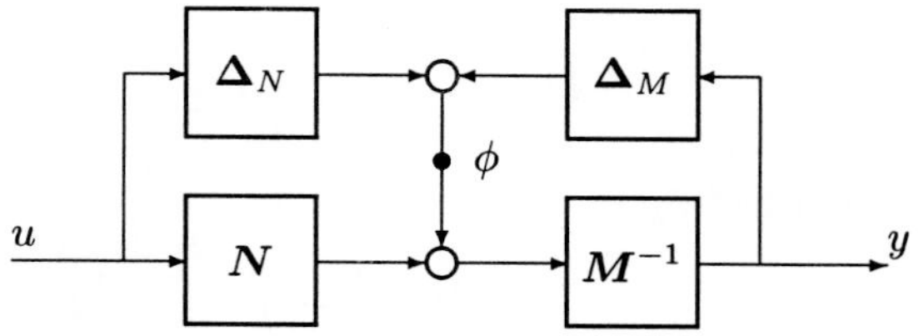

Figure 12.1: Plant with coprime factor perturbations.

Notice that if y and u arise from the nominal model $y = \boldsymbol{M}^{-1}\boldsymbol{N}u$, we have $\boldsymbol{M}y - \boldsymbol{N}u = 0$. If y and u do not arise from the nominal model, we have the "equation error" $\boldsymbol{M}y - \boldsymbol{N}u = \phi$. The norm bound in the normalized coprime factor model set requires that the equation error ϕ satisfies the two-norm bound

$$\|\phi\|_2 < \gamma^{-1} \left\| \begin{bmatrix} u \\ y \end{bmatrix} \right\|_2, \qquad \begin{bmatrix} u \\ y \end{bmatrix} \neq 0.$$

To illustrate the benefits of the normalized coprime factor representation of model error, we return to Example 12.2.1.

Example 12.2.2. As before,

$$\boldsymbol{G} = \frac{2\sqrt{2}}{s^2+1}, \qquad \boldsymbol{G}_\Delta = \frac{2\sqrt{2}}{s^2+1+\alpha}.$$

A normalized coprime factorization of $\boldsymbol{G}$ is

$$\begin{bmatrix} \boldsymbol{N} & \boldsymbol{M} \end{bmatrix} = \frac{1}{s^2+2s+3} \begin{bmatrix} 2\sqrt{2} & s^2+1 \end{bmatrix}.$$

Since

$$\boldsymbol{G}_\Delta = \left(\frac{s^2+1}{s^2+2s+3} + \frac{\alpha}{s^2+2s+3} \right)^{-1} \times \frac{2\sqrt{2}}{s^2+2s+3},$$

we see that $\boldsymbol{\Delta}_N = 0$ and $\boldsymbol{\Delta}_M = \frac{\alpha}{s^2+2s+3}$. Hence $\boldsymbol{G}_\Delta \in \mathcal{G}_\gamma$ for any $\gamma^{-1} > \|\frac{\alpha}{s^2+2s+3}\|_\infty$. ▽

We now give a brief summary of the theory of robust stability optimization for normalized coprime factors and loop-shaping design. We refer the reader to the notes and references at the end of the chapter for details regarding the relevant literature.

The optimization problem

We are interested in the stabilization of closed-loop systems constructed from plants $\boldsymbol{G}_p \in \mathcal{G}_\gamma$, with $\mathcal{G}_\gamma$ the normalized coprime factor perturbation model set defined in (12.2.4). The aim is to design a controller that minimizes the achievable value of γ, thereby maximizing the size of the admissible perturbation. Figure 12.2 gives an illustration of the optimization problem we are about to solve. From this diagram we see that

$$\begin{aligned} \begin{bmatrix} u \\ y \end{bmatrix} &= \begin{bmatrix} \boldsymbol{K} \\ I \end{bmatrix} (I - \boldsymbol{G}\boldsymbol{K})^{-1} \boldsymbol{M}^{-1} \phi \\ \phi &= \begin{bmatrix} \boldsymbol{\Delta}_N & \boldsymbol{\Delta}_M \end{bmatrix} \begin{bmatrix} u \\ y \end{bmatrix}. \end{aligned}$$

Therefore, by the small gain theorem (see Theorems 3.4.1 and Theorem 3.6.1),

$$\left\| \begin{bmatrix} \boldsymbol{K} \\ I \end{bmatrix} (I - \boldsymbol{G}\boldsymbol{K})^{-1} \boldsymbol{M}^{-1} \right\|_\infty \leq \gamma \tag{12.2.5}$$

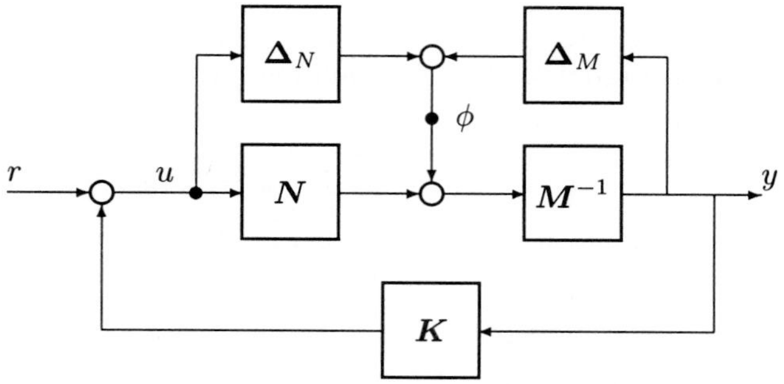

Figure 12.2: The robust controller design problem for the normalized coprime factor model error representation.

ensures that the loop will be stable for all plant in the normalized coprime factor perturbation model set $\mathcal{G}_\gamma$ defined by (12.2.4). Indeed, (12.2.5) ensures that the closed-loop will be stable provided $\left[\begin{array}{cc} \Delta_M & \Delta_N \end{array}\right]$ is stable and has incremental gain less than γ^{-1}, a generalization that allows for nonlinear and time-varying perturbations. In order to maximize the robust stability of the closed-loop, we require a stabilizing feedback controller that minimizes γ.

Since $\left[\begin{array}{cc} N & M \end{array}\right]$ is normalized and $\left[\begin{array}{cc} G & I \end{array}\right] = M^{-1}\left[\begin{array}{cc} N & M \end{array}\right]$,

$$\begin{aligned} & \left\| \left[\begin{array}{c} K \\ I \end{array}\right] (I - GK)^{-1} M^{-1} \right\|_\infty \\ = & \left\| \left[\begin{array}{c} K \\ I \end{array}\right] (I - GK)^{-1} \left[\begin{array}{cc} G & I \end{array}\right] \right\|_\infty . \end{aligned} \qquad (12.2.6)$$

As explained in Chapter 2, each of the four transfer function matrices on the right-hand side has a performance and/or robust stability interpretation. Thus, minimizing γ in (12.2.5) has many robust stability and performance interpretations via the identity (12.2.6).

State-space models for normalized coprime factors

If G has stabilizable and detectable realization (A, B, C, D), then

$$\left[\begin{array}{cc} N & M \end{array}\right] \stackrel{s}{=} \left[\begin{array}{c|cc} A - HC & B - HD & H \\ \hline -R^{-\frac{1}{2}}C & R^{-\frac{1}{2}}D & R^{-\frac{1}{2}} \end{array}\right] \qquad (12.2.7)$$

are normalized coprime factors of G if $H = (BD' + YC')R^{-1}$ and $R = I + DD'$. The matrix $Y \geq 0$ is the unique stabilizing solution to the Kalman filter algebraic Riccati equation

$$(A - BS^{-1}D'C)Y + Y(A - BS^{-1}D'C)' - YC'R^{-1}CY + BS^{-1}B' = 0,$$

in which $S = I + D'D$. The fact that (12.2.7) defines a left coprime factorization follows from results presented in Appendix A. Since the matrix Y is the controllability gramian of the given realization of $\begin{bmatrix} \boldsymbol{N} & \boldsymbol{M} \end{bmatrix}$ and

$$\begin{aligned} R^{-\frac{1}{2}} \begin{bmatrix} D & I \end{bmatrix} \begin{bmatrix} B' - D'H' \\ H' \end{bmatrix} + R^{-\frac{1}{2}} CY &= 0 \\ R^{-\frac{1}{2}} \begin{bmatrix} D & I \end{bmatrix} \begin{bmatrix} D' \\ I \end{bmatrix} R^{-\frac{1}{2}} &= I, \end{aligned}$$

Theorem 3.2.1 implies that $\begin{bmatrix} \boldsymbol{N} & \boldsymbol{M} \end{bmatrix}$ satisfies (12.2.3). Therefore (12.2.7) defines a normalized left coprime factorization.

The optimal stability margin

If $X \geq 0$ is the unique stabilizing solution to the general control algebraic Riccati equation

$$X(A - BS^{-1}D'C) + (A - BS^{-1}D'C)'X - XBS^{-1}B'X + C'R^{-1}C = 0,$$

the theory of Chapter 8 (see Problem 8.12) can be used to show that the lowest achievable value of γ is

$$\gamma_{opt} = \sqrt{1 + \lambda_{\max}(XY)}. \tag{12.2.8}$$

An alternative formula for γ_{opt} is

$$\gamma_{opt} = (1 - \| \begin{bmatrix} \boldsymbol{M} & \boldsymbol{N} \end{bmatrix} \|_H^2)^{-\frac{1}{2}} \tag{12.2.9}$$

where $\| \cdot \|_H$ denotes the Hankel norm. We will not verify this fact here, but a reference to the relevant literature appears in the notes.

An optimal controller

A controller $\boldsymbol{K}_0$ that achieves the bound (12.2.5) can be derived via the results of Chapter 8 (see Problem 8.12). One such controller is described by the descriptor state-space equations

$$\begin{aligned} W\dot{\widehat{x}} &= (W(A - BF) - \gamma^2 YC'(C - DF))\widehat{x} + \gamma^2 YC'y && (12.2.10) \\ u &= -B'X\widehat{x} - D'y, && (12.2.11) \end{aligned}$$

in which

$$\begin{aligned} F &= S^{-1}(D'C + B'X) \\ W &= (\gamma^2 - 1)I - YX. \end{aligned}$$

This controller always satisfies the norm criterion (12.2.5), but it is a stabilizing controller if and only if $\gamma \geq \gamma_{opt}$. When $\gamma = \gamma_{opt}$, it follows from (12.2.8) that the matrix W is singular and the controller degree is reduced.

12.2.2 Loop-shaping design procedure

We now summarize the design procedure we shall use in both of our case studies. In the first step of the design, the transfer function matrix $\boldsymbol{G}$ is shaped using a dynamic weighting function $\boldsymbol{W}$ so that the singular values of $\boldsymbol{GW}$ have desirable characteristics. Typically, we would like high low-frequency gain to ensure adequate attenuation of low-frequency disturbances and accurate tracking of step commands. Model errors and limits on actuator bandwidth usually require that the high-frequency gain be kept low. For example, we may require that the singular values of $\boldsymbol{GW}$ do not enter the cross-hatched areas in Figure 12.3. These "forbidden" areas are problem dependent and may be constructed from the design specifications. Roughly speaking, any penetration of the lower region constitutes a violation of the robust performance specifications, while a penetration of the upper region leads to a violation of the robust stability specifications. We remind the reader that these issues have been treated in detail in Chapter 2.

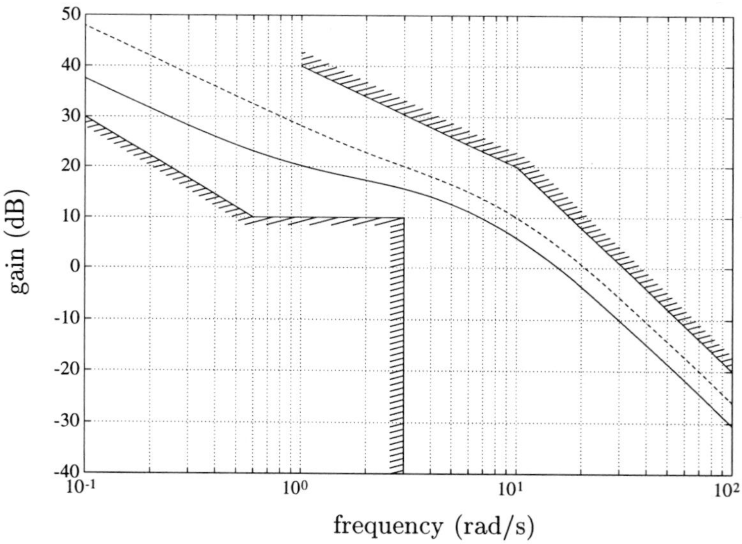

Figure 12.3: The standard loop shaping situation.

In a typical application, $\boldsymbol{W}$ will be used to increase the low-frequency gain, since this leads to better closed-loop reference tracking and forward-path disturbance attenuation. It will also be used to reduce the roll-off rate of $\boldsymbol{GW}$ in the unity-gain range of frequencies. This is motivated by the Bode gain-phase relations (and their multivariable generalizations), which imply that the lower the rate of gain reduction through the cross-over frequency, the smaller the phase lag. Thus a low rate of gain reduction through the unity-gain range of frequencies will help ensure the phase margin is not too small and that the closed-loop step response is reasonably well damped.[2] Finally, $\boldsymbol{W}$ will be used to roll off the open-loop gain at high frequencies. Here, the motivation comes from a need to ensure adequate robust stability margins—the plant model is usually least reliable at high frequencies. Since rolling off $\boldsymbol{GW}$ also has the effect of reducing the controller bandwidth, it will also result in a reduction in the high-frequency actuator activity and actuator saturation.

Since the first stage takes no account of the phase of $\boldsymbol{GW}$, a second design step is required to secure the stability of the closed loop.[3] This is achieved by synthesizing a controller that robustly stabilizes a normalized left coprime factorization of the shaped closed-loop transfer function matrix $\boldsymbol{GW}$. If the resulting value of γ_{opt} in equation (12.2.8) is small, the controller will not have to adjust the loop shape too much—the loop shape is consistent with ensuring a high level of stability robustness. If on the other hand γ_{opt} is too large, the loop should be reshaped (usually by compromising on some aspect of the desired performance) until an acceptable value is achieved. The fact that γ_{opt} is an upper bound on the infinity norm of the four transfer functions in (12.2.6) should be used in assessing the effectiveness of the design.

A four stage procedure is now given:

1. **Loop shaping**: Select an open-loop pre-compensator $\boldsymbol{W}$ so that the singular values of $\boldsymbol{GW}$ satisfy the robust performance specifications. If this is not possible, adjustments will have to be made to the specifications, the plant or both.

2. **Robust stabilization**: Determine the optimal stability margin γ_{opt} for the shaped plant $\boldsymbol{GW}$ from (12.2.8). If the resulting value of γ_{opt} is too high, modify $\boldsymbol{W}$ and repeat until a satisfactory compromise is found. Once a loop shape that produces an acceptable γ_{opt} has been obtained, compute the corresponding optimal controller $\boldsymbol{K}_0$ from (12.2.10) and (12.2.11).

3. **Weight absorption**: Because $\boldsymbol{W}$ is not part of the plant, it must be absorbed into the controller by replacing $\boldsymbol{K}_0$ with $\boldsymbol{K} = \boldsymbol{W}\boldsymbol{K}_0$. The final controller degree will be bounded above by the degree of the plant plus twice that of the weight. Since $\boldsymbol{K}$ is obtained by post-multiplying $\boldsymbol{K}_0$ by $\boldsymbol{W}$, it is clear that rolling off $\boldsymbol{W}$ will roll off $\boldsymbol{K}$.

---

[2] A high rate of gain reduction incurs a large phase-lag penalty. Thus, a high rate of gain reduction through the unity-gain range of frequencies results in small phase margins and therefore a poorly damped closed-loop step response.

[3] The selection of the loop shape is guided primarily by gain considerations. However, the Bode gain-phase relation and its consequences need to be kept in mind, which is why we do not attempt to select a loop shape that has a rapid gain roll-off through the cross-over frequency. Thus, although phase is not explicitly a part of the loop shape selection, a naive approach that completely ignores the likely consequences of the chosen loop shape will result in many unnecessary design iterations.

4. **Prefilter**: If $\boldsymbol{W}$ contains integral action (which it often does), accurate low-frequency command tracking will be achieved if the constant prefilter $-\boldsymbol{K}(0)$ is introduced. To see how this works, refer to Figure 12.2 and observe that if $u(0) = 0$, then $\boldsymbol{K}(0)y(0) = -r$ where r is the constant reference being fed into the loop. If the reference r is generated by the prefilter $r = -\boldsymbol{K}(0)y_{des}$, then $\boldsymbol{K}(0)y(0) = \boldsymbol{K}(0)y_{des}$. Therefore, provided $\boldsymbol{K}(0)$ has full column rank, we have $y = y_{des}$ as required.[4]

Main points of the section

1. To use the additive and multiplicative model error representations, we must know the number of right-half-plane poles in the system, and this must be constant for all plants in the model set. A further disadvantage of these model error representations is that they cannot represent uncertain resonances (poles on the imaginary axis).
2. The representation of model errors as a stable perturbation to the factors of a normalized coprime factorization of the nominal plant model provides a more general robust stability problem formulation.
3. The optimal stability margin for normalized coprime factor perturbations provides a bound on the infinity norm of other transfer function matrices of interest in assessing closed-loop performance and robustness.
4. The robust stability margin for normalized coprime factor perturbations can be computed via an eigenvalue calculation from the solution of two Riccati equations—no so called "γ iteration" is required.
5. The loop-shaping design procedure is based on selecting a weighting function such that the weighted loop gain has desirable magnitude characteristics as assessed by singular value plots, followed by a robust stabilization of the weighted loop gain.

12.3 Tokamak plasma control

Radioactive waste and greenhouse gases represent an escalating problem associated with conventional methods of electric power generation. The successful development of a nuclear fusion reactor will offer an almost limitless source of power which does not produce greenhouse gases or long-lived radioactive by-products such as plutonium.

[4]Note that $u(0)$, $\boldsymbol{K}(0)$, and so on, denote evaluations of frequency domain representations of the signals and systems. That is, $\boldsymbol{K}(0)$ is the steady-state or DC gain of the controller and $u(0)$ is the steady-state value of u.

Nuclear fusion occurs when light nuclei fuse to form heavier ones with a subsequent release of energy. One such reaction, which is the basis of modern fusion reactors, occurs between deuterium and tritium, which are both isotopes of hydrogen:

$${}^2_1D + {}^3_1T \rightarrow {}^4_2He + {}^1_0n + 17.6\ MeV.$$

To achieve reactor conditions, in which there is a net output of energy, a hot dense mixture of deuterium and tritium must be confined for a sufficiently long time. If a gaseous mixture of deuterium and tritium is held at an average temperature of 5 KeV (approximately 50 million degrees Kelvin), ignition will occur once the product of particle density and the energy confinement time exceeds $3 \times 10^{20}\ m^{-3}s$, which is known as the Lawson criterion. At these high temperatures, the gaseous mixture is completely ionized—it is in the plasma state. To achieve these very high temperatures and maintain the plasma purity in a practical engineering system, the plasma must avoid any contact with physical materials. In a tokamak, the plasma containment is achieved with the aid of a complex system of magnetic fields, which form a "magnetic cage" around the plasma. The main component of the magnetic field is produced by the toroidal field coils, which are shown in Figure 12.4. This field, together with that produced by the plasma current, form the basis of the magnetic confinement system. In addition to the toroidal field coils there are poloidal and active control coils, which are used to shape and position the plasma. These coils may be seen in Figure 12.5.

The field produced by the plasma current "pinches" the plasma, thereby providing a force balance between the kinetic and magnetic pressures. It has been shown that by increasing the plasma current both the particle density and the plasma temperature can be increased. The drawback is the need for an associated increase in the toroidal field in order to maintain magnetohydrodynamic (MHD) stability. In order to increase the plasma current stably, for a fixed toroidal field, the plasma cross-section is deliberately elongated by the application of external quadrupole fields. Unfortunately, the shaping process gives rise to a vertical instability in the plasma's centroid position with a fast growth rate. The aim of our work is to design a control system that will regulate the voltage applied to the active control coils in such a way as to stabilize the elongated plasma's vertical position. This vertical position instability can be observed in the open-loop nonlinear simulations shown in Figure 12.6, which show the plasma drifting into the containment vessel wall.

12.3.1 The system model

In order to describe the vertical dynamics of the plasma, it was necessary to model the main electromagnetic features of the reactor. This task was accomplished by making a number of simplifying assumptions regarding the geometry of the magnetic part of the structure and ignoring μ and certain other aspects of the plasma's

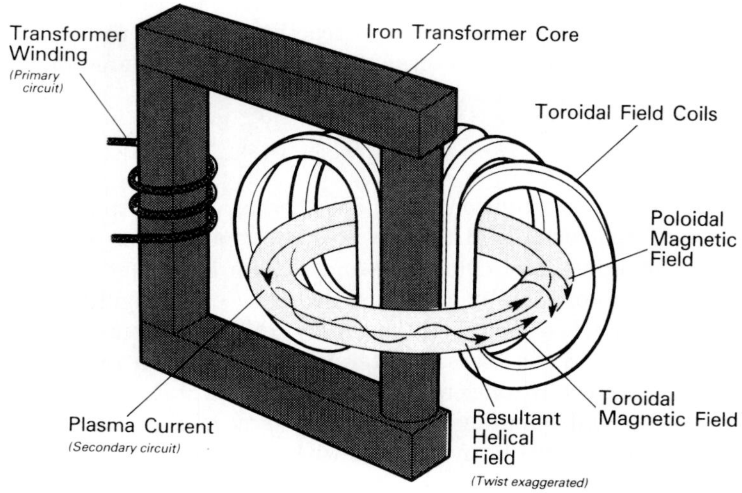

Figure 12.4: The magnetic confinement system of a toroidal fusion reactor.

behavior.[5] By linearizing a finite element model around various operating conditions, it was possible to obtain low-order, time-invariant, state-space models that describe the local vertical dynamics of the plasma. These models will be used only for design. A full nonlinear MHD model is used in all the controller simulation tests.

In the study we make use of two low-order models that map changes in the applied field control voltage to changes in the vertical component of the plasma position. The first is associated with a steady-state plasma current of 10 MA, while the second corresponds to a plasma current of 22 MA. The 10 MA model is given by

$$G_{10} \stackrel{s}{=} \left[\begin{array}{cccc|c} -7.1355e+00 & -3.9087e-01 & -5.0764e+00 & 0 & 8.2143e-02 \\ 3.9087e-01 & -3.5346e-01 & -3.4166e+01 & 0 & -2.2168e-03 \\ -5.0764e+00 & 3.4166e+01 & -8.6596e+01 & 0 & 2.9531e-02 \\ 0 & 0 & 0 & 9.8987e+00 & 8.6248e+02 \\ \hline -8.2143e-02 & -2.2168e-03 & -2.9531e-02 & 1.0400e-05 & 0 \end{array}\right]$$

[5] μ is the plasma viscosity.

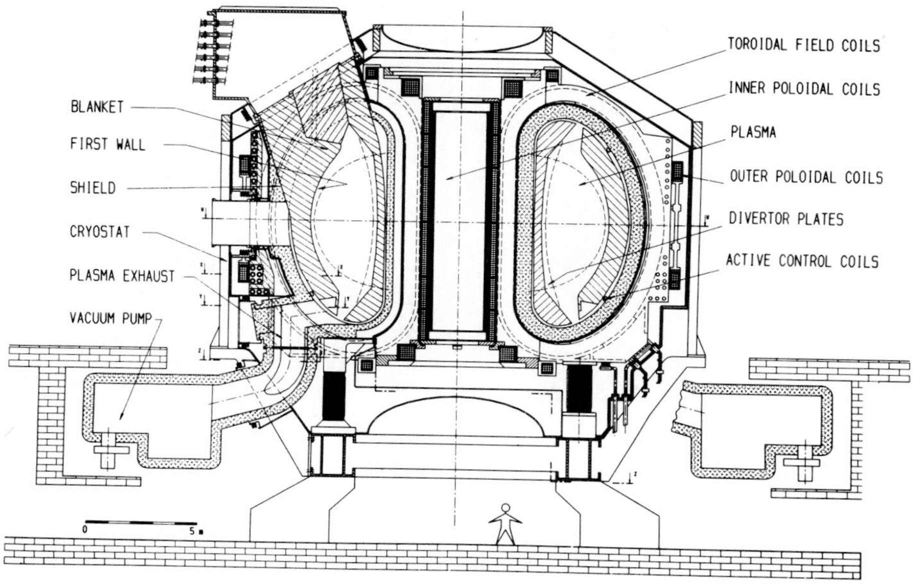

Figure 12.5: Cross-section of a large fusion reactor.

and the 22 MA model us given by

$$
G_{22} \stackrel{s}{=} \left[\begin{array}{cccc|c}
-7.7366e+00 & 6.6515e+00 & -7.8538e-01 & 0 & 5.7242e-02 \\
6.6515e+00 & -6.8347e+01 & 2.8251e+01 & 0 & -2.5144e-02 \\
7.8538e-01 & -2.8251e+01 & -2.0050e+00 & 0 & -2.8772e-03 \\
0 & 0 & 0 & 3.0762e+01 & 1.2588e+03 \\
\hline
-5.7242e-02 & 2.5144e-02 & -2.8772e-03 & 3.9832e-06 & 0
\end{array}\right].
$$

Since the $(4,4)$-entries of the A-matrices in the above models indicate the presence of a pole in the right-half plane, the vertical dynamics of the plasma are unstable. In addition, one can see that the instability growth rate increases with plasma current.

12.3.2 The design problem

Although the instability in the plasma's vertical position may be slowed down by surrounding the plasma with a set of damping coils, in much the same way that damping coils are used in electrical machines, the instability can only be removed completely with active control. The key objectives for such a control system are:

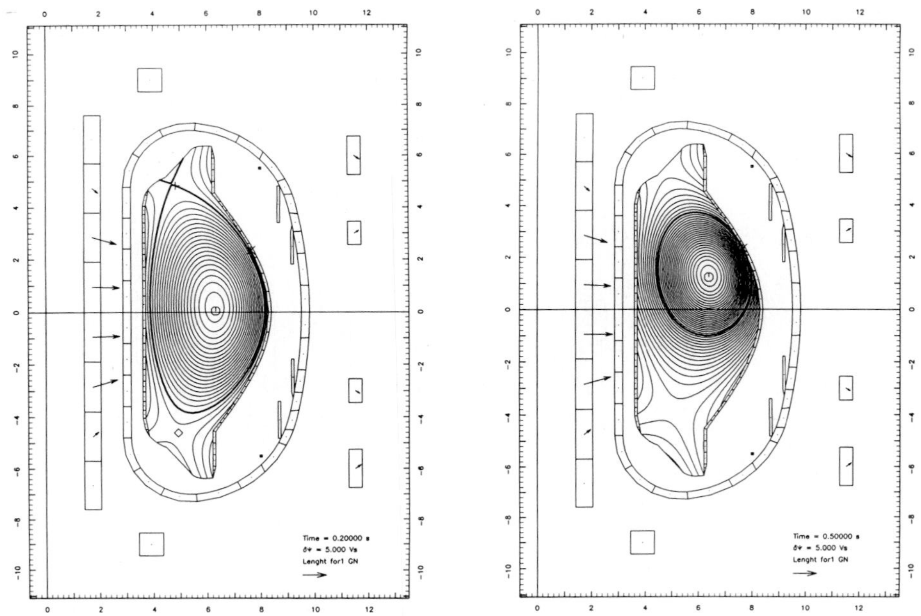

Figure 12.6: The evolution of the plasma shape after a small disturbance: (a) 0.2 s after the disturbance and (b) 0.5 s after the disturbance.

1. The robust stabilization of the plasma's vertical position.
2. The control voltage demand must not exceed $\pm\ 1\ kV$—these are the saturation limits of the power amplifiers driving the control coils.
3. The settling time should be no greater than 50 ms.
4. There should be a nonoscillatory return of the plasma to the reference equilibrium position.
5. There should be a high level of output disturbance attenuation.
6. There should be a high level of sensor error attenuation.

Because of the crude modelling of the plasma's vertical dynamics and the presence of unpredictable changes in the plasma's state during the machine's operation, robust stabilization is an important feature of the control system. Any loss of vertical control will terminate the tokamak discharge in a disruptive manner, which will induce severe electromagnetic and thermal loads on the containment structures.

Power amplifier saturation can lead to system instability and must therefore be considered, and if possible, prevented. The disturbance attenuation requirement stems from the need to reject time-varying error fields. Since it is impossible to measure the plasma position directly, there are "sensor disturbances" associated with any vertical position estimation procedure, and it is therefore important to guarantee good sensor error attenuation.

The control system design is based on the normalized coprime factor loop-shaping procedure introduced in Section 12.2.2.

12.3.3 Control system design

The aim of this section is to evaluate the control system design procedure presented in Section 12.2.2 on the tokamak plasma stabilization problem. We restrict our presentation to the results obtained for the 22 MA plasma model.

When selecting the loop-shaping (or weighting) function, our aim was to satisfy the six requirements listed in Section 12.3.2 and to find a controller with a high low-frequency gain and a low bandwidth. The loop-shaping function we selected to achieve these goals was

$$\boldsymbol{w} = \frac{6.4 \times 10^4(s+1)}{s(10^{-4}s+1)(2.5 \times 10^{-4}s+1)},$$

and Figure 12.7 gives the corresponding shaped and unshaped open-loop frequency responses.

The weighting function was selected by considering the low, intermediate and high ranges of frequency separately. Briefly,

1. The integrator in the weighting function increases the low-frequency gain.
2. The zero at -1 decreases the unity-gain roll-off rate. This roll-off rate reduction has a beneficial effect on the damping of the closed-loop response.
3. The poles at -4000 and -10^4 increase the controller's high-frequency roll-off rate.

This loop-shaping function gives $\gamma_{opt} = 2.1271$ for the normalized coprime factor robustness problem associated with $\boldsymbol{gw}$. Figure 12.8 gives a number of closed-loop frequency responses relevant to this design. The plot of $|(1-\boldsymbol{gk})^{-1}|$, shown in Figure 12.8 (a), highlights the effect of integral action on the sensitivity function. This weighting function results in very good low-frequency output disturbance attenuation. Figure 12.8 (b) shows $|(1-\boldsymbol{gk})^{-1}\boldsymbol{g}|$, from which one deduces that the closed loop is able to attenuate both low-frequency and high-frequency disturbances at the plant input. The low-frequency disturbance attenuation comes from the integral action while the high-frequency disturbance attenuation comes about due to the strictly proper nature of $\boldsymbol{gw}$. Figure 12.8 (c) shows the allowable additive plant uncertainty as given by $1/|\boldsymbol{k}(1-\boldsymbol{gk})^{-1}|$. For frequencies below 100 rad/s,

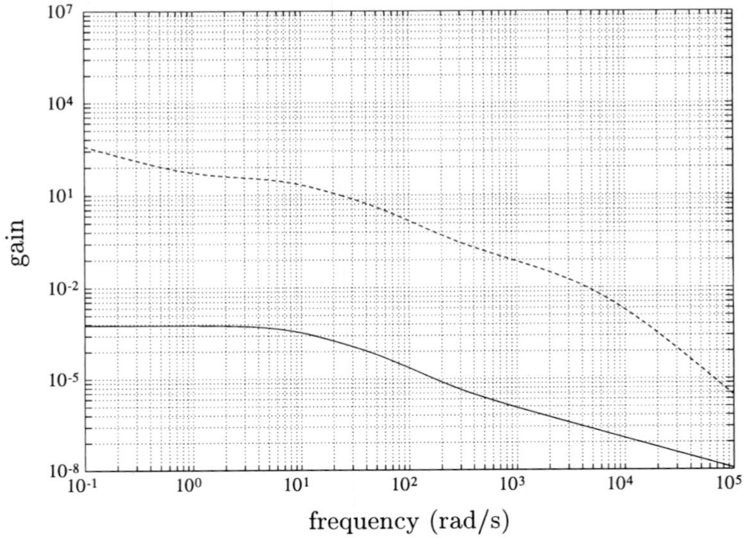

Figure 12.7: The unshaped (solid) and shaped (dashed) open-loop Bode magnitude for the 22 MA model.

the closed-loop system tolerates a level of additive uncertainty comparable to the magnitude of the plant. This is because $1/|\boldsymbol{k}(1-\boldsymbol{gk})^{-1}| \approx |\boldsymbol{g}|$ when $\boldsymbol{gk} \gg 1$. Figure 12.8 (d) shows $1/|\boldsymbol{gk}(1-\boldsymbol{gk})^{-1}|$, which has a robustness interpretation when the uncertainty is represented in a multiplicative form.

Preliminary simulation study

In order to assess the performance of this control system, it was tested by simulation in a full nonlinear MHD environment. Figure 12.9 shows the transient performance of the closed-loop system for an initial plasma displacement of 1 cm. The design specifications are met in that the closed-loop is stable, the plasma current centroid returns to its initial equilibrium position in about 50 ms and the maximum control voltage magnitude is approximately 1 kV. The system response shows a small overshoot with no oscillations.

12.3.4 Antiwindup scheme

The power amplifiers that drive the active coil can only produce voltages between ± 1 kV. If integral action is combined with such actuators, integrator windup may

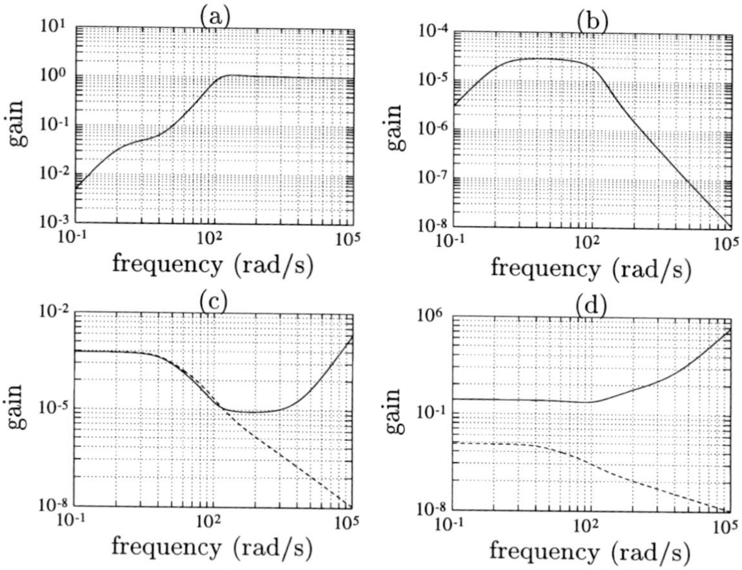

Figure 12.8: (a) The sensitivity function magnitude $|(1-\boldsymbol{gk})^{-1}|$. (b) The tolerance to plant input disturbance: $|(1-\boldsymbol{gk})^{-1}\boldsymbol{g}|$. (c) The robustness to additive uncertainty: $1/|\boldsymbol{k}(1-\boldsymbol{gk})^{-1}|$ (solid) and $|\boldsymbol{g}|$ (dashed). (d) The robustness to multiplicative uncertainty: $1/|\boldsymbol{gk}(1-\boldsymbol{gk})^{-1}|$ (solid) and $|\boldsymbol{g}|$ (dashed).

occur whenever the actuator saturates. In the event of large persistent commands, the integrator builds up a large output thereby forcing the actuator to remain saturated for an extended period of time.

In this section we consider the antiwindup scheme illustrated in Figure 12.10, which inhibits the unlimited growth of the controller output. The scheme consists of a feedback loop around the controller that is activated as soon as $u > u_{max}$ (or $< u_{min}$). If $u = u_c$, everything proceeds as normal in a linear manner. If u saturates at u_{max} (alternatively u_{min}), we see that

$$\begin{aligned} u_c &= \boldsymbol{k}\big(e - f(u_c - u_{max/min})\big) \\ &= (1+\boldsymbol{k}f)^{-1}\boldsymbol{k}(e + f u_{max/min}). \end{aligned}$$

By choosing a constant f such that $|f| \gg 1$ and $|f\boldsymbol{k}| \gg 1$, we get

$$\begin{aligned} u_c &\approx (f\boldsymbol{k})^{-1}\boldsymbol{k}(e + f u_{max/min}) \\ &\approx u_{max/min}. \end{aligned}$$

Thus, during saturation, u_c is clamped at $u_{max/min}$ and windup is prevented. The

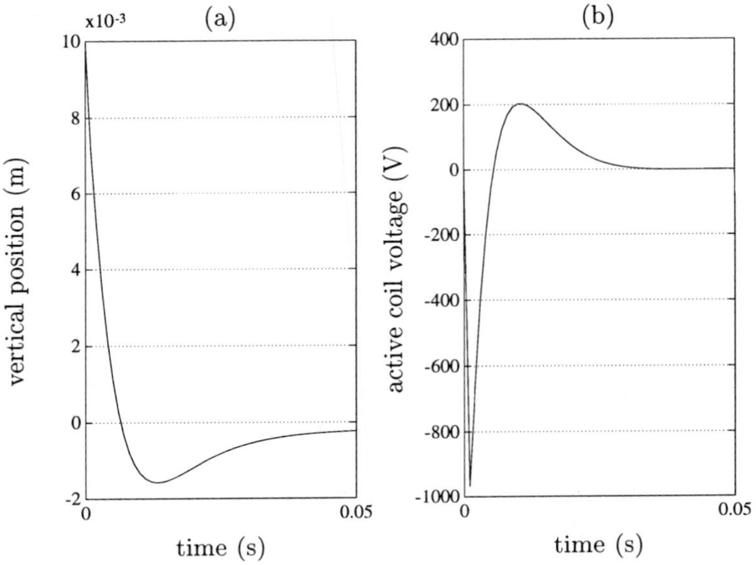

Figure 12.9: The transient performance with the robust coprime factor controller for the 22 MA model. (a) The plasma vertical position. (b) The active coil amplifier voltage.

controller will then come out of saturation as soon as e returns to normal levels.

Figures 12.11 (a) and (b) show the closed-loop performance of the 22 MA plasma for a 10 cm step change in the set-point position demand; both the antiwindup protected mode and the unprotected mode are illustrated. The initial responses of the protected and unprotected loops are similar, since the amplifier is only saturated at $+1$ kV for 10 ms. When the applied voltage switches to -1 kV, however, the antiwindup protected system goes into saturation for approximately 20 ms while the unprotected system applies -1 kV to the active coils for over 95 ms. The antiwindup compensator allows the protected system to come out of saturation a long time before its unprotected counterpart. As a result the plasma settles to its steady-state position in approximately 60 ms with very little overshoot. In contrast, the unprotected system overshoots by 150% and takes 160 ms to reach the 10 cm off-set position. The large overshoot associated with the unprotected controller causes the plasma to make contact with the shields that protect the vessel walls. Frequent contact between the protective shields and the plasma cannot be sustained, because impurities enter the plasma causing its temperature and current to drop, thereby inducing MHD instabilities. These instabilities result in the catastrophic collapse of the plasma current and large stresses are induced in the vessel superstructure. The

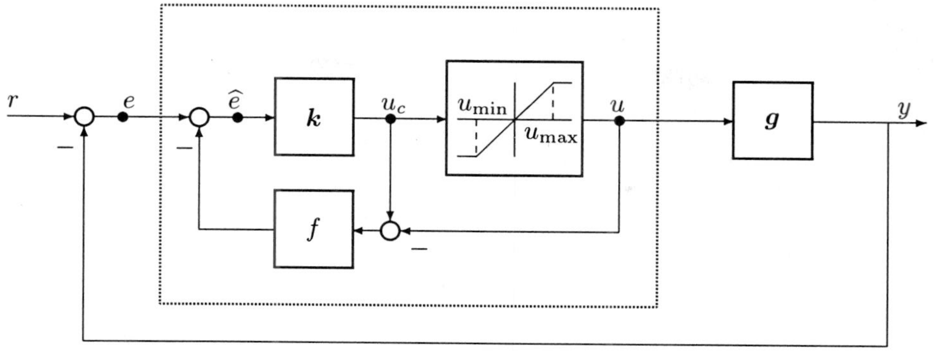

Figure 12.10: Antiwindup scheme for plant input saturation.

applied voltage evolution plots shown in Figure 12.11 (b) show that the protected and unprotected systems behave very differently after 10 ms. The control voltage in the protected system drops to -400 V after 50 ms, while the unprotected system continues to fluctuate for over 200 ms.

12.3.5 Bumpless transfer scheme

It is often the case that a nonlinear plant cannot be controlled by a single, linear controller, because the plant dynamics vary too widely during the operating duty cycle. Tokamaks are pulsed machines and their operating cycle is divided into a startup, a fuel burning phase and a shutdown phase. In order to obtain an adequate level of robust performance during the duty cycle, a controller scheduling scheme is required.

We consider the case of two controllers, $\boldsymbol{k}_1$ and $\boldsymbol{k}_2$, which were designed to meet the performance requirements at their respective operating points of 10 MA and 22 MA. Figure 12.12 shows the proposed bumpless transfer scheme. At the time instant being illustrated, $\boldsymbol{k}_1$ is operating in closed loop, while $\boldsymbol{k}_2$ is in open loop. From this diagram we see that

$$\begin{aligned} u_i &= \boldsymbol{k}_i\big(e - f_i(u_i - u)\big) \\ &= (1 + \boldsymbol{k}_i f_i)^{-1}\boldsymbol{k}_i(e + f_i u) \end{aligned}$$

and

$$\begin{aligned} \widehat{e}_i &= \boldsymbol{k}_i(e - f_i\widehat{e}_i) - u \\ &= (1 + \boldsymbol{k}_i f_i)^{-1}(\boldsymbol{k}_i e - u). \end{aligned}$$

If we choose the constant f_i's so that $|f_i| \gg 1$ and $|f_i\boldsymbol{k}_i| \gg 1$, we obtain $\widehat{e}_i \approx 0$. This means that $u_i \approx u$ and a bumpless transfer is possible. Once the switch is

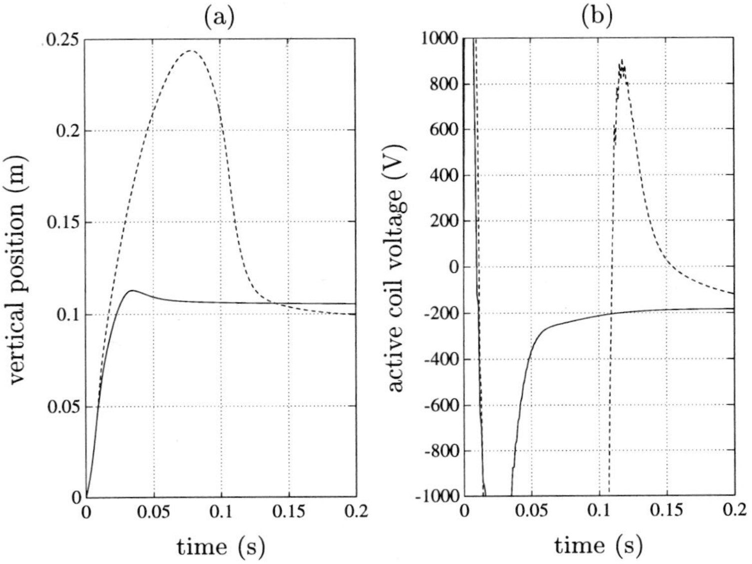

Figure 12.11: The transient performance with the robust coprime factor controller for the rigid displacement model in wind-up protected mode (solid) and unprotected mode: (dashed). (a) Plasma vertical position. (b) Active coil amplifier voltage.

toggled, $\boldsymbol{k}_1$ and $\boldsymbol{k}_2$ exchange roles. Under the new regime, controller $\boldsymbol{k}_1$ operates in open loop while controller $\boldsymbol{k}_2$ operates in closed loop. After the controller transfer, f_1, because of its high gain, acts rapidly to take $\widehat{e}_1$ to zero so that $u_1 \approx u$, thereby facilitating a second bumpless transfer if one is required. After reflection, we see that an antiwindup feature is obtained for free and that the scheme can be extended to any number of controllers. The bumpless transfer scheme suggested above was implemented as part of the tokamak position control system.

12.3.6 Simulations

The performance of the control system was evaluated by conducting simulation studies using a nonlinear MHD simulation code. This section presents some of the results of two of these studies.

Disturbance attenuation and bumpless transfer

In the first simulation, we wanted to check the disturbance attenuation properties of the control system and test the bumpless transfer scheme. The bumpless transfer

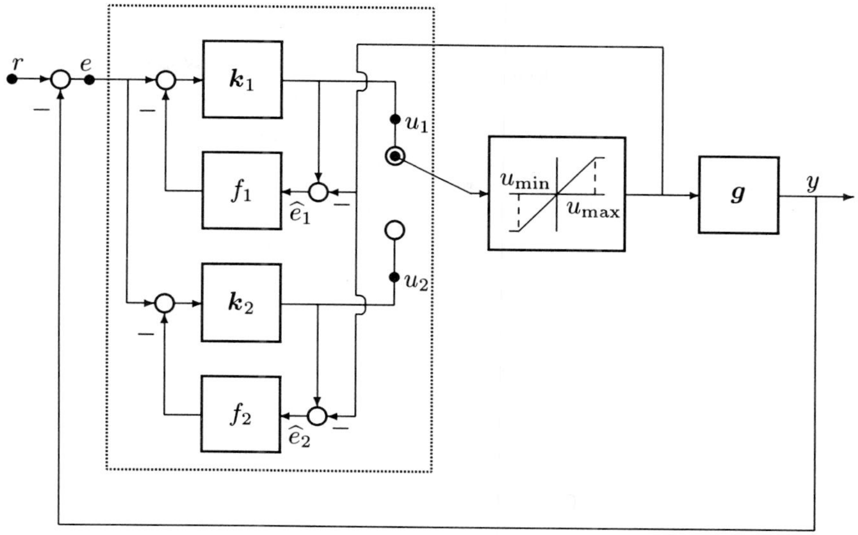

Figure 12.12: Controller bumpless transfer scheme with anti windup protection.

scheme is required during the start-up phase of the tokamak, during which the plasma current increases and the plasma is elongated. Although the start-up phase of the tokamak has a duration of 90 s, we will only examine certain subintervals of this period that are of particular interest to us.

For this study, the plasma current is 12 MA 20 s into the start-up phase and it is ramped linearly to 12.54 MA at 20.5 s. During this period the plasma changes from being only slightly elongated to being strongly elongated. During this time, a 10 Hz sinusoidally-varying, radial error magnetic field located near the vessel wall was used to disturb the plasma's position. The peak value of this disturbance field at the plasma center was 1.5×10^{-3} T. The plasma set-point was fixed at zero, which denotes the center of the containment vessel. The results of the simulation are shown in Figure 12.13.

The 10 MA controller $\boldsymbol{k}_1$ remains in the feedback loop until 20.3 s at which time the 22 MA controller $\boldsymbol{k}_2$ is brought into service—there is no visible evidence of a "bumpy" transfer. The spikes in the plasma position (and the control action), visible at 20.24 s, are the result of the poor computation of the plasma current distribution during this phase of the plasma evolution.

Since the source of the error field is located near the vessel wall, and since the plasma moves away from the wall as it elongates, the error field at the plasma center decreases with the increase in plasma current. The decreasing influence of the error field is clearly visible in Figure 12.13. As a final observation, we see that the outputs of the two controllers track each other closely over the entire simulation interval.

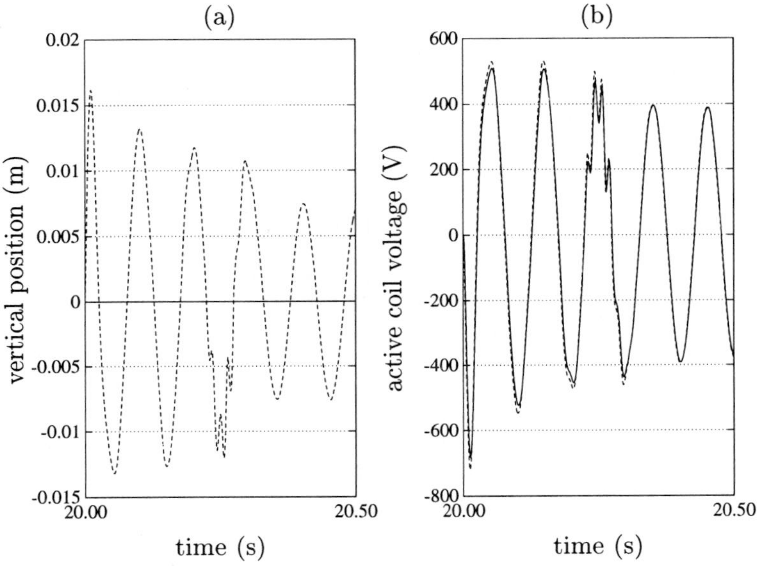

Figure 12.13: The rejection of a sinusoidal error field during the plasma ramp up phase: (a) Plasma centroid position (dashed). (b) Requested active coil voltages for the 22 MA controller (dashed) and for the 10 MA controller (solid).

Reference tracking and bumpless transfer

The aim of the second simulation is to check the reference tracking properties of the control system. In this case, the current is ramped linearly from 12 MA at 20 s to 12.54 MA at 20.1 s, it is then held constant at this value. There is no error field present. The plasma position reference is a 10 Hz sinusoid with a peak value of 1 cm—the plasma is required to move ± 1 cm around the machine's central plane. The results of this trial are shown in Figure 12.14. Since the plasma reaches its maximum elongation at 20.1 s, at which time it moves away from the vessel wall, we selected this moment for the controller interchange. The transfer "bump" is only just visible. Although both controllers track the reference well, $\boldsymbol{k}_2$ has a slightly superior performance. As we can see from Figure 12.14 (b), the second controller is using a marginally lower amplitude control signal as compared to the first. This is probably due to changes in the plant dynamics, rather than the superiority of the second controller design.

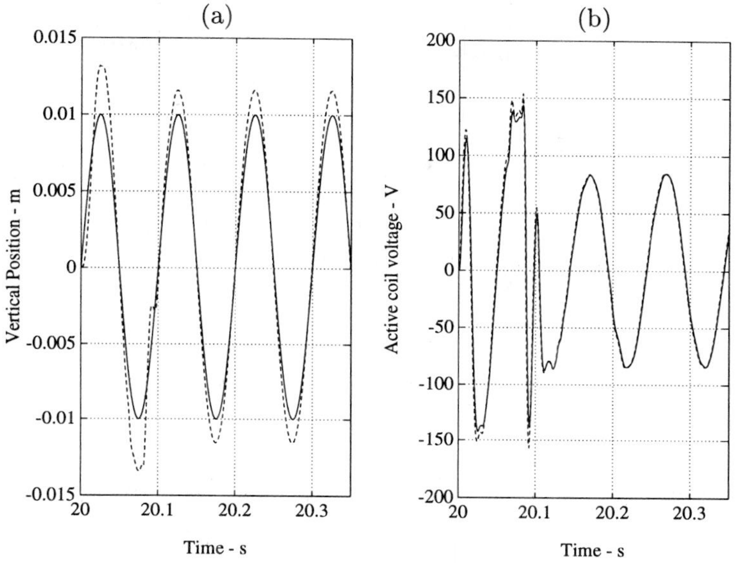

Figure 12.14: Tracking a sinusoidal set-point change during the plasma current ramp-up phase: (a) Plasma centroid position (dashed), set point change (solid). (b) Requested active coil voltages for the 22 MA controller (dashed), for the 10 MA controller (solid).

12.4 High-purity distillation

This case study is concerned with the design of a two-degree-of-freedom (TDF) product-composition controller for a high-purity distillation column. The $\mathcal{H}_\infty$ optimization problem is set up to ensure a guaranteed level of robust stability, robust disturbance attenuation and robust reference tracking performance.

Distillation is an important process in the separation and purification of chemicals that exploits the difference in the boiling points of multicomponent liquids. A typical distillation column is shown in Figure 12.15. Unfortunately, the control of distillation columns is difficult, because the distillation process is highly nonlinear and the associated linearized models are often ill-conditioned with respect to directional gain. The ill-conditioning is especially pronounced around the operating point with which we will be concerned.

The prototypical distillation column contains a series of trays that are located along its length. The liquid in the column flows over the trays from top to bottom, while the vapor in the column rises from bottom to top. The constant contact between the vapor and liquid facilitates a mass transfer between the phases. This

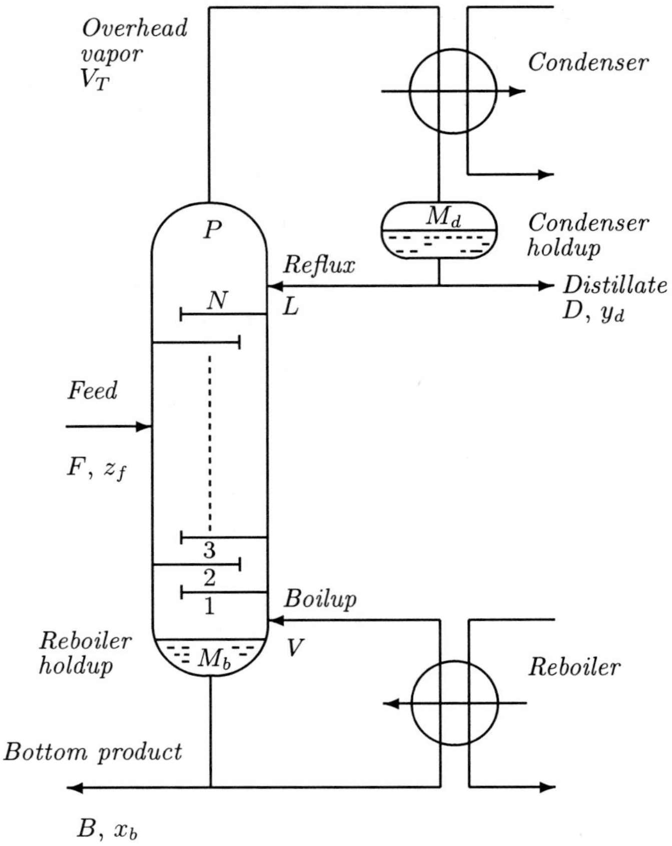

Figure 12.15: The distillation column system.

interchange has the effect of increasing the concentration of the more volatile component in the vapor, while simultaneously increasing the concentration of the less volatile component in the liquid.

The raw material enters the column at a flow rate of F *kmol/min* and with composition z_f. The top product, the distillate, is condensed and removed at a flow rate of D *kmol/min* and with composition y_d. The bottom product, "the bottoms", is removed as a liquid at a flow rate of B *kmol/min* and with composition x_b. The operation of the column requires that some of the bottoms is reboiled at a rate of V *kmol/min* to ensure the continuity of the vapor flow. In the same way, some of the distillate is refluxed to the top tray at a rate of L *kmol/min* to ensure the continuity of the liquid flow.

12.4.1 Design specification

The column operating point used for this design study is case 1 of operating point A in Morari and Zafiriou [151], page 440. The operating conditions are summarized in Table 12.1, while the column data can be found on pages 462-463 of [151]. A hydraulic time constant of $\tau_l = 0.063\ min$ was used and it was assumed that the feed was saturated liquid ($q_f = 1.0$).

Flows (kmol/minute)	Compositions
$F = 1$	$y_d = 0.99$
$L = 2.7063$	$x_b = 0.01$
$V = 3.2063$	$z_f = 0.5$
$D = 0.5$	
$B = 0.5$	

Table 12.1: Column operating conditions.

The specifications for the control system design are as follows:

1. Disturbances of ±30% in the feed flow rate F, and changes of ±0.05 in the feed composition z_f, should be rejected to within 10% of steady-state within 30 minutes.

2. For all product compositions, where a change is demanded, the composition should be within ±10% of the desired final value within 30 minutes.

3. The design should allow for a worst-case time delay of one minute on the control action and for ±20% uncertainty in the actuator gains.

4. The final steady-state values of all variables should be within 1% of their desired values.

5. For product compositions where no change is demanded, deviations of less than 5×10^{-3} in y_d and 10^{-3} in x_b are required.

6. Variations in the manipulated variables should be less than ±50% of their nominal values. In addition, the control action should not be oscillatory.

7. The above specifications should be satisfied for both the linear and nonlinear models.

12.4.2 The system model

All the simulation results were obtained using an 82-state nonlinear model which includes the liquid dynamics. There are two states per tray, one which represents the liquid composition and one which represents the liquid holdup. The nonlinear model was linearized about the operating point given in Table 12.1 and reduced from 82nd order to 8th order.

The manipulated variables are the reflux flow L and the vapor boilup V. Since the holdup dynamics are fast, it is possible to implement two single-input-single-output proportional controllers for level control. This facilitates the design of a multivariable controller for the product compositions, which is independent of the level controllers.

The plant model can be split into two 2-input 2-output sections. The first part $\boldsymbol{G}_c$ represents the transfer function matrix mapping the manipulated inputs u_c to the output y, while the second part $\boldsymbol{G}_d$ represents the transfer function matrix mapping the disturbances u_d to the output y. This gives

$$\dot{x} = Ax + \begin{bmatrix} B_c & B_d \end{bmatrix} \begin{bmatrix} u_c \\ u_d \end{bmatrix}$$

and

$$y = Cx + \begin{bmatrix} D_c & D_d \end{bmatrix} \begin{bmatrix} u_c \\ u_d \end{bmatrix},$$

in which

$$u_c = \begin{bmatrix} L \\ V \end{bmatrix}; \qquad u_d = \begin{bmatrix} F \\ z_f \end{bmatrix}; \qquad y = \begin{bmatrix} y_d \\ x_b \end{bmatrix}.$$

Thus

$$\boldsymbol{G}_c \stackrel{s}{=} \left[\begin{array}{c|c} A & B_c \\ \hline C & D_c \end{array}\right]$$

and

$$\boldsymbol{G}_d \stackrel{s}{=} \left[\begin{array}{c|c} A & B_d \\ \hline C & D_d \end{array}\right].$$

The reduced order linear models of $\boldsymbol{G}_c$ and $\boldsymbol{G}_d$ are:

$$A = \begin{bmatrix} 4.0417 & -7.9022 & 6.2980 & -20.3317 & -11.8555 & -37.2006 & -9.8382 & -40.7807 \\ 3.8444 & -5.5722 & 2.9794 & -16.0011 & -5.2481 & -12.0674 & 4.8702 & -21.8897 \\ 0.0000 & 0.0000 & -0.3636 & -4.6970 & 3.6110 & -1.6446 & -6.1630 & 5.1258 \\ 0.0000 & 0.0000 & 0.3156 & -1.2008 & -0.0371 & -2.3575 & -0.9795 & -2.1296 \\ 0.0000 & 0.0000 & 0.0000 & 0.0000 & -0.4216 & -3.1276 & -0.7429 & -0.8648 \\ 0.0000 & 0.0000 & 0.0000 & 0.0000 & 0.0105 & -0.1349 & -0.0409 & -0.2360 \\ 0.0000 & 0.0000 & 0.0000 & 0.0000 & 0.0000 & 0.0000 & -0.0817 & 0.1399 \\ 0.0000 & 0.0000 & 0.0000 & 0.0000 & 0.0000 & 0.0000 & 0.0000 & -0.0052 \end{bmatrix}$$

$$\begin{bmatrix} B_c & B_d \end{bmatrix} = \begin{bmatrix} 53.1999 & 9.1346 & -70.9407 & -37.7852 \\ 24.2212 & 1.6750 & -75.0731 & 21.0103 \\ -55.4147 & -6.4358 & -14.5560 & -18.3519 \\ -7.6347 & -1.2712 & -7.3427 & -9.6092 \\ 6.3548 & -0.7513 & 0.1240 & -14.1825 \\ 0.0405 & -0.1135 & 0.0416 & -1.9818 \\ 0.0398 & -0.2678 & 1.2365 & 0.2129 \\ -0.0219 & 0.0218 & -0.0110 & -0.0232 \end{bmatrix}$$

$$C = \begin{bmatrix} 0.0000 & 0.0000 & 0.0000 & 0.0000 & -0.0001 & 0.0026 & -0.0021 & -0.1967 \\ -0.0001 & 0.0000 & -0.0002 & 0.0013 & -0.0004 & 0.0039 & 0.0045 & -0.2564 \end{bmatrix}$$

$$\begin{bmatrix} D_c & D_d \end{bmatrix} = \begin{bmatrix} 0 & 0 & 0 & 0 \\ 0 & 0 & 0 & 0 \end{bmatrix}.$$

According to the design specification, the design must cater for a worst case time delay of 1 *min* on the plant input. This is incorporated into the nominal linear model via a first-order Padé approximation—this is the model we will use for design. The time delays are incorporated into the simulation model using a sixth-order Padé approximation. The design model has the actuator gains set to unity, while the simulation model will allow the actuator gains to vary. The design model is therefore

$$\boldsymbol{G}_{nc} = \boldsymbol{G}_c \begin{bmatrix} \left(\frac{1-sT/2}{1+sT/2}\right) & 0 \\ 0 & \left(\frac{1-sT/2}{1+sT/2}\right) \end{bmatrix},$$

while $\boldsymbol{G}_d$ remains unchanged.

12.4.3 Two-degree-of-freedom controller design

Since this problem has demanding time-response specifications, we make use of a two-degree-of-freedom (TDF) controller structure that can be designed within the generalized regulator framework. An alternative TDF design procedure involves the separate optimization of the prefilter and feedback controller, but requires the parameterization theory for all TDF controllers. The interested reader will find several references to this material in the notes at the end of the chapter. A distillation column design, which makes full use of TDF control, is covered in one of the cited papers.

The optimization problem

The configuration we will study is give in Figure 12.16, in which

$$\boldsymbol{M}^{-1} \begin{bmatrix} \boldsymbol{N}_c & \boldsymbol{N}_d \end{bmatrix} = \begin{bmatrix} \boldsymbol{G}_{nc}\boldsymbol{W}_c & \boldsymbol{G}_d\boldsymbol{W}_d \end{bmatrix},$$

such that $\boldsymbol{M}^{-1}\boldsymbol{N}_c$ is a normalized left coprime factorization. The model set we consider is therefore

$$\mathcal{G}_{\hat{\gamma}} = \left\{ (\boldsymbol{M} - \boldsymbol{\Delta}_M)^{-1}(\boldsymbol{N}_c + \boldsymbol{\Delta}_N) : \begin{array}{l} \begin{bmatrix} \boldsymbol{\Delta}_N & \boldsymbol{\Delta}_M \end{bmatrix} \in \mathcal{H}_\infty, \\ \| \begin{bmatrix} \boldsymbol{\Delta}_N & \boldsymbol{\Delta}_M \end{bmatrix} \|_\infty < \hat{\gamma}^{-1} \end{array} \right\}.$$

It is not difficult to modify the design to allow for perturbations to $\boldsymbol{N}_d$, but we have not done this in the interests of simplifying the presentation. The weight $\boldsymbol{W}_c$ is used to shape the loop, while $\boldsymbol{W}_d$ contains spectral information about expected disturbances. The scaling factor ρ is used to weight the relative importance of robust stability as compared to robust model matching and robust disturbance rejection.

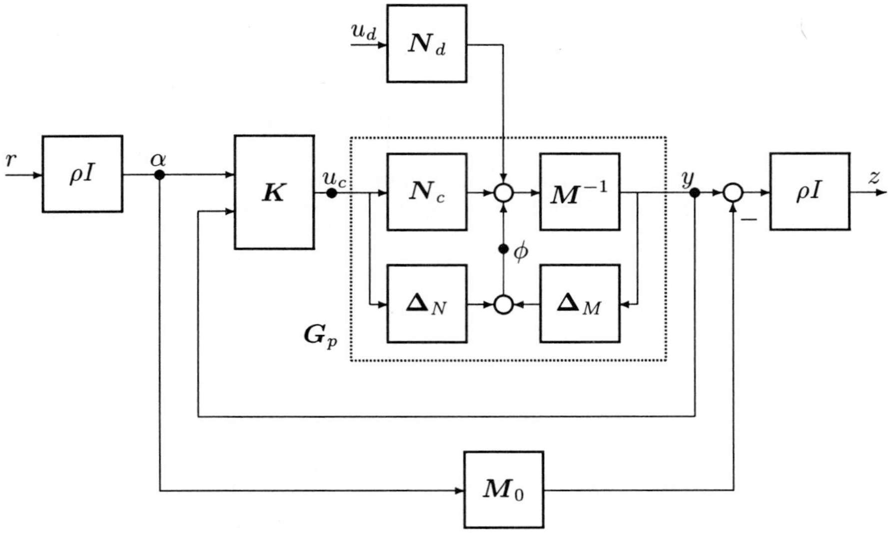

Figure 12.16: The design problem configuration.

It follows from Figure 12.16 that the closed-loop system of interest is described by the linear fractional transformation

$$\left[\begin{array}{c} z \\ y \\ u_c \\ \hline \alpha \\ y \end{array}\right] = \left[\begin{array}{ccc|c} -\rho^2 \boldsymbol{M}_0 & \rho \boldsymbol{G}_d \boldsymbol{W}_d & \rho \boldsymbol{M}^{-1} & \rho \boldsymbol{G}_{nc} \boldsymbol{W}_c \\ 0 & \boldsymbol{G}_d \boldsymbol{W}_d & \boldsymbol{M}^{-1} & \boldsymbol{G}_{nc} \boldsymbol{W}_c \\ 0 & 0 & 0 & I \\ \hline \rho I & 0 & 0 & 0 \\ 0 & \boldsymbol{G}_d \boldsymbol{W}_d & \boldsymbol{M}^{-1} & \boldsymbol{G}_{nc} \boldsymbol{W}_c \end{array}\right] \left[\begin{array}{c} r \\ u_d \\ \phi \\ \hline u_c \end{array}\right]$$

$$u_c = \left[\begin{array}{cc} \boldsymbol{K}_1 & \boldsymbol{K}_2 \end{array}\right] \left[\begin{array}{c} \alpha \\ y \end{array}\right],$$

which we denote by $\boldsymbol{R}$.[6] We are required to find an internally-stabilizing controller such that $\|\boldsymbol{R}\|_\infty \leq \hat{\gamma}$. This is a generalized regulator problem, which may be solved using the theory of Chapter 8. Commercial implementations of this theory are available in the Robust Control Toolbox for MATLAB and other software packages.[7]

Solving the loop equations shows that the closed-loop transfer function matrix $\boldsymbol{R}$ is given by

$$\left[\begin{array}{c} z \\ y \\ u_c \end{array}\right] = \left[\begin{array}{ccc} \rho^2(\boldsymbol{S}\boldsymbol{G}_p\boldsymbol{K}_1 - \boldsymbol{M}_0) & \rho \boldsymbol{S}\boldsymbol{G}_d\boldsymbol{W}_d & \rho \boldsymbol{S}\boldsymbol{M}^{-1} \\ \rho \boldsymbol{S}\boldsymbol{G}_p\boldsymbol{K}_1 & \boldsymbol{S}\boldsymbol{G}_d\boldsymbol{W}_d & \boldsymbol{S}\boldsymbol{M}^{-1} \\ \rho \tilde{\boldsymbol{S}}\boldsymbol{K}_1 & \boldsymbol{K}_2\boldsymbol{S}\boldsymbol{G}_d\boldsymbol{W}_d & \boldsymbol{K}_2\boldsymbol{S}\boldsymbol{M}^{-1} \end{array}\right] \left[\begin{array}{c} r \\ u_d \\ \phi \end{array}\right],$$

[6]The disturbance "model" $\boldsymbol{W}_d$ and the loop-shaping weight $\boldsymbol{W}_c$ are not shown in Figure 12.16.

[7]MATLAB is a registered trademark of The MathWorks, Inc.

in which $\boldsymbol{S} = (I - \boldsymbol{G}_p\boldsymbol{K}_2)^{-1}$ is the sensitivity operator and $\tilde{\boldsymbol{S}} = (I - \boldsymbol{K}_2\boldsymbol{G}_p)^{-1}$. Therefore, once a controller such that $\|\boldsymbol{R}\|_\infty \leq \hat{\gamma}$ has been found, we see that:

1. The loop will remain stable for all $\boldsymbol{G} \in \mathcal{G}_{\hat{\gamma}}$. This follows from the $(2,3)$ and $(3,3)$-blocks of $\boldsymbol{R}$, $\|\boldsymbol{R}\|_\infty \leq \hat{\gamma}$ and the small gain theorem (see equation (12.2.5)).

2. By considering the linear fractional transformation $\mathcal{F}_\ell(\boldsymbol{R}, \left[\begin{array}{cc} \boldsymbol{\Delta}_M & \boldsymbol{\Delta}_N \end{array}\right])$, we conclude from Theorem 4.3.2 that $\|\boldsymbol{S}\boldsymbol{G}_p\boldsymbol{K}_1 - \boldsymbol{M}_0\|_\infty \leq \hat{\gamma}\rho^{-2}$ for all $\boldsymbol{G}_p \in \mathcal{G}_{\hat{\gamma}}$. This is a guaranteed robust performance property.

3. In the same way, $\|\boldsymbol{S}\boldsymbol{G}_d\boldsymbol{W}_d\|_\infty \leq \hat{\gamma}$ for all $\boldsymbol{G}_p \in \mathcal{G}_{\hat{\gamma}}$. This is the robust disturbance attenuation property.

4. If ρ is set to zero, the TDF problem reduces to the normalized coprime factor robust stability problem of Section 12.2.

A prescriptive design procedure

The purpose of this section is to describe an extension to the loop-shaping design procedure given in Section 12.2.2. This extension gives one way of optimizing the TDF controller, although many others are possible. Each of the seven steps refer to the configuration given in Figure 12.16.

1. Select a loop-shaping weight $\boldsymbol{W}_c$ for $\boldsymbol{G}_{nc}$. As with the earlier procedure, $\boldsymbol{W}_c$ is used to meet some of the closed-loop performance specifications.

2. Find the minimal value γ_{opt} in the pure robust stabilization problem of Section 12.2; this may be calculated using equation (12.2.8). A high value of γ_{opt} indicates that the specified loop shapes are inconsistent with robust stability requirements and that the feedback controller will significantly alter the loop shapes. In this case they should be adjusted via a revised $\boldsymbol{W}_c$.

3. Select the weighting function $\boldsymbol{W}_d$. This is used to shape the closed-loop disturbance rejection transfer functions.

4. Select a simple target model, $\boldsymbol{M}_0$, for the closed-loop system. This is usually a diagonal matrix of first- or second-order lags that represent desired closed-loop, time-domain command response properties. As with any other weight selection, the target model must be realistic, or the resulting closed-loop system will have poor robust stability properties and the controller will produce excessive control action.

5. Select a ρ value for the TDF configuration in Figure 12.16. In our experience, one obtains good results on process control problems when ρ is in the range $0.8 \leq \rho \leq 2$.

6. Find the optimal value of $\hat{\gamma}$. In distillation applications we found that $1.2 \times \gamma_{opt} \leq \hat{\gamma} \leq 3 \times \gamma_{opt}$ gave a good compromise between the robust stability and robust performance objectives.

7. Calculate the optimal controller, post-multiply it by $\boldsymbol{W}_c$, and rescale the prefilter to achieve perfect steady-state model matching. To do this, make the substitution $\boldsymbol{K}_1 \to \boldsymbol{K}_1 S$ where S is a scaling matrix defined by $S = \boldsymbol{R}_{y\alpha}^{-1}(0)\boldsymbol{M}_0(0)$. We have observed that this re-scaling tends to produce better model matching at all frequencies, because the $\mathcal{H}_\infty$ optimization process gives $\boldsymbol{R}_{y\alpha}$ roughly the same frequency response as the model $\boldsymbol{M}_0$. The final controller degree will be bounded above by $\deg(\boldsymbol{G}_{nc}) + \deg(\boldsymbol{W}_d) + \deg(\boldsymbol{M}_0) + 2 \times \deg(\boldsymbol{W}_c)$.

12.4.4 Design weight selection

We are now ready to use the design procedure described in Section 12.4.3 to design the product-composition controller. We remind the reader that in the design model the uncertain input time delays were set to unity and modeled using first-order Padé approximations. The uncertain actuator gains were also set to unity. In contrast, the nonlinear simulation model allowed variable actuator gains and the delays were represented by more accurate sixth-order Padé approximations.

Following the prescriptive design method, the loop-shaping weight was selected to meet the robust stability and robust performance specification given in Section 12.4.1. After several design iterations we decided on

$$\boldsymbol{W}_c = \frac{40(s+1)}{s(s+0.1)} I_2. \tag{12.4.1}$$

The integral action ensures zero steady-state error, and the pole at -0.1 ensures a low controller bandwidth and restricts the control demand level. The zero at -1 is used to reduce the roll-off rate to approximately 20 dB/dec in the unity gain range of frequencies. This has a beneficial effect on the closed-loop command and disturbance rejection response. Note that $\boldsymbol{W}_c$ is well-conditioned—ill-conditioned compensators for ill-conditioned plants can give very poor robustness properties at certain points in the loop. This is because some of the closed-loop transfer functions can have a very high condition number in these cases (see Example 2.1.1). The shaped and unshaped singular value plots are given in Figure 12.17. The loop-shaping function in (12.4.1) gives $\gamma_{opt} = 6.9610$ for the pure robustness problem associated with $\boldsymbol{G}_{nc}$.

The disturbance weighting function $\boldsymbol{W}_d$ was chosen to be the identity matrix and the time-response model we selected was

$$\boldsymbol{M}_0 = \frac{0.12}{s+0.12} I_2,$$

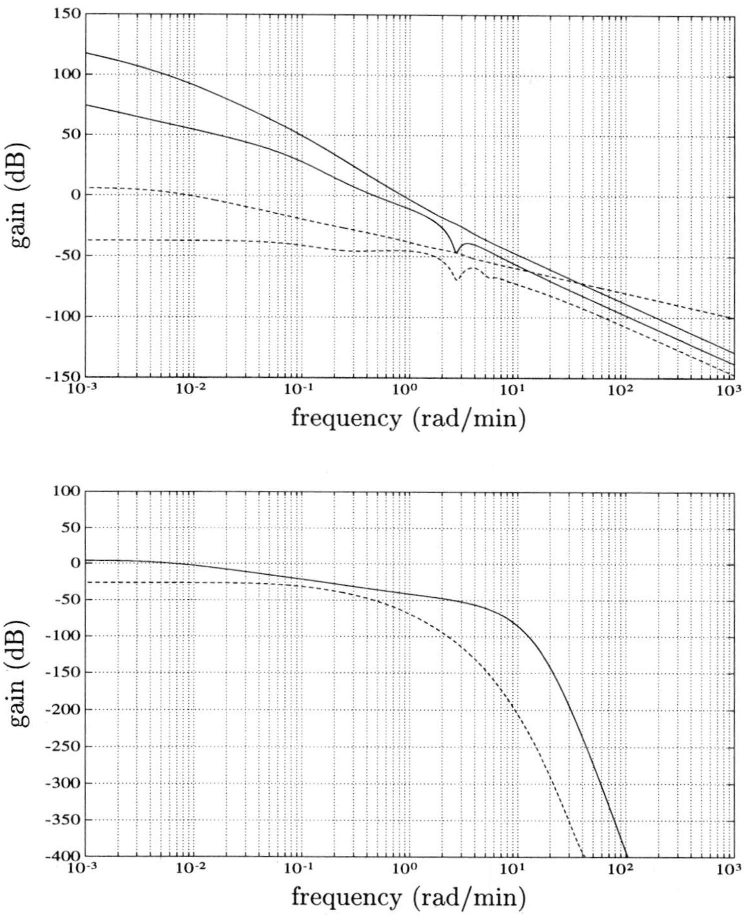

Figure 12.17: Top: the singular value plots of $\boldsymbol{G}_{nc}\boldsymbol{W}$ (solid) and $\boldsymbol{G}_c$ (dashed). Bottom: the singular value plots of $\boldsymbol{G}_d$.

which is fast enough to meet the time-domain specification while still being realistic.

All that remains is for us to obtain an acceptable value of ρ. We discovered that $\rho = 1.0$ gave a good compromise between acceptable stability, disturbance attenuation and time-domain performance requirements. This leads to $\hat{\gamma}_{opt} = 8.4657$ for the lowest achievable infinity norm for the optimization problem described in Section 12.4.3. Figures 12.18 show the Bode magnitude plots for the controller; both the prefilter and the feedback part of the controller have an acceptably low bandwidth.

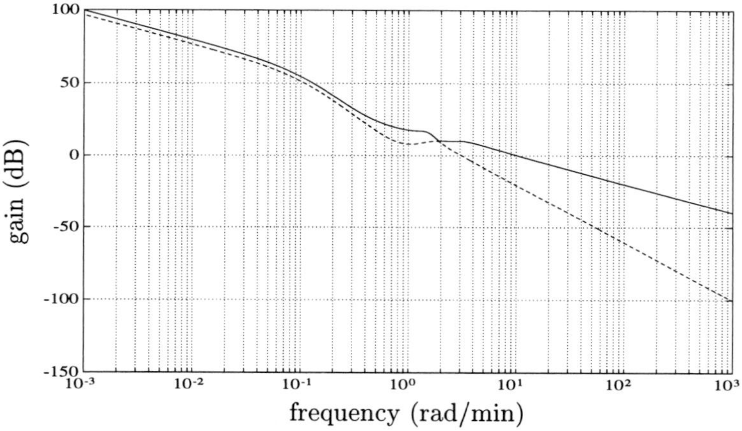

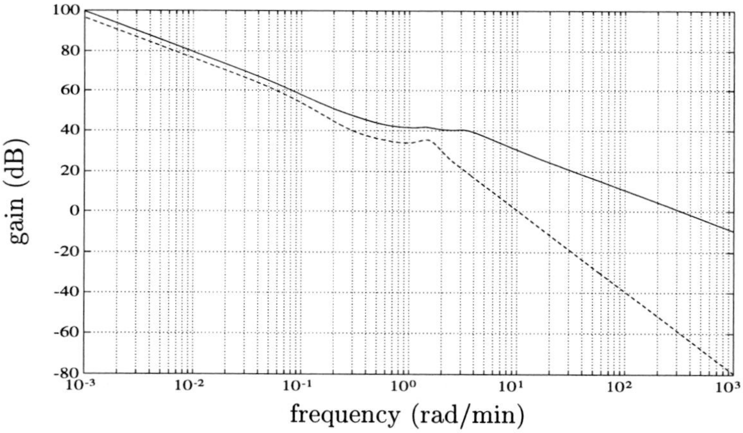

Figure 12.18: Top: the singular values of the prefilter. Bottom: the singular values of the feedback part of the controller.

12.4.5 Simulation results

The remainder of this section is concerned with the presentation of various simulation results. These were all calculated using the 82 state nonlinear simulation model with the input delays, τ_1 and τ_2, represented by sixth order Padé approximations. We set $\tau_1 = \tau_2 = 1\ min$ throughout, while checking the following five combinations of actuator gains: $k_1 = k_2 = 1.0$; $k_1 = k_2 = 1.2$; $k_1 = k_2 = 0.8$; $k_1 = 0.8$ and $k_2 = 1.2$; and $k_1 = 1.2$ and $k_2 = 0.8$.

Figure 12.19 gives the response to a step change in the distillate composition demand. The reference value of y_d was changed from 0.990 to 0.995. Although such a demand change is not common in practice, this simulation does provide a good way of testing the closed-loop response.

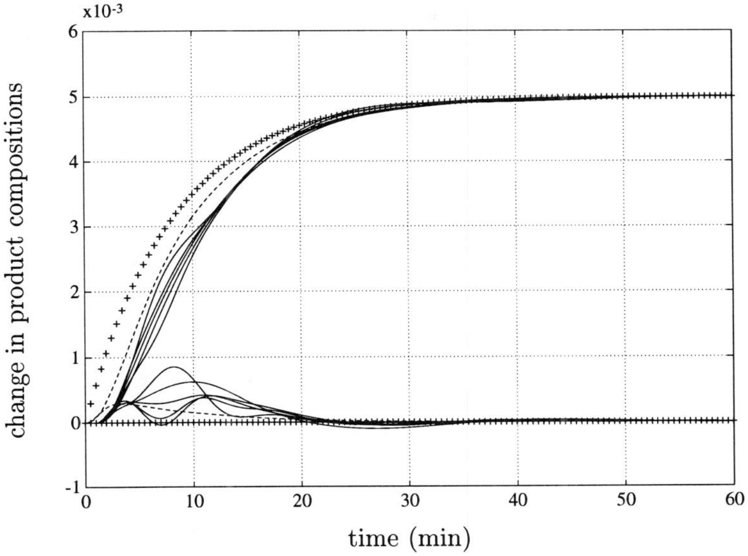

Figure 12.19: Response to a step change in the distillate composition demand: reference model (+++); nominal linear model (dashed); nonlinear results for the five combinations of actuator gains (solid).

Figure 12.20 gives the response to a step change in the bottoms composition demand. The reference value of x_b was changed from 0.0100 to 0.0095.

Figure 12.21 illustrates the response of the column to a step change in the feed flow rate from 1.0 $kmol/min$ to 1.3 $kmol/min$, which provides a convenient way of checking the controller design under extreme operating conditions.

Our last simulation result, which is given in Figure 12.22, shows the response of the closed loop to a step change in the feed-stream composition.

The responses given in Figures 12.19 and 12.20 show that the closed-loop system has a response which is close to that of the reference model response. The closed-loop disturbance attenuation properties are also very good—each disturbance is attenuated to within $\pm 10\%$ within the required 30 minutes. Each response shows a zero steady-state offset and indicates that the robust stability, robust disturbance attenuation and robust performance specifications are met for the entire range of uncertain actuator gains and the worst-case time delay. In addition, the controller

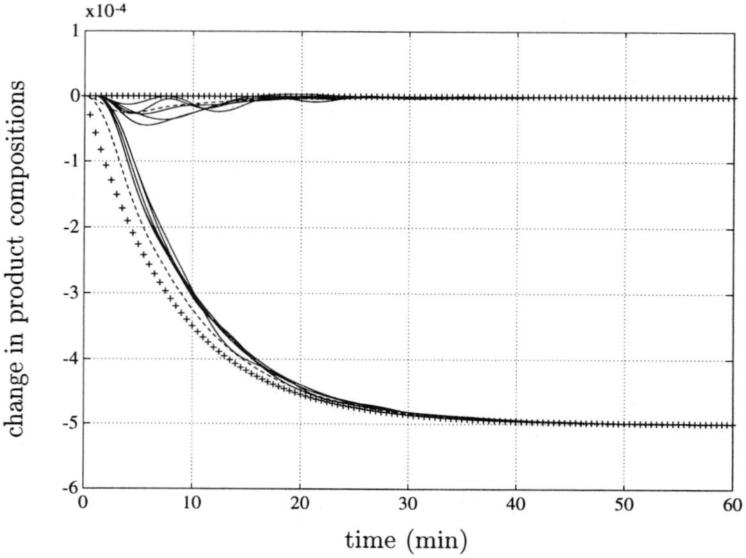

Figure 12.20: Response to a step change in the bottom product composition demand: reference model (+++); nominal linear model (dashed); nonlinear results for the five combinations of actuator gains (solid).

designed for the reduced-order linear model performs to specification on the high-order nonlinear simulation model.

12.5 Notes and References

In this chapter we have illustrated how analytical design theory may be applied to practical design problems. The key difficulties in applications work are concerned with modelling the plant and translating design specifications into a manageable optimization problem and weight selection. Although the tasks of modelling the plant and selecting an optimization problem can and should be guided by the robust stability and performance theory described in Chapter 2, this process still relies on engineering judgement and leaps of faith of one form or another. For example, in the tokamak study, we used a fourth-order linear model to describe the magnetohydrodynamics of a burning plasma! When we began this work, it was far from clear that such a simple model was going to provide an adequate description of the relevant plasma dynamics. The task of selecting an optimization problem that will to some degree reflect the performance specifications is also a challenge.

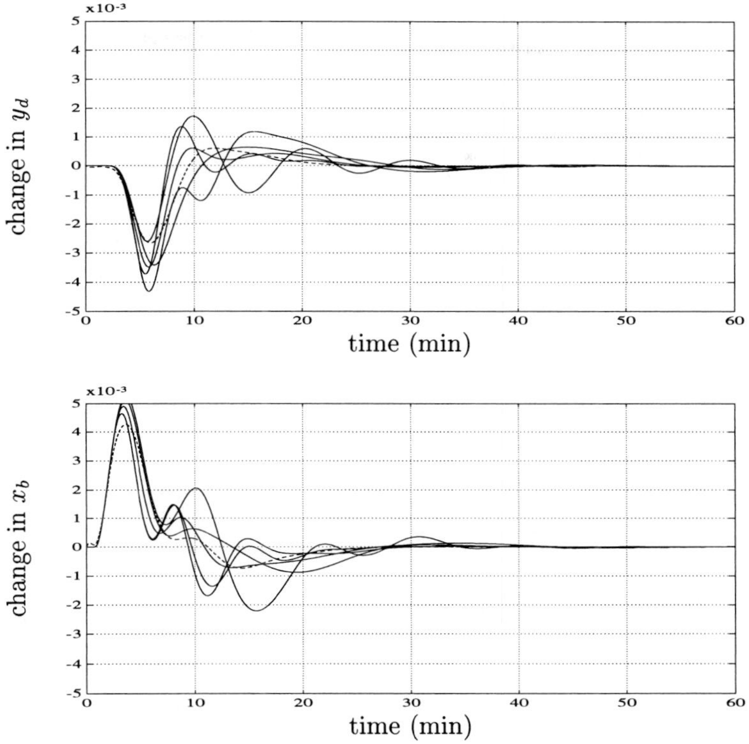

Figure 12.21: Response to a step disturbance in the feed flow rate: nominal linear model (dashed); nonlinear results for the five combinations of actuator gains (solid).

In order to assess the extent to which one has been successful, both in modelling and design, it is necessary to embark on a detailed program of simulation studies before any hardware trials can begin. The hope is that theoretical advances of the type described in this book will help to systematize the design process and reduce the time spent on the iterative design-and-simulate procedure.

The classic books of Bode [31], Horowitz [95] and Newton, Gould and Kaiser [158] have had a marked impact on contemporary design philosophy. Although computers and theoretical advances have rendered some of the perspectives of these authors obsolete, much of the material in these books is as relevant today as it was at the time they were written. As an illustration, we point out a passage on page 245 of [158], which was written prior to 1957:

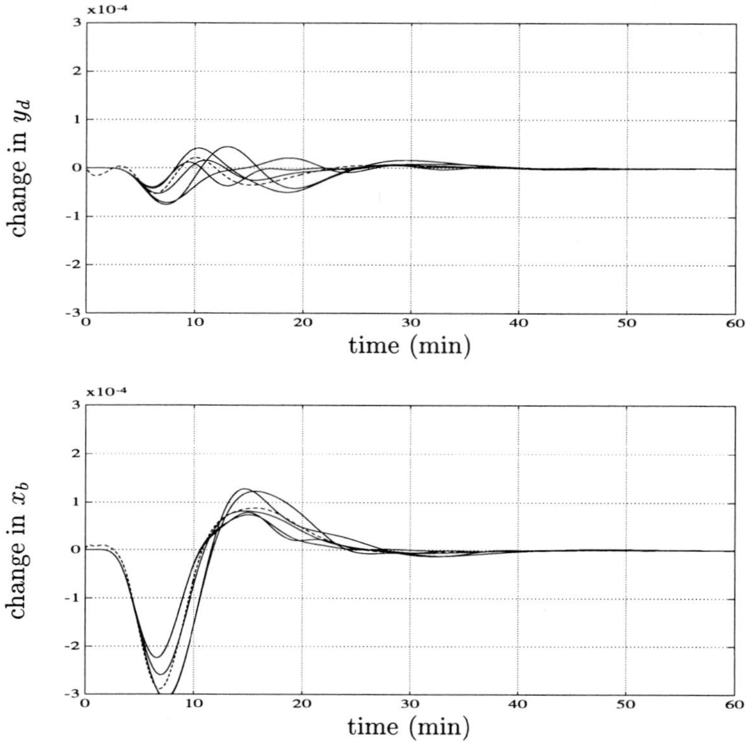

Figure 12.22: Response to a step change in the feed-stream composition: nominal linear model (dashed); nonlinear results for the five combinations of actuator gains (solid).

> "...These [mean-square error] performance indices have been used in this book because they are the only ones of engineering usefulness that lead to a reasonably straightforward mathematical analysis. Many other performance indices might have engineering usefulness, but they lead to formulations of the design problem that are not tractable by analysis. An example of such a class of performance indices involves the absolute value of the error..."

Stable coprime factor representations of model error were introduced by Vidyasagar and Kimura [206]. They also showed that this problem could be set up as a standard two-block $\mathcal{H}_\infty$ optimization problem. Glover and McFarlane [79, 148] demonstrated that in the case of normalized coprime factor perturbations, the optimal robustness problem has a particularly simple solution and derived the Hankel norm formula (12.2.9) for the optimal stability margin. We refer the reader to these papers for an account of the theoretical development, which is only mentioned in passing in this chapter. Georgiou and Smith [70] show that robustness optimization for normalized coprime factor perturbations is equivalent to robustness optimization in the gap metric, thereby extending the work of [79] in several respects.

The work on tokamak control is based on a series of papers written by workers at Imperial College and the Max Planck Institute for Plasma Physics [3, 112, 113]. The two fourth-order design models were obtained by reducing high-order linearized models generated by CARRIDI [8] and NAPS [37]. The simulation results were obtained from the MHD simulation code PROTEUS [7].

An early design methodology for two-degree-of-freedom (TDF) controllers is due to Horowitz [95]. The work of Bongiorno and Youla [220] put TDF design on a firm theoretical footing and gave a complete parameterization theory for all TDF controllers in terms of a pair of stable parameters. Another readable account may be found in Vidyasagar [205]. The TDF distillation column design case study is based on the work of Hoyle, Hyde, Kasenally, Limebeer and Perkins [96, 136], although the particular problem presented here is new.

The case studies we have presented here rely, in an essential way, on the work of several of our students and colleagues. In particular, Ebrahim Kasenally helped with both design studies. Alfredo Portone made a major contribution to the tokamak design study and ran countless simulations on our behalf; we are grateful to the Max Planck Institute for Plasma Physics for the use of their supercomputer facilities. Nefyn Jones did the lion's share of the work in the distillation column design study under the knowledgeable eye of John Perkins. We would also like to thank Elling Jacobsen for making his nonlinear simulation code for the distillation problem available to us. All the workers are employees of the Centre for Process Systems Engineering at Imperial College.

Appendix A

Internal Stability Theory

A.1 Introduction

A fundamental requirement of any feedback control system design is the stability of the closed-loop system. The design problem may therefore be considered as a search or optimization over the class of all stabilizing controllers. By finding a characterization of all stabilizing controllers as the first step of the controller design process, a constrained search or optimization may be replaced with an unconstrained one.

In this appendix, we develop a parametrization of all stabilizing controllers. The parametrization is linear fractional in character and can be written in the form

$$\boldsymbol{K} = \mathcal{F}_\ell(\boldsymbol{K}_s, \boldsymbol{Q}), \qquad \boldsymbol{Q} \in \mathcal{RH}_\infty. \tag{A.1.1}$$

A suitable $\boldsymbol{K}_s$ may be constructed from any stabilizing state-feedback gain matrix and any stabilizing observer gain matrix. The parameter $\boldsymbol{Q}$ is stable, but otherwise arbitrary.[1]

If we are concerned with the characteristics of the closed-loop system arising from the linear fractional transformation $\mathcal{F}_\ell(\boldsymbol{P}, \boldsymbol{K})$ shown in Figure A.1, in which $\boldsymbol{K}$ is required to be stabilizing, substitution from (A.1.1) allows us to write $\mathcal{F}_\ell(\boldsymbol{P}, \boldsymbol{K}) = \mathcal{F}_\ell(\boldsymbol{T}, \boldsymbol{Q})$, in which $\boldsymbol{T}$ is obtained from $\boldsymbol{P}$ and $\boldsymbol{K}_s$ according to the composition of LFT's formula (see Chapter 4). This replaces a design problem in which we select a stabilizing controller with a design problem in which we select a stable $\boldsymbol{Q}$. It turns out that $\boldsymbol{T}$ has the form

$$\boldsymbol{T} = \begin{bmatrix} \boldsymbol{T}_{11} & \boldsymbol{T}_{12} \\ \boldsymbol{T}_{21} & 0 \end{bmatrix},$$

so that

$$\mathcal{F}_\ell(\boldsymbol{P}, \boldsymbol{K}) = \mathcal{F}_\ell(\boldsymbol{T}, \boldsymbol{Q}) = \boldsymbol{T}_{11} + \boldsymbol{T}_{12}\boldsymbol{Q}\boldsymbol{T}_{21}. \tag{A.1.2}$$

[1]That is, any stable $\boldsymbol{Q}$ leads to a stabilizing controller via (A.1.1), and conversely any stabilizing controller may be written in the form (A.1.1) for some stable $\boldsymbol{Q}$.

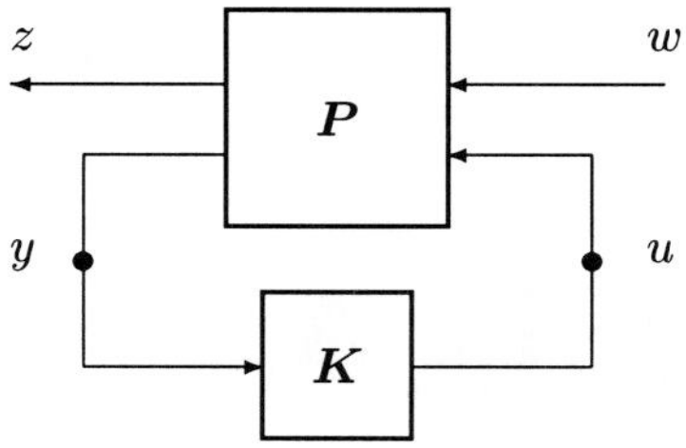

Figure A.1: A linear fractional transformation.

Thus the parametrization of all stabilizing controllers achieves two important simplifications:

1. It replaces a search or optimization over the class of stabilizing controllers with a search or optimization over $\boldsymbol{Q} \in \mathcal{RH}_\infty$;

2. It replaces the linear fractional parametrization $\mathcal{F}_\ell(\boldsymbol{P}, \boldsymbol{K})$ of the objective with the affine parametrization $\boldsymbol{T}_{11} + \boldsymbol{T}_{12}\boldsymbol{Q}\boldsymbol{T}_{21}$.

In view of (A.1.2), a generalized regulator problem in which $\|\mathcal{F}_\ell(\boldsymbol{P}, \boldsymbol{K})\|_2$ or $\|\mathcal{F}_\ell(\boldsymbol{P}, \boldsymbol{K})\|_\infty$ is required to be small is a model matching problem in which we seek a stable $\boldsymbol{Q}$ such that $\boldsymbol{T}_{12}\boldsymbol{Q}\boldsymbol{T}_{21}$ is approximately equal to $-\boldsymbol{T}_{11}$.

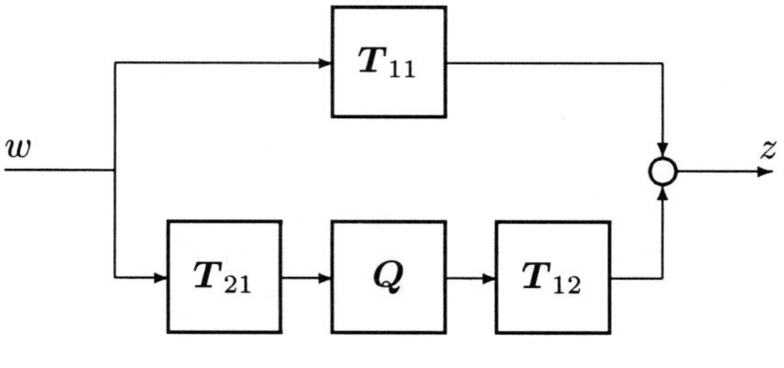

Figure A.2: The model matching problem.

The reader may recall that a parametrization of all stabilizing controllers for a stable single-input-single-output plant was presented in Chapter 1. The generalization to stable, multi-input-multi-output plants is trivial, and our main concern is the generalization to the case of plants which may be unstable. Because we focus on a state-space development of $\mathcal{H}_\infty$ and LQG controller synthesis theory, we have decided to emphasize the role of the state-space in our development of stability theory. Readers should also note that our treatment is aimed at obtaining the results we need, rather than providing a comprehensive account of this area of linear systems theory.

A.1.1 Basics

Throughout this appendix, we consider only linear, time-invariant systems that are finite dimensional. These systems can be represented by rational transfer function matrices.

As in Chapter 1, the definition of internal stability is:

Definition A.1.1 *The feedback loop in Figure A.3 is internally stable if the system mapping* $\begin{bmatrix} w' & v' \end{bmatrix}'$ *to* $\begin{bmatrix} u' & y' \end{bmatrix}'$ *is stable.*

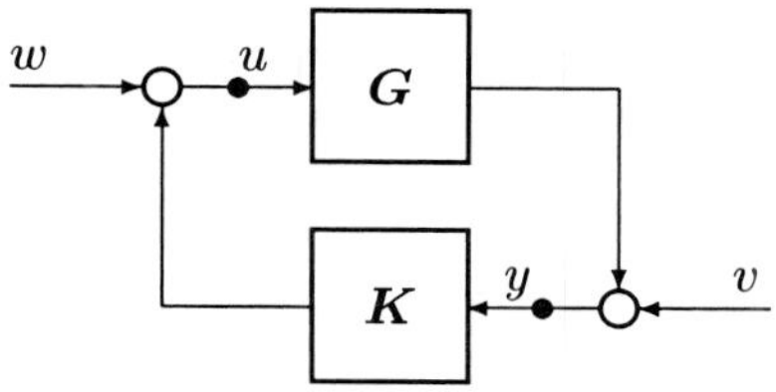

Figure A.3: Diagram for internal stability definition.

Our first result is a consequence of the definition of internal stability.

Lemma A.1.1 *The feedback loop of Figure A.3 is internally stable if and only if*

$$\begin{bmatrix} I & -\boldsymbol{K} \\ -\boldsymbol{G} & I \end{bmatrix}^{-1} \in \mathcal{RH}_\infty. \tag{A.1.3}$$

Proof. From Figure A.3,

$$\begin{bmatrix} w \\ v \end{bmatrix} = \begin{bmatrix} I & -\boldsymbol{K} \\ -\boldsymbol{G} & I \end{bmatrix} \begin{bmatrix} u \\ y \end{bmatrix}.$$

Hence

$$\begin{bmatrix} u \\ y \end{bmatrix} = \begin{bmatrix} I & -\boldsymbol{K} \\ -\boldsymbol{G} & I \end{bmatrix}^{-1} \begin{bmatrix} w \\ v \end{bmatrix}$$

and the result is immediate from Definition A.1.1. ■

For certain controllers, the 2×2 block matrix in (A.1.3) may not be proper, even though $\boldsymbol{G}$ and $\boldsymbol{K}$ are. This means that for some inputs w and v, the algebraic loop cannot be solved and the feedback loop is said to be ill-posed. Controllers with this property are not permitted in our applications. If either $\boldsymbol{G}$ or $\boldsymbol{K}$ is strictly proper, well-posedness is assured.

In order to develop the parametrization theory for all stabilizing controllers in the unstable plant case, we will need some of the properties of coprime factorizations.

A.2 Coprime factorization

This section covers those results on coprime factorizations most relevant to internal stability theory. We begin with a definition of coprimeness.

Definition A.2.1 *Two transfer function matrices $\boldsymbol{N}, \boldsymbol{D} \in \mathcal{RH}_\infty$ with the same number of columns are right coprime (r.c.) if there exist matrices $\boldsymbol{X}, \boldsymbol{Y} \in \mathcal{RH}_\infty$ such that*

$$\boldsymbol{X}\boldsymbol{N} + \boldsymbol{Y}\boldsymbol{D} = I. \tag{A.2.1}$$

Equations of this form are known as Bezout equations.

Example A.2.1. Two integers n and d are coprime if ± 1 is their only common factor. It follows from Euclid's algorithm that n and d are coprime if and only if there exist integers x, y such that $xn + yd = 1$. For example, 3 and 4 are coprime, since $1 = 4 \times 4 - 3 \times 5$. On the other hand, 2 and 4 are not coprime, since $2x + 4y = 2(x + 2y)$, which can never equal 1 if x and y are integers. ∇

Example A.2.2. The transfer functions $\boldsymbol{n} = \frac{s-1}{s+1}$ and $\boldsymbol{d} = \frac{s-1}{s+2}$ are not coprime, since for any stable functions $\boldsymbol{x}$ and $\boldsymbol{y}$, $\boldsymbol{x}\boldsymbol{n} + \boldsymbol{y}\boldsymbol{d}$ will have a zero at $+1$. Thus there cannot exist stable $\boldsymbol{x}, \boldsymbol{y}$ such that $\boldsymbol{x}\boldsymbol{n} + \boldsymbol{y}\boldsymbol{d} = 1$. In fact, $\boldsymbol{n}$ and $\boldsymbol{d}$ are coprime if and only if they have no common zeros in the closed right-half plane (including infinity). ∇

Definition A.2.2 *If $\boldsymbol{N}$ and $\boldsymbol{D}$ are right coprime and $\boldsymbol{D}$ is nonsingular (in the sense of transfer function matrices), then $\boldsymbol{N}\boldsymbol{D}^{-1}$ is called right coprime factorization (r.c.f.).*

Left coprimeness and left coprime plant descriptions may be defined in a similar way.

Definition A.2.3 *Two transfer function matrices $\tilde{\boldsymbol{N}}, \tilde{\boldsymbol{D}} \in \mathcal{RH}_\infty$ with the same number of rows are left coprime (l.c.) if there exist matrices $\tilde{\boldsymbol{X}}, \tilde{\boldsymbol{Y}} \in \mathcal{RH}_\infty$ such that*

$$\tilde{\boldsymbol{N}}\tilde{\boldsymbol{X}} + \tilde{\boldsymbol{D}}\tilde{\boldsymbol{Y}} = I.$$

If $\tilde{\boldsymbol{N}}$ and $\tilde{\boldsymbol{D}}$ are left coprime and $\tilde{\boldsymbol{D}}$ is nonsingular, then $\tilde{\boldsymbol{D}}^{-1}\tilde{\boldsymbol{N}}$ is called a left coprime factorization (l.c.f.).

The next example shows that coprime factorizations of a given system are not unique.

Example A.2.3. Consider the scalar transfer function

$$\boldsymbol{g} = \frac{(s-1)(s+2)}{(s-3)(s+4)}.$$

To obtain a r.c.f. of $\boldsymbol{g}$, we make all the stable poles of $\boldsymbol{g}$ poles of $\boldsymbol{n}$, all the left-half-plane zeros of $\boldsymbol{g}$ poles of $\boldsymbol{d}$, and then fill in the zeros of $\boldsymbol{n}$ and $\boldsymbol{d}$ so that the identity $\boldsymbol{g} = \boldsymbol{n}\boldsymbol{d}^{-1}$ holds. Thus

$$\boldsymbol{n} = \frac{s-1}{s+4}, \qquad \boldsymbol{d} = \frac{s-3}{s+2}$$

is a coprime factorization. Alternatively,

$$\boldsymbol{n} = \frac{(s-1)(s+k_1)}{(s+4)(s+k_2)}, \qquad \boldsymbol{d} = \frac{(s-3)(s+k_1)}{(s+2)(s+k_2)}$$

is a r.c.f. of $\boldsymbol{g}$ for any k_1, $k_2 > 0$. ▽

The following lemma establishes that all right coprime factorizations of the same transfer function matrix are related by a $\boldsymbol{W} \in \mathcal{RH}_\infty$ such that $\boldsymbol{W}^{-1} \in \mathcal{RH}_\infty$.

Lemma A.2.1 *Let $\boldsymbol{N}_1\boldsymbol{D}_1{}^{-1} = \boldsymbol{N}_2\boldsymbol{D}_2{}^{-1}$ be right coprime factorizations. Then*

$$\begin{bmatrix} \boldsymbol{N}_2 \\ \boldsymbol{D}_2 \end{bmatrix} = \begin{bmatrix} \boldsymbol{N}_1 \\ \boldsymbol{D}_1 \end{bmatrix} \boldsymbol{W}, \tag{A.2.2}$$

in which $\boldsymbol{W}$ and $\boldsymbol{W}^{-1}$ are in $\mathcal{RH}_\infty$.

In particular, if $\boldsymbol{G} = \boldsymbol{N}\boldsymbol{D}^{-1} \in \mathcal{RH}_\infty$ with $\boldsymbol{N}$, $\boldsymbol{D}$ right coprime, then $\boldsymbol{D}^{-1} \in \mathcal{RH}_\infty$.

(If $\boldsymbol{G} \in \mathcal{RH}_\infty$, then $\boldsymbol{G} = \boldsymbol{G}I^{-1}$ is a r.c.f. Therefore, if $\boldsymbol{G} = \boldsymbol{N}\boldsymbol{D}^{-1}$ is also a r.c.f., it follows that $\boldsymbol{W} = \boldsymbol{D}^{-1}$.)

Proof. Define $\boldsymbol{W} = \boldsymbol{D}_1^{-1}\boldsymbol{D}_2$, so that (A.2.2) holds. Let $\boldsymbol{X}_2\boldsymbol{N}_2 + \boldsymbol{Y}_2\boldsymbol{D}_2 = I$. From (A.2.2), $(\boldsymbol{X}_2\boldsymbol{N}_1 + \boldsymbol{Y}_2\boldsymbol{D}_1)\boldsymbol{W} = I$ and hence $\boldsymbol{W}^{-1} = \boldsymbol{X}_2\boldsymbol{N}_1 + \boldsymbol{Y}_2\boldsymbol{D}_1 \in \mathcal{RH}_\infty$. Similarly, $\boldsymbol{X}_1\boldsymbol{N}_1 + \boldsymbol{Y}_1\boldsymbol{D}_1 = I$ implies that $\boldsymbol{W} = \boldsymbol{X}_1\boldsymbol{N}_2 + \boldsymbol{Y}_1\boldsymbol{D}_2 \in \mathcal{RH}_\infty$.

If $\boldsymbol{G} \in \mathcal{RH}_\infty$, then $\boldsymbol{X}\boldsymbol{N} + \boldsymbol{Y}\boldsymbol{D} = I \Rightarrow \boldsymbol{X}\boldsymbol{G} + \boldsymbol{Y} = \boldsymbol{D}^{-1} \in \mathcal{RH}_\infty$. ■

A.2.1 Coprime factorization and internal stability

The relationship between coprime factorizations and stabilizing controllers is as follows. Suppose $\boldsymbol{G} = \boldsymbol{N}\boldsymbol{D}^{-1}$ is a r.c.f. and let $\boldsymbol{X}$, $\boldsymbol{Y} \in \mathcal{RH}_\infty$ satisfy the Bezout equation $\boldsymbol{X}\boldsymbol{N} + \boldsymbol{Y}\boldsymbol{D} = I$. If $\boldsymbol{Y}$ is nonsingular, then $\boldsymbol{K} = -\boldsymbol{Y}^{-1}\boldsymbol{X}$ is a stabilizing controller for $\boldsymbol{G}$. To see this, we simply note that

$$\begin{bmatrix} I & -\boldsymbol{K} \\ -\boldsymbol{G} & I \end{bmatrix} = \begin{bmatrix} \boldsymbol{Y}^{-1} & \boldsymbol{Y}^{-1}\boldsymbol{X} \\ 0 & I \end{bmatrix} \begin{bmatrix} \boldsymbol{D}^{-1} & 0 \\ -\boldsymbol{N}\boldsymbol{D}^{-1} & I \end{bmatrix},$$

which gives

$$\begin{bmatrix} I & -\boldsymbol{K} \\ -\boldsymbol{G} & I \end{bmatrix}^{-1} = \begin{bmatrix} \boldsymbol{D} & 0 \\ \boldsymbol{N} & I \end{bmatrix} \begin{bmatrix} \boldsymbol{Y} & -\boldsymbol{X} \\ 0 & I \end{bmatrix} \in \mathcal{RH}_\infty.$$

For the converse, we use the generalized Nyquist criterion (Theorem 2.4.2). By this theorem, $\boldsymbol{K}$ is stabilizing if and only if the number of anticlockwise encirclements of the origin by $\det(I - \boldsymbol{K}\boldsymbol{G})(s)$ as s traverses the Nyquist contour is equal to $n_K + n_G$, with n_K and n_G being respectively the number of poles of $\boldsymbol{K}$ and $\boldsymbol{G}$ in the closed-right-half plane. If $\boldsymbol{G} = \boldsymbol{N}\boldsymbol{D}^{-1}$ is a r.c.f. and $\boldsymbol{K} = -\tilde{\boldsymbol{Y}}^{-1}\tilde{\boldsymbol{X}}$ is a l.c.f., then $-n_G$ is the number of anticlockwise encirclements of the origin by $\det \boldsymbol{D}(s)$ and $-n_K$ is the number of anticlockwise encirclements of the origin by $\det \tilde{\boldsymbol{Y}}(\mathrm{s})$ as s traverses the Nyquist contour. Since

$$\det(\tilde{\boldsymbol{Y}}\boldsymbol{D} + \tilde{\boldsymbol{X}}\boldsymbol{N}) = \det \tilde{\boldsymbol{Y}} \det \boldsymbol{D} \det(I - \boldsymbol{K}\boldsymbol{G}),$$

it follows that $\det(\tilde{\boldsymbol{Y}}\boldsymbol{D}+\tilde{\boldsymbol{X}}\boldsymbol{N})(s)$ makes no encirclements of the origin as s traverse the Nyquist contour. Therefore, $\boldsymbol{V} = \tilde{\boldsymbol{Y}}\boldsymbol{D} + \tilde{\boldsymbol{X}}\boldsymbol{N} \in \mathcal{RH}_\infty$ cannot have any zeros in the closed-right-half plane, giving $\boldsymbol{V}^{-1} \in \mathcal{RH}_\infty$. Hence $\boldsymbol{K} = -\boldsymbol{Y}^{-1}\boldsymbol{X}$, in which $\boldsymbol{X} = \boldsymbol{V}^{-1}\tilde{\boldsymbol{X}}$ and $\boldsymbol{Y} = \boldsymbol{V}^{-1}\tilde{\boldsymbol{Y}}$, is a l.c.f. of $\boldsymbol{K}$ and $\boldsymbol{X}\boldsymbol{N} + \boldsymbol{Y}\boldsymbol{D} = I$.

Thus $\boldsymbol{K}$ is a stabilizing controller for $\boldsymbol{G} = \boldsymbol{N}\boldsymbol{D}^{-1}$ if and only if $\boldsymbol{K}$ has a l.c.f $\boldsymbol{K} = -\boldsymbol{Y}^{-1}\boldsymbol{X}$ such that the Bezout identity $\boldsymbol{X}\boldsymbol{N} + \boldsymbol{Y}\boldsymbol{D} = I$ is satisfied.

A.2.2 Doubly coprime factorization

Suppose $\boldsymbol{G} = \boldsymbol{N}_r\boldsymbol{D}_r^{-1}$ is a r.c.f. and $\boldsymbol{X}_r$, $\boldsymbol{Y}_r \in \mathcal{RH}_\infty$ satisfy $\boldsymbol{X}_r\boldsymbol{N}_r + \boldsymbol{Y}_r\boldsymbol{D}_r = I$. Suppose also that $\boldsymbol{G} = \boldsymbol{D}_l^{-1}\boldsymbol{N}_l$ is a l.c.f. and that $\boldsymbol{X}_l$, $\boldsymbol{Y}_l \in \mathcal{RH}_\infty$ satisfy $\boldsymbol{N}_l\boldsymbol{X}_l + \boldsymbol{D}_l\boldsymbol{Y}_l = I$. Then

$$\begin{bmatrix} \boldsymbol{Y}_r & \boldsymbol{X}_r \\ -\boldsymbol{N}_l & \boldsymbol{D}_l \end{bmatrix} \begin{bmatrix} \boldsymbol{D}_r & \boldsymbol{D}_r\boldsymbol{R} - \boldsymbol{X}_l \\ \boldsymbol{N}_r & \boldsymbol{N}_r\boldsymbol{R} + \boldsymbol{Y}_l \end{bmatrix} = \begin{bmatrix} I & 0 \\ 0 & I \end{bmatrix},$$

in which $\boldsymbol{R} = \boldsymbol{Y}_r\boldsymbol{X}_l - \boldsymbol{X}_r\boldsymbol{Y}_l$.

This shows that for any right and left coprime factorizations of the same transfer function matrix (*i.e.*, $\boldsymbol{N}_r\boldsymbol{D}_r^{-1} = \boldsymbol{D}_l^{-1}\boldsymbol{N}_l$), there exist transfer function matrices $\boldsymbol{U}_r$, $\boldsymbol{V}_r$, $\boldsymbol{U}_l$ and $\boldsymbol{V}_l$, all in $\mathcal{RH}_\infty$, such that the generalized Bezout equation

$$\begin{bmatrix} \boldsymbol{V}_r & \boldsymbol{U}_r \\ -\boldsymbol{N}_l & \boldsymbol{D}_l \end{bmatrix} \begin{bmatrix} \boldsymbol{D}_r & -\boldsymbol{U}_l \\ \boldsymbol{N}_r & \boldsymbol{V}_l \end{bmatrix} = \begin{bmatrix} I & 0 \\ 0 & I \end{bmatrix} \tag{A.2.3}$$

is satisfied. This is known as a *doubly coprime factorization*, and we shall use it to parametrize all stabilizing controllers. The following result establishes the existence of, and state-space formulae for, a doubly coprime factorization of a given transfer function matrix.

Theorem A.2.2 *Suppose $\boldsymbol{G} = D + C(sI - A)^{-1}B$ is a stabilizable and detectable realization of a transfer function matrix $\boldsymbol{G}$. Let F be a state-feedback gain matrix such that $A - BF$ is asymptotically stable, and let H be an observer gain matrix such that $A - HC$ is asymptotically stable. Define*

$$\begin{bmatrix} \boldsymbol{D}_r & -\boldsymbol{U}_l \\ \boldsymbol{N}_r & \boldsymbol{V}_l \end{bmatrix} \stackrel{s}{=} \left[\begin{array}{c|cc} A - BF & B & H \\ \hline -F & I & 0 \\ C - DF & D & I \end{array}\right] \tag{A.2.4}$$

$$\begin{bmatrix} \boldsymbol{V}_r & \boldsymbol{U}_r \\ -\boldsymbol{N}_l & \boldsymbol{D}_l \end{bmatrix} \stackrel{s}{=} \left[\begin{array}{c|cc} A-HC & B-HD & H \\ \hline F & I & 0 \\ -C & -D & I \end{array}\right]. \tag{A.2.5}$$

Then the generalized Bezout equation (A.2.3) holds and $\boldsymbol{G} = \boldsymbol{N}_r\boldsymbol{D}_r{}^{-1} = \boldsymbol{D}_l{}^{-1}\boldsymbol{N}_l$ are right and left coprime factorizations of $\boldsymbol{G}$.

Proof. The verification of equation (A.2.3) is a calculation which is left as an exercise (Problem A.3). Since $A - HC$ and $A - BF$ are asymptotically stable, the transfer function matrices defined by (A.2.4) and (A.2.5) are both in $\mathcal{RH}_\infty$. From the $(1,1)$- and $(2,2)$-blocks of (A.2.3) we have the Bezout equations, $\boldsymbol{V}_r\boldsymbol{D}_r + \boldsymbol{U}_r\boldsymbol{N}_r = I$ and $\boldsymbol{N}_l\boldsymbol{U}_l + \boldsymbol{D}_l\boldsymbol{V}_l = I$, which establishes that $\boldsymbol{N}_r$, $\boldsymbol{D}_r$ are right coprime and that $\boldsymbol{D}_l$, $\boldsymbol{N}_l$ are left coprime. The verification of the idenities $\boldsymbol{G} = \boldsymbol{N}_r\boldsymbol{D}_r{}^{-1} = \boldsymbol{D}_l{}^{-1}\boldsymbol{N}_l$ is another calculation which is left as an exercise (Problem A.3). ■

By the result of Section A.2.1, $\boldsymbol{K} = -\boldsymbol{V}_r^{-1}\boldsymbol{U}_r$ is a stabilizing controller. This controller is simply

$$\dot{\widehat{x}} = A\widehat{x} + Bu + H\big(y - (C\widehat{x} + Du)\big) \tag{A.2.6}$$

$$u = -F\widehat{x}, \tag{A.2.7}$$

which is a combination of a stable observer and a stabilizing state (estimate) feedback (Problem A.3).

Main points of the section

1. Coprime factorizations are unique up to a matrix $\boldsymbol{W} \in \mathcal{RH}_\infty$ such that $\boldsymbol{W}^{-1} \in \mathcal{RH}_\infty$. In particular, if $\boldsymbol{G} = \boldsymbol{N}\boldsymbol{D}^{-1}$ is a r.c.f. and $\boldsymbol{G} \in \mathcal{RH}_\infty$, then $\boldsymbol{D}^{-1} \in \mathcal{RH}_\infty$.
2. Coprime factorization and stabilization are intimately connected. A controller $\boldsymbol{K}$ stabilizes a plant $\boldsymbol{G}$ if and only if there exist $\boldsymbol{N}$, $\boldsymbol{D}$, $\boldsymbol{X}$ and $\boldsymbol{Y}$ such that $\boldsymbol{G} = \boldsymbol{N}\boldsymbol{D}^{-1}$, $\boldsymbol{K} = -\boldsymbol{Y}^{-1}\boldsymbol{X}$ and $\boldsymbol{X}\boldsymbol{N} + \boldsymbol{Y}\boldsymbol{D} = I$.
3. State-space formulae for left and right coprime factors have been given. The computation of a coprime factorization involves selecting stabilizing state-feedback and observer gain matrices.
4. A doubly coprime factorization is defined by a generalized Bezout equation and can be obtained from any right and left coprime factorizations of the same transfer function matrix.
5. A doubly coprime factorization defines a stabilizing controller for the plant. State-space formulae for a doubly coprime factorization and the implied stabilizing controller have been given. The controller has the form of a stable observer combined with a stabilizing state (estimate) feedback.

A.3 All stabilizing controllers

We now show that a doubly coprime factorization can be used to parametrize all the stabilizing controllers for the feedback loop given in Figure A.3.

Theorem A.3.1 *Let* $\boldsymbol{G} = \boldsymbol{N}_r \boldsymbol{D}_r^{-1} = \boldsymbol{D}_l^{-1} \boldsymbol{N}_l$ *be right and left coprime factorizations respectively of* $\boldsymbol{G}$*, and let*

$$\begin{bmatrix} \boldsymbol{V}_r & \boldsymbol{U}_r \\ -\boldsymbol{N}_l & \boldsymbol{D}_l \end{bmatrix} \begin{bmatrix} \boldsymbol{D}_r & -\boldsymbol{U}_l \\ \boldsymbol{N}_r & \boldsymbol{V}_l \end{bmatrix} = \begin{bmatrix} I & 0 \\ 0 & I \end{bmatrix},$$

with each of these transfer functions in $\mathcal{RH}_\infty$ *(i.e., we have a doubly coprime factorization). The following are equivalent:*

1. $\boldsymbol{K}$ *is an internally-stabilizing controller for the feedback loop in Figure A.3.*

2. $\boldsymbol{K} = \boldsymbol{K}_1 \boldsymbol{K}_2^{-1}$*, in which*

$$\begin{bmatrix} \boldsymbol{K}_1 \\ \boldsymbol{K}_2 \end{bmatrix} = \begin{bmatrix} \boldsymbol{D}_r & -\boldsymbol{U}_l \\ \boldsymbol{N}_r & \boldsymbol{V}_l \end{bmatrix} \begin{bmatrix} \boldsymbol{Q} \\ I \end{bmatrix}, \qquad \boldsymbol{Q} \in \mathcal{RH}_\infty. \tag{A.3.1}$$

3. $\boldsymbol{K} = \boldsymbol{K}_4^{-1} \boldsymbol{K}_3$*, in which*

$$\begin{bmatrix} \boldsymbol{K}_4 & -\boldsymbol{K}_3 \end{bmatrix} = \begin{bmatrix} I & -\boldsymbol{Q} \end{bmatrix} \begin{bmatrix} \boldsymbol{V}_r & \boldsymbol{U}_r \\ -\boldsymbol{N}_l & \boldsymbol{D}_l \end{bmatrix}, \quad \boldsymbol{Q} \in \mathcal{RH}_\infty. \tag{A.3.2}$$

4.
$$\boldsymbol{K} = \mathcal{F}_\ell(\boldsymbol{K}_s, \boldsymbol{Q}), \tag{A.3.3}$$

in which

$$\boldsymbol{K}_s = \begin{bmatrix} -\boldsymbol{V}_r^{-1}\boldsymbol{U}_r & \boldsymbol{V}_r^{-1} \\ \boldsymbol{V}_l^{-1} & -\boldsymbol{V}_l^{-1}\boldsymbol{N}_r \end{bmatrix}. \tag{A.3.4}$$

If the doubly coprime factorization takes the form given in Theorem A.2.2, then

$$\boldsymbol{K}_s \stackrel{s}{=} \left[\begin{array}{c|cc} A - BF - H(C - DF) & H & B - HD \\ \hline -F & 0 & I \\ -(C - DF) & I & -D \end{array}\right]. \tag{A.3.5}$$

Proof.

3 ⇒1: Since we may write

$$\begin{bmatrix} I & -\boldsymbol{K} \\ -\boldsymbol{G} & I \end{bmatrix} = \begin{bmatrix} \boldsymbol{K}_4 & 0 \\ 0 & \boldsymbol{D}_l \end{bmatrix}^{-1} \begin{bmatrix} I & -\boldsymbol{Q} \\ 0 & I \end{bmatrix} \begin{bmatrix} \boldsymbol{V}_r & \boldsymbol{U}_r \\ -\boldsymbol{N}_l & \boldsymbol{D}_l \end{bmatrix},$$

we see that

$$\begin{bmatrix} I & -\boldsymbol{K} \\ -\boldsymbol{G} & I \end{bmatrix}^{-1} = \begin{bmatrix} \boldsymbol{D}_r & -\boldsymbol{U}_l \\ \boldsymbol{N}_r & \boldsymbol{V}_l \end{bmatrix} \begin{bmatrix} I & \boldsymbol{Q} \\ 0 & I \end{bmatrix} \begin{bmatrix} \boldsymbol{K}_4 & 0 \\ 0 & \boldsymbol{D}_l \end{bmatrix} \in \mathcal{RH}_\infty.$$

This shows that any controller generated by (A.3.2) is internally stabilizing.

$1 \Rightarrow 3$: Let $\boldsymbol{K}$ be a stabilizing controller and $\boldsymbol{K} = \boldsymbol{X}^{-1}\boldsymbol{Y}$ be a l.c.f. of $\boldsymbol{K}$. Then

$$\begin{bmatrix} I & -\boldsymbol{K} \\ -\boldsymbol{G} & I \end{bmatrix} = \begin{bmatrix} \boldsymbol{X} & 0 \\ 0 & \boldsymbol{D}_l \end{bmatrix}^{-1} \begin{bmatrix} \boldsymbol{X} & -\boldsymbol{Y} \\ -\boldsymbol{N}_l & \boldsymbol{D}_l \end{bmatrix}$$

gives

$$\begin{bmatrix} I & -\boldsymbol{K} \\ -\boldsymbol{G} & I \end{bmatrix}^{-1} = \begin{bmatrix} \boldsymbol{X} & -\boldsymbol{Y} \\ -\boldsymbol{N}_l & \boldsymbol{D}_l \end{bmatrix}^{-1} \begin{bmatrix} \boldsymbol{X} & 0 \\ 0 & \boldsymbol{D}_l \end{bmatrix}. \tag{A.3.6}$$

If $\boldsymbol{A}, \boldsymbol{B} \in \mathcal{RH}_\infty$ satisfy

$$\boldsymbol{X}\boldsymbol{A} + \boldsymbol{Y}\boldsymbol{B} = I,$$

then

$$\begin{bmatrix} \boldsymbol{X} & 0 \\ 0 & \boldsymbol{D}_l \end{bmatrix} \begin{bmatrix} \boldsymbol{A} & \boldsymbol{U}_l \\ \boldsymbol{B} & \boldsymbol{V}_l \end{bmatrix} + \begin{bmatrix} \boldsymbol{X} & -\boldsymbol{Y} \\ -\boldsymbol{N}_l & \boldsymbol{D}_l \end{bmatrix} \begin{bmatrix} 0 & -\boldsymbol{U}_l \\ -\boldsymbol{B} & 0 \end{bmatrix} = \begin{bmatrix} I & 0 \\ 0 & I \end{bmatrix},$$

which shows that (A.3.6) is a l.c.f. of $\begin{bmatrix} I & -\boldsymbol{K} \\ -\boldsymbol{G} & I \end{bmatrix}^{-1}$. Invoking Lemma A.2.1, we see that

$$\begin{bmatrix} I & -\boldsymbol{K} \\ -\boldsymbol{G} & I \end{bmatrix}^{-1} \in \mathcal{RH}_\infty \Rightarrow \begin{bmatrix} \boldsymbol{X} & -\boldsymbol{Y} \\ -\boldsymbol{N}_l & \boldsymbol{D}_l \end{bmatrix}^{-1} \in \mathcal{RH}_\infty.$$

Now

$$\begin{bmatrix} \boldsymbol{X} & -\boldsymbol{Y} \\ -\boldsymbol{N}_l & \boldsymbol{D}_l \end{bmatrix} \begin{bmatrix} \boldsymbol{D}_r & -\boldsymbol{U}_l \\ \boldsymbol{N}_r & \boldsymbol{V}_l \end{bmatrix} = \begin{bmatrix} \boldsymbol{X}\boldsymbol{D}_r - \boldsymbol{Y}\boldsymbol{N}_r & -\boldsymbol{X}\boldsymbol{U}_l - \boldsymbol{Y}\boldsymbol{V}_l \\ 0 & I \end{bmatrix}.$$

Since both matrices on the left-hand side are invertible in $\mathcal{RH}_\infty$, it follows that $(\boldsymbol{X}\boldsymbol{D}_r - \boldsymbol{Y}\boldsymbol{N}_r)^{-1} \in \mathcal{RH}_\infty$. Equation (A.3.2) follows from

$$\begin{aligned} \begin{bmatrix} \boldsymbol{X} & -\boldsymbol{Y} \end{bmatrix} &= \begin{bmatrix} \boldsymbol{X} & -\boldsymbol{Y} \end{bmatrix} \begin{bmatrix} \boldsymbol{D}_r & -\boldsymbol{U}_l \\ \boldsymbol{N}_r & \boldsymbol{V}_l \end{bmatrix} \begin{bmatrix} \boldsymbol{V}_r & \boldsymbol{U}_r \\ -\boldsymbol{N}_l & \boldsymbol{D}_l \end{bmatrix} \\ &= \begin{bmatrix} \boldsymbol{X}\boldsymbol{D}_r - \boldsymbol{Y}\boldsymbol{N}_r & -\boldsymbol{X}\boldsymbol{U}_l - \boldsymbol{Y}\boldsymbol{V}_l \end{bmatrix} \begin{bmatrix} \boldsymbol{V}_r & \boldsymbol{U}_r \\ -\boldsymbol{N}_l & \boldsymbol{D}_l \end{bmatrix}, \end{aligned}$$

which may be rewritten as

$$\begin{aligned} (\boldsymbol{X}\boldsymbol{D}_r - \boldsymbol{Y}\boldsymbol{N}_r)^{-1} \begin{bmatrix} \boldsymbol{X} & -\boldsymbol{Y} \end{bmatrix} &= \begin{bmatrix} I & -\boldsymbol{Q} \end{bmatrix} \begin{bmatrix} \boldsymbol{V}_r & \boldsymbol{U}_r \\ -\boldsymbol{N}_l & \boldsymbol{D}_l \end{bmatrix} \\ &= \begin{bmatrix} \boldsymbol{K}_4 & -\boldsymbol{K}_3 \end{bmatrix}, \end{aligned}$$

in which $\boldsymbol{Q} = (\boldsymbol{X}\boldsymbol{D}_r - \boldsymbol{Y}\boldsymbol{N}_r)^{-1}(\boldsymbol{X}\boldsymbol{U}_l + \boldsymbol{Y}\boldsymbol{V}_l) \in \mathcal{RH}_\infty$.

$2 \Leftrightarrow 3$: Since

$$\begin{bmatrix} I & -\boldsymbol{Q} \\ 0 & I \end{bmatrix} \begin{bmatrix} \boldsymbol{V}_r & \boldsymbol{U}_r \\ -\boldsymbol{N}_l & \boldsymbol{D}_l \end{bmatrix} \begin{bmatrix} \boldsymbol{D}_r & -\boldsymbol{U}_l \\ \boldsymbol{N}_r & \boldsymbol{V}_l \end{bmatrix} \begin{bmatrix} I & \boldsymbol{Q} \\ 0 & I \end{bmatrix} = \begin{bmatrix} I & 0 \\ 0 & I \end{bmatrix},$$

it follows that

$$\begin{bmatrix} \boldsymbol{K}_4 & -\boldsymbol{K}_3 \\ -\boldsymbol{N}_l & \boldsymbol{D}_l \end{bmatrix} \begin{bmatrix} \boldsymbol{D}_r & \boldsymbol{K}_1 \\ \boldsymbol{N}_r & \boldsymbol{K}_2 \end{bmatrix} = \begin{bmatrix} I & 0 \\ 0 & I \end{bmatrix}.$$

The (1,2)-block gives $\boldsymbol{K}_4\boldsymbol{K}_1 - \boldsymbol{K}_3\boldsymbol{K}_2 = 0$, so $\boldsymbol{K}_4{}^{-1}\boldsymbol{K}_3 = \boldsymbol{K}_1\boldsymbol{K}_2{}^{-1}$.

2 ⇔ 4: This is an algebraic calculation. Since $\boldsymbol{D}_r = \boldsymbol{V}_r{}^{-1} - \boldsymbol{V}_r{}^{-1}\boldsymbol{U}_r\boldsymbol{N}_r$, and $\boldsymbol{U}_l\boldsymbol{V}_l{}^{-1} = \boldsymbol{V}_r{}^{-1}\boldsymbol{U}_r$ it follows that

$$\begin{aligned} &(\boldsymbol{D}_r\boldsymbol{Q} - \boldsymbol{U}_l)(\boldsymbol{N}_r\boldsymbol{Q} + \boldsymbol{V}_l)^{-1} \\ &= (\boldsymbol{V}_r{}^{-1}\boldsymbol{Q} - \boldsymbol{V}_r{}^{-1}\boldsymbol{U}_r\boldsymbol{N}_r\boldsymbol{Q} - \boldsymbol{U}_l)(I + \boldsymbol{V}_l{}^{-1}\boldsymbol{N}_r\boldsymbol{Q})^{-1}\boldsymbol{V}_l{}^{-1} \\ &= -\boldsymbol{U}_l\boldsymbol{V}_l{}^{-1} + \boldsymbol{V}_r{}^{-1}\boldsymbol{Q}(I + \boldsymbol{V}_l{}^{-1}\boldsymbol{N}_r\boldsymbol{Q})^{-1}\boldsymbol{V}_l{}^{-1} \\ &= \mathcal{F}_\ell\left(\begin{bmatrix} -\boldsymbol{V}_r^{-1}\boldsymbol{U}_r & \boldsymbol{V}_r^{-1} \\ \boldsymbol{V}_l^{-1} & -\boldsymbol{V}_l^{-1}\boldsymbol{N}_r \end{bmatrix}, \boldsymbol{Q}\right). \end{aligned}$$

This verifies that $\boldsymbol{K}$ is given by (A.3.1) if and only if it is given by (A.3.3), in which $\boldsymbol{K}_s$ is as in (A.3.4). We leave the verification of (A.3.5) as an exercise. ■

When $\boldsymbol{G}$ is stable, it follows that

$$\begin{bmatrix} \boldsymbol{D}_r & -\boldsymbol{U}_l \\ \boldsymbol{N}_r & \boldsymbol{V}_l \end{bmatrix} = \begin{bmatrix} I & 0 \\ \boldsymbol{G} & I \end{bmatrix}.$$

Substituting this into (A.3.1) yields $\boldsymbol{K} = \boldsymbol{Q}(I + \boldsymbol{G}\boldsymbol{Q})^{-1}$, which is the parametrization for all stabilizing controllers for stable plants described in Chapter 1.

Examining (A.3.5), we see that all stabilizing controllers have the form

$$\begin{aligned} \dot{\widehat{x}} &= (A - BF - H(C - DF))\widehat{x} + Hy + (B - HD)r \\ u &= -F\widehat{x} + r \\ \eta &= y - (C - DF)\widehat{x} - Dr \\ r &= \boldsymbol{Q}\eta \end{aligned}$$

These equations may be manipulated to yield

$$\begin{aligned} \dot{\widehat{x}} &= A\widehat{x} + Bu + H\big(y - (C\widehat{x} + Du)\big) \\ u &= -F\widehat{x} + \boldsymbol{Q}\big(y - (C\widehat{x} + Du)\big), \end{aligned}$$

which shows that every stabilizing controller is a combination of a stable observer and a stabilizing state (estimate) feedback, plus $\boldsymbol{Q}\eta$, with $\eta = y - (C\widehat{x} + Du)$ being the "innovations" process.[2] That is, one may "corrupt" the stabilizing control signal $-F\widehat{x}$ by any stable system acting on the "innovations" process, as shown in Figure A.4.

[2]The term innovations process is used for the signal $y - (C\widehat{x} + Du)$ when $\widehat{x}$ is the optimal state estimate arising from the Kalman filter. That is, when H is the Kalman gain. When H is not the Kalman gain, $y - (C\widehat{x} + Du)$ does not have a statistical interpretation and we use the term "innovations process" purely as an analogy—it still represents the difference between the actual output y and our estimate of it, which is $C\widehat{x} + Du$.

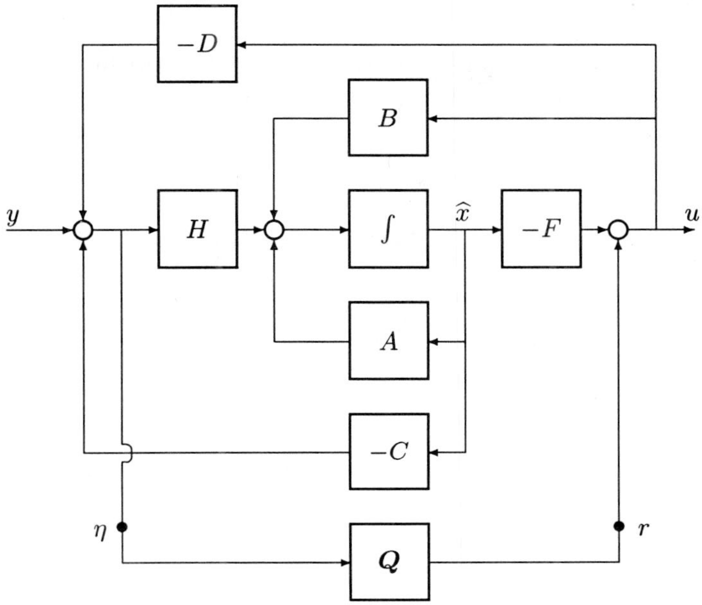

Figure A.4: A representation of all stabilizing controllers.

Main points of the section

1. All stabilizing controllers can be represented as a coprime factorization involving the elements of a doubly coprime factorization and a stable but otherwise arbitrary free parameter. Since the doubly coprime factorization is equivalent to the choice of a single stabilizing controller, this shows how every stabilizing controller can be constructed from a given stabilizing controller.

2. All stabilizing controllers are generated by a linear fractional transformation $\boldsymbol{K} = \mathcal{F}_\ell(\boldsymbol{K}_s, \boldsymbol{Q})$, in which $\boldsymbol{Q}$ is stable but otherwise arbitrary. This is known as the Q-parametrization or Youla parametrization.

   In particular, a suitable $\boldsymbol{K}_s$ may be constructed from any stabilizing state feedback gain matrix and any stabilizing observer gain matrix.

3. All stabilizing controllers have the form of a state estimator (observer) combined with a stabilizing state estimate feedback "corrupted" by a stable system driven by the "innovations" process.

A.4 Internal stability of LFTs

Linear fractional transformations are important in controller synthesis theory because they provides a framework in which one may study a wide variety of different optimization problems (see Chapter 4). With this as motivation, we will now analyze the internal stability of the linear fractional transformation given in Figure A.5.

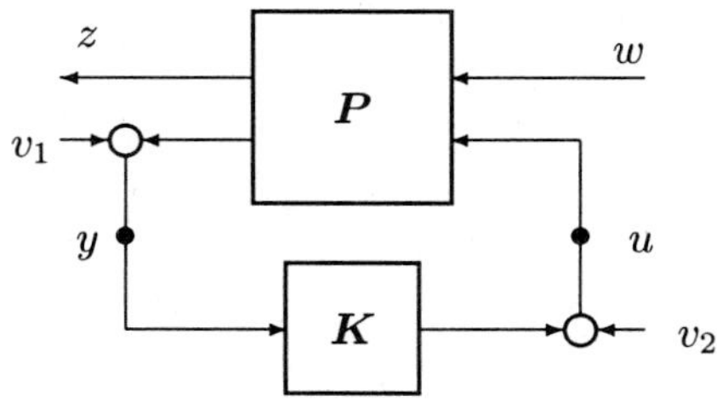

Figure A.5: Linear fractional transformation: Set-up for internal stability definition.

Definition A.4.1 *The linear fractional transformation $\mathcal{F}_\ell(\boldsymbol{P}, \boldsymbol{K})$ internally stable if the nine transfer function matrices mapping w, v_1, and v_2 to z, y and u in Figure A.5 are all stable.*

All the results in this section will be proved using state-space arguments. We shall work with the following *stabilizable and detectable* realizations for $\boldsymbol{P}$ and $\boldsymbol{K}$.[3]

$$\boldsymbol{P} = \begin{bmatrix} \boldsymbol{P}_{11} & \boldsymbol{P}_{12} \\ \boldsymbol{P}_{21} & \boldsymbol{P}_{22} \end{bmatrix} \tag{A.4.1}$$

$$\stackrel{s}{=} \left[\begin{array}{c|cc} A & B_1 & B_2 \\ \hline C_1 & D_{11} & D_{12} \\ C_2 & D_{21} & 0 \end{array}\right] \tag{A.4.2}$$

$$\boldsymbol{K} \stackrel{s}{=} \left[\begin{array}{c|c} \widehat{A} & \widehat{B} \\ \hline \widehat{C} & \widehat{D} \end{array}\right]. \tag{A.4.3}$$

The assumption that $D_{22} = 0$ in (A.4.1) is made in order to limit the proliferation of an unwieldy number of terms. If $D_{22} \neq 0$, one may restore the $D_{22} = 0$ situation by a loop shifting argument that absorbs D_{22} into $\boldsymbol{K}$ (see Section 4.6 for details). We do not make any assumptions concerning the dimensions of D_{21}, D_{12} or their rank. We also make no assumptions about the zeros of $\boldsymbol{P}_{12}$ or $\boldsymbol{P}_{21}$. That is, we are considering the internal stability of general linear fractional transformations,

[3]In what follows, it will be assumed without comment that any realization of $\boldsymbol{P}$ or $\boldsymbol{K}$ that we write down is stablizable and detectable. That is, (A, B, C) and $(\widehat{A}, \widehat{B}, \widehat{C})$ are stabilizable and detectable.

which do not have to satisfy the assumptions of the generalized regulator problem given in Section 4.2.1, although the results here do apply to that case.

By way of preparation, we begin by finding a realization for the closed-loop transfer function matrix that maps $\begin{bmatrix} w' & v_1' & v_2' \end{bmatrix}'$ to $\begin{bmatrix} z' & y' & u' \end{bmatrix}'$ in Figure A.5. Letting x denote the state of $\boldsymbol{P}$ and $\widehat{x}$ denote the state of $\boldsymbol{K}$, it follows by direct calculation that

$$\begin{aligned} \begin{bmatrix} \dot{x} \\ \dot{\widehat{x}} \end{bmatrix} &= \begin{bmatrix} A + B_2\widehat{D}C_2 & B_2\widehat{C} \\ \widehat{B}C_2 & \widehat{A} \end{bmatrix} \begin{bmatrix} x \\ \widehat{x} \end{bmatrix} \\ &\quad + \begin{bmatrix} B_1 + B_2\widehat{D}D_{21} & B_2\widehat{D} & B_2 \\ \widehat{B}D_{21} & \widehat{B} & 0 \end{bmatrix} \begin{bmatrix} w \\ v_1 \\ v_2 \end{bmatrix} \end{aligned} \tag{A.4.4}$$

$$\begin{aligned} \begin{bmatrix} z \\ y \\ u \end{bmatrix} &= \begin{bmatrix} C_1 + D_{12}\widehat{D}C_2 & D_{12}\widehat{C} \\ C_2 & 0 \\ \widehat{D}C_2 & \widehat{C} \end{bmatrix} \begin{bmatrix} x \\ \widehat{x} \end{bmatrix} \\ &\quad + \begin{bmatrix} D_{11} + D_{12}\widehat{D}D_{21} & D_{12}\widehat{D} & D_{12} \\ D_{21} & I & 0 \\ \widehat{D}D_{21} & \widehat{D} & I \end{bmatrix} \begin{bmatrix} w \\ v_1 \\ v_2 \end{bmatrix}. \end{aligned} \tag{A.4.5}$$

Our first result provides a state-space condition for internal stability.

Lemma A.4.1 *The linear fractional transformation $\mathcal{F}_\ell(\boldsymbol{P}, \boldsymbol{K})$ is internally stable if and only if the matrix*

$$\begin{bmatrix} A + B_2\widehat{D}C_2 & B_2\widehat{C} \\ \widehat{B}C_2 & \widehat{A} \end{bmatrix}$$

is asymptotically stable (i.e., has no eigenvalue in the closed-right-half plane).

Proof. To establish this result, all we need show is that the realization in (A.4.4) and (A.4.5) is stabilizable and detectable, since in this case the stability of the transfer function matrix is equivalent to the negativity of the real parts of all the eigenvalues of the realization's A-matrix.

Suppose that

$$\begin{bmatrix} A + B_2\widehat{D}C_2 - \lambda I & B_2\widehat{C} \\ \widehat{B}C_2 & \widehat{A} - \lambda I \\ C_1 + D_{12}\widehat{D}C_2 & D_{12}\widehat{C} \\ C_2 & 0 \\ \widehat{D}C_2 & \widehat{C} \end{bmatrix} \begin{bmatrix} w_1 \\ w_2 \end{bmatrix} = \begin{bmatrix} 0 \\ 0 \\ 0 \\ 0 \\ 0 \end{bmatrix}.$$

Then: row 4 $\Rightarrow C_2 w_1 = 0$; row 5 $\Rightarrow \widehat{C} w_2 = 0$; row 3 $\Rightarrow C_1 w_1 = 0$; row 1 $\Rightarrow (\lambda I - A) w_1 = 0$; and row 2 $\Rightarrow (\lambda I - \widehat{A}) w_2 = 0$. By the assumed detectability of

$(A, \begin{bmatrix} C_1 \\ C_2 \end{bmatrix})$ and $(\widehat{A}, \widehat{C})$, we conclude that $\mathrm{R_e}(\lambda) < 0$, or that $w_1 = 0$ and $w_2 = 0$. This proves the realization in (A.4.4) and (A.4.5) is detectable. The stabilizability of the realization may be established by a dual sequence of arguments which are omitted. ■

Some linear fractional transformations are not stabilizable by any controller. To see this one need only consider the case of $\boldsymbol{P}_{11}$ unstable and $\boldsymbol{P}_{21} = 0$. This means that $z = \boldsymbol{P}_{11}w$, and at least one of the nine transfer functions given in Definition A.4.1 is unstable no matter what the controller is. We now give necessary and sufficient conditions for the LFT to be stabilizable.

Lemma A.4.2 *$\boldsymbol{P}$ is stabilizable if and only if (A, B_2, C_2) is stabilizable and detectable.*

Proof. Suppose a stabilizing controller $\boldsymbol{K} \stackrel{s}{=} \left[\begin{array}{c|c} \widehat{A} & \widehat{B} \\ \hline \widehat{C} & \widehat{D} \end{array}\right]$ exists. By Lemma A.4.1

$$\begin{bmatrix} A + B_2\widehat{D}C_2 & B_2\widehat{C} \\ \widehat{B}C_2 & \widehat{A} \end{bmatrix} = \begin{bmatrix} A & 0 \\ \widehat{B}C_2 & \widehat{A} \end{bmatrix} + \begin{bmatrix} B_2 \\ 0 \end{bmatrix} \begin{bmatrix} \widehat{D}C_2 & \widehat{C} \end{bmatrix}$$

is stable, and the decomposition above proves that

$$\left(\begin{bmatrix} A & 0 \\ \widehat{B}C_2 & \widehat{A} \end{bmatrix}, \begin{bmatrix} B_2 \\ 0 \end{bmatrix} \right)$$

is stabilizable. It follows that (A, B_2) must be stabilizable. The detectability of (A, C_2) follows from a similar argument based on the decomposition

$$\begin{bmatrix} A + B_2\widehat{D}C_2 & B_2\widehat{C} \\ \widehat{B}C_2 & \widehat{A} \end{bmatrix} = \begin{bmatrix} A & B_2\widehat{C} \\ 0 & \widehat{A} \end{bmatrix} + \begin{bmatrix} B_2\widehat{D} \\ \widehat{B} \end{bmatrix} \begin{bmatrix} C_2 & 0 \end{bmatrix}.$$

Conversely, suppose (A, B_2, C_2) is stabilizable and detectable. Let F be a state-feedback gain such that $A - B_2F$ is asymptotically stable and let H be an observer gain such that $A - HC_2$ is asymptotically stable. The controller

$$\begin{aligned} \dot{\widehat{x}} &= (A - B_2F)\widehat{x} + H(y - C_2\widehat{x}) \\ u &= -F\widehat{x} + v_1, \end{aligned}$$

that is

$$\left[\begin{array}{c|c} \widehat{A} & \widehat{B} \\ \hline \widehat{C} & \widehat{D} \end{array}\right] = \left[\begin{array}{c|c} A - B_2F - HC_2 & H \\ \hline -F & 0 \end{array}\right],$$

leads to

$$\begin{bmatrix} A+B_2\widehat{D}C_2 & B_2\widehat{C} \\ \widehat{B}C_2 & \widehat{A} \end{bmatrix} = \begin{bmatrix} A & -B_2F \\ HC_2 & A-B_2F-HC_2 \end{bmatrix}$$
$$= \begin{bmatrix} I & 0 \\ I & I \end{bmatrix} \begin{bmatrix} A-B_2F & -B_2F \\ 0 & A-HC_2 \end{bmatrix} \begin{bmatrix} I & 0 \\ -I & I \end{bmatrix}$$

and the controller is seen to be stabilizing by Lemma A.4.1. ■

We now show that stabilizing $\boldsymbol{P}$ is equivalent to stabilizing $\boldsymbol{P}_{22}$.

Lemma A.4.3 *Suppose $\boldsymbol{P}$ is stabilizable. Then $\boldsymbol{K}$ is an internally-stabilizing controller for $\boldsymbol{P}$ if and only if it is an internally-stabilizing controller for $\boldsymbol{P}_{22}$.*

Proof. If $\boldsymbol{K}$ stabilizes $\boldsymbol{P}$, then it also stabilizes $\boldsymbol{P}_{22}$ (since the four transfer function matrices mapping v_1 and v_2 to y and u are stable). Now suppose that $\boldsymbol{K}$ stabilizes $\boldsymbol{P}_{22}$. It follows from this assumption and the stabilizability and detectability of (A, B_2, C_2) that

$$\begin{bmatrix} A+B_2\widehat{D}C_2 & B_2\widehat{C} \\ \widehat{B}C_2 & \widehat{A} \end{bmatrix}$$

must be stable; review the calculations in the proof of Lemma A.4.1. It now follows that $\boldsymbol{K}$ stabilizes $\boldsymbol{P}$. ■

Combining this with the parametrization of all stabilizing controllers for $\boldsymbol{P}_{22}$, we have:

Theorem A.4.4 *Suppose $\boldsymbol{P}$ is stabilizable. Let $\boldsymbol{P}_{22} = \boldsymbol{N}_r\boldsymbol{D}_r{}^{-1} = \boldsymbol{D}_l{}^{-1}\boldsymbol{N}_l$ be right and left coprime factorizations of $\boldsymbol{P}_{22}$, and let*

$$\begin{bmatrix} \boldsymbol{V}_r & \boldsymbol{U}_r \\ -\boldsymbol{N}_l & \boldsymbol{D}_l \end{bmatrix} \begin{bmatrix} \boldsymbol{D}_r & -\boldsymbol{U}_l \\ \boldsymbol{N}_r & \boldsymbol{V}_l \end{bmatrix} = \begin{bmatrix} I & 0 \\ 0 & I \end{bmatrix},$$

be the generalized Bezout equation of the corresponding doubly coprime factorization. Then the following are equivalent:

1. *$\boldsymbol{K}$ is an internally-stabilizing controller for the feedback loop in Figure A.5.*
2. *$\boldsymbol{K} = \boldsymbol{K}_1\boldsymbol{K}_2{}^{-1}$, in which*

$$\begin{bmatrix} \boldsymbol{K}_1 \\ \boldsymbol{K}_2 \end{bmatrix} = \begin{bmatrix} \boldsymbol{D}_r & -\boldsymbol{U}_l \\ \boldsymbol{N}_r & \boldsymbol{V}_l \end{bmatrix} \begin{bmatrix} \boldsymbol{Q} \\ I \end{bmatrix}, \qquad \boldsymbol{Q} \in \mathcal{RH}_\infty \tag{A.4.6}$$

3. *$\boldsymbol{K} = \boldsymbol{K}_4{}^{-1}\boldsymbol{K}_3$, in which*

$$\begin{bmatrix} \boldsymbol{K}_4 & -\boldsymbol{K}_3 \end{bmatrix} = \begin{bmatrix} I & -\boldsymbol{Q} \end{bmatrix} \begin{bmatrix} \boldsymbol{V}_r & \boldsymbol{U}_r \\ -\boldsymbol{N}_l & \boldsymbol{D}_l \end{bmatrix}, \quad \boldsymbol{Q} \in \mathcal{RH}_\infty \tag{A.4.7}$$

4.

$$\boldsymbol{K} = \mathcal{F}_l\left(\begin{bmatrix} -\boldsymbol{V}_r^{-1}\boldsymbol{U}_r & \boldsymbol{V}_r^{-1} \\ \boldsymbol{V}_l^{-1} & -\boldsymbol{V}_l^{-1}\boldsymbol{N}_r \end{bmatrix}, \boldsymbol{Q}\right). \tag{A.4.8}$$

With $\boldsymbol{K}$ as in (A.4.6), (A.4.7) or (A.4.8) above, the closed loop is given by

$$\begin{aligned} \mathcal{F}_l\left(\begin{bmatrix} \boldsymbol{P}_{11} & \boldsymbol{P}_{12} \\ \boldsymbol{P}_{21} & \boldsymbol{P}_{22} \end{bmatrix}, \boldsymbol{K}\right) &= \mathcal{F}_l\left(\begin{bmatrix} \boldsymbol{T}_{11} & \boldsymbol{T}_{12} \\ \boldsymbol{T}_{21} & 0 \end{bmatrix}, \boldsymbol{Q}\right) \\ &= \boldsymbol{T}_{11} + \boldsymbol{T}_{12}\boldsymbol{Q}\boldsymbol{T}_{21}, \end{aligned}$$

in which

$$\begin{bmatrix} \boldsymbol{T}_{11} & \boldsymbol{T}_{12} \\ \boldsymbol{T}_{21} & 0 \end{bmatrix} = \begin{bmatrix} \boldsymbol{P}_{11} - \boldsymbol{P}_{12}\boldsymbol{U}_l\boldsymbol{D}_l\boldsymbol{P}_{21} & \boldsymbol{P}_{12}\boldsymbol{D}_r \\ \boldsymbol{D}_l\boldsymbol{P}_{21} & 0 \end{bmatrix}. \tag{A.4.9}$$

This is an affine parametrization in $\boldsymbol{Q}$.

Proof. The result is a direct consequence of Theorem A.3.1 and Lemma A.4.3.
The formula for the closed loop is obtained by substituting for $\boldsymbol{K}$ from (A.4.6):

$$\begin{aligned} &\boldsymbol{P}_{11} + \boldsymbol{P}_{12}\boldsymbol{K}(I - \boldsymbol{P}_{22}\boldsymbol{K})^{-1}\boldsymbol{P}_{21} \\ &= \boldsymbol{P}_{11} + \boldsymbol{P}_{12}(\boldsymbol{D}_r\boldsymbol{Q} - \boldsymbol{U}_l)(\boldsymbol{N}_r\boldsymbol{Q} + \boldsymbol{V}_l)^{-1} \\ &\quad \times\left(I - \boldsymbol{D}_l^{-1}\boldsymbol{N}_l(\boldsymbol{D}_r\boldsymbol{Q} - \boldsymbol{U}_l)(\boldsymbol{N}_r\boldsymbol{Q} + \boldsymbol{V}_l)^{-1}\right)^{-1}\boldsymbol{P}_{21} \\ &= \boldsymbol{P}_{11} + \boldsymbol{P}_{12}(\boldsymbol{D}_r\boldsymbol{Q} - \boldsymbol{U}_l)\big(\boldsymbol{D}_l(\boldsymbol{N}_r\boldsymbol{Q} + \boldsymbol{V}_l) - \boldsymbol{N}_l(\boldsymbol{D}_r\boldsymbol{Q} - \boldsymbol{U}_l)\big)^{-1}\boldsymbol{D}_l\boldsymbol{P}_{21} \\ &= \boldsymbol{P}_{11} + \boldsymbol{P}_{12}(\boldsymbol{D}_r\boldsymbol{Q} - \boldsymbol{U}_l)\big((\boldsymbol{D}_l\boldsymbol{N}_r - \boldsymbol{N}_l\boldsymbol{D}_r)\boldsymbol{Q} + (\boldsymbol{D}_l\boldsymbol{V}_l + \boldsymbol{N}_l\boldsymbol{U}_l)\big)^{-1}\boldsymbol{D}_l\boldsymbol{P}_{21} \\ &= \boldsymbol{P}_{11} + \boldsymbol{P}_{12}(\boldsymbol{D}_r\boldsymbol{Q} - \boldsymbol{U}_l)\boldsymbol{D}_l\boldsymbol{P}_{21} \\ &= (\boldsymbol{P}_{11} - \boldsymbol{P}_{12}\boldsymbol{U}_l\boldsymbol{D}_l\boldsymbol{P}_{21}) + (\boldsymbol{P}_{12}\boldsymbol{D}_r)\boldsymbol{Q}(\boldsymbol{D}_l\boldsymbol{P}_{21}). \end{aligned}$$

Therefore, $\mathcal{F}_\ell(\boldsymbol{P}, \boldsymbol{K}) = \boldsymbol{T}_{11} + \boldsymbol{T}_{12}\boldsymbol{Q}\boldsymbol{T}_{21}$, with the $\boldsymbol{T}_{ij}$'s as in (A.4.9). ■

We now give a state-space realization for each of the $\boldsymbol{T}_{ij}$'s in equation (A.4.9) and for the generator of all controllers.

Lemma A.4.5 *Let the doubly coprime factorization in Theorem A.4.4 arise from a realization of $\boldsymbol{P}_{22}$ according to the state-space construction of Theorem A.2.2. Then all stabilizing controllers for $\boldsymbol{P}_{22}$ may be generated by*

$$\boldsymbol{K} = \mathcal{F}_\ell(\boldsymbol{K}_s, \boldsymbol{Q}),$$

in which

$$\boldsymbol{K}_s \stackrel{s}{=} \left[\begin{array}{c|cc} A - B_2F - HC_2 & H & B_2 \\ \hline -F & 0 & I \\ -C_2 & I & 0 \end{array}\right]. \tag{A.4.10}$$

Furthermore, a state-space realization of the $\boldsymbol{T}_{ij}$'s given in (A.4.9) is

$$\left[\begin{array}{cc} \boldsymbol{T}_{11} & \boldsymbol{T}_{12} \\ \boldsymbol{T}_{21} & 0 \end{array}\right] \stackrel{s}{=} \left[\begin{array}{cc|cc} A-B_2F & HC_2 & HD_{21} & B_2 \\ 0 & A-HC_2 & B_1-HD_{21} & 0 \\ \hline C_1-D_{12}F & C_1 & D_{11} & D_{12} \\ 0 & C_2 & D_{21} & 0 \end{array}\right].$$

Note that all the $\boldsymbol{T}_{ij}$'s are stable.

Proof. The state-space realization of the representation formula for all stabilizing controllers is immediate upon substituting $\boldsymbol{P}_{22} \stackrel{s}{=} \left[\begin{array}{c|c} A & B_2 \\ \hline C_2 & 0 \end{array}\right]$ into (A.3.5).

Now $\boldsymbol{T}$ is obtained as the composition of the two LFTs $\boldsymbol{P}$ and $\boldsymbol{K}$. That is, $\boldsymbol{T} = \mathcal{C}_\ell(\boldsymbol{P}, \boldsymbol{K}_s)$. The state-space formula for $\boldsymbol{T}$ is obtained by applying Lemma 4.1.1 and using the state transformation $\left[\begin{array}{cc} I & I \\ 0 & -I \end{array}\right]$. ■

A.4.1 The full-information configuration

The full-information configuration is a special case of a linear fractional transformation in which $\boldsymbol{P}$ has the state-space realization

$$\left[\begin{array}{c} \dot{x} \\ z \\ \left[\begin{array}{c} w \\ x \end{array}\right] \end{array}\right] = \left[\begin{array}{ccc} A & B_1 & B_2 \\ C_1 & D_{11} & D_{12} \\ \left[\begin{array}{c} 0 \\ I \end{array}\right] & \left[\begin{array}{c} I \\ 0 \end{array}\right] & \left[\begin{array}{c} 0 \\ 0 \end{array}\right] \end{array}\right] \left[\begin{array}{c} x \\ w \\ u \end{array}\right].$$

That is, the measurement is $y = \left[\begin{array}{cc} w' & x' \end{array}\right]'$. Choose any F such that $A - B_2F$ is asymptotically stable, and any $H = \left[\begin{array}{cc} H_1' & H_2' \end{array}\right]'$ such that $A - H_2$ is asymptotically stable (the choice of H_1 is completely arbitrary). Then by Lemma A.4.5, all stabilizing controllers are generated by

$$\begin{aligned} \dot{\widehat{x}} &= (A - B_2F)\widehat{x} + H_1w + H_2(x - \widehat{x}) + B_2r \\ u &= -F\widehat{x} + r \\ r &= \left[\begin{array}{cc} \boldsymbol{Q}_1 & \boldsymbol{Q}_2 \end{array}\right] \left[\begin{array}{c} w \\ x - \widehat{x} \end{array}\right]. \end{aligned}$$

Note that setting the free parameter $\boldsymbol{Q} = \left[\begin{array}{cc} \boldsymbol{Q}_1 & \boldsymbol{Q}_2 \end{array}\right]$ equal to zero results in the state estimate feedback law $u = -F\widehat{x}$, rather than the state feedback law $u = -Fx$, which is also a stabilizing controller (it is generated by choosing $\boldsymbol{Q}_2 = -F$ and $\boldsymbol{Q}_1 = 0$). It is therefore convenient to re-parametrize the generator of all controllers for the full-information problem.

Choose the matrix $H_2 = B_2F$ and write $\tilde{r} = r + F(x - \widehat{x})$. This results in the new parametrization

$$\dot{\widehat{x}} = (A - B_2F)\widehat{x} + H_1w + B_2\tilde{r}$$

$$
\begin{aligned}
u &= -Fx + \tilde{r} \\
\tilde{r} &= \begin{bmatrix} Q_1 & \tilde{Q}_2 \end{bmatrix} \begin{bmatrix} w \\ x - \widehat{x} \end{bmatrix},
\end{aligned}
$$

in which $\tilde{Q}_2 = Q_2 + F$. Now setting $\tilde{r}$ to zero (by setting $\begin{bmatrix} Q_1 & \tilde{Q}_2 \end{bmatrix} = 0$) results in $u = -Fx$.

The matrix H_1 is irrelevant from a stability view point, but the choice $H_1 = B_1$ seems sensible—it leads to the intuitively appealing dynamics

$$
\dot{\widehat{x}} = A\widehat{x} + B_1 w + B_2 u + B_2 F(x - \widehat{x})
$$

for the state of the controller. If $\widehat{x}(0) = x(0)$, then $\widehat{x}(t) = x(t)$ for all $t \geq 0$. That is, the state of the controller is a copy of the state of the plant.

Main points of the section

1. If P in the LFT $\mathcal{F}_\ell(P, K)$ has a stabilizable and detectable realization
$$
P \stackrel{s}{=} \left[\begin{array}{c|cc} A & B_1 & B_2 \\ \hline C_1 & D_{11} & D_{12} \\ C_2 & D_{21} & D_{22} \end{array}\right],
$$
then P is stabilizable if and only if (A, B_2, C_2) is stabilizable and detectable.
2. If P is stabilizable, K stabilizes P if and only if it stabilizes P_{22}.
3. The parametrization of all stabilizing controllers leads to an affine parametrization $T_{11} + T_{12}QT_{21}$ of all closed-loop transfer functions.
4. All stabilizing controllers for the full-information configuration may be obtained as a special case of the parametrization theory for linear fractional transformations.

A.5 Notes and References

The parametrization of all stabilizing controllers is a surprisingly recent development in linear system theory. It was first developed by Youla, Jabr and Bongiorno [41] and Kucera [122] using coprime polynomial matrix fraction descriptions. The methodology presented here, in which coprime factorizations over $\mathcal{RH}_\infty$ are used, was introduced by Desoer, Liu, Murray and Saeks [46]. These matters and more are developed in considerable detail in the book by Vidyasagar [205], and there is also a treatment in Doyle, Francis and Tannenbaum [53].

The parametrization of all stabilizing controllers for a stable plant has a longer history. Newton, Gould and Kaiser [158] use it to convert a closed-loop design problem into an open-loop one, and it is used in much the same way in the seminal

$\mathcal{H}_\infty$ paper by Zames [227]. It is often referred to as "the Q-parametrization", and is closely related to what the process control community calls internal model control (IMC)—see Morari and Zafiriou [151]. If $\boldsymbol{G}$ is stable, then all stabilizing controllers for the unity feedback configuration in Figure A.6 are given by $\boldsymbol{K} = \boldsymbol{Q}(I - \boldsymbol{GQ})^{-1}$. Substituting this formula for $\boldsymbol{K}$ shows that a stabilizing controller has the IMC

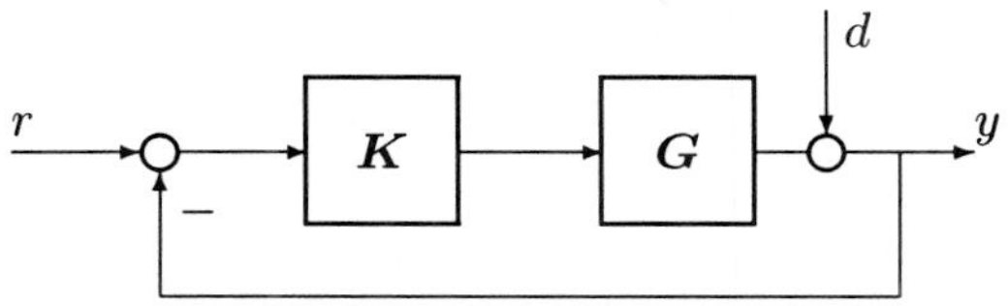

Figure A.6: Unity feedback loop with stable plant.

structure shown in Figure A.7. Provided $\boldsymbol{G}$ is stable, the IMC structure is stable

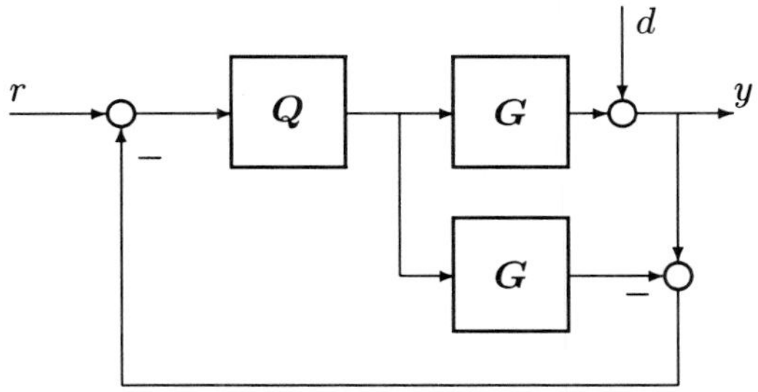

Figure A.7: IMC structure: stable plant.

for any stable $\boldsymbol{Q}$. The closed-loop transfer function matrix mapping r to y is $\boldsymbol{GQ}$, while the transfer function mapping d to y is $I - \boldsymbol{GQ}$. An obvious choice for $\boldsymbol{Q}$ is $\boldsymbol{Q} = \boldsymbol{G}^{-1}$, which will be stable provided the plant is minimum phase (and has no zeros at infinity either). Failing that, we can choose a constant $Q = \boldsymbol{G}^{-1}(0)$, or even $\boldsymbol{Q} \approx \boldsymbol{G}^{-1}$ over the range of frequencies in which good command response properties are desired. (We would naturally think to minimize $\|\boldsymbol{GQ} - \boldsymbol{M}\|_\infty$, in which $\boldsymbol{M}$ is the desired closed-loop transfer function.) The parallel-model-and-plant structure of IMC is also a feature of Smith predictors, which date from the 1950s. Further interpretations may be found in [151].

State-space formulae for coprime factorizations over $\mathcal{RH}_\infty$ were first given by Khargonekar and Sontag [117]; the converse result, that all coprime factorizations arise in this way (see Problem A.4), is due to Nett, Jacobson and Balas [156], who give the state-space formulae for doubly coprime factorizations.

The internal stability of the generalized regulator is considered in Doyle [52], Francis [65] and Safonov, Jonckheere, Verma and Limebeer [181]. There is a purely transfer function matrix approach in Green [84].

The internal stability of the full-information configuration has received special attention from Zhou [229] and Liu, Mita and Kawatani [138].

A.6 Problems

Problem A.1. Suppose $\boldsymbol{N}$, $\boldsymbol{D}$ are $\mathcal{RH}_\infty$ transfer function matrices such that $\boldsymbol{N}\boldsymbol{D}^{-1} = \boldsymbol{N}_c\boldsymbol{D}_c^{-1}$, in which $\boldsymbol{N}_c$ and $\boldsymbol{D}_c$ are right coprime. Show that

$$\begin{bmatrix} \boldsymbol{N} \\ \boldsymbol{D} \end{bmatrix} = \begin{bmatrix} \boldsymbol{N}c \\ \boldsymbol{D}_c \end{bmatrix} \boldsymbol{W},$$

in which $\boldsymbol{W} \in \mathcal{RH}_\infty$.

Problem A.2. Show that $\boldsymbol{N}, \boldsymbol{D} \in \mathcal{RH}_\infty$ are r.c. if and only if $\begin{bmatrix} \boldsymbol{N}' & \boldsymbol{D}' \end{bmatrix}'(s)$ has full column rank for all s in the closed-right-half plane (including infinity). Conclude that the number of poles of $\boldsymbol{G}$ in the closed-right-half plane is equal to the number of zeros of $\det \boldsymbol{D}(s)$ in the closed-right-half plane.

Problem A.3.

1. Verify all the calculations requested to complete the proof of Theorem A.2.2.
2. Verify the state-space equations (A.2.6) and (A.2.7) for the controller $\boldsymbol{K} = -\boldsymbol{V}_r^{-1}\boldsymbol{U}_r$.

Problem A.4. Suppose $\boldsymbol{G} = \boldsymbol{N}\boldsymbol{D}^{-1}$ is a r.c.f. and $\boldsymbol{G}$ is proper. Show that there exist matrices A, B, C, D, F and W such that (A, B, C, D) is a stabilizable and detectable realization of $\boldsymbol{G}$, W is nonsingular, $A - BW^{-1}F$ is asymptotically stable and

$$\begin{bmatrix} \boldsymbol{D} \\ \boldsymbol{N} \end{bmatrix} \stackrel{s}{=} \left[\begin{array}{c|c} A - BW^{-1}F & BW^{-1} \\ \hline -W^{-1}F & W^{-1} \\ C - DW^{-1}F & DW^{-1} \end{array}\right].$$

(Hint: Write down a minimal realization of $\begin{bmatrix} \boldsymbol{D} \\ \boldsymbol{N} \end{bmatrix}$ and work out $\boldsymbol{N}\boldsymbol{D}^{-1}$.)

Problem A.5. Verify the state-space formula (A.3.5) for all stabilizing controllers.

Problem A.6. Suppose $\boldsymbol{G}$ is stable and $\boldsymbol{G}(0)$ is nonsingular. For the loop in Figure A.3, find all stabilizing controllers such that the steady-state value of y is zero when v is a step input and $w = 0$.

Problem A.7. Show that any proper rational transfer function matrix $\boldsymbol{G}$ has a r.c.f. $\boldsymbol{G} = \boldsymbol{N}\boldsymbol{D}^{-1}$ such that

$$\begin{bmatrix} \boldsymbol{D}^\sim & \boldsymbol{N}^\sim \end{bmatrix} \begin{bmatrix} \boldsymbol{D} \\ \boldsymbol{N} \end{bmatrix} = I.$$

Such a r.c.f. is called a normalized right coprime factorization. Now suppose $\boldsymbol{G}$ has stabilizable and detectable realization (A, B, C, D). Find state-space formulae for a normalized coprime factorization of $\boldsymbol{G}$.

(Hint: Use the general state-space formula for $\boldsymbol{N}$ and $\boldsymbol{D}$ given in Problem A.4 and apply the state-space characterization of allpass systems in Theorem 3.2.1. (You may find it helpful to consider the case when $D = 0$ first.) You will obtain a Riccati equation that is identical to one required in the LQ problem of minimizing $\|z\|_2^2$, in which

$$\dot{x} = Ax + Bu, \qquad z = \begin{bmatrix} C \\ 0 \end{bmatrix} x + \begin{bmatrix} D \\ I \end{bmatrix} u.$$

Can you explain why these problems are related?)

The aim of the following problems is to show how to reduce the generalized regulator problem to a four-block problem.

Assume that $\boldsymbol{P}$ has the simplified form

$$\boldsymbol{P} = \left[\begin{array}{c|cc} A & B_1 & B_2 \\ \hline C_1 & 0 & D_{12} \\ C_2 & D_{21} & 0 \end{array}\right],$$

in which (A, B_2, C_2) is stabilizable and detectable and $D_{12}'D_{12} = I$, $D_{21}D_{21}' = I$. Assume also that

$$\begin{bmatrix} A - j\omega I & B_2 \\ C_1 & D_{12} \end{bmatrix}, \qquad \begin{bmatrix} A - j\omega I & B_1 \\ C_2 & D_{21} \end{bmatrix}$$

have full column and row rank respectively, for all real ω.

Problem A.8. Choose F and H to be the state feedback and Kalman filter gain matrices from the solution of the LQG problem associated with the generalized plant $\boldsymbol{P}$. Show that the transfer function matrices $\boldsymbol{T}_{12}$ and $\boldsymbol{T}_{21}$ in Lemma A.4.5 satisfy $\boldsymbol{T}_{12}^{\sim}\boldsymbol{T}_{12} = I$ and $\boldsymbol{T}_{21}\boldsymbol{T}_{21}^{\sim} = I$.

Problem A.9. Suppose that $\boldsymbol{T}$ results from choosing F and H as in Problem A.8. Let X and Y denote the solutions of the control and filter Riccati equations for the LQG problem, and let $\widehat{D}_{12}$ and $\widehat{D}_{21}$ be orthogonal completions of D_{12} and D_{21}. Show that

$$\begin{bmatrix} \widehat{\boldsymbol{T}}_{12} & \boldsymbol{T}_{12} \end{bmatrix} \stackrel{s}{=} \left[\begin{array}{c|cc} A - B_2F & \widehat{B} & B_2 \\ \hline C_1 - D_{12}F & \widehat{D}_{12} & D_{12} \end{array}\right]$$

$$\begin{bmatrix} \widehat{\boldsymbol{T}}_{21} \\ \boldsymbol{T}_{21} \end{bmatrix} \stackrel{s}{=} \left[\begin{array}{c|c} A - HC_2 & B_1 - HD_{21} \\ \hline \widehat{C} & \widehat{D}_{21} \\ C_2 & D_{21} \end{array}\right]$$

are square and allpass if $\widehat{B} = -X^{\#}C_1'\widehat{D}_{12}$ and $\widehat{C} = -\widehat{D}_{21}B_1'Y^{\#}$, in which $X^{\#}$, $Y^{\#}$ are Moore-Penrose pseudo inverses of X and Y.

Problem A.10.

1. Show that if $\boldsymbol{K}$ is a stabilizing controller for $\boldsymbol{P}$, then

$$\|\mathcal{F}_\ell(\boldsymbol{P}, \boldsymbol{K})\|_{2,\infty} = \left\| \begin{bmatrix} \boldsymbol{R}_{11} & \boldsymbol{R}_{12} \\ \boldsymbol{R}_{21} & \boldsymbol{R}_{22} + \boldsymbol{Q} \end{bmatrix} \right\|_{2,\infty}$$

   for some $\boldsymbol{Q} \in \mathcal{RH}_\infty$. The notation $\|\cdot\|_{2,\infty}$ means that the norm is either the 2-norm or the infinity norm. Find a state-space realization of $\boldsymbol{R}$ and show that $\boldsymbol{R} \in \mathcal{RH}_\infty^-$.

   (Hint: For suitable $\boldsymbol{T}$, $\boldsymbol{R} = \begin{bmatrix} \widehat{\boldsymbol{T}}_{12}^\sim \\ \boldsymbol{T}_{12}^\sim \end{bmatrix} \boldsymbol{T}_{11} \begin{bmatrix} \widehat{\boldsymbol{T}}_{21}^\sim & \boldsymbol{T}_{21}^\sim \end{bmatrix}$.)

2. Conclude that the controller that minimizes $\|\mathcal{F}_\ell(\boldsymbol{P}, \boldsymbol{K})\|_2$ is obtained by setting $\boldsymbol{Q} = 0$ and that the minimum norm is $\|\boldsymbol{R}\|_2$.

   (Hint: use the result of Problem 11.2.)

Appendix B

Discrete-Time $\mathcal{H}_\infty$ Synthesis Theory

B.1 Introduction

This Appendix offers a brief development of $\mathcal{H}_\infty$ synthesis theory for discrete-time systems. Our approach parallels that adopted for the continuous-time theory, in which the solution to the infinite-horizon problem is obtained via limiting arguments from the finite-horizon case. In order to contain the treatment to a reasonable length, we will not offer detailed commentary or hesitate to leave parts of the development to the exercises.

With the continuous-time synthesis theory complete, a natural approach to the discrete-time synthesis problem is to transform it into continuous-time via the bilinear transformation $z \mapsto s = \frac{z-1}{z+1}$. A continuous-time controller may then be found and transformed back to discrete-time via the inverse map $z = \frac{1+s}{1-s}$. Although this procedure is valid, it has a number of disadvantages including:

1. The bilinear transformation cannot be used for time-varying or finite-horizon problems.

2. Since properness is not preserved by the bilinear transformation, special care needs to be taken to avoid nonproper controllers.[1]

3. The selection of weighting functions in design problems is made more difficult by frequency warping phenomena.

4. Although the bilinear transformation will lead to controller formulas for the discrete-time synthesis problem, there are theoretical advantages to be gained from a solution in "natural coordinates".

[1] A linear time-invariant system $\boldsymbol{G}$ is causal if and only if it's transfer function matrix is proper—that is $\|\boldsymbol{G}(\infty)\| < \infty$.

B.1.1 Definitions

We shall be concerned with signals that are sequences. We write $f = \{f_k\}_{-\infty}^{\infty}$, in which each f_k is in $\mathbb{R}^n$. The spaces $\ell_2(-\infty,\infty)$ and $\ell_2[0,N]$ are defined by

$$\begin{aligned}\ell_2(-\infty,\infty) &= \{f : \|f\|_2 < \infty\}\\ \ell_2[0,N] &= \left\{f : f_k = 0 \text{ for } k \notin [0,N], \|f\|_{2,[0,N]} < \infty\right\},\end{aligned}$$

in which the norms are defined by

$$\begin{aligned}\|f\|_2 &= \left\{\sum_{k=-\infty}^{\infty} f_k' f_k\right\}^{\frac{1}{2}}\\ \|f\|_{2,[0,N]} &= \left\{\sum_{k=0}^{N} f_k' f_k\right\}^{\frac{1}{2}}.\end{aligned}$$

(We will often use the shorthand $f \in \ell_2[0,N]$ for the statement that the projection of f obtained by setting $f_k = 0$ for $k \notin [0,N]$ is an element of $\ell_2[0,N]$.) The space $\ell_2[0,\infty)$ is

$$\ell_2[0,\infty) = \{f \in \ell_2(-\infty,\infty) : f_k = 0 \text{ for } k \leq -1\}.$$

Theorem B.1.1 *Consider a signal z generated by*

$$\begin{bmatrix} x_{k+1} \\ z_k \end{bmatrix} = \begin{bmatrix} A(k) \\ C(k) \end{bmatrix} x_k,$$

in which every entry of $A(k)$ and $C(k)$ is bounded.

1. The finite-horizon case*:*

   (a) $z \in \ell_2[0,N]$ for all x_0 and all finite $N \geq 0$.

   (b) $\|z\|_{2,[0,N]}^2 = x_0' Q(0) x_0$, with $Q(0)$ generated by

$$Q(k) = A'(k)Q(k+1)A(k) + C'(k)C(k), \qquad Q(N+1) = 0.$$

2. The infinite-horizon case*: Assume that A and C are constant.*

   (a) The following are equivalent:

   (i) $z \in \ell_2[0,\infty)$ for all x_0.

   (ii) $CA^k \to 0$ as $k \to \infty$.

   (iii) Every observable eigenspace of A is asymptotically stable.

   (iv) The solution to the Lyapunov equation

$$Q(k) = A'Q(k+1)A + C'C, \qquad Q(N+1) = 0,$$

is uniformly bounded on $k \le N$.
In this case, $Q = \lim_{k\to-\infty} Q(k)$ *exists, is independent of* N *and satisfies*

$$Q = A'QA + C'C. \tag{B.1.1}$$

Furthermore, $Q \ge 0$.

(v) *There exists* $Q \ge 0$ *satisfying (B.1.1). (Such a* Q *may not be equal to* $\lim_{k\to-\infty} Q(k)$, *which is the smallest nonnegative definite solution to (B.1.1).)*

(b) *If the conditions in Item 2a hold, then* $\|z\|_2^2 = x_0'Qx_0$, *in which* $Q = \lim_{k\to-\infty} Q(k)$.

Proof. This is left as an exercise (Problem B.1). ■

For a system $\boldsymbol{G}$, we define the finite-horizon norm to be

$$\|\boldsymbol{G}\|_{[0,N]} = \sup_{w\neq 0\in\ell_2[0,N]} \frac{\|\boldsymbol{G}w\|_{2,[0,N]}}{\|w\|_{2,[0,N]}}$$

and the infinite-horizon norm to be

$$\|\boldsymbol{G}\|_\infty = \sup_{w\neq 0\in\ell_2(-\infty,\infty)} \frac{\|\boldsymbol{G}w\|_2}{\|w\|_2}.$$

The space $\mathcal{L}_\infty$ consists of all linear time-invariant systems for which $\|\boldsymbol{G}\|_\infty$ is finite. If $\boldsymbol{G}$ is the transfer function matrix of such a system (*i.e.*, $\boldsymbol{G}$ is the Z-transform of the system's pulse response), then

$$\|\boldsymbol{G}\|_\infty = \sup_{\theta\in(-\pi,\pi]} \overline{\sigma}\big(\boldsymbol{G}(e^{j\theta})\big).$$

A system $\boldsymbol{G}$ is *stable* if $\boldsymbol{G}w \in \ell_2[0,\infty)$ for any $w \in \ell_2[0,\infty)$. A linear time-invariant system described by a transfer function matrix $\boldsymbol{G}$ is stable if and only if $\boldsymbol{G}(z)$ is analytic in $|z| > 1$ and $\|\boldsymbol{G}\|_\infty < \infty$. This space is known as $\mathcal{H}_\infty$. If $\boldsymbol{G} : w \mapsto z$ according to

$$\begin{bmatrix} x_{k+1} \\ z_k \end{bmatrix} = \begin{bmatrix} A & B \\ C & D \end{bmatrix} \begin{bmatrix} x_k \\ w_k \end{bmatrix},$$

then $\boldsymbol{G} \in \mathcal{H}_\infty$ if and only if $Ax = \lambda x$, $x \neq 0$ implies that: (a) $|\lambda| < 1$ or (b) λ is an unobservable or uncontrollable mode. The matrix A is called *asymptotically stable* if $|\lambda_i(A)| < 1$ for all i.

B.1.2 Problem statement

We consider the generalized regulator problem defined by the LFT

$$\begin{aligned} \begin{bmatrix} z \\ y \end{bmatrix} &= \begin{bmatrix} \boldsymbol{P}_{11} & \boldsymbol{P}_{12} \\ \boldsymbol{P}_{21} & \boldsymbol{P}_{22} \end{bmatrix} \begin{bmatrix} w \\ u \end{bmatrix}, \\ u &= \boldsymbol{K} y. \end{aligned}$$

The generalized plant $\boldsymbol{P} = \begin{bmatrix} \boldsymbol{P}_{11} & \boldsymbol{P}_{12} \\ \boldsymbol{P}_{21} & \boldsymbol{P}_{22} \end{bmatrix}$ is defined by the linear difference equation

$$\begin{bmatrix} x_{k+1} \\ z_k \\ y_k \end{bmatrix} = \begin{bmatrix} A(k) & B_1(k) & B_2(k) \\ C_1(k) & D_{11}(k) & D_{12}(k) \\ C_2(k) & D_{21}(k) & D_{22}(k) \end{bmatrix} \begin{bmatrix} x_k \\ w_k \\ u_k \end{bmatrix}. \tag{B.1.2}$$

In (B.1.2), w_k is an l-dimensional exogenous input (or model error output—see Section 4.2.1), u_k is an m-dimensional control, y is a q-dimensional vector of controller inputs and z_k is a p-dimensional objective signal. The state vector x_k has dimension n.

We assume that $D_{12}(k)$ has full column rank and $D_{21}(k)$ has full row rank for all k of interest. Equivalently, we assume

$$D_{12}'(k)D_{12}(k) > 0 \qquad \text{and} \qquad D_{21}(k)D_{21}'(k) > 0 \tag{B.1.3}$$

for all k of interest. We do not assume that $D_{11}(k) = 0$, or that $D_{12}'(k)D_{12}(k) = I$, or that $D_{21}(k)D_{21}'(k) = I$, since these assumptions only produce slight simplifications in the formulas. We shall, however, assume that the loop-shifting transformation that enables us to set $D_{22}(k) = 0$ has been carried out (see Section 4.6).

The finite-horizon case

In the case of a finite horizon, we seek necessary and sufficient conditions for the existence of a causal, linear controller $\boldsymbol{K}$ such that

$$\|z\|_{2,[0,N]}^2 - \gamma^2\|w\|_{2,[0,N]}^2 + x_{N+1}'\Delta x_{N+1} \le -\epsilon\|w\|_{2,[0,N]}^2, \tag{B.1.4}$$

when $x_0 = 0$. We assume that (B.1.3) holds for all $k = 0, \ldots, N$ and that the terminal penalty matrix Δ is nonnegative definite. As in the continuous-time case, we will use Δ to ensure that a stabilizing controller is obtained when we consider the limit $N \to \infty$. If $\Delta = 0$, then (B.1.4) is equivalent to

$$\|\mathcal{F}_\ell(\boldsymbol{P}, \boldsymbol{K})\|_{[0,N]} < \gamma.$$

When such controllers exist, we would like a parametrization of all of them.

The infinite-horizon case

In the case of an infinite horizon, we assume the system (B.1.2) is *time-invariant* and satisfies:

1. (A, B_2, C_2) is stabilizable and detectable;
2. $D_{12}'D_{12} > 0$ and $D_{21}D_{21}' > 0$;
3. $$\text{rank}\begin{bmatrix} A - e^{j\theta}I & B_2 \\ C_1 & D_{12} \end{bmatrix} = n + m, \qquad \text{for all } \theta \in (-\pi, \pi]; \tag{B.1.5}$$
4. $$\text{rank}\begin{bmatrix} A - e^{j\theta}I & B_1 \\ C_2 & D_{21} \end{bmatrix} = n + q, \qquad \text{for all } \theta \in (-\pi, \pi]. \tag{B.1.6}$$

We seek a causal, linear, time-invariant and finite-dimensional controller such that the closed-loop system $\mathcal{F}_\ell(\boldsymbol{P}, \boldsymbol{K})$ is internally stable and satisfies

$$\|\mathcal{F}_\ell(\boldsymbol{P}, \boldsymbol{K})\|_\infty < \gamma. \tag{B.1.7}$$

This is equivalent to

$$\|z\|_2^2 - \gamma^2\|w\|_2^2 \leq -\epsilon\|w\|_2^2 \tag{B.1.8}$$

for all $w \in \ell_2[0, \infty)$ and some $\epsilon > 0$ when $x_0 = 0$.

B.2 Full information

In the full-information problem, we drop the requirement that the control signal be generated from y and seek a linear, full-information controller

$$u = \boldsymbol{K}\begin{bmatrix} x \\ w \end{bmatrix} \tag{B.2.1}$$

such that (B.1.4) or (B.1.8) is satisfied.

B.2.1 Finite horizon

It is convenient to define

$$\phi_k = \begin{bmatrix} w_k \\ u_k \end{bmatrix} \text{ and } \psi_k = \begin{bmatrix} z_k \\ w_k \end{bmatrix},$$

which enables us to write

$$\|z\|_{2,[0,N]}^2 - \gamma^2\|w\|_{2,[0,N]}^2 = \sum_{k=0}^{N} \psi_k' J \psi_k,$$

in which

$$J = \begin{bmatrix} I_p & 0 \\ 0 & -\gamma^2 I_l \end{bmatrix}.$$

The relevant system equations now take the simple form

$$\begin{bmatrix} x_{k+1} \\ \psi_k \end{bmatrix} = \begin{bmatrix} A(k) & B(k) \\ \overline{C}(k) & \overline{D}(k) \end{bmatrix} \begin{bmatrix} x_k \\ \phi_k \end{bmatrix}, \tag{B.2.2}$$

in which

$$\begin{bmatrix} A(k) & B(k) \\ \overline{C}(k) & \overline{D}(k) \end{bmatrix} = \left[\begin{array}{c|cc} A(k) & B_1(k) & B_2(k) \\ \hline C_1(k) & D_{11}(k) & D_{12}(k) \\ 0 & I_l & 0 \end{array}\right].$$

In dynamic programming terms, the controller is a causal, linear decision maker that chooses the $N+1$ vectors u_k, $k = 0, 1, \ldots, N$. An iterative argument, which proceeds backwards from the terminal time $k = N$, determines the control policy, *i.e.*, the strategy for choosing the vectors u_k, $k = 0, 1, \ldots, N$.

At time k, the decision u_k is taken, w_k occurs and

$$z_k' z_k - \gamma^2 w_k' w_k + x_{k+1}' X_\infty(k+1) x_{k+1}$$

is the cost of stage k. The matrix $X_\infty(k+1)$ is a "cost-to-go" matrix that will be determined by the dynamic programming argument—at this point of the development, however, $X_\infty(k+1)$ is an arbitrary nonnegative definite matrix.

The stage k cost may be determined via the dynamics from x_k, w_k and u_k, since

$$\begin{aligned} & z_k' z_k - \gamma^2 w_k' w_k + x_{k+1}' X_\infty(k+1) x_{k+1} \\ &= \begin{bmatrix} x_{k+1}' & \psi_k' \end{bmatrix} \begin{bmatrix} X_\infty(k+1) & 0 \\ 0 & J \end{bmatrix} \begin{bmatrix} x_{k+1} \\ \psi_k \end{bmatrix} \\ &= \begin{bmatrix} x_k \\ \phi_k \end{bmatrix}' \begin{bmatrix} A & B \\ \overline{C} & \overline{D} \end{bmatrix}' \begin{bmatrix} X_\infty(k+1) & 0 \\ 0 & J \end{bmatrix} \begin{bmatrix} A & B \\ \overline{C} & \overline{D} \end{bmatrix} \begin{bmatrix} x_k \\ \phi_k \end{bmatrix} \\ &= \begin{bmatrix} x_k \\ \phi_k \end{bmatrix}' \begin{bmatrix} A' X_\infty(k+1) A + \overline{C}' J \overline{C} & L' \\ L & R \end{bmatrix} \begin{bmatrix} x_k \\ \phi_k \end{bmatrix}, \end{aligned} \tag{B.2.3}$$

in which

$$R(k) = \overline{D}'(k) J \overline{D}(k) + B'(k) X_\infty(k+1) B(k) \tag{B.2.4}$$

$$L(k) = \overline{D}'(k) J \overline{C}(k) + B'(k) X_\infty(k+1) A(k). \tag{B.2.5}$$

Partition the matrices R and L conformably with $\phi = \begin{bmatrix} w' & u' \end{bmatrix}'$, viz

$$R = \begin{bmatrix} R_1 & R_2' \\ R_2 & R_3 \end{bmatrix}, \qquad L = \begin{bmatrix} L_1 \\ L_2 \end{bmatrix}, \tag{B.2.6}$$

with R_3 $m \times m$ and L_2 $m \times n$.

The dynamic programming argument will show $R_3(k) > 0$ and $\nabla(k) \leq -\epsilon I$ for $k = N, N-1, \ldots, 0$ are necessary for the existence of a controller satisfying (B.1.4). A sequence $\nabla(k)$ will be defined in terms of a sequence of matrices $X_\infty(k+1)$ that satisfy a Riccati difference equation with the terminal condition $X_\infty(N+1) = \Delta \geq 0$. This iterative process will also generate a candidate controller. In the sufficiency proof, following the theorem statement, we show that this controller does indeed satisfy (B.1.4) for some $\epsilon > 0$ when $x_0 = 0$.

Schur decomposition of R

Suppose that at stage k, $X_\infty(k+1)$ is some given nonnegative definite matrix. Since $D_{12}'(k)D_{12}(k) > 0$, we have

$$R_3(k) = D_{12}'(k)D_{12}(k) + B_2'(k)X_\infty(k+1)B_2(k) > 0,$$

and we may write the Schur decomposition

$$\begin{bmatrix} R_1 & R_2' \\ R_2 & R_3 \end{bmatrix} = \begin{bmatrix} I & R_2'R_3^{-1} \\ 0 & I \end{bmatrix} \begin{bmatrix} \nabla & 0 \\ 0 & R_3 \end{bmatrix} \begin{bmatrix} I & 0 \\ R_3^{-1}R_2 & I \end{bmatrix}, \tag{B.2.7}$$

in which

$$\nabla(k) = (R_1 - R_2'R_3^{-1}R_2)(k). \tag{B.2.8}$$

This means we may write

$$\phi_k' R \phi_k = w_k' \nabla w_k + (u_k + R_3^{-1}R_2 w_k)' R_3 (u_k + R_3^{-1}R_2 w_k), \tag{B.2.9}$$

in which the time dependence of the $R_2(k)$, $R_3(k)$ and $\nabla(k)$ matrices has been suppressed.

A necessary condition

Suppose that $X_\infty(k+1) \geq 0$ and that there exists a causal, linear controller that satisfies

$$\|z\|_{2,[0,k]}^2 - \gamma^2 \|w\|_{2,[0,k]}^2 + x_{k+1}' X_\infty(k+1) x_{k+1} \leq -\epsilon \|w\|_{2,[0,k]}^2 \tag{B.2.10}$$

for all $w \in \ell_2[0,k]$ when $x_0 = 0$. If the exogenous input w is such that $w_i = 0$ for all $i < k$, then the initial condition $x_0 = 0$ implies that $u_i = 0$ for $i < k$ and $x_i = 0$ for $i \leq k$, since the controller is causal and the state dynamics are strictly causal. Hence

$$\begin{aligned} -\epsilon w_k' w_k &= -\epsilon \|w\|_{[0,k]}^2 \\ &\geq \|z\|_{2,[0,k]}^2 - \gamma^2 \|w\|_{2,[0,k]} + x_{k+1}' X_\infty(k+1) x_{k+1} \\ &= z_k' z_k - \gamma^2 w_k' w_k + x_{k+1}' X_\infty(k+1) x_{k+1} \\ &= \phi_k' R(k) \phi_k \\ &= w_k' \nabla(k) w_k + (u_k + R_3^{-1}R_2 w_k)' R_3 (u_k + R_3^{-1}R_2 w_k) \\ &\geq w_k' \nabla(k) w_k, \end{aligned}$$

in which we have invoked (B.2.10), (B.2.3) and (B.2.9). Since w_k is arbitrary, we conclude that $\nabla(k) \leq -\epsilon I_l$.

Thus $X_\infty(k+1) \geq 0$ (and $D_{12}'(k)D_{12}(k) > 0$) implies $R_3(k) > 0$ and the existence of a controller that satisfies (B.2.10) when $x_0 = 0$ implies that $\nabla(k) \leq -\epsilon I_l$.

A consequence of $R_3 > 0$ and $\nabla \leq -\epsilon I$

Suppose that $R_3(k) > 0$ and that $\nabla(k) \leq -\epsilon I$. From the Schur decomposition (B.2.7), we see that $R(k)$ is nonsingular, so we may take Schur complements with respect to $R(k)$ in (B.2.3) to obtain

$$\begin{aligned} & z_k'z_k - \gamma^2 w_k'w_k + x_{k+1}'X_\infty(k+1)x_{k+1} \\ = & \begin{bmatrix} x_k \\ \phi_k + R^{-1}Lx_k \end{bmatrix}' \begin{bmatrix} X_\infty(k) & 0 \\ 0 & R(k) \end{bmatrix} \begin{bmatrix} x_k \\ \phi_k + R^{-1}Lx_k \end{bmatrix}, \end{aligned} \quad \text{(B.2.11)}$$

in which we have defined $X_\infty(k)$ according to the Riccati difference equation

$$\begin{aligned} X_\infty(k) &= A'(k)X_\infty(k+1)A(k) + \overline{C}'(k)J\overline{C}(k) \\ &\quad - L'(k)R^{-1}(k)L(k). \end{aligned} \quad \text{(B.2.12)}$$

Substituting the Schur decomposition of $R(k)$ into (B.2.11), we see that the stage cost is given by

$$\begin{aligned} & z_k'z_k - \gamma^2 w_k'w_k + x_{k+1}'X_\infty(k+1)x_{k+1} \\ &= x_k'X_\infty(k)x_k + (w_k - w_k^*)'\nabla(k)(w_k - w_k^*) \\ &\quad + (u_k - u_k^*)'R_3(k)(u_k - u_k^*), \end{aligned} \quad \text{(B.2.13)}$$

in which

$$\begin{bmatrix} w_k - w_k^* \\ u_k - u_k^* \end{bmatrix} = \begin{bmatrix} I & 0 \\ R_3^{-1}R_2 & I \end{bmatrix} \left(\begin{bmatrix} w_k \\ u_k \end{bmatrix} + R^{-1}Lx_k \right).$$

Expanding R^{-1} using (B.2.7) reveals that

$$\begin{bmatrix} w_k^* \\ u_k^* \end{bmatrix} = - \begin{bmatrix} \nabla^{-1}L_\nabla & 0 \\ R_3^{-1}L_2 & R_3^{-1}R_2 \end{bmatrix} \begin{bmatrix} x_k \\ w_k \end{bmatrix}, \quad \text{(B.2.14)}$$

in which

$$L_\nabla(k) = (L_1 - R_2'R_3^{-1}L_2)(k). \quad \text{(B.2.15)}$$

Equation (B.2.13) is an algebraic identity which holds for any x_k, u_k and w_k. Setting $u_k = u_k^*$ and $w_k = 0$ in (B.2.13), we see that

$$x_k'X_\infty(k)x_k = z_k'z_k + x_{k+1}'X_\infty(k+1)x_{k+1} - (w_k^*)'\nabla(k)w_k^* \geq 0 \quad \text{(B.2.16)}$$

for any x_k and we conclude that $X_\infty(k) \geq 0$.

Decomposition of the cost function

The necessary condition $\nabla(k) \leq -\epsilon I$ was obtained by considering exogenous inputs w that are zero up to time k. We now turn our attention to general inputs.

For any $k \geq 1$, we may write

$$\begin{aligned} &\|z\|_{2,[0,k]}^2 - \gamma^2\|w\|_{2,[0,k]}^2 + x_{k+1}' X_\infty(k+1)x_{k+1} \\ &= \|z\|_{2,[0,k-1]}^2 - \gamma^2\|w\|_{2,[0,k-1]}^2 \\ &\quad + z_k' z_k - \gamma^2 w_k' w_k + x_{k+1}' X_\infty(k+1)x_{k+1} \\ &= \|z\|_{2,[0,k-1]}^2 - \gamma^2\|w\|_{2,[0,k-1]}^2 + \text{(cost of stage } k). \end{aligned}$$

Now suppose that $R_3(k) > 0$ and that $\nabla(k) \leq -\epsilon I$. Then w_k^* and u_k^* are well defined and from (B.2.13) we have

$$\begin{aligned} &\|z\|_{2,[0,k]}^2 - \gamma^2\|w\|_{2,[0,k]}^2 + x_{k+1}' X_\infty(k+1)x_{k+1} \\ &= \|z\|_{2,[0,k-1]}^2 - \gamma^2\|w\|_{2,[0,k-1]}^2 + x_k' X_\infty(k)x_k \\ &\quad + (u_k - u_k^*)' R_3(u_k - u_k^*) + (w_k - w_k^*)'\nabla(w_k - w_k^*). \end{aligned} \tag{B.2.17}$$

If u_k is generated by a causal controller, then x_k and w_k^* do not depend on u_k, since the state dynamics are strictly causal. We conclude that whatever (causal) control law is applied on the time interval $[0, k]$, and what ever exogenous input occurs, the cost $\|z\|_{2,[0,k]}^2 - \gamma^2\|w\|_{2,[0,k]}^2 + x_{k+1}' X_\infty(k+1)x_{k+1}$ is no less than the cost that would be incurred by the implementing $u_k = u_k^*$.

Iterative generation of a candidate controller

Suppose $X_\infty(k+1) \geq 0$ and that $\boldsymbol{K}$ is any causal linear controller that satisfies (B.2.10) when $x_0 = 0$. Then

1. $R_3(k) > 0$, $\nabla(k) \leq -\epsilon I$, $X_\infty(k) \geq 0$.
2. The causal, linear controller

$$u_i = \begin{cases} \boldsymbol{K}\begin{bmatrix} x \\ w \end{bmatrix} & \text{for} \quad i \leq k-1 \\ u_k = u_k^* & \text{for} \quad i = k \end{cases} \tag{B.2.18}$$

   also satisfies (B.2.10) when $x_0 = 0$, since $u_k = u_k^*$ does not increase the left-hand side of (B.2.10).

3. If the exogenous signal is $w_k = w_k^*$, (B.2.17) implies that any controller that satisfies (B.2.10) also satisfies

$$\begin{aligned} \|z\|_{2,[0,k-1]}^2 - \gamma^2\|w\|_{2,[0,k-1]}^2 + x_k' X_\infty(k)x_k &\leq -\epsilon\|w\|_{2,[0,k]}^2 \\ &\leq -\epsilon\|w\|_{[0,k-1]}. \end{aligned}$$

Thus, if $\boldsymbol{K}$ satisfies (B.2.10), the controller (B.2.18) also satisfies this inequality and if $k \geq 1$ it also satisfies (B.2.10) with k replaced by $k-1$. Iterating this procedure from $k = N$ to $k = 0$ we obtain the necessity proof of the following theorem.

Theorem B.2.1 *Suppose $D_{12}'(k)D_{12}(k) > 0$ for all $k = 0, \ldots, N$, $\Delta \geq 0$ and $x_0 = 0$ in (B.2.2). There exists a causal, linear, full-information controller such that the closed-loop system satisfies (B.1.4) for all $w \in \ell_2[0, N]$ and some $\epsilon > 0$ if and only if*

$$\begin{aligned} R_3(k) &> 0, \qquad k = 0, \ldots, N && \text{(B.2.19)} \\ (R_1 - R_2' R_3^{-1} R_2)(k) &\leq -\alpha I_l, \qquad k = 0, \ldots, N && \text{(B.2.20)} \end{aligned}$$

for some $\alpha \geq \epsilon$. The matrices R_1, R_2 and R_3 are defined by (B.2.6) and (B.2.4), in which $X_\infty(k)$ satisfies the Riccati difference equation (B.2.12) with terminal condition $X_\infty(N+1) = \Delta$.

In this case, $X_\infty(k) \geq 0$ for $k = 0, \ldots, N+1$, and a full-information controller that achieves the objective (B.1.4) is

$$u_k^* = -R_3^{-1}(k) \begin{bmatrix} L_2(k) & R_2(k) \end{bmatrix} \begin{bmatrix} x_k \\ w_k \end{bmatrix}. \qquad \text{(B.2.21)}$$

In connection with this result we note the following:

- The control law (B.2.21) is not generally a state feedback law, since

  $$R_2(k) = D_{12}'(k)D_{11}(k) + B_2'(k)X_\infty(k+1)B_1(k)$$

  is nonzero in general. At first sight, it may appear that this is a fundamental difference between the discrete-time and the continuous-time theories. It is not. The same phenomenon occurs in the general continuous-time case when $D_{12}'D_{11} \neq 0$, since the full-information control law $u^*(t)$ is a memoryless function of both $x(t)$ and $w(t)$.

- Since $R_2(k) \neq 0$ in general, the control law u_k^* is not *strictly* causal and must be generated instantaneously from w_k (and x_k). If a full-information controller that is a strictly causal function of w is required[2], condition (B.2.20) must be replaced with

  $$R_1(k) \leq -\alpha I, \qquad k = 0, \ldots, N \qquad \text{(B.2.22)}$$

  for some $\alpha \geq \epsilon$. If condition (B.2.22) is satisfied, then a control law that achieves the objective (B.1.4) is the memoryless state feedback controller

  $$u_k^* = -(R_3 - R_2 R_1^{-1} R_2')^{-1}(k)(L_2 - R_2 R_1^{-1} L_1)(k) x_k.$$

[2]That is, u_k can be a function of w_i, $i \leq k-1$ and x_i, $i \leq k$.

Sufficiency: Completing the square

Suppose that the conditions (B.2.19) and (B.2.20) hold. Then u^* and w^* are well defined for $k = 0, \ldots, N$ and (B.2.17) yields

$$\begin{aligned} z_k' z_k - \gamma^2 w_k' w_k + x_{k+1} X_\infty(k+1) x_{k+1} - x_k X_\infty(k) x_k \\ = (u_k - u_k^*)' R_3(k)(u_k - u_k^*) + (w_k - w_k^*)' \nabla(k)(w_k - w_k^*). \end{aligned}$$

Since

$$\sum_{k=0}^{N} x_{k+1}' X_\infty(k+1) x_{k+1} - x_k' X_\infty(k) x_k = x_{N+1}' X_\infty(N+1) x_{N+1} - x_0' X_\infty(0) x_0$$

we obtain the identity

$$\begin{aligned} &\sum_{k=0}^{N} z_k' z_k - \gamma^2 w_k' w_k + x_{N+1}' \Delta x_{N+1} - x_0' X_\infty(0) x_0 \\ &\quad = \sum_{k=0}^{N} (u_k - u_k^*)' R_3(k)(u_k - u_k^*) + (w_k - w_k^*)' \nabla(k)(w_k - w_k^*). \end{aligned} \quad \text{(B.2.23)}$$

Setting $x_0 = 0$ and $u = u^*$ gives

$$\begin{aligned} \|z\|_{2,[0,N]}^2 - \gamma^2 \|w\|_{[0,N]}^2 + x_{N+1}' \Delta x_{N+1} &= \sum_{k=0}^{N} (w_k - w_k^*)' \nabla (w_k - w_k^*) \\ &\leq -\alpha \|w - w^*\|_{2,[0,N]}^2 \\ &\leq -\epsilon \|w\|_{2,[0,N]}^2, \end{aligned}$$

for some $0 < \epsilon \leq \alpha$. The final inequality follows from the fact that the system $\boldsymbol{L} : w \mapsto (w - w^*)$ when $u = u^*$ is causally invertible and $\epsilon = \alpha / \|\boldsymbol{L}^{-1}\|_{[0,N]}^2$, with $\|\boldsymbol{L}^{-1}\|\|_{[0,N]} \geq 1$. We leave the verification of this fact as an exercise. This shows that u^* satisfies (B.1.4).

All solutions

Suppose that the conditions (B.2.19) and (B.2.20) hold. Let $V_{12}(k)$ be an $m \times m$ matrix such that

$$V_{12}'(k) V_{12}(k) = R_3(k)$$

and let $V_{21}(k)$ be an $l \times l$ matrix such that

$$V_{21}'(k) V_{21}(k) = -\gamma^{-2}(R_1 - R_2' R_3^{-1} R_2)(k) = -\gamma^{-2} \nabla(k).$$

Defining

$$\begin{bmatrix} s_k \\ r_k \end{bmatrix} = \begin{bmatrix} V_{21}(k) & 0 \\ 0 & V_{12}(k) \end{bmatrix} \begin{bmatrix} w_k - w_k^* \\ u_k - u_k^* \end{bmatrix}, \quad \text{(B.2.24)}$$

in which w^* and u^* are given in (B.2.14), we obtain

$$\begin{aligned}\|z\|^2_{2,[0,N]} - \gamma^2\|w\|^2_{2,[0,N]} + x'_{N+1}\Delta x_{N+1} \\ = \; x'_0 X(0)x_0 + \|r\|^2_{2,[0,N]} - \gamma^2\|s\|^2_{2,[0,N]}\end{aligned} \tag{B.2.25}$$

from (B.2.23). This formula is vital to most of our subsequent work.

Arguments that are virtually identical to those used in the continuous-time case show that any control signal leading to a closed-loop system satisfying (B.1.4) can be generated in terms of a causal linear system $\boldsymbol{U}$ such that

$$r = \boldsymbol{U}s, \quad \|\boldsymbol{U}\|_{[0,N]} < \gamma.$$

This gives

$$u_k = u_k^* + V_{12}^{-1}\boldsymbol{U}\big(V_{21}(w_k - w_k^*)\big),$$

or, in LFT form,

$$\begin{aligned}\begin{bmatrix} u_k \\ s_k \end{bmatrix} &= \begin{bmatrix} -R_3^{-1}L_2 & -R_3^{-1}R_2 & V_{12}^{-1} \\ -(\gamma^2 V'_{21})^{-1}L_\nabla & V_{21} & 0 \end{bmatrix}\begin{bmatrix} x_k \\ w_k \\ r_k \end{bmatrix} \\ r &= \boldsymbol{U}s.\end{aligned}$$

To obtain all controllers, we use the duplicate state

$$\begin{aligned}\widehat{x}_{k+1} &= A\widehat{x}_k + B_1 w_k + B_2 u_k \\ &= A\widehat{x}_k + B_1 w_k + B_2(-R_3^{-1}L_2\widehat{x}_k - R_3^{-1}R_2 w_k + V_{12}^{-1}r_k) \\ &= (A - B_2R_3^{-1}L_2)\widehat{x}_k + (B_1 - B_2R_3^{-1}R_2)w_k + B_2V_{12}^{-1}r_k\end{aligned}$$

and augment the controller to

$$u_k = u_k^* + V_{12}^{-1}(k)\boldsymbol{U}\big(V_{21}^{-1}(w_k - w_k^*)\big) + V_{12}^{-1}(k)\boldsymbol{V}(x_k - \widehat{x}_k),$$

in which $\boldsymbol{V}$ is an arbitrary causal, linear system.

Game theoretic interpretation

Consider the difference game with dynamics (B.2.2) and pay-off functional

$$\begin{aligned}J(\boldsymbol{K}, w, x_0, N, \Delta) &= \sum_{k=0}^{N} z'_k z_k - \gamma^2 w'_k w_k + x'_{N+1}\Delta x_{N+1} \\ &= \|z\|^2_{2,[0,N]} - \gamma^2\|w\|^2_{2,[0,N]} + x'_{N+1}\Delta x_{N+1}.\end{aligned}$$

The designer's aim is to minimize J by choosing $\boldsymbol{K}$, which generates a control that is a causal, linear function of x and w. The aim of the w-player is to choose $w \in \ell_2[0,N]$ to maximize J.

It follows from the fundamental identity (B.2.3) that a unique minimizing $\boldsymbol{K}$ exists for any w if and only if $R_3(k) > 0$ for $k \in [0, N]$. In this case, the minimizing controller $\boldsymbol{K}^*$ is given by (B.2.21). With the controller $\boldsymbol{K}^*$ implemented, a unique w that maximizes $J(\boldsymbol{K}^*, w, N, \Delta)$ exists if and only if $\nabla(k) < 0$ for $k \in [0, N]$. In this case, the controller $\boldsymbol{K}^*$ and the disturbance w_k^* generated by

$$\begin{bmatrix} x_{k+1}^* \\ w_k^* \end{bmatrix} = \begin{bmatrix} A - BR^{-1}L \\ -\nabla^{-1}L_\nabla \end{bmatrix} x_k^*, \qquad x_0^* = x_0$$

satisfy the saddle point condition

$$J(\boldsymbol{K}^*, w, x_0, N, \Delta) \leq J(\boldsymbol{K}^*, w^*, x_0, N, \Delta) \leq J(\boldsymbol{K}, w^*, x_0, N, \Delta),$$

with $J(\boldsymbol{K}^*, w^*, x_0, N, \Delta) = x_0' X_\infty(0) x_0$.

Notice that the maximization over w occurs with the controller $\boldsymbol{K}^*$ in place. We do not require that $J(\boldsymbol{K}, w, x_0, N, \Delta)$ has a maximum in w for any $\boldsymbol{K}$. If it is demanded that $J(\boldsymbol{K}, w, x_0, N, \Delta)$ has a maximum in w for any $\boldsymbol{K}$, one needs the stronger condition $R_1(k) < 0$ for $k \in [0, N]$.

B.2.2 Infinite horizon

We will now generalize Theorem B.2.1 to the infinite-horizon case.

Theorem B.2.2 *Suppose that (A, B_2) is stabilizable, that $D_{12}'D_{12} > 0$ and that condition (B.1.5) holds. Then there exists a causal, linear, time-invariant and stabilizing full-information controller such that (B.1.7) is satisfied if and only if the Riccati equation*

$$X_\infty = \overline{C}' J \overline{C} + A' X_\infty A - L' R^{-1} L, \tag{B.2.26}$$

with

$$\begin{aligned} R &= \overline{D}' J \overline{D} + B' X_\infty B && \text{(B.2.27)} \\ L &= \overline{D}' J \overline{C} + B' X_\infty A && \text{(B.2.28)} \end{aligned}$$

has a solution such that $A - BR^{-1}L$ asymptotically stable and

$$\begin{aligned} X_\infty &\geq 0 && \text{(B.2.29)} \\ R_1 - R_2' R_3^{-1} R_2 = \nabla &< 0. && \text{(B.2.30)} \end{aligned}$$

In this case a stabilizing, full-information controller that achieves the objective (B.1.7) is

$$u_k^* = -R_3^{-1} \begin{bmatrix} L_2 & R_2 \end{bmatrix} \begin{bmatrix} x_k \\ w_k \end{bmatrix}. \tag{B.2.31}$$

Remark B.2.1. As noted in the finite-horizon case, the controller (B.2.31) is not a state-feedback law. If a state-feedback law is desired, condition (B.2.30) must be replaced with the more stringent condition $R_1 < 0$, and then one controller which satisfies (B.1.7) is given by

$$u_k = -(R_3 - R_2 R_1^{-1} R_2')^{-1}(L_2 - R_2 R_1^{-1} L_1) x_k.$$

Proof of sufficiency

The control law (B.2.31) yields the closed-loop system

$$\begin{bmatrix} x_{k+1} \\ z_k \end{bmatrix} = \begin{bmatrix} A - B_2 R_3^{-1} L_2 & B_1 - B_2 R_3^{-1} R_2 \\ C_1 - D_{12} R_3^{-1} L_2 & D_{11} - D_{12} R_3^{-1} R_2 \end{bmatrix} \begin{bmatrix} x_k \\ w_k \end{bmatrix},$$

which we will now show is stable. Using the Schur decomposition of R in (B.2.7), the Riccati equation for X_∞ may be written in the form

$$X_\infty = C_1' C_1 + A' X_\infty A - L_2' R_3^{-1} L_2 - L_\nabla' \nabla^{-1} L_\nabla.$$

Combining this with the definitions of R_3 and L_2, we may write

$$\begin{aligned} &\begin{bmatrix} A & B_2 \\ C_1 & D_{12} \end{bmatrix}' \begin{bmatrix} X_\infty & 0 \\ 0 & I \end{bmatrix} \begin{bmatrix} A & B_2 \\ C_1 & D_{12} \end{bmatrix} \\ &= \begin{bmatrix} X_\infty + L_\nabla' \nabla^{-1} L_\nabla & 0 \\ 0 & 0 \end{bmatrix} + \begin{bmatrix} L_2' \\ R_3 \end{bmatrix} R_3^{-1} \begin{bmatrix} L_2 & R_3 \end{bmatrix}. \end{aligned}$$

Multiplying this equation by $\begin{bmatrix} I & 0 \\ -R_3^{-1} L_2 & I \end{bmatrix}$ on the right, by its transpose on the left, and writing out only the $(1,1)$-block, yields the equation

$$\begin{aligned} X_\infty \;=\; & (A - B_2 R_3^{-1} L_2)' X_\infty (A - B_2 R_3^{-1} L_2) - L_\nabla' \nabla^{-1} L_\nabla \\ & + (C_1 - D_{12} R_3^{-1} L_2)'(C_1 - D_{12} R_3^{-1} L_2). \end{aligned} \qquad \text{(B.2.32)}$$

Since $\nabla < 0$ and $X_\infty \geq 0$, (B.2.32) implies that $|\lambda_i(A - B_2 R_3^{-1} L_2)| \leq 1$ for all i. To conclude that strict inequality holds, we show that $(A - B_2 R_3^{-1} L_2, L_\nabla)$ is detectable. Using the Schur decomposition of R again, we see that

$$A - BR^{-1}L = (A - B_2 R_3^{-1} L_2) - (B_1 - B_2 R_3^{-1} R_2)\nabla^{-1} L_\nabla. \qquad \text{(B.2.33)}$$

This implies that $(A - B_2 R_3^{-1} L_2, L_\nabla)$ is detectable, since $A - BR^{-1}L$ is asymptotically stable. Therefore, we may conclude from the Lyapunov equation (B.2.32) that $A - B_2 R_3^{-1} L_2$ is asymptotically stable.

Since $A - B_2R_3^{-1}L_2$ is asymptotically stable, $x \in \ell_2[0,\infty)$ for any $w \in \ell_2[0,\infty)$ and we may invoke (B.2.25) to obtain

$$\|z\|_2^2 - \gamma^2\|w\|_2^2 = -\gamma^2\|s\|_2^2, \tag{B.2.34}$$

since $u = u^*$ and $x_0 = 0$. The vector sequence s is given by

$$\begin{bmatrix} x_{k+1} \\ s_k \end{bmatrix} = \begin{bmatrix} A - B_2R_3^{-1}L_2 & B_1 - B_2R_3^{-1}R_2 \\ V_{21}\nabla^{-1}L_\nabla & V_{21} \end{bmatrix} \begin{bmatrix} x_k \\ w_k \end{bmatrix}.$$

This system is stable with a stable inverse, since by (B.2.33) the A-matrix of the inverse is $A - BR^{-1}L$. Therefore, there exists an $\epsilon > 0$ such that $\|s\|_2^2 \geq \epsilon\|w\|_2^2/\gamma^2$ and substitution into (B.2.34) yields

$$\|z\|_2^2 - \gamma^2\|w\|_2^2 \leq -\epsilon\|w\|_2^2.$$

Necessity

Let X_2 be the unique matrix such that

$$x_0'X_2x_0 = \min_{\boldsymbol{K}} \|z\|_2^2$$

for arbitrary x_0. That is, X_2 is the unique nonnegative definite solution to the discrete-time algebraic Riccati equation

$$\begin{aligned} X_2 &= C_1'C_1 + A'X_2A \\ &\quad -(D_{12}'C_1 + B_2'X_2A)'(D_{12}'D_{12} + B_2'X_2B_2)^{-1}(D_{12}'C_1 + B_2'X_2A) \end{aligned}$$

such that $A - B_2(D_{12}'D_{12} + B_2'X_2B_2)^{-1}(D_{12}'C_1 + B_2'X_2A)$ is asymptotically stable. (The theory of the discrete-time LQ regulator may be found in books such as [29], and is also developed in Problems B.5 and B.7.)

As in the continuous-time synthesis theory, we shall prove necessity by showing that when a stabilizing controller satisfying (B.1.7) exists, the Riccati difference equation converges to a stabilizing solution to the algebraic Riccati equation.

B.2.3 Convergence of the Riccati equation

It is assumed that there exists a causal, linear, time-invariant, stabilizing, full-information controller such that (B.1.8) holds when $x_0 = 0$. The arguments that show that the required solution to the Riccati difference equation (B.2.12) converges to the stabilizing solution of the algebraic Riccati equation (B.2.26) mimic those used in the continuous-time case.

Let $X_\infty(k, N+1, \Delta)$ denote the solution of the Riccati equation (B.2.12) for a general terminal condition. Our aim is to show that $X(k, N+1, X_2)$ (*i.e.*, the solution with terminal condition X_2) converges to a stabilizing, nonnegative definite solution to the algebraic Riccati equation (B.2.26) such that $R_1 - R_2'R_3^{-1}R_2 < 0$.

$X_\infty(k, N+1, X_2)$ **exists**

For any w such that $w_k = 0$ for $k \geq N+1$, we have

$$\begin{aligned}
&\|z\|_2^2 - \gamma^2\|w\|_2^2 \\
&= \|z\|_{2,[0,N]}^2 - \gamma^2\|w\|_{2,[0,N]}^2 + \sum_{k=N+1}^{\infty} z_k' z_k \\
&\geq \|z\|_{2,[0,N]}^2 - \gamma^2\|w\|_{2,[0,N]}^2 + \min_{\boldsymbol{K}} \sum_{k=N+1}^{\infty} z_k' z_k \\
&= \|z\|_{2,[0,N]}^2 - \gamma^2\|w\|_{2,[0,N]}^2 + x_{N+1}' X_2 x_{N+1}.
\end{aligned} \tag{B.2.35}$$

Hence, any controller with the property

$$\|z\|_2^2 - \gamma^2\|w\|_2^2 \leq -\epsilon\|w\|_2^2$$

for all $w \in \ell_2[0,\infty)$ when $x_0 = 0$ also satisfies

$$\|z\|_{2,[0,N]}^2 - \gamma^2\|w\|_{2,[0,N]}^2 + x_{N+1}' X_2 x_{N+1} \leq -\epsilon\|w\|_{2,[0,N]}^2$$

for all $w \in \ell_2[0,N]$ when $x_0 = 0$. By our finite-horizon results, we conclude that $X_\infty(k, N+1, X_2)$ exists for any finite $k \leq N+1$ and also that

$$\begin{aligned}
X_\infty(k, N+1, X_2) &\geq 0 \\
\nabla(k) = (R_1 - R_2' R_3^{-1} R_2)(k) &\leq -\alpha I
\end{aligned} \tag{B.2.36}$$

for some $\alpha \geq \epsilon$. Take $\alpha = \epsilon$, since this is independent of the horizon length N.

$X_\infty(k, N+1, X_2)$ **is uniformly bounded**

When $x_0 \neq 0$, the response z of the closed-loop system depends both on x_0 and w. By linearity, z may be decomposed as $z = z_{x_0} + z_w$, with z_{x_0} and z_w denoting the contributions to the response due to x_0 and w respectively. By hypothesis, $\|z_w\|_2^2 - \gamma^2\|w\|_2^2 \leq -\epsilon\|w\|_2^2$ and, since the controller is also stabilizing, $\|z_{x_0}\|_2 \leq \delta\|x_0\|$ for some number δ. The triangle inequality gives

$$\|z\|_2^2 \leq \|z_{x_0}\|_2^2 + \|z_w\|_2^2 + 2\|z_{x_0}\|_2\|z_w\|_2.$$

Therefore

$$\begin{aligned}
&\|z\|_2^2 - \gamma^2\|w\|_2^2 \\
&\leq \|z_w\|_2^2 - \gamma^2\|w\|_2^2 + \|z_{x_0}\|_2^2 + 2\|z_{x_0}\|_2\|z_w\|_2 \\
&\leq -\epsilon\|w\|_2^2 + \delta^2\|x_0\|^2 + 2\gamma\delta\|x_0\|\ \|w\|_2 \\
&= \delta^2\|x_0\|^2 - \epsilon(\|w\|_2^2 - \frac{2\gamma\delta}{\epsilon}\|x_0\|\ \|w\|_2) \\
&= (\delta^2 + \frac{\gamma^2\delta^2}{\epsilon})\|x_0\|^2 - \epsilon(\|w\|_2 - \frac{\gamma\delta}{\epsilon}\|x_0\|)^2 \\
&\leq (\delta^2 + \frac{\gamma^2\delta^2}{\epsilon})\|x_0\|^2 = \beta\|x_0\|^2
\end{aligned} \tag{B.2.37}$$

for all x_0 and all $w \in \ell_2[0,\infty)$.

Now choose N finite and let w be the particular $\ell_2[0,\infty)$ signal

$$w_k = \begin{cases} -\nabla(k)^{-1}L_\nabla(k)x_k & \text{if} \quad k \le N \\ 0 & \text{if} \quad k \ge N+1. \end{cases}$$

(*i.e.*, $w = w^*$ for the finite-horizon problem.) Since $w_k = 0$ for $x \ge N+1$, (B.2.35) holds and by (B.2.25)

$$\begin{aligned} \|z\|_2^2 - \gamma^2\|w\|_2^2 &\ge x_0' X_\infty(0, N+1, X_2)x_0 + \|r\|_{2,[0,N]}^2 \\ &\ge x_0' X_\infty(0, N+1, X_2)x_0. \end{aligned}$$

(r is defined by (B.2.24)). Combining this with (B.2.37), we have that for any finite N and any x_0 that

$$x_0' X_\infty(0, N+1, X_2)x_0 \le \beta\|x_0\|^2,$$

which shows that $X_\infty(0, N+1, X_2)$ is uniformly bounded. By time invariance, it follows that $X_\infty(k, N+1, X_2)$ is uniformly bounded on $k \le N+1$.

$X_\infty(k, N+1, X_2)$ is monotonic

Using (B.2.25) on $[k, N]$ gives

$$\begin{aligned} &\|z\|_{2,[k,N]}^2 - \gamma^2\|w\|_{2,[k,N]}^2 + x_{N+1}' X_2 x_{N+1} \\ &\quad = \|r\|_{2,[k,N]}^2 - \gamma^2\|s\|_{2,[k,N]}^2 + x_k' X_\infty(k, N+1, X_2)x_k. \end{aligned}$$

In the same way we obtain

$$\begin{aligned} &\|z\|_{2,[k,N+1]}^2 - \gamma^2\|w\|_{2,[k,N+1]}^2 + x_{N+2}' X_2 x_{N+2} \\ &\quad = \|\overline{r}\|_{2,[k,N+1]}^2 - \gamma^2\|\overline{s}\|_{2,[k,N+1]}^2 + x_k' X_\infty(k, N+2, X_2)x_k, \end{aligned}$$

in which $\overline{s}$ and $\overline{r}$ are the corresponding signals for the finite-horizon problem on the interval $[k, N+1]$. Set $u_i = \overline{u}_i^*$ for $i = k, \ldots, N+1$ and $w_i = w_i^*$ for $i = k, \ldots, N$ and $w_{N+1} = 0$. This gives $\overline{r}_i = 0$ for $i = k, \ldots, N+1$ and $s_i = 0$ for $i = k, \ldots, N$. Subtracting the above identities yields

$$\begin{aligned} &x_k[X_\infty(k, N+2, X_2) - X_\infty(k, N+1, X_2)]x_k \\ &\quad = \|r\|_{2,[k,N]}^2 + \gamma^2\|\overline{s}\|_{2,[k,N+1]}^2 \\ &\qquad - x_{N+1}' X_2 x_{N+1} + z_{N+1}' z_{N+1} + x_{N+2} X_2 x_{N+2} \\ &\quad \ge -x_{N+1}' X_2 x_{N+1} + z_{N+1}' z_{N+1} + x_{N+2}' X_2 x_{N+2} \\ &\quad \ge -x_{N+1}' X_2 x_{N+1} + \min_{u_{N+1}} \left\{ z_{N+1}' z_{N+1} + x_{N+2}' X_2 x_{N+2} \right\} \\ &\quad = -x_{N+1}' X_2 x_{N+1} + x_{N+1}' X_2 x_{N+1} \\ &\quad \ge 0. \end{aligned}$$

Because x_k may be regarded as an arbitrary initial condition, $X_\infty(k, N+2, X_2) \ge X_\infty(k, N+1, X_2)$ as required.

A solution to the algebraic Riccati equation exists

Since $X(k, N+1, X_2)$ is nonnegative definite, uniformly bounded and monotonic, we conclude that

$$X_\infty = \lim_{N\to\infty} X(k, N+1, X_2)$$

exists, is independent of k and is nonnegative definite also. From (B.2.36), since $\alpha \geq \epsilon$, which is independent independent of the horizon length, we conclude that $\nabla < 0$. Hence R is nonsingular and X_∞ is a solution to (B.2.26). We also note that $X_\infty \geq X_2$ by monotonicity.

The best control and the worst disturbance

Define

$$\begin{bmatrix} w_k^* \\ u_k^* \end{bmatrix} = -\begin{bmatrix} \nabla^{-1} Z_2 & 0 \\ R_3^{-1} L_2 & R_3^{-1} R_2 \end{bmatrix} \begin{bmatrix} x_k \\ w_k \end{bmatrix}$$

and

$$\begin{bmatrix} s_k \\ r_k \end{bmatrix} = \begin{bmatrix} V_{21} & 0 \\ 0 & V_{12} \end{bmatrix} \begin{bmatrix} w_k - w_k^* \\ u_k - u_k^* \end{bmatrix},$$

in which Z, V_{12} and V_{21} are as per the finite-horizon case, *mutatis mutandi.*

Invoking an infinite-horizon version of (B.2.25) gives

$$\|z\|_2^2 - \gamma^2 \|w\|_2^2 = x_0' X_\infty x_0 + \|r\|_2^2 - \gamma^2 \|s\|_2^2 \tag{B.2.38}$$

for any controller that stabilizes the system and any $w \in \ell_2[0, \infty)$.

u^* is stabilizing

The control $u_k = u_k^*$ leads to the dynamics

$$x_{k+1} = (A - B_2 R_3^{-1} L_2) x_k + (B_1 - B_2 R_3^{-1} R_2) w_k.$$

To show that this is asymptotically stable, we note that $\Gamma = X_\infty - X_2$ satisfies

$$\begin{aligned} \Gamma \;=\;& (A - B_2 R_3^{-1} L_2)' \left(\Gamma + \Gamma B_2 (R_3 - B_2' \Gamma B_2)^{-1} B_2' \Gamma\right) (A - B_2 R_3^{-1} L_2) \\ & - L_\nabla' \nabla^{-1} L_\nabla. \end{aligned} \tag{B.2.39}$$

Since $R_3 - B_2' \Gamma B_2 = D_{12}' D_{12} + B_2' X_2 B_2$, the inverse exists and is indeed positive definite. Furthermore,

$$\left(A - B_2 R_3^{-1} L_2, B_2' \Gamma (A - B_2 R_3^{-1} L_2)\right)$$

is detectable, since

$$\begin{aligned} & A - B_2 R_3^{-1} L_2 + B_2 (R_3 - B_2' \Gamma B_2)^{-1} B_2' \Gamma (A - B_2 R_3^{-1} L_2) \\ &= A - B_2 (D_{12}' D_{12} + B_2' X_2 B_2)^{-1} (D_{12}' C_1 + B_2' X_2 A), \end{aligned}$$

which is asymptotically stable, since it is the closed-loop dynamics associated with the LQ problem. The calculations required to verify the above are requested in Problem B.9. Since $\Gamma \geq 0$ and $\nabla < 0$, we conclude from the Lyapunov equation (B.2.39) that $A - B_2R_3^{-1}L_2$ is asymptotically stable.

Parametrization of the closed-loop

The closed loop is also generated by a controller of the form

$$u_k = u_k^* + V_{12}^{-1}\boldsymbol{U}V_{21}(w_k - w_k^*).$$

For such a controller, the closed loop is given by

$$\begin{aligned}\begin{bmatrix} x_{k+1} \\ z_k \\ s_k \end{bmatrix} &= \begin{bmatrix} A - B_2R_3^{-1}L_2 & B_1 - B_2R_3^{-1}R_2 & B_2V_{12}^{-1} \\ C_1 - D_{12}R_3^{-1}L_2 & D_{11} - D_{12}R_3^{-1}R_2 & D_{12}V_{12}^{-1} \\ -(\gamma^2V_{21}')^{-1}L_\nabla & V_{21} & 0 \end{bmatrix}\begin{bmatrix} x_k \\ w_k \\ r_k \end{bmatrix} \\ r &= \boldsymbol{U}s.\end{aligned}$$

That is, the closed loop is generated by a LFT $\mathcal{F}_\ell(\boldsymbol{R}_a, \boldsymbol{U})$, in which $\boldsymbol{R}_a$ maps $\begin{bmatrix} w \\ r \end{bmatrix}$ to $\begin{bmatrix} z \\ s \end{bmatrix}$. Setting $x_0 = 0$ in (B.2.38), we have

$$\|z\|_2^2 + \gamma^2\|s\|_2^2 = \gamma^2\|w\|_2^2 + \|r\|_2^2. \tag{B.2.40}$$

When $\gamma = 1$ (which may be assumed without loss of generality), this identity shows that $\boldsymbol{R}_a$ is allpass.

$A - BR^{-1}L$ has no eigenvalue on the unit circle

In order to avoid having to re-scale, assume (without loss of generality) that $\gamma = 1$. Then $\boldsymbol{R}_a$ is allpass by (B.2.40). By assumption, there exists a controller such that the closed loop $\boldsymbol{R}$ is internally stable and $\|\boldsymbol{R}\|_\infty < \gamma = 1$. Therefore, there exists a $\boldsymbol{U}$ such that $\|\mathcal{F}_\ell(\boldsymbol{R}_a, \boldsymbol{U})\|_\infty < 1$. Consequently, by a discrete-time version of Theorem 4.3.2, the $(2,1)$ block of $\boldsymbol{R}_a$ has no zeros on the unit circle. Because $A - B_2R_3^{-1}L_2$ is asymptotically stable, this implies that

$$A - B_2R_3^{-1}L_2 - (B_1 - B_2R_3^{-1}R_2)\nabla^{-1}L_\nabla$$

has no eigenvalue on the unit circle. By (B.2.33), we conclude that $A - BR^{-1}L$ has no eigenvalue on the unit circle.

$A - BR^{-1}L$ is asymptotically stable

The sequence $\Gamma(k) = X_\infty - X_\infty(k, N+1, X_2)$ is the solution to the Riccati difference equation

$$\begin{aligned}\Gamma(k) &= (A - BR^{-1}L)'\big(\Gamma(k+1) \\ &\quad + \Gamma(k+1)B(R - B'\Gamma(k+1)B)^{-1}B'\Gamma(k+1)\big)(A - BR^{-1}L),\end{aligned}$$

with terminal condition $\Gamma(N+1) = X_\infty - X_2$ (Problem B.10).

Assume that $\Gamma(k)$ is nonsingular for $k \leq N+1$ (the extension to the case in which $\Gamma(k)$ may be singular is also requested in Problem B.10). Clearly, this implies that $\widehat{A} = A - BR^{-1}L$ is nonsingular. Taking inverses using the matrix inversion lemma (see [105], page 656) we obtain

$$\Gamma^{-1}(k) = \widehat{A}^{-1}[\Gamma^{-1}(k+1) - BR^{-1}B'](\widehat{A}')^{-1}.$$

Now define $\Omega(k) = \Gamma^{-1}(N+1-k)$. Since $\Gamma(k) \to 0$ as $k \to -\infty$, $x^*\Omega(k)x \to \infty$ as $k \to \infty$ for any x. Let $(\widehat{A}')^{-1}x = \frac{1}{\lambda}x$. Then

$$x^*\Omega(k+1)x = \frac{x^*\Omega(k)x}{|\lambda|^2} - \frac{x^*BR^{-1}B'x}{|\lambda|^2}.$$

Since $x^*\Omega(k)x \to \infty$, we must have $|\lambda| \leq 1$ and since $\widehat{A}$ has no eigenvalue on the unit circle, we must have $|\lambda| < 1$. Therefore, $\widehat{A} = A - BR^{-1}L$ is asymptotically stable.

All solutions

By a discrete-time version of Theorem 4.3.3, we see that all control signals and all closed-loop systems that satisfy (B.1.8) are generated by controllers of the form $u = u^* + V_{12}^{-1}\boldsymbol{U}V_{21}(w - w^*)$, in which $\boldsymbol{U} \in \mathcal{H}_\infty$ and $\|\boldsymbol{U}\|_\infty < \gamma$. That is,

$$\begin{aligned} \begin{bmatrix} u_k \\ s_k \end{bmatrix} &= \begin{bmatrix} -R_3^{-1}L_2 & -R_3^{-1}R_2 & V_{12}^{-1} \\ -(\gamma^2 V_{21}')^{-1}L_\nabla & V_{21} & 0 \end{bmatrix}(k) \begin{bmatrix} x_k \\ w_k \\ r_k \end{bmatrix} \\ r &= \boldsymbol{U}s. \end{aligned}$$

To obtain all controllers, we use the duplicate state

$$\begin{aligned} \widehat{x}_{k+1} &= A\widehat{x}_k + B_1 w_k + B_2 u_k \\ &= A\widehat{x}_k + B_1 w_k + B_2(-R_3^{-1}L_2\widehat{x}_k - R_3^{-1}R_2 w_k + V_{12}^{-1}r_k) \\ &= (A - B_2R_3^{-1}L_2)\widehat{x}_k + (B_1 - B_2R_3^{-1}R_2)w_k + B_2V_{12}^{-1}r_k \end{aligned}$$

and augment the controller to

$$u_k = u_k^* + V_{12}^{-1}\boldsymbol{U}\big(V_{21}^{-1}(w_k - w_k^*)\big) + V_{12}^{-1}\boldsymbol{V}(x_k - \widehat{x}_k),$$

in which $\boldsymbol{V} \in \mathcal{H}_\infty$ is arbitrary.

B.3 Filtering

We now consider the discrete-time $\mathcal{H}_\infty$ filter. As the development parallels that presented in Chapter 7, we will do little more than write down the appropriate formulae.

B.3.1 Finite horizon

Consider the signal generator

$$\begin{bmatrix} x_{k+1} \\ z_k \\ y_k \end{bmatrix} = \begin{bmatrix} A(k) & B_1(k) \\ -C_1(k) & -D_{11}(k) \\ C_2(k) & D_{21}(k) \end{bmatrix} \begin{bmatrix} x_k \\ w_k \end{bmatrix}, \qquad x_0 = 0. \tag{B.3.1}$$

We assume that $D_{21}(k)D'_{21}(k) > 0$ for all k of interest. Our aim is to find an estimate of z of the form

$$\widehat{z} = \boldsymbol{F}y$$

such that

$$\|\widehat{z} - z\|^2_{2,[0,N]} - \gamma^2\|w\|^2_{2,[0,N]} \leq -\epsilon\|w\|^2_{2,[0,N]} \tag{B.3.2}$$

for some positive ϵ and all $w \in \ell_2[0,N]$.

This problem may be cast as the LFT problem

$$\begin{aligned} \begin{bmatrix} x_{k+1} \\ \widehat{z}_k - z_k \\ y_k \end{bmatrix} &= \begin{bmatrix} A & B_1 & 0 \\ C_1 & D_{11} & I \\ C_2 & D_{21} & 0 \end{bmatrix} (k) \begin{bmatrix} x_k \\ w_k \\ \widehat{z}_k \end{bmatrix}, \qquad x_0 = 0, \\ \widehat{z} &= \boldsymbol{F}y. \end{aligned}$$

The adjoint of this LFT is given by

$$\begin{aligned} \begin{bmatrix} p_{k-1} \\ \tilde{z}_k \\ \tilde{w}_k \end{bmatrix} &= \begin{bmatrix} A' & C'_1 & C'_2 \\ B'_1 & D'_{11} & D'_{21} \\ 0 & I & 0 \end{bmatrix} (k) \begin{bmatrix} p_k \\ \tilde{w}_k \\ \tilde{u}_k \end{bmatrix}, \qquad p_N = 0, \\ \tilde{u} &= \boldsymbol{F}^{\sim}\tilde{w}. \end{aligned}$$

This is a control problem in which the controller has access to $\tilde{w}$, but not to p. Fortunately, this does not affect the conditions for the existence of a controller since we may use a copy of the state generated by

$$\widehat{p}_{k-1} = A'(k)\widehat{p}_k + C'_1(k)\tilde{w}_k + C'_2(k)\tilde{u}_k.$$

rather than the state p_k itself. It is now immediate from the full-information control results that a suitable $\boldsymbol{F}$ exists if and only if the solution to the Riccati difference equation

$$\begin{aligned} Y_\infty(k+1) &= \tilde{B}(k)\tilde{J}\tilde{B}'(k) + A(k)Y_\infty(k)A'(k) \\ &\quad - M(k)S^{-1}(k)M'(k), \qquad Y_\infty(0) = 0, \end{aligned} \tag{B.3.3}$$

satisfies

$$S_3(k) > 0, \qquad k = 0, \ldots, N \tag{B.3.4}$$

$$(S_1 - S_2S_3^{-1}S'_2)(k) \leq -\alpha I_p, \qquad k = 0, \ldots, N, \tag{B.3.5}$$

for some positive $\alpha \geq \epsilon$. In the above, the matrices S and M are defined by

$$\begin{aligned} S(k) &= \tilde{D}(k)\tilde{J}\tilde{D}'(k) + C(k)Y_\infty(k)C'(k) = \begin{bmatrix} S_1 & S_2 \\ S_2' & S_3 \end{bmatrix}(k) \\ M(k) &= \tilde{B}(k)\tilde{J}\tilde{D}'(k) + A(k)Y_\infty(k)C'(k), \end{aligned}$$

in which

$$\begin{bmatrix} A(k) & \tilde{B}(k) \\ C(k) & \tilde{D}(k) \end{bmatrix} = \left[\begin{array}{c|cc} A(k) & B_1(k) & 0 \\ \hline C_1(k) & D_{11}(k) & I_p \\ C_2(k) & D_{21}(k) & 0 \end{array}\right]$$

and

$$\tilde{J} = \begin{bmatrix} I_l & 0 \\ 0 & -\gamma^2 I_p \end{bmatrix}.$$

If (B.3.4) and (B.3.5) hold, let

$$\begin{aligned} W_{21}(k)W_{21}'(k) &= S_3(k) \\ W_{12}(k)W_{12}'(k) &= -\gamma^{-2}(S_1 - S_2S_3^{-1}S_2')(k). \end{aligned}$$

Then $\boldsymbol{F}$ is a filter that satisfies (B.3.2) if and only if

$$\boldsymbol{F} = \mathcal{F}_\ell(\boldsymbol{F}_a, \boldsymbol{U}), \qquad \|\boldsymbol{U}\|_{[0,N]}\| < \gamma \tag{B.3.6}$$

for some causal $\boldsymbol{U}$. The generator of all filters, $\boldsymbol{F}_a$, is the system with state-space realization

$$\left[\begin{array}{c|cc} A - M_2S_3^{-1}C_2 & M_2S_3^{-1} & (M_1 - M_2S_3^{-1}S_2)(\gamma^2 W_{12}')^{-1} \\ \hline -(C_1 - S_2S_3^{-1}C_2) & -S_2S_3^{-1} & W_{12} \\ -W_{21}^{-1}C_2 & W_{21}^{-1} & 0 \end{array}\right].$$

Choosing $\boldsymbol{U} = 0$ results in the filter

$$\begin{aligned} \widehat{x}_{k+1} &= A(k)\widehat{x}_k + M_2(k)S_3^{-1}(k)(y_k - C_2(k)\widehat{x}_k) \\ \widehat{z}_k &= -C_1(k)\widehat{x}_k - S_2(k)S_3^{-1}(k)(y_k - C_2(k)\widehat{x}_k), \end{aligned}$$

which has a discrete-time observer structure driven by the "innovations process" $y - C_2\widehat{x}$. The signal s is just a normalized version of the innovations, since $s = W_{21}^{-1}[y - C_2\widehat{x}]$. The normalization is introduced so that the norm constraint on the $\boldsymbol{U}$ parameter mimics the closed-loop norm bound. Note also that it is not necessary to calculate the matrices W_{21} and W_{12} if only this "central filter" is of interest. Finally, we see that this filter has the property

$$\mathcal{E}\{(\widehat{x}_k - x_k)(\widehat{x}_k - x_k)'\} \leq Y_\infty(k) \tag{B.3.7}$$

when w is a unit intensity white noise process (Problem B.12).

Finally, it will be convenient in the application of these results to the measurement feedback $\mathcal{H}_\infty$ synthesis problem to write the state-space realization of $\boldsymbol{F}_a$ in the form

$$\begin{bmatrix} I & 0 & -M_2(W_{21}')^{-1} \\ 0 & I & S_2(W_{21}')^{-1} \\ 0 & 0 & W_{21} \end{bmatrix} \begin{bmatrix} \widehat{x}_{k+1} \\ \widehat{z}_k \\ s_k \end{bmatrix} = \begin{bmatrix} A & 0 & (M_1 - M_2 S_3^{-1} S_2)(\gamma^2 W_{12}')^{-1} \\ -C_1 & 0 & W_{12} \\ -C_2 & I & 0 \end{bmatrix} \begin{bmatrix} \widehat{x}_k \\ y_k \\ r_k \end{bmatrix}. \tag{B.3.8}$$

Remark B.3.1. The filters above generally require immediate use of the current measurement y_k to generate $\widehat{z}_k$. If this is not acceptable, the existence condition (B.3.5) must be modified to $S_1(k) \le -\alpha I$, $k = 0, \dots, N$. In this case the filter also has to be modified. One such filter is

$$\begin{aligned} \widehat{x}_{k+1} &= A\widehat{x}_k + (M_2 - M_1 S_1^{\dagger} S_2)(S_3 - S_2' S_1^{\dagger} S_2)^{-1}(y_k - C_2\widehat{x}_k) \\ \widehat{z}_k &= -C_1\widehat{x}_k. \end{aligned}$$

B.3.2 Infinite horizon

In the case of an infinite-horizon filtering problem, we assume: (a) that the matrices A, $\tilde{B}$, C and $\tilde{D}$ are constant; (b) that $D_{21}D_{21}' > 0$; and (c) that the rank condition (B.1.6) holds. We seek a causal, linear and stable filter such that the map $\boldsymbol{R} : w \mapsto \widehat{z} - z$ is stable and satisfies $\|\boldsymbol{R}\|_\infty < \gamma$.

Such a filter exists if and only if the Riccati equation

$$Y_\infty = \tilde{B}\tilde{J}\tilde{B}' + AY_\infty A' - MS^{-1}M' \tag{B.3.9}$$

has a solution such that

$$\begin{aligned} Y_\infty &\ge 0 && \text{(B.3.10)} \\ S_1 - S_2 S_3^{-1} S_2' &< 0, && \text{(B.3.11)} \end{aligned}$$

with $A - MS^{-1}C$ asymptotically stable. In this case, all such filters are generated by the LFT (B.3.6), in which $\boldsymbol{U} \in \mathcal{H}_\infty$ with $\|\boldsymbol{U}\|_\infty < \gamma$.

B.4 Measurement feedback

We now consider the full generalized regulator problem in which $\boldsymbol{P}$ is described by (B.1.2), with $D_{22} = 0$.

B.4.1 Finite horizon

We assume that (B.1.3) holds for all k of interest and that $x_0 = 0$.

If there is a causal, linear controller $u = \boldsymbol{K}y$ such that (B.1.4) holds, then

$$u = \boldsymbol{K}\begin{bmatrix} C_2 & D_{21} \end{bmatrix}\begin{bmatrix} x \\ w \end{bmatrix}$$

is a causal, linear full-information controller that satisfies (B.1.4). Therefore, the Riccati equation (B.2.12) as a solution satisfying (B.2.19) and (B.2.20). Furthermore, from the identity (B.2.25), the controller $\boldsymbol{K}$ satisfies (B.1.4) if and only if it also satisfies

$$\|r\|_{2,[0,N]}^2 - \gamma^2\|s\|_{2,[0,N]}^2 \le -\epsilon\|s\|_{2,[0,N]}^2. \tag{B.4.1}$$

for some $\epsilon > 0$. (Recall that the map from w to s is causally invertible.)

Now

$$s_k = V_{21}(k)(w_k + \nabla^{-1}L_\nabla(k)x_k),$$

so

$$w_k = V_{21}^{-1}(k)s_k - \nabla^{-1}L_\nabla(k)x_k.$$

Substituting into the formulae for x_{k+1}, y_k and r_k, we obtain the LFT

$$\begin{aligned}\begin{bmatrix} x_{k+1} \\ r_k \\ y_k \end{bmatrix} &= \begin{bmatrix} A - B_1\nabla^{-1}L_\nabla & B_1V_{21}^{-1} & B_2 \\ V_{12}R_3^{-1}(L_2 - R_2\nabla^{-1}L_\nabla) & V_{12}R_3^{-1}R_2V_{21}^{-1} & V_{12} \\ C_2 - D_{21}\nabla^{-1}L_\nabla & D_{21}V_{21}^{-1} & 0 \end{bmatrix}\begin{bmatrix} x_k \\ s_k \\ u_k \end{bmatrix} \\ u &= \boldsymbol{K}y.\end{aligned}$$

(The k dependence of the matrices has been suppressed.) Since $r = V_{12}(u - u^*)$, this signal is a scaled version of $u - u^*$. The objective (B.4.1) requires us to choose $\boldsymbol{K}$ so that the closed-loop system mapping s to r has induced norm less than γ. Therefore, as in the continuous-time case, we need to choose $\boldsymbol{K}$ so that u is not too far from the u^* we would use if we had full information. This is an $\mathcal{H}_\infty$ estimation problem in which we seek a filter $\boldsymbol{K}$ such that $r = V_{12}(u - u^*)$ is sufficiently small.

We will solve this modified objective problem using our filtering results. The LFT describing this estimation problem has two differences from the situation we considered in our discussion of the filter. Firstly, the output of the filter $\boldsymbol{K}$ affects the dynamics. This makes no difference to the conditions for a solution, but merely modifies the prediction equation for $\widehat{x}_{k+1}$ by the inclusion of a B_2u_k term. The other difference is the term V_{12} in the map between the output of the filter (*i.e.* u) and the "estimation error" (*i.e.* r). This makes no difference to the conditions for a solution because V_{12} is nonsingular. All we need do is scale the filter output by V_{12}^{-1}, since $\boldsymbol{K} = V_{12}^{-1}[V_{12}\boldsymbol{K}]$.

Therefore, define

$$\begin{bmatrix} A_t(k) & \tilde{B}_t(k) \\ C_t(k) & \tilde{D}_t(k) \end{bmatrix} = \left[\begin{array}{c|cc} A - B_1\nabla^{-1}L_\nabla & B_1V_{21}^{-1} & 0 \\ \hline V_{12}R_3^{-1}(L_2 - R_2\nabla^{-1}L_\nabla) & V_{12}R_3^{-1}R_2V_{21}^{-1} & I \\ C_2 - D_{21}\nabla^{-1}L_\nabla & D_{21}V_{21}^{-1} & 0 \end{array}\right](k)$$

and

$$\begin{aligned} Z_\infty(k+1) &= B_t(k)\hat{J}B_t'(k) + A_t(k)Z_\infty(k)A_t'(k) \\ &\quad - M_t(k)S_t^{-1}(k)M_t'(k), \qquad Z_\infty(0) = 0, \end{aligned}$$

in which

$$\begin{aligned} S_t(k) &= \tilde{D}_t(k)\hat{J}\tilde{D}_t'(k) + C_t(k)Z_\infty(k)C_t'(k) = \begin{bmatrix} S_{t1} & S_{t2} \\ S_{t2}' & S_{t3} \end{bmatrix}(k) \\ M_t(k) &= \tilde{B}_t(k)\hat{J}\tilde{D}_t{}'(k) + A_t(k)Z_\infty(k)C_t'(k) \\ \hat{J} &= \begin{bmatrix} I_l & 0 \\ 0 & -\gamma^2 I_m \end{bmatrix}. \end{aligned}$$

A necessary and sufficient condition for the existence of a causal linear controller satisfying (B.4.1), and hence (B.1.4), is that

$$S_{t3}(k) > 0, \qquad k = 0, \ldots, N \tag{B.4.2}$$

$$(S_{t1} - S_{t2}S_{t3}^{-1}S_{t2}')(k) \leq -\alpha I_p, \qquad k = 0, \ldots, N \tag{B.4.3}$$

for some positive α. In this case, a controller that achieves the objective is

$$\begin{aligned} \widehat{x}_{k+1} &= A_t(k)\widehat{x}_k + B_2(k)u_k + M_{t2}(k)S_{t3}^{-1}(k)(y_k - C_{t2}(k)\widehat{x}_k) \\ V_{12}(k)u_k &= -C_{t1}(k)\widehat{x}_k - S_{t2}(k)S_{t3}^{-1}(k)(y_k - C_{t2}(k)\widehat{x}_k). \end{aligned}$$

As in the continuous-time case, this controller has an observer structure. Since $C_{2t} = C_2 - D_{21}\nabla^{-1}L_\nabla$, the observer assumes that the input is w^*, the worst input for the full-information problem and hence also the worst input for the measurement feedback problem.

The generator of all controllers is obtained from the solution to the filtering problem in (B.3.8). If we recall the need to add $B_2 u_k$ to the prediction equation for $\widehat{x}_{k+1}$ and scale the output by V_{12} as discussed above, the generator $\boldsymbol{K}_a$ of all filters, and hence all controllers, is given by the state-space system

$$\begin{bmatrix} I & -B_2 & -M_{t2}(X_{21}')^{-1} \\ 0 & V_{12} & S_{t2}(X_{21}')^{-1} \\ 0 & 0 & X_{21} \end{bmatrix} \begin{bmatrix} \widehat{x}_{k+1} \\ u_k \\ \eta_k \end{bmatrix} = \begin{bmatrix} A_t & 0 & (M_{t1} - M_{t2}S_{t3}^{-1}S_{t2})(\gamma^2 X_{12}')^{-1} \\ -C_{t1} & 0 & X_{12} \\ -C_{t2} & I & 0 \end{bmatrix} \begin{bmatrix} \widehat{x}_k \\ y_k \\ \varphi_k \end{bmatrix}. \tag{B.4.4}$$

(The time dependence is not explicitly shown.) That is, all controllers are generated by the LFT $\boldsymbol{K} = \mathcal{F}_\ell(\boldsymbol{K}_a, \boldsymbol{U})$, in which $\boldsymbol{U}$ is a causal linear system such that $\|\boldsymbol{U}\|_{[0,N]} < \gamma$. The matrices X_{12} and X_{21} are given by

$$\begin{aligned} X_{21}(k)X_{21}'(k) &= S_{t3}(k) \\ X_{12}(k)X_{12}'(k) &= -\gamma^{-2}(S_{t1} - S_{t2}S_{t3}^{-1}S_{t2}')(k). \end{aligned}$$

B.4.2 Infinite horizon

The extension of the theory to infinite-horizon, measurement feedback problems follows arguments that are identical to those presented in the continuous-time case in Chapter 8.

Suppose that the matrices (A, B, C, D) are constant; that (A, B_2, C_2) is stabilizable and detectable; that $D_{12}'D_{12} > 0$ and $D_{21}D_{21}' > 0$; and that (B.1.5) and (B.1.6) hold. Then a causal, linear, finite-dimensional stabilizing controller that satisfies (B.1.7) exists if and only if

1. There exists a solution to the Riccati equation (B.2.26) satisfying (B.2.29) and (B.2.30) such that $A - BR^{-1}L$ is asymptotically stable.
2. There exists a solution to the Riccati equation

$$Z_\infty = B_t\hat{J}B_t' + A_tZ_\infty A_t' - M_tS_t^{-1}M_t', \tag{B.4.5}$$

in which

$$\begin{aligned} S_t &= \tilde{D}_t\hat{J}\tilde{D}_t' + C_tZ_\infty C_t' = \begin{bmatrix} S_{t1} & S_{t2} \\ S_{t2}' & S_{t3} \end{bmatrix} \\ M_t &= \tilde{B}_t\hat{J}\tilde{D}_t{}' + A_t'Z_\infty C_t' \end{aligned}$$

such that

$$\begin{aligned} Z_\infty &\geq 0 \\ S_{t1} - S_{t2}S_{t3}^{-1}S_{t2}' &< 0, \end{aligned}$$

with $A_t - M_tS_t^{-1}C_t$ asymptotically stable.

In this case, a controller that achieves the objective is

$$\begin{aligned} \widehat{x}_{k+1} &= A_t\widehat{x}_k + B_2u_k + M_{t2}S_{t3}^{-1}(y_k - C_{t2}\widehat{x}_k) \\ V_{12}u_k &= -C_{t1}\widehat{x}_k - S_{t2}S_{t3}^{-1}(y_k - C_{t2}\widehat{x}_k). \end{aligned}$$

All controllers that achieve the objective are generated by the LFT $\boldsymbol{K} = \mathcal{F}_\ell(\boldsymbol{K}_a, \boldsymbol{U})$ with $\boldsymbol{U} \in \mathcal{RH}_\infty$ satisfying the norm bound $\|\boldsymbol{U}\|_\infty < \gamma$ and $\boldsymbol{K}_a$ given in (B.4.4).

Remark B.4.1. It is possible to rephrase condition 2 in terms of the existence of a solution Y_∞ to (B.3.9) satisfying (B.3.10) and (B.3.11) such that $A - MS^{-1}C$ asymptotically stable. As in the continuous time case, substituting Z_∞ with Y_∞ means that the condition $\rho(X_\infty X_\infty) < \gamma^2$ must be satisfied. Furthermore, $Z_\infty = Y_\infty(I - \gamma^{-2}X_\infty Y_\infty)^{-1}$ and the generator of all controllers can be re-written in terms of X_∞ and Y_∞. The calculations required to show this are lengthy and should not be attempted by anyone without time on their hands.

B.5 Notes and References

Discrete-time $\mathcal{H}_\infty$ synthesis theory has been developed by a number of authors. The principal references are Limebeer, Green and Walker [131], Green [84], Stoorvogel [200], Yaesh and Shaked [217, 218, 216], Başar [18] and Iglesias and Glover [99]. Some early work was contributed by Gu, Tsai and Postlethwaite [89]. Liu, Mita and Kimura [139] have an approach based on J-lossless conjugation. Iglesias, Mustafa and Glover [100] show that the central ($\boldsymbol{U} = 0$) controller minimizes an entropy integral.

Başar [18] considers the problem in which the controller is required to be strictly causal. He exploits the connection with game theory and the results of Başar and Olsder [22]. Similar results can be found in the book by Başar and Bernhard [20].

The approach to the finite-horizon problem presented here follows that given in Limebeer, Green and Walker [131]. The limiting arguments that show that the solution to the Riccati difference equation converges to a stabilizing solution to the algebraic Riccati equation are new. These results generalize the corresponding results that are well known for Riccati equations associated with LQ-optimal control and Kalman filtering problems—see, for example, de Souza, Gevers and Goodwin [42]; Anderson and Moore [12]; Poubelle, Bitmead and Gevers [167] and Bitmead, Gevers and Wertz [29].

Pappas, Laub and Sandell [159] is the seminal reference on the solution of the discrete-time algebraic Riccati equation via eigenvalue methods.

The *optimal* full-information $\mathcal{H}_\infty$ synthesis problem is treated in Green and Limebeer [86]. No complete treatment of the optimal measurement feedback case has been given, although the bilinear transformation based approach may be used for the infinite-horizon case.

B.6 Problems

Problem B.1. Prove Theorem B.1.1.

Problem B.2. Verify that the system $\boldsymbol{L} : w \mapsto (w - w^*)$ when $u = u^*$ is causally invertible. Show that $\|\boldsymbol{L}^{-1}\|_{[0,N]} \geq 1$ by considering the impulse response.

Problem B.3. Prove the statements following Theorem B.2.1 regarding the case when the control u_k is not allowed to be a function of w_k.

(Hint: Use the fact that

$$\begin{bmatrix} R_1 & R_2' \\ R_2 & R_3 \end{bmatrix} = \begin{bmatrix} I & 0 \\ R_2 R_1^{-1} & I \end{bmatrix} \begin{bmatrix} R_1 & 0 \\ 0 & R_3 - R_2 R_1^{-1} R_2' \end{bmatrix} \begin{bmatrix} I & R_1^{-1} R_2' \\ 0 & I \end{bmatrix}$$

to derive an alternative to (B.2.13).)

Problem B.4. Suppose $X_\infty(k)$ and $\overline{X}_\infty(k)$ satisfy the Riccati equation (B.2.12) with the terminal conditions

$$\begin{aligned} X_\infty(N+1) &= \Delta \\ \overline{X}_\infty(N+1) &= \overline{\Delta} \end{aligned}$$

and suppose that the corresponding matrices R and $\overline{R}$ defined by (B.2.4) satisfy

$$\begin{array}{llllll} R_3(i) > 0 & \text{and} & (R_1 - R_2' R_3^{-1} R_2)(i) & \le & -\alpha I, & \text{for } i = k, \ldots, N \\ \overline{R}_3(i) > 0 & \text{and} & (\overline{R}_1 - \overline{R}_2'(\overline{R}_3)^{-1}\overline{R}_2)(i) & \le & -\alpha I, & \text{for } i = k, \ldots, N \end{array}$$

for some $\alpha > 0$. Show that $\Delta - \overline{\Delta} \ge 0$ implies $X_\infty(k) - \overline{X}_\infty(k) \ge 0$.

(Hint: Complete the square using X_∞ and $\overline{X}_\infty$, subtract the results and choose the inputs u and w so that the inequality

$$x_0'\big(X_\infty(k) - \overline{X}_\infty(k)\big)x_0 \ge x_{N+1}(\Delta - \overline{\Delta})x_{N+1}$$

is obtained.)

Problem B.5. (Finite-horizon LQ-optimal control). Consider the system

$$\begin{bmatrix} x_{k+1} \\ z_k \end{bmatrix} = \begin{bmatrix} A(k) & B_2(k) \\ C_1(k) & D_{12}(k) \end{bmatrix} \begin{bmatrix} x_k \\ u_k \end{bmatrix}$$

and the performance index $J(u, x_0, N, \Delta) = \|z\|_{2,[0,N]}^2 + x_{N+1}'\Delta x_{N+1}$. It is assumed that $D_{12}'(k)D_{12}(k) > 0$ for all times of interest and that $\Delta \ge 0$.

1. Show that

$$\begin{aligned} & z_k' z_k + x_{k+1}' X_2(k+1) x_{k+1} \\ &= \begin{bmatrix} x_k \\ u_k \end{bmatrix}' \begin{bmatrix} A'(k)X_2(k+1)A(k) + C_1'(k)C_1(k) & L'(k) \\ L(k) & R(k) \end{bmatrix} \begin{bmatrix} x_k \\ u_k \end{bmatrix}, \end{aligned}$$

in which

$$\begin{aligned} R(k) &= D_{12}'(k)D_{12}(k) + B_2'(k)X_2(k+1)B_2(k) \\ L(k) &= D_{12}'(k)C_1(k) + B_2'(k)X_2(k+1)A(k). \end{aligned}$$

2. If $X_2(k+1) \ge 0$, show that $R(k) > 0$ and that

$$z_k' z_k + x_{k+1}' X_2(k+1) x_{k+1} = x_k' X_2(k) x_k + (u_k - u_k^*)' R(k)(u_k - u_k^*),$$

in which $u_k^* = -R^{-1}(k)L(k)x_k$ and

$$X_2(k) = A'(k)X_2(k+1)A(k) + C_1'(k)C_1(k) - L'(k)R^{-1}(k)L(k).$$

Conclude that $X_2(k) \ge 0$.

3. Conclude that the Riccati equation for $X_2(k)$, with $X_2(N+1) = \Delta \geq 0$, has a solution on $[0, N]$ for any finite $N \geq 0$, and that

$$\begin{aligned} &\|z\|^2_{2,[0,N]} + x'_{N+1}\Delta x_{N+1} \\ &= x'_0 X_2(0) x_0 + \sum_{k=0}^{N} (u_k - u^*_k)' R(k)(u_k - u^*_k). \end{aligned} \quad \text{(B.6.1)}$$

4. Show that

$$\min_u \left\{ \|z\|^2_{2,[0,N]} + x'_{N+1}\Delta x_{N+1} \right\} = x'_0 X_2(0) x_0$$

and that the optimal control is u^*.

Problem B.6. (Removing cross terms). Consider the problem set up described in Problem B.5. Define

$$\begin{aligned} \tilde{A}(k) &= A(k) - B_2(k)\big(D_{12}(k)'D_{12}(k)\big)^{-1} D'_{12}(k)C_1(k) \\ \tilde{C}'(k)\tilde{C}(k) &= C'_1(k)\big(I - D_{12}(k)(D'_{12}(k)D_{12}(k))^{-1} D_{12}(k)'\big)C_1(k). \end{aligned}$$

Show that $X_2(k)$ satisfies the Riccati equation

$$X_2(k) = \tilde{A}(k)'\big(X_2(k+1) - X_2(k+1)B_2R(k)^{-1}B'_2X_2(k+1)\big)\tilde{A}(k) + \tilde{C}'(k)\tilde{C}(k)$$

and that

$$A(k) - B_2(k)R^{-1}(k)L(k) = \tilde{A}(k) - B_2(k)R^{-1}(k)B'_2(k)X_2(k+1)\tilde{A}(k).$$

Problem B.7. (Infinite-horizon LQ-optimal control). Consider the time-invariant system

$$\begin{bmatrix} x_{k+1} \\ z_k \end{bmatrix} = \begin{bmatrix} A & B_2 \\ C_1 & D_{12} \end{bmatrix} \begin{bmatrix} x_k \\ u_k \end{bmatrix}, \quad \text{(B.6.2)}$$

in which $D'_{12}D_{12} > 0$ and (A, B) is stabilizable. Let $\Delta \geq 0$ be any matrix such that

$$\begin{aligned} \Delta \;\geq\; & A'\Delta A + C'_1 C_1 \\ & -(D'_{12}C_1 + B'_2\Delta A)'(D'_{12}D_{12} + B'_2\Delta B_2)^{-1}(D'_{12}C_1 + B'_2\Delta A) \end{aligned} \quad \text{(B.6.3)}$$

and

$$\begin{bmatrix} A - \lambda I & B_2 \\ C_1 & D_{12} \\ \Delta & 0 \end{bmatrix} \quad \text{(B.6.4)}$$

has full column rank for all $|\lambda| \geq 1$.

1. Let K be any stabilizing state feedback control law (*i.e.*, $|\lambda_i(A - B_2K)| < 1$). Show that $u = -Kx$ results in $\|z\|^2_2 = x'_0 P x_0$, in which

$$P = (A - B_2K)'P(A - B_2K) + (C_1 - D_{12}K)'(C_1 - D_{12}K). \quad \text{(B.6.5)}$$

Show that the choice $\Delta = P$ satisfies (B.6.3) and (B.6.4).

2. Let $X_2(k)$ be the solution to

$$\begin{aligned} X_2(k) &= A'X_2(k+1)A - L'(k)R^{-1}(k)L(k) + C_1'C_1, \quad X_2(N+1) = \Delta, \\ R(k) &= D_{12}'D_{12} + B_2'X_2(k+1)B_2 \\ L(k) &= D_{12}'C_1 + B_2'X_2(k+1)A. \end{aligned}$$

Show that $X_2(k) \leq X_2(k+1)$.
(Hint: Use the completion of squares identity on $[0, N]$ and $[0, N+1]$.)

3. Show that as $k \to -\infty$, $X_2(k)$ converges to a matrix X_2 that satisfies the algebraic Riccati equation

$$\begin{aligned} X_2 &= A'X_2A - L'R^{-1}L + C_1'C_1 \\ R &= D_{12}'D_{12} + B_2'X_2B_2 \\ L &= D_{12}'C_1 + B_2'X_2A. \end{aligned} \qquad \text{(B.6.6)}$$

Define $u_k^* = -R^{-1}Lx_k$ and by completing the square show that

$$\|z\|_2^2 = x_0'X_2x_0 + \|R^{\frac{1}{2}}(u - u^*)\|_2^2$$

for any stabilizing controller.

4. Show that the control law $u_k = -F_M x_k$ with F_M defined by

$$F_M = R^{-1}(N-M)L(N-M)$$

is stabilizing (*i.e.*, $|\lambda_i(A - BF_M)|$), for any finite $M = 0, 1, \ldots$.
(Hint: First consider the case in which $\Delta = 0$ is allowed—use the fake algebraic Riccati technique. In the general case, it is useful to use the completion of squares identity to show that $(A - BF_M)x = \lambda x$ and $X_M x = 0$ implies that $\Delta\lambda^M x = 0$.
Show also that the control law $u_k = -F_M x_k$ results in $\|z\|_2^2 \leq x_0 X_2(N+1-M)x_0$.

5. Show that the control law $u_k = -R^{-1}Lx_k$ is stabilizing if and only if

$$\begin{bmatrix} A - e^{j\theta}I & B_2 \\ C_1 & D_{12} \end{bmatrix} \qquad \text{(B.6.7)}$$

has full column rank for all real θ.

6. Conclude that a stabilizing controller that *minimizes* $\|z\|_2^2$ exists if and only if (B.6.7) has full column rank for all real θ. Show that in this case the minimizing control law is $u_k = -R^{-1}Lx_k$ and the optimal cost is $x_0'X_2x_0$.

Problem B.8. Consider the system (B.6.2). Let u° be the optimal control associated with the cost function $\|z\|_{2,[0,N]}^2 + x'_{N+1}\Delta x_{N+1}$ and let u^* be the optimal control associated with the cost function $\|z\|_{2,[0,N]}^2 + x'_{N+1}X_2x_{N+1}$. Here, X_2 is any solution to the Riccati equation (B.6.6).

1. Using two applications of the completion of squares identity (see (B.6.1)), show that

$$\sum_{k=0}^{N}(u_k - u_k^*)'R(u_k - u_k^*) + x_{N+1}'(\Delta - X_2)x_{N+1}$$
$$= \sum_{k=0}^{N}(u_k - u_k^\circ)'R(k)(u_k - u_k^\circ) + x_0'(X_2(0, N+1, \Delta) - X_2)x_0 \quad \text{(B.6.8)}$$

By considering the problem of minimizing the left-hand side of the above identify conclude that the solution of the Riccati equation

$$\begin{aligned}\Gamma(k) &= (A - B_2F)'\big(\Gamma(k+1) \\ &\quad -\Gamma(k+1)B_2(R + B_2'\Gamma(k+1)B_2)^{-1}B_2'\Gamma(k+1)\big)(A - B_2F),\end{aligned} \quad \text{(B.6.9)}$$

with terminal condition $\Gamma(N+1) = \Delta - X_2$ is $\Gamma(k) = X_2(k, N+1, \Delta) - X_2$.

2. Verify that $\Gamma(k) = X_2(k, N+1, \Delta) - X_2$ is indeed the solution to (B.6.9) by subtracting the Riccati equations defining X_2 and $X_2(k)$. It is not necessary to assume the existence of any inverses other than R^{-1} and $R^{-1}(k)$. (Hint: Write

$$\begin{aligned}L(k) &= L + B_2'(X_2(k+1) - X_2)A \\ R(k) &= R + B_2'(X_2(k+1) - X_2)B_2.)\end{aligned}$$

Problem B.9. Suppose $X_\infty \geq 0$ satisfying

$$\begin{aligned}X_\infty &= A'X_\infty A - L'R^{-1}L + \overline{C}'J\overline{C} \\ R &= \overline{D}'J\overline{D} + B'X_\infty B \\ L &= \overline{D}'J\overline{C} + B'X_\infty A\end{aligned}$$

exists. Partition R and L as in the text, and suppose $\nabla = R_1 - R_2'R_3^{-1}R_2 < 0$. Suppose also that X_2 is the stabilizing solution to the LQ Riccati equation

$$\begin{aligned}X_2 &= C_1'C_1 + A'X_2A \\ &\quad - (D_{12}'C_1 + B_2'X_2A)'(D_{12}'D_{12} + B_2'X_2B_2)^{-1}(D_{12}'C_1 + B_2'X_2A).\end{aligned}$$

1. Show that $\Gamma = X_\infty - X_2$ satisfies

$$\begin{aligned}\Gamma &= (A - B_2R_3^{-1}L_2)'\big(\Gamma + \Gamma B_2(R_3 - B_2'\Gamma B_2)^{-1}\big)B_2'\Gamma\big)(A - B_2R_3^{-1}L_2) \\ &\quad - L_\nabla'\nabla^{-1}L_\nabla.\end{aligned}$$

2. Show that $X_\infty - X_2 \geq 0$ implies that $A - B_2R_3^{-1}L_2$ is asymptotically stable.

3. Show that $(X_\infty - X_2)x = 0$ implies $(A - BR^{-1}L)x = (A - B_2R_3^{-1}L_2)x$.

Problem B.10.

1. Show that $\Gamma(k) = X_\infty - X_\infty(k)$ is the solution to the Riccati difference equation

$$\begin{aligned}\Gamma(k) &= (A - BR^{-1}L)'\big(\Gamma(k+1) \\ &\quad + \Gamma(k+1)B(R - B'\Gamma(k+1)B)^{-1}B'\Gamma(k+1)\big)(A - BR^{-1}L),\end{aligned}$$

with terminal condition $\Gamma(N+1) = X_\infty - X_2$.
(Hint: Write

$$\begin{aligned}L(k) &= L - B'(X_\infty - X_\infty(k+1))A \\ R(k) &= R - B'(X_\infty - X_\infty(k+1))B.)\end{aligned}$$

2. Show that $X_\infty = \lim_{N\to\infty} X_\infty(k, N+1, X_2)$ is such that $A - BR^{-1}L$ is asymptotically stable *without* assuming that $X_\infty - X_\infty(k, N+1, \Delta)$ is nonsingular for all $k \leq N+1$.
(Hint: Complete the square on [k,N] using $X_\infty(k, N+1, X_2)$ and also using X_∞. Use these two identities to show that if $x_k \in \ker\big(X_\infty - X_\infty(k, N, X_2)\big)$, then $x_{N+1} \in \ker\big(X_\infty - X_2\big)$.)

Problem B.11. Show that the $\ell_2[0, N]$-adjoint of the discrete-time system

$$\begin{bmatrix} x_{k+1} \\ z_k \end{bmatrix} = \begin{bmatrix} A(k) & B(k) \\ C(k) & D(k) \end{bmatrix} \begin{bmatrix} x_k \\ w_k \end{bmatrix}, \qquad x_0 = 0,$$

is

$$\begin{bmatrix} p_{k-1} \\ y_k \end{bmatrix} = \begin{bmatrix} A'(k) & C'(k) \\ B'(k) & D'(k) \end{bmatrix} \begin{bmatrix} p_k \\ u_k \end{bmatrix}, \qquad p_N = 0.$$

Problem B.12. Verify equation (B.3.7).

Bibliography

[1] V.M. Adamjan, D.Z. Arov, and M.G. Krein. Analytic properties of Schmidt pairs for a Hankel operator and the generalized Schur-Takagi problem. *Math. USSR Sbornik*, 15:31–73, 1971.

[2] V.M. Adamjan, D.Z. Arov, and M.G. Krein. Infinite block Hankel matrices and related extension problems. *American Mathematical Society Translations*, 111:133–156, 1978.

[3] M.M. Al-Husari, B. Hendel, I.M. Jaimoukha, E.M. Kasenally D.J.N. Limebeer, and A. Portone. Vertical stabilisation of tokamak plasmas. In *Proceedings of the IEEE Conference on Decision and Control*, pages 1165–1170, Brighton, England, 1991.

[4] M.M Al-Hussari, I.M. Jaimoukha, and D.J.N. Limebeer. A descriptor approach for the solution of the one-block distance problem. In *Proceedings of the IFAC World Congress*, Sydney, Australia, 1993.

[5] U.M. Al-Saggaf and G.F. Franklin. An error bound for a discrete reduced order model of a linear multivariable system. *IEEE Transactions on Automatic Control*, 32:815–819, 1987.

[6] U.M. Al-Saggaf and G.F. Franklin. Model reduction via balanced realization: An extension and frequency weighting techniques. *IEEE Transactions on Automatic Control*, 33:681–692, 1988.

[7] R. Albanese, J. Blum, and O. DeBarbieri. Numerical studies of the Next European Torus via the PROTEUS code. In *27th Conference on Numerical Simulation of Plasmas*, San Francisco, 1987.

[8] R. Albanese and G. Rubinacci. Integral formulation for 3D eddy-current computation using edge elements. *Proc IEE, Part A*, 135(7):457–462, 1988.

[9] B.D.O. Anderson. A system theory criterion for positive real matrices. *SIAM Journal of Control and Optimization*, 6(2):171–192, 1967.

[10] B.D.O. Anderson. Weighted Hankel norm approximation: Calculation of bounds. *Systems and Control Letters*, 7:247–255, 1986.

[11] B.D.O. Anderson and J.B. Moore. *Linear Optimal Control.* Prentice-Hall, Englewood Cliffs, N.J., 1971.

[12] B.D.O. Anderson and J.B. Moore. *Optimal Filtering.* Prentice-Hall, Englewood Cliffs, N.J., 1979.

[13] B.D.O. Anderson and J.B. Moore. *Optimal Control: Linear Quadratic Methods.* Prentice-Hall, Englewood Cliffs, N.J., 1989.

[14] B.D.O. Anderson and S. Vongpanitlerd. *Network Analysis and Synthesis: A Modern Systems Theory Approach.* Prentice-Hall, Englewood Cliffs, N.J., 1973.

[15] M.A. Athans. Editorial on the LQG problem. *IEEE Transactions on Automatic Control*, 16(6):528, 1971.

[16] M.A. Athans. The role and use of the stochastic Linear-Quadratic-Gaussian problem. *IEEE Transactions on Automatic Control*, 16(6):529–552, 1971.

[17] M.A. Athans (Guest Editor). Special issue on the LQG problem. *IEEE Transactions on Automatic Control*, 16(6):527–869, 1971.

[18] T. Başar. A dynamic games approach to controller design: Disturbance rejection in discrete-time. In *Proceedings of the IEEE Conference on Decision and Control*, pages 407–414, Tampa, 1989.

[19] T. Başar. Optimum performance levels for $\mathcal{H}_\infty$ filters, predictors and smoothers. *Systems and Control Letters*, 16:309–317, 1991.

[20] T. Başar and P. Bernhard. *$\mathcal{H}_\infty$-Optimal Control and Related Minimax Design Problems: A Dynamic Game Approach.* Systems and Control: Foundations and Applications. Birkhäuser, Boston, 1991.

[21] T. Başar and M. Mintz. Minimax terminal state estimation for linear plants with unknown forcing functions. *International Journal of Control*, 16:49–70, 1972.

[22] T. Başar and G.J. Olsder. *Dynamic Non-Cooperative Game Theory.* Academic Press, New York, 1982.

[23] J.A. Ball and N. Cohen. Sensitivity minimization in an $\mathcal{H}_\infty$ norm: Parametrization of all solutions. *International Journal of Control*, 46:785–816, 1987.

[24] J.A. Ball and E. A. Jonckheere. The four block Adamjan Arov Krein problem. *Journal of Mathematical Analysis and Applications*, 170(2):322–342, 1992.

[25] J.A. Ball and A.C.M. Ran. Optimal Hankel norm model reductions and Wiener-Hopf factorization I: The canonical case. *SIAM*, 25(2):362–382, 1987.

[26] M. Banker. Linear stationary quadratic games. In *Proceedings of the IEEE Conference on Decision and Control*, pages 193–197, San Diego, 1973.

[27] L.D. Berkovitz. A variational approach to differential games. In *Advances in Game Theory*, volume 52 of *Annals. of Math. Study*, pages 127–174. Princeton University Press, Princeton, N.J., 1964.

[28] D.S. Bernstein and W. Haddad. Steady-state Kalman filtering with an $\mathcal{H}_\infty$ error bound. *Systems and Control Letters*, 12:9–16, 1989.

[29] R.R. Bitmead, M. Gevers, and W. Wertz. *Adaptive Optimal Control: The Thinking Man's GPC.* Prentice-Hall, Sydney, 1990.

[30] H.S. Black. Inventing the negative feedback amplifier. *IEEE Spectrum*, pages 55–60, December 1977.

[31] H.W. Bode. *Network Analysis and Feedback Amplifier Design.* D. Van Nostrand, Princeton, N.J., 1945.

[32] S. Boyd and C.A. Desoer. Subharmonic functions and performance bounds on linear time-invariant feedback systems. *IMA Journal of Mathematical Control and Information*, 2:153–170, 1985.

[33] R.W. Brockett. *Finite Dimensional Linear Systems.* John Wiley and Sons, New York, 1970.

[34] A.E. Bryson and Y.C. Ho. *Applied Optimal Control.* Blaisdell, Waltham, Mass., 1969.

[35] R.Y. Chiang and M.G. Safonov. *Robust Control Toolbox User's Guide.* The MathWorks, Inc., Natick, Mass., 1992.

[36] C.C. Chu, J.C. Doyle, and E.B. Lee. The general distance problem in $\mathcal{H}_\infty$ optimal control theory. *International Journal of Control*, 44:565–596, 1986.

[37] E. Coccorese and F. Garofalo. Plasma position control in tokamak startup. *E. Majorana Series Ed. by Knöpfel*, 26:337–349, 1986.

[38] J.B. Cruz Jr. and W.R. Perkins. A new approach to the sensitivity problem in multivariable feedback system design. *IEEE Transactions on Automatic Control*, 9:216–223, 1964.

[39] C. Davis, W.M. Kahan, and H.F. Weinberger. Norm preserving dilations and their application to optimal error bounds. *SIAM Journal of Numerical Analysis*, 19:445–469, 1982.

[40] M.H.A. Davis. *Linear Estimation and Stochastic Control.* Chapman and Hall, London, 1977.

[41] D.C.Youla, H.A. Jabr, and J.J. Bongiorno. Modern Weiner-Hopf design of optimal controllers, Part II: The multivariable case. *IEEE Transactions on Automatic Control*, 21:319–338, 1976.

[42] C. de Souza, M.R. Gevers, and G.C. Goodwin. Riccati equations in optimal filtering of nonstabilizable systems having singular state transition matrices. *IEEE Transactions on Automatic Control*, 31(9):831–838, 1986.

[43] P. Delsarte, Y. Genin, and Y. Kamp. The Nevanlinna-Pick problem for matrix valued functions. *SIAM Journal of Applied Mathematics*, 36:47–61, 1979.

[44] P. Delsarte, Y. Genin, and Y. Kamp. On the role of the Nevanlinna-Pick problem in circuit theory. *Circuit Theory and Applications*, 9:177–187, 1981.

[45] U.B. Desai and D. Pal. A transformation approach to stochastic model reduction. *IEEE Transactions on Automatic Control*, 29(12):1097–1100, 1984.

[46] C.A. Desoer, R.W. Liu, J. Murray, and R. Saeks. Feedback system design: The fractional representation approach to analysis and synthesis. *IEEE Transactions on Automatic Control*, 25:339–412, 1980.

[47] C.A. Desoer and M. Vidyasagar. *Feedback Systems: Input-Output Properties.* Academic Press, New York, 1975.

[48] P. Dewilde, A. Vieira, and T. Kailath. On a generalized Szegö-Levinson realization algorithm for optimal linear predictors based on a network synthesis approach. *IEEE Transactions on Circuits and Systems*, 25:663–675, 1978.

[49] J.C. Doyle. Guaranteed margins for LQG regulators. *IEEE Transactions on Automatic Control*, 23:756–757, 1978.

[50] J.C. Doyle. Robustness of multiloop linear feedback systems. In *Proceedings of the IEEE Conference on Decision and Control*, pages 12–18, San Diego, 1979.

[51] J.C. Doyle. Analysis of feedback systems with structured uncertainties. *Proceedings of the IEE, Part D*, 129(6):242–250, 1982.

[52] J.C. Doyle. Lecture notes in advanced multivariable control. ONR/Honeywell Workshop, Minneapolis, 1984.

[53] J.C. Doyle, B. Francis, and A. Tannenbaum. *Feedback Control Theory.* Macmillan Publishing Co., New York, 1991.

[54] J.C. Doyle, K. Glover, P.P. Khargonekar, and B.A. Francis. State-space solutions to standard $\mathcal{H}_2$ and $\mathcal{H}_\infty$ control problems. *IEEE Transactions on Automatic Control*, 34:831–847, 1989.

[55] J.C. Doyle and G. Stein. Multivariable feedback design: Concepts for a classical /modern synthesis. *IEEE Transactions on Automatic Control*, 26:4–16, 1981.

[56] P.L. Duren. *Theory of $\mathcal{H}_p$ Spaces.* Academic Press, New York, 1970.

[57] D.F. Enns. Model reduction with balanced realizations: An error bound and frequency weighted generalization. In *Proceedings of the IEEE Conference on Decision and Control*, pages 127–132, Las Vegas, 1984.

[58] H.C. Vivian *et al.* Flexible structure control laboratory development and technology demonstration. JPL Publication 88-29, California Institute of Technology, 1987.

[59] Ky Fan. Maximum properties and inequalities for the eigenvalues of completely continuous operators. *Proc. Nat. Acad. Sciences*, 37:760–766, 1951.

[60] A. Feintuch and B. A. Francis. Uniformly optimal control of linear systems. *Automatica*, 21(5):563–574, 1985.

[61] J.M. Fernandes, C.E. de Souza, and G.C. Goodwin. Novel techniques for the design of robust state estimators. In *IFAC symposium*, 1990.

[62] K.V. Fernando and H. Nicholson. Singular perturbational model reduction of balanced systems. *IEEE Transactions on Automatic Control*, 27:466–468, 1982.

[63] C. Foias and A. Tannenbaum. On the four block problem, I. In I. Gohberg and M.A. Kaashoek, editors, *Topics in Operator Theory: Constantin Apostol Memorial Issue*, volume 32 of *Operator theory: Advances and applications*, pages 93–112. Birkäuser, Basel, 1988.

[64] C. Foias and A. Tannenbaum. On the singular values of the four block operator and certain generalized interpolation problems. In Sadovsky, editor, *Analysis and partial differential equations*, pages 483–493. Marcel Dekker, New York, 1990.

[65] B.A. Francis. *A Course in $\mathcal{H}_\infty$ Control.* Number 88 in Lecture Notes in Control and Information Sciences. Springer-Verlag, Berlin, 1987.

[66] B.A. Francis and G. Zames. On $\mathcal{H}_\infty$-optimal sensitivity theory for SISO feedback systems. *IEEE Transactions on Automatic Control*, 29(1):9–16, 1984.

[67] J.S. Freudenberg and D.P. Looze. Right-half-plane poles and zeros and design trade-offs in feedback systems. *IEEE Transactions on Automatic Control*, 30(6):555–565, 1985.

[68] J.S. Freudenberg and D.P. Looze. *Frequency Domain Properties of Scalar and Multivariable Feedback Systems*. Springer-Verlag, New-York, 1988.

[69] J.B. Garnett. *Bounded Analytic Functions*. Academic Press, New York, 1981.

[70] T.T. Georgiou and M.C. Smith. Optimal robustness in the gap metric. *IEEE Transactions on Automatic Control*, 35(6):673–686, 1990.

[71] K. Glover. All optimal hankel-norm approximations of linear multivariable systems and their $\mathcal{L}_\infty$-error bounds. *International Journal of Control*, 39(6):1115–1193, 1984.

[72] K. Glover. Multiplicative approximation of linear multivariable systems with $\mathcal{H}_\infty$ error bounds. In *Proceedings of the IEEE Conference on Decision and Control*, pages 1705–1709, 1986.

[73] K. Glover. Robust stabilization of linear multivariable systems: Relations to approximation. *International Journal of Control*, 43(3):741–766, 1986.

[74] K. Glover. Model reduction: A tutorial on Hankel norm methods and lower bounds on $\mathcal{L}_2$ errors. In *Proceedings of the Xth Triennial IFAC World Congress*, volume 10, pages 288–293, Munich, 1987. Pergamon Press.

[75] K. Glover. A tutorial on model reduction. In J.C. Willems, editor, *From Data to Model*, pages 26–48. Springer-Verlag, Berlin, 1989.

[76] K. Glover and J.C. Doyle. State-space formulae for all stabilizing controllers that satisfy a $\mathcal{H}_\infty$ norm bound and relations to risk sensitivity. *Systems and Control Letters*, 11:167–172, 1988.

[77] K. Glover, D. J. N. Limebeer, and Y. S. Hung. A structured approximation problem with applications to frequency weighted model reduction. *IEEE Transactions on Automatic Control*, 37(4):447–465, 1992.

[78] K. Glover, D.J.N. Limebeer, J.C. Doyle, E.M. Kasenally, and M.G. Safonov. A characterization of all solutions to the four block general distance problem. *SIAM Journal of Control and Optimization*, 29(2):283–324, 1991.

[79] K. Glover and D. McFarlane. Robust stabilization of normalized coprime factor plant descriptions with $\mathcal{H}_\infty$-bounded uncertainty. *IEEE Transactions on Automatic Control*, 34(8):821–830, 1989.

[80] K. Glover and D. Mustafa. Derivation of the maximum entropy $\mathcal{H}_\infty$ controller and a state-space formula for its entropy. *International Journal of Control*, 50:899–916, 1989.

[81] G.H. Golub and C.F. van Loan. *Matrix Computations.* North Oxford Academic, Oxford, 1983.

[82] M. Green. Balanced stochastic realizations. *Linear Algebra and its Applications*, 98:211–247, 1988.

[83] M. Green. A relative error bound for balanced stochastic truncation. *IEEE Transactions on Automatic Control*, 33(10):961–965, 1988.

[84] M. Green. $\mathcal{H}_\infty$ controller synthesis by J-lossless coprime factorization. *SIAM Journal of Control and Optimization*, 28:522–547, 1992.

[85] M. Green, K. Glover, D.J.N. Limebeer, and J.C. Doyle. A J-spectral factorization approach to $\mathcal{H}_\infty$ control. *SIAM Journal of Control and Optimization*, 28:1350–1371, 1990.

[86] M. Green and D.J.N. Limebeer. $\mathcal{H}_\infty$ optimal full information control for discrete time systems. In *Proceedings of the IEEE Conference on Decision and Control*, pages 1769–1774, Honolulu, 1990.

[87] M.J. Grimble. $\mathcal{H}_\infty$ design of optimal linear filters. In C.I. Byrnes, C.F. Martin, and R.E. Saeks, editors, *Linear Circuits, Systems and Signal Processing; Theory and Application*, pages 533–540. North-Holland, Amsterdam, 1988. Proceedings of MTNS, Phoenix, Arizona, 1987.

[88] M.J. Grimble, R. Ho, and A. Elsayed. $\mathcal{H}_\infty$ robust linear estimators. In *IFAC symposium*, 1989.

[89] D.W. Gu, M.C. Tsai, and I. Postlethwaite. State-space formulae for discrete-time $\mathcal{H}_\infty$ optimization. *International Journal of Control*, 49(5):1683–1723, 1989.

[90] J.W. Helton. Operator theory and broadband matching. In *Proceedings of the 11th Annual Allerton Conference on Communications, Control and Computing*, 1976.

[91] P. Heuberger. A famililly of reduced order models based on open-loop balancing. In *Selected Topics in Identification, Modelling and Control*, volume 1, pages 1–10. 1990.

[92] G. Hexner and M. Mintz. On the solution of a minimax terminal state estimation problem: A Hilbert space setting. *International Journal of Control*, 27:821–830, 1989.

[93] K. Hoffman. *Banach Spaces of Analytic Functions.* Prentice-Hall, Englewood Cliffs, N.J., 1962.

[94] R.A. Horn and C.A. Johnson. *Matrix Analysis.* Cambridge University Press, Cambridge, England, 1985.

[95] I.M. Horowitz. *Synthesis of Feedback Systems.* Academic Press, New York, 1963.

[96] D. Hoyle, R. Hyde, and D.J.N. Limebeer. An $\mathcal{H}_\infty$ approach to two-degree-of-freedom design. In *Proceedings of the IEEE Conference on Decision and Control*, pages 1581–1585, Brighton, England, 1991.

[97] Y.S. Hung. $\mathcal{H}_\infty$ optimal control: Part I model matching. *International Journal of Control*, 49(4):1291–1331, 1989.

[98] Y.S. Hung. $\mathcal{H}_\infty$ optimal control: Part II solutions for controllers. *International Journal of Control*, 49(4):1331–1359, 1989.

[99] P. Iglesias and K. Glover. State-space approach to discrete-time $\mathcal{H}_\infty$-control. *International Journal of Control*, 54(5):1031–1074, 1991.

[100] P. Iglesias, D. Mustafa, and K. Glover. Discrete-time $\mathcal{H}_\infty$-controllers satisfying minimum entropy criterion. *Systems and Control Letters*, 14:275–286, 1990.

[101] R. Isaacs. Differential games, I, II, III, IV. Research Memoranda RM-1391, RM-1399, RM-1411, RM-1486, The Rand Corporation, 1954.

[102] R. Isaacs. *Differential Games.* John Wiley and Sons, New York, 1965.

[103] D.H. Jacobson. Optimal stochastic linear systems with exponential performance criteria and their relation to deterministic games. *IEEE Transactions on Automatic Control*, 18:124–131, 1973.

[104] I.M. Jaimoukha, E.M. Kasenally, and D.J.N. Limebeer. Numerical solution of large scale lyapunov equations using krylov subspace methods. In *Proceedings of the IEEE Conference on Decision and Control*, pages 1927–1932, Tuscon, 1992.

[105] T. Kailath. *Linear Systems.* Prentice-Hall, Englewood Cliffs, N.J., 1980.

[106] R.E. Kalman. A new approach to linear filtering and prediction theory. *ASME Transactions, Series D: Journal of Basic Engineering*, 82:35–45, 1960.

[107] R.E. Kalman. Lyapunov functions for the problem of Lur'e in automatic control. *Proceedings of the National Academy of Sciences, USA*, 49(2):201–205, 1963.

[108] R.E. Kalman. On a new characterization of linear passive systems. In *Proceedings of the First Allerton Conference on Circuit and System Theory*, pages 456–470, University of Illinois, Urbana, 1963.

[109] R.E. Kalman. When is a control system optimal? *ASME Transactions, Series D: Journal of Basic Engineering*, 86:1–10, 1964.

[110] R.E. Kalman and R.S. Bucy. New results in linear filtering and prediction theory. *ASME Transactions, Series D: Journal of Basic Engineering*, 83:95–108, 1960.

[111] E. M. Kasenally and D. J. N. Limebeer. Closed formulae for a parametric mixed sensitivity problem. *Systems and Control Letters*, 12:1–7, 1989.

[112] E.M. Kasenally, D.J.N. Limebeer, and A. Portone. A new approach to tokamak vertical instability control. In *Proceedings of IAEA Technical Meeting on the Avoidance and Control of Tokamak Disruptions*, Culham Laboratories, 1991.

[113] E.M. Kasenally, D.J.N. Limebeer, and A. Portone. Robust instability control of tokamak plasmas. In *Proceedings of the IFAC World Congress*, Sydney Australia, 1993.

[114] S.A. Kassan and V. Poor. Robust techniques for signal processing. *Proceedings of the IEEE*, 73:433–481, 1985.

[115] P.P. Khargonekar and K.M. Nagpal. Filtering and smoothing in an $\mathcal{H}_\infty$ setting. *IEEE Transactions on Automatic Control*, 36(2):152–166, 1991.

[116] P.P. Khargonekar, I.R. Petersen, and M.A. Rotea. $\mathcal{H}_\infty$-optimal control with state feedback. *IEEE Transactions on Automatic Control*, 33:786–788, 1988.

[117] P.P. Khargonekar and E. Sontag. On the relation between stable matrix fraction factorizations and regulable realizations of linear systems over rings. *IEEE Transactions on Automatic Control*, 27:627–638, 1982.

[118] H. Kimura. Robust stabilizability for a class of transfer functions. *IEEE Transactions on Automatic Control*, 29:788–793, 1984.

[119] H. Kimura. Directional interpolation approach to $\mathcal{H}_\infty$-optimization and robust stabilization. *IEEE Transactions on Automatic Control*, 32:1085–1093, 1987.

[120] H. Kimura, Y. Lu, and R. Kawtani. On the structure of $\mathcal{H}_\infty$ control systems and related questions. *IEEE Transactions on Automatic Control*, 36(6):653–667, 1991.

[121] P.J. Kootsookos, R.R. Bitmead, and M. Green. The Nehari schuffle: FIR(q) filter design with guaranteed error bounds. *IEEE Transactions on Acoustics, Speech and Signal Processing*, 40:1876–1883, 1992.

[122] V. Kucera. *Discrete Linear Control: The Polynomial Equation Approach.* Wiley, New York, 1979.

[123] H. Kwakernaak. Robustness optimization of linear feedback systems. In *Proceedings of the IEEE Conference on Decision and Control*, pages 618–624, San Antonio, 1983.

[124] H. Kwakernaak. The polynomial approach to $\mathcal{H}_\infty$-optimal regulation. In *$\mathcal{H}_\infty$-Control Theory*, volume 1496 of *Lecture Notes in Mathematics*. Springer-Verlag, Berlin, 1991.

[125] H. Kwakernaak and R. Sivan. *Linear Optimal Control Systems.* Wiley-Interscience, New York, 1972.

[126] H. Kwakernaak and R. Sivan. *Modern Signals and Systems.* Prentice-Hall, Englewood Cliffs, N.J., 1991.

[127] G. A. Latham and B.D.O. Anderson. Frequency weighted optimal Hankel-norm approximation of stable transfer functions. *Systems and Control Letters*, 5:229–236, 1986.

[128] A.J. Laub, M.T. Heath, C.C Page, and R.C. Ward. Computation of balacing transformations and other applications of simultaneous diagonalization algorithms. *IEEE Transactions on Automatic Control*, 32:115–122, 1987.

[129] D.J.N. Limebeer and B.D.O. Anderson. An interpolation theory approach to $\mathcal{H}_\infty$ controller degree bounds. *Linear Algebra and its Applications*, 98:347–386, 1988.

[130] D.J.N. Limebeer, B.D.O. Anderson, P.P. Khargonekar, and M. Green. A game theoretic approach to $\mathcal{H}_\infty$ control for time varying systems. *SIAM Journal of Control and Optimization*, 30(2):262–283, 1992.

[131] D.J.N. Limebeer, M. Green, and D. Walker. Discrete-time $\mathcal{H}_\infty$ control. In *Proceedings of the IEEE Conference on Decision and Control*, pages 392–396, Tampa, 1989.

[132] D.J.N. Limebeer and G. Halikias. An analysis of pole zero cancellations in $\mathcal{H}_\infty$ control problems of the second kind. *SIAM Journal of Control and Optimization*, 25:1457–1493, 1987.

[133] D.J.N. Limebeer, G. Halikias, and K. Glover. State-space algorithm for the computation of superoptimal matrix interpolating functions. *International Journal of Control*, 50(6):2431–2466, 1989.

[134] D.J.N. Limebeer and Y.S. Hung. An analysis of pole zero cancellations in $\mathcal{H}_\infty$ control problems of the first kind. *SIAM Journal of Control and Optimization*, 26:646–667, 1988.

[135] D.J.N. Limebeer, E. Kasenally, I. Jaimouka, and M.G. Safonov. All solutions to the four-block general distance problem. In *Proceedings of the IEEE Conference on Decision and Control*, pages 875–880, Austin, 1988.

[136] D.J.N. Limebeer, E.M. Kasenally, and J.D. Perkins. On the design of robust two-degree-of-freedom-controllers. *Automatica*, 29(1):157–168, 1993.

[137] D.J.N. Limebeer and U. Shaked. New results on $\mathcal{H}_\infty$ optimal filtering. In H. Kimura and S. Kodama, editors, *Recent Advances in the Mathematical Theory of Systems, Control, Networks and Signal Processing*, volume 1, pages 317–322. MITA Press, Osaka, Japan, 1992. Proceedings of MTNS, Kobe, Japan, 1991.

[138] K.Z. Liu, T. Mita, and R. Kawtani. Parametrization of state feedback $\mathcal{H}_\infty$ controllers. *International Journal of Control*, 51(3):535–551, 1990.

[139] K.Z. Liu, T. Mita, and H. Kimura. Complete solution to the standard four-block $\mathcal{H}_\infty$ control problem for discrete-time systems. In *Proceedings of the IEEE Conference on Decision and Control*, pages 1786–1793, Honolulu, 1990.

[140] Y. Liu and B.D.O. Anderson. Singular perturbation approximation of balanced systems. *International Journal of Control*, 50:1379–1405, 1989.

[141] D.G. Luenberger. An introduction to observers. *IEEE Transactions on Automatic Control*, 16(6):596–602, 1971.

[142] A.G.J. MacFarlane and D.F.A. Scott-Jones. Vector gain. *International Journal of Control*, 29:65–91, 1979.

[143] A.G.J. MacFarlane (Editor). *Frequency Response Methods in Control Systems.* IEEE Press, New York, 1979.

[144] J.M. Maciejowski. *Multivariable Feedback Design.* Addison Wesley, New York, 1989.

[145] E.F. Mageirou. Values and strategies for infinite time linear quadratic games. *IEEE Transactions on Automatic Control*, 21(4):547–550, 1976.

[146] E.F. Mageirou and Y.C. Ho. Decentralized stabilization via game theoretic methods. *Automatica*, 13:393–399, 1977.

[147] P.S. Maybeck. *Stochastic Models, Estimation and Control, Volume 1.* Academic Press, New York, 1979.

[148] D. McFarlane and K. Glover. Robust controller design using normalized coprime factor plant descriptions. *IEEE Transactions on Automatic Control*, 37:759–769, 1992.

[149] J.M. Mendel and D.L. Gieseking. Bibliography on the Linear-Quadratic-Gaussian problem. *IEEE Transactions on Automatic Control*, 16(6):847–869, 1971.

[150] T. Mita, K.Z. Liu, and S. Ohuchi. Correction of the fi results in $\mathcal{H}_\infty$ control and parametrization of $\mathcal{H}_\infty$ state feedback controllers. *IEEE Transactions on Automatic Control*, 38(2):343–347, 1993.

[151] M. Morari and E. Zafiriou. *Robust Process Control.* Prentice-Hall, Englewood Cliffs, N.J., 1989.

[152] M.S.Tombs and I. Postlethwaite. Truncated balanced realizations of a stable non-minimal state-space system. *Rpt. No. OUEL 1647/86, Engineering Dept., Oxford.*, 1986.

[153] C.T. Mullis and R.A. Roberts. Synthesis of minimum roundoff noise fixed point digital filters. *IEEE Transactions of Circuits and Systems*, 23:551–562, 1976.

[154] D. Mustafa, K. Glover, and D.J.N. Limebeer. Solutions to the $\mathcal{H}_\infty$ general distance problem which minimize an entropy integral. *Automatica*, 27:193–199, 1991.

[155] Z. Nehari. On bounded bilinear forms. *Annals of Mathematics*, 15(1):153–162, 1957.

[156] C.N. Nett, C.A. Jacobson, and M.J. Balas. A connection between state-space and doubly coprime fractional representations. *IEEE Transactions on Automatic Control*, 29:831–832, 1984.

[157] R. Nevanlinna and V. Paatero. *Complex analysis.* Chelsea, New York, 2nd edition, 1982.

[158] G.C. Newton, L.A. Gould, and J.F. Kaiser. *Analytic Design of Linear Feedback Control Systems.* Wiley, New York, 1957.

[159] T. Pappas, A.J. Laub, and N. R. Sandell Jr. On the numerical solution of the discrete-time algebraic Riccati equation. *IEEE Transactions on Automatic Control*, 25(4):631–641, 1980.

[160] S. Parrott. On a quotient norm and the Sz-Nagy-Foias lifting theorem. *Journal of Functional Analysis*, 30:311–328, 1978.

[161] J.R. Partington. *An Introduction to Hankel Operators*, volume 13 of *London Mathematical Society Student Texts.* Cambridge University Press, 1988.

[162] L. Pernebo and L.M. Silverman. Model reduction by balanced state space representations. *IEEE Transactions on Automatic Control*, 27:382–387, 1982.

[163] I.R. Petersen. Disturbance attenuation and $\mathcal{H}_\infty$ optimization: A design method based on the algebraic Riccati equation. *IEEE Transactions on Automatic Control*, 32:427–429, 1987.

[164] I.R. Petersen and C.V. Hollot. A Riccati equation approach to the stabilization of uncertain linear systems. *Automatica*, 22:397–411, 1986.

[165] V.M. Popov. Absolute stability of nonlinear systems of automatic control. *Automation and Remote Control*, pages 857–875, 1962.

[166] I. Postlethewaite, J.M. Edmunds, and A.G.J. MacFarlane. Principal gains and principal phases in the analysis of linear multivariable feedback systems. *IEEE Transactions on Automatic Control*, 26(1):32–46, 1981.

[167] M.A. Poubelle, R.R. Bitmead, and M. Gevers. Fake algebraic Riccati techniques and stability. *IEEE Transactions on Automatic Control*, 33:379–381, 1988.

[168] S.C. Power. *Hankel Operators on Hilbert Space.* Pitman advanced publishing programme, Boston, 1981.

[169] R. Ravi, K.M. Nagpal, and P.P. Khargonekar. $\mathcal{H}_\infty$ control of linear time-varying systems: A state-space approach. *SIAM Journal of Control and Optimization*, 29(6):1394–1413, 1991.

[170] R. Redheffer. Inequalities for a matrix Riccati equation. *Journal of Mathematical Mechanics*, 8(3):349–367, 1959.

[171] R. Redheffer. On a certain linear fractional transformation. *Journal of Mathematics and Physics*, 39:269–286, 1960.

[172] H.H. Rosenbrock. *Computer-Aided Control System Design.* Academic Press, New York, 1974.

[173] H.H. Rosenbrock and P.D. Moran. Good, bad, or optimal? *IEEE Transactions on Automatic Control*, 16(6):552–554, 1971.

[174] W. Rudin. *Real and Complex Analysis.* McGraw-Hill, New York, 1966.

[175] M.G. Safonov. *Stability and Robustness of Multivariable Feedback Systems.* PhD thesis, M.I.T., Cambridge, Mass., 1977.

[176] M.G. Safonov. Tight bounds on the response of multivariable systems with component uncertainty. In *Proceedings of the 16th Annual Allerton Conference on Communications, Control and Computing*, pages 451–460, 1978.

[177] M.G. Safonov. *Stability and Robustness of Multivariable Feedback Systems.* M.I.T. Press, Cambridge, Mass., 1980.

[178] M.G. Safonov. Stability margins of diagonally perturbed multivariable feedback systems. *Proceedings of the IEE, Part D*, 129(6):251–256, 1982.

[179] M.G. Safonov and M. Athans. Gain and phase margins for multiloop LQG regulators. *IEEE Transactions on Automatic Control*, 22(2):173–178, 1977.

[180] M.G. Safonov and R.Y. Chiang. A Schur method for balanced-truncation model reduction. *IEEE Transactions on Automatic Control*, 43(7):729–733, 1989.

[181] M.G. Safonov, E.A. Jonckheere, M. Verma, and D.J.N. Limebeer. Synthesis of positive real multivariable feedback systems. *International Journal of Control*, 45(3):817–842, 1987.

[182] M.G. Safonov, A.J. Laub, and G.L. Hartmann. Feedback properties of multivariable systems: The role and use of the return difference matrix. *IEEE Transactions on Automatic Control*, 26(1):47–65, 1981.

[183] M.G. Safonov and D.J.N. Limebeer. Simplifying the $\mathcal{H}_\infty$ theory via loop shifting. In *Proceedings of the IEEE Conference on Decision and Control*, pages 1399–1404, Austin, 1988.

[184] M.G. Safonov, D.J.N. Limebeer, and R.Y. Chiang. Simplifying the $\mathcal{H}_\infty$ theory via loop shifting, matrix pencil and descriptor concepts. *International Journal of Control*, 50(6):2467–2488, 1990.

[185] M.K. Sain (Guest Editor). Special issue on linear multivariable control systems. *IEEE Transactions on Automatic Control*, 26:1–295, 1981.

[186] I.W. Sandberg. Frequency-domain criteria for the stability of feedback systems containing a single time-varying nonlinear element. *Bell System Technical Journal*, 43:1601–1608, 1964.

[187] I.W. Sandberg. Frequency domain criteria for the stability of nonlinear feedback systems. In *Proceedings of the National Electronics Conference*, volume 20, pages 737–741, 1964.

[188] I.W. Sandberg. On the $\mathcal{L}_2$-boundedness of solutions of nonlinear functional equations. *Bell System Technical Journal*, 43:1581–1599, 1964.

[189] I.W. Sandberg. An observation concerning the application of the contraction mapping fixed-point theorem and a result concerning the norm-boundedness of solution of nonlinear functional equations. *Bell System Technical Journal*, 44:1809–1812, 1965.

[190] N.R. Sandell Jr. Robust stability of multivariable feedback systems. In *Proceedings of the 16th Annual Allerton Conference on Communications, Control and Computing*, pages 471–478, 1978.

[191] D. Sarason. Generalized interpolation in $\mathcal{H}_\infty$. *Transactions of the American Mathematical Society*, 127:179–203, 1967.

[192] C. Scherer. $\mathcal{H}_\infty$-control for plants with zeros on the imaginary axis. *SIAM Journal of Control and Optimization*, 30(1):123–142, 1992.

[193] C. Scherer. $\mathcal{H}_\infty$ optimization without assumptions on finite or infinite zeros. *SIAM Journal of Control and Optimization*, 30(1):143–166, 1992.

[194] I. Schur. Bemerkungen zur Theorie der beschänkten Bilinearformen mit unendlich vielen Veränderlichen. *Journal für die reine und angewandte Mathematik*, 140:1–28, 1911.

[195] U. Shaked. $\mathcal{H}_\infty$-minimum error state estimation of linear stationary processes. *IEEE Transactions on Automatic Control*, 35:554–558, 1990.

[196] J.L. Speyer, J. Deyst, and D.H. Jacobson. Optimization of stochastic linear systems with additive measurement and process noise using exponential performance criteria. *IEEE Transactions on Automatic Control*, 19:358–366, 1974.

[197] G. Stein and J.C. Doyle. Singular values and feedback: Design examples. In *Proceedings of the 16th Annual Allerton Conference on Communications, Control and Computing*, pages 461–470, 1978.

[198] G.W. Stewart. *Introduction to Matrix Computations.* Academic Press, New York, 1973.

[199] A.A. Stoorvogel. The singular $\mathcal{H}_\infty$ control problem with dynamic measurement feedback. *SIAM Journal of Control and Optimization*, 29(1):160–184, 1991.

[200] A.A. Stoorvogel. The discrete-time $\mathcal{H}_\infty$ control problem with measurement feedback. *SIAM Journal of Control and Optimization*, 30:180–202, 1992.

[201] A.A. Stoorvogel. *The $\mathcal{H}_\infty$ Control Problem.* Prentice-Hall, New York, 1992.

[202] A.A. Stoorvogel and H.L. Trentleman. The quadratic matrix inequality in singular $\mathcal{H}_\infty$ control with state feedback. *SIAM Journal of Control and Optimization*, 28(5):1190–1208, 1990.

[203] B. Szokefalvi-Nagy and C. Foias. *Harmonic Analysis of Operators on Hilbert Space.* North-Holland, 1970.

[204] G. Tadmor. Worst-case design in the time domain: The maximum principle and the standard $\mathcal{H}_\infty$ problem. *Mathematics of Control, Signals and Systems*, 3(4):301–325, 1990.

[205] M. Vidyasagar. *Control System Synthesis: A Factorization Approach.* M.I.T. Press, Cambridge, Mass. 1985.

[206] M. Vidyasagar and H. Kimura. Robust controllers for uncertain linear multivariable systems. *Automatica*, 22(1):85–94, 1986.

[207] J.L. Walsh. *Interpolation and Approximation by Rational Functions in the Complex Domain.* American Math. Society, Providence, RI, 5th edition, 1969.

[208] W. Wang and M.G. Safonov. A tighter relative-error bound for balanced stochastic truncation. *Systems and Control Letters*, 14(4):307–317, 1990.

[209] P. Whittle. Risk sensitive LQG control. *Advances in Applied Probability*, 13:764–777, 1981.

[210] J.C. Willems. *The Analysis of Feedback Systems.* M.T.T. Press, Cambridge, Mass., 1971.

[211] J.C. Willems. Least squares stationary optimal control and the algebraic Riccati equation. *IEEE Transactions on Automatic Control*, 16(6):621–634, 1971.

[212] D. Williamson. *Digital Control and Implementation : Finite Wordlength Considerations.* Prentice-Hall, Englewood Cliffs, N.J., 1990.

[213] W.M. Wonham. On the separation theorem of stochastic control. *SIAM Journal of Control and Optimization*, 6:312–326, 1968.

[214] L. Xie, C.E. de Souza, and M. Fu. $\mathcal{H}_\infty$ estimation for discrete-time linear uncertain systems. *International Journal of Robust and Nonlinear Control*, 1:111–123, 1991.

[215] I. Yaesh and U. Shaked. Game theory approach to optimal linear estimation in the minimum $\mathcal{H}_\infty$ norm sense. In *Proceedings of the IEEE Conference on Decision and Control*, pages 421–425, Tampa, 1989.

[216] I. Yaesh and U. Shaked. Minimum $\mathcal{H}_\infty$-norm regulation of linear discrete-time systems and its relation to linear quadratic discrete games. In *Proceedings of the IEEE Conference on Decision and Control*, pages 942–947, Tampa, 1989.

[217] I. Yaesh and U. Shaked. $\mathcal{H}_\infty$-optimal one step-ahead output feedback control of discrete-time systems. *IEEE Transactions on Automatic Control*, 37(8):1245–1250, 1992.

[218] I. Yaesh and U. Shaked. A transfer function approach to the problems of discrete-time systems: $\mathcal{H}_\infty$-optimal linear control and filtering. *IEEE Transactions on Automatic Control*, 36(11):1264–1271, 1992.

[219] V.A. Yakubovič. The solution of certain matrix inequalities in automatic control theory. *Doklady Akademii Nauk, USSR*, 143:1304–1307, 1962.

[220] D.C. Youla and J.J. Bongiorno. A feedback theory of two-degree-of-freedom optimal wiener-hopf design. *IEEE Transactions on Automatic Control*, 30(7):652–665, 1985.

[221] D.C. Youla and M. Saito. Interpolation with positive real functions. *Journal of the Franklin Institute*, 2:77–108, 1967.

[222] N. Young. *An Introduction to Hilbert Space.* Cambridge University Press, Cambridge, U.K., 1988.

[223] N.J. Young. The Nevanlinna-Pick problem for matrix valued functions. *Journal of Operator Theory*, 15:239–320, 1986.

[224] G. Zames. On the stability of nonlinear, time-varying feedback systems. In *Proceedings of the National Electronics Conference*, volume 20, pages 725–730, 1964.

[225] G. Zames. On the input-ouput stability of nonlinear time-varying feedback systems, Part I: Conditions derived using concepts of loop gain, conicity and positivity. *IEEE Transactions on Automatic Control*, 11(2):228–238, 1966.

[226] G. Zames. On the input-ouput stability of nonlinear time-varying feedback systems, Part II: Conditions involving circles in the frequency plane and sector nonlinearities. *IEEE Transactions on Automatic Control*, 11(3):465–476, 1966.

[227] G. Zames. Feedback and optimal sensitivity: Model reference transformations, multiplicative seminorms, and approximate inverses. *IEEE Transactions on Automatic Control*, 26:301–320, 1981.

[228] G. Zames and B.A. Francis. Feedback, minimax sensitivity, and optimal robustness. *IEEE Transactions on Automatic Control*, 28:585–601, 1983.

[229] K. Zhou. On the parametrization of $\mathcal{H}_\infty$ controllers. *IEEE Transactions on Automatic Control*, 37(9):1442–1446, 1992.

Index